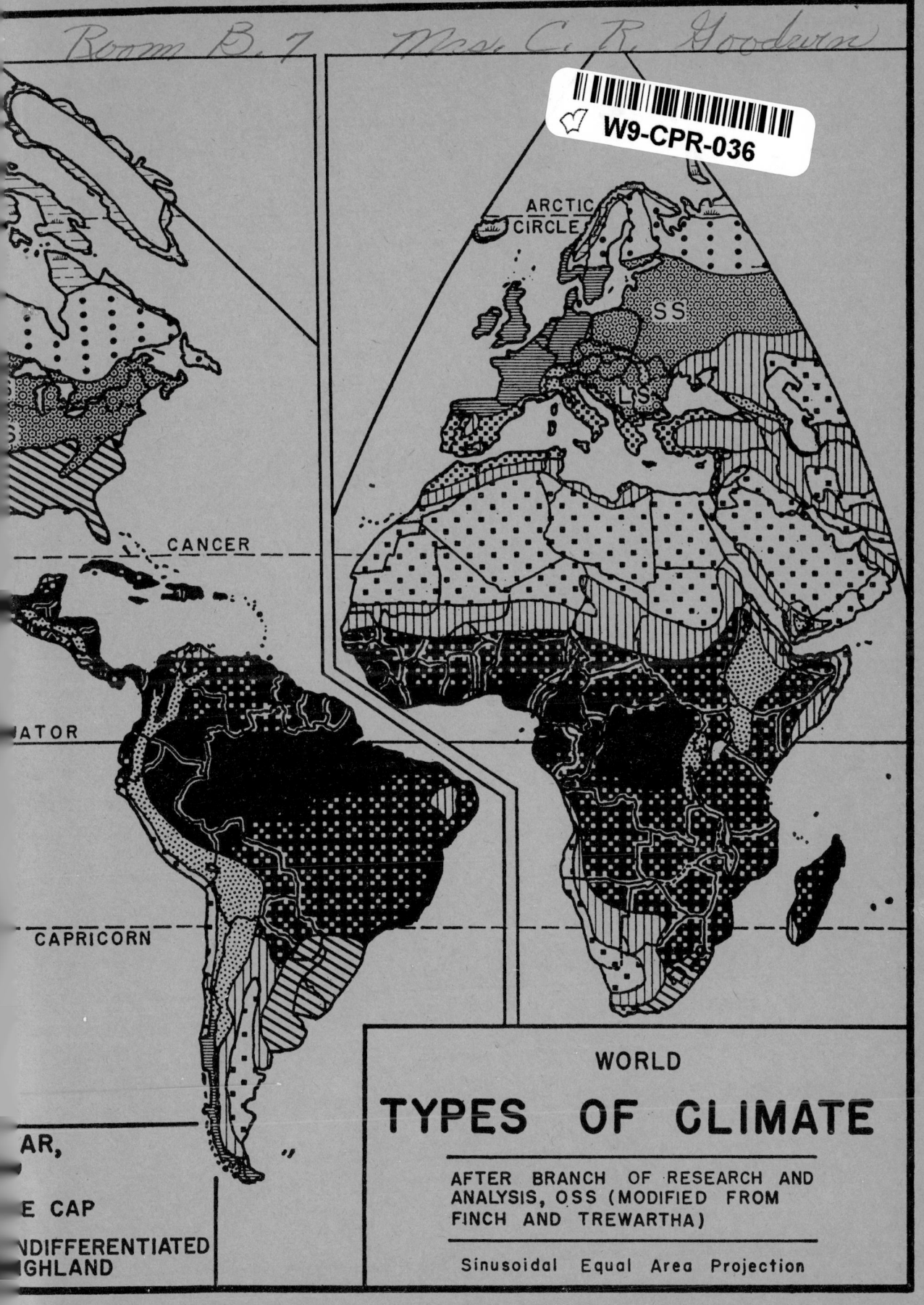

ARCTIC CIRCLE

SS

LS

CANCER

EQUATOR

CAPRICORN

WORLD

# TYPES OF CLIMATE

AFTER BRANCH OF RESEARCH AND ANALYSIS, OSS (MODIFIED FROM FINCH AND TREWARTHA)

Sinusoidal Equal Area Projection

AR,

E CAP

NDIFFERENTIATED
GHLAND

# REGIONAL GEOGRAPHY

# OF THE WORLD

# REGIONAL
## OF THE

*An Introductory*

**JESSE H. WHEELER, JR.**
UNIVERSITY OF MISSOURI

**J. TRENTON KOSTBADE**
UNIVERSITY OF MISSOURI

**RICHARD S. THOMAN**
QUEEN'S UNIVERSITY

# GEOGRAPHY WORLD

*Survey* · REVISED

HOLT, RINEHART AND WINSTON

New York · Chicago · San Francisco · Toronto · London

Cartography for the revised edition by Lois Grotewold,
assisted by Phyllis Johnson.

April 1964

# Preface

This revised edition, like the first edition, seeks to assist college and university students in acquiring certain basic ideas and supporting facts about contemporary world geography which a person with a college education might reasonably be expected to know. Its aim, in short, is general education in world geography.

It surveys the world importance, geographical characteristics, and major problems of eight world regions—Europe, the Soviet Union, the Middle East, the Orient, the Pacific World, Africa, Latin America, and Anglo-America. Attention is also given to important individual countries and regional groups of countries within each world region. Pertinent background material on systematic physical and cultural geography is presented at appropriate places. A general introduction to geography as a field of study is presented in Chapter 1. The book is designed as a text for courses in world regional geography on an introductory college level.

In the revised edition the basic structure of the book remains unchanged, although every effort has been made to bring all material up to date. Much rewriting has been done in certain chapters, particularly those on the British Isles, France, Germany, the Soviet Union, the Middle East, the Chinese Realm, and Africa. Extensive changes and improvements have also been made in the maps. Many first-edition maps have been redrawn, and a considerable number and variety of new maps have been added.

Instructors may not find it necessary to require students to purchase an atlas. Nearly all of the place names mentioned in the text are shown on maps. A considerable number of maps showing the world or regional distribution of population, types of climate, major crops, and other elements of geographical significance are included.

The photographs in the volume are not intended to give a comprehensive coverage, although it is hoped that each photo will convey at least one significant idea about the country or region portrayed. Teachers are urged to make such use as time permits of movies, slides, and film strips to illustrate, amplify, and supplement the ideas contained in the text and to give students the "feel" of the areas considered.

Statistics have been employed in various places to reinforce important concepts. It was not felt necessary in an introductory textbook to give full documentation for all statistics. They have been drawn from a wide variety of standard sources.

Although most of the text has been specially written, a variety of readings, mostly short, are included. In editing the readings, minor changes in spelling, capitalization, and punctuation have been made in order to give uniformity to the book as a whole. Most of the sectional headings within the body of the readings represent editorial additions. Elision marks are not used at the beginning of an opening paragraph or the end of a selection.

The senior author has carried the over-all editorial responsibility for the book and the chief responsibility for the planning and supervision of the cartography and the selection and captioning of photographs. Chapters 1, 2, 10, 11, 12, 13, 14, 15, 22, and 23 were prepared by the senior author. Mr. Kostbade prepared Chapters 6, 7, 8, 9, 16, 17, 21, 26, and 27, and Chapters 3, 4, 18, 19, and 20 were prepared jointly by Mr. Kostbade and the senior author. Chapters

24 and 25 were prepared by Mr. Thoman, while Chapter 5 was prepared jointly by Mr. Thoman and the senior author. The basic core of ideas in the book was to a large extent a product of many hours of discussion among the three authors during a fruitful association at the University of Missouri extending over a period of several years.

The authors extend sincere thanks to a number of other geographers who were kind enough to offer their comments on portions of the manuscript submitted for criticism, or who otherwise rendered assistance. Their suggestions proved exceedingly useful and were heeded in the great majority of cases. They are, of course, absolved of any responsibility for errors of fact or interpretation in the book. The men to whom acknowledgment is due include the following:

*First edition:* John E. Brush, Rutgers University; Wesley Calef, University of Chicago; Charles C. Colby, University of Chicago (Emeritus); Jerome D. Fellman, University of Illinois; Gerard Foster; Norton S. Ginsburg, University of Chicago; William A. Hance, Columbia University; Robert A. Harper, Southern Illinois University; Chauncy D. Harris, University of Chicago; Howard F. Hirt, University of Missouri; William Horbaly; Rayburn W. Johnson, Memphis State University; James B. Kenyon; H. Louis Kostanick, University of California, Los Angeles; Trevor Lloyd, Dartmouth College; James S. Matthews, Memphis State University; Edwin S. Munger, University of Chicago and American Universities Field Staff; Howard J. Nelson, University of California, Los Angeles; Jerome P. Pickard; Robert S. Platt, University of Chicago (Emeritus); Paul H. Sisco, Memphis State University; Joseph E. Spencer, University of California, Los Angeles; Edward J. Taaffe, Northwestern University; Philip True; Philip L. Wagner, University of Chicago; R. Kenton Wibking, Kansas State Teachers College, Emporia; and James R. Wray.

*Revised edition:* David H. K. Amiran, Hebrew University, Jerusalem; James E. Collier, University of Missouri; Kenneth B. Cumberland, University of Auckland; Andreas Grotewold, University of Missouri; Howard F. Hirt, University of Missouri; W. R. Mead, University College, London; and Alexander Melamid, New York University.

Lois Grotewold was the principal cartographer for the revised edition, with much assistance by Phyllis Johnson. Thanks are due them for their careful and skillful work.

The senior author expresses his continued appreciation to the Fund for the Advancement of Education of the Ford Foundation for its award of a Faculty Study Fellowship in 1951–1952. This grant made possible a school year of work devoted to organizing a new general education course in world regional geography at the University of Missouri and led eventually to the preparation of the present book.

Thanks are expressed to the individuals, firms, and government agencies or other organizations who permitted the use of copyrighted textual matter, photographs, and maps. Such permissions are separately acknowledged. Design did not permit specific acknowledgment along with the illustrations for the part titles. Therefore, the authors wish to thank the following organizations at this point: Standard Oil Company (N. J.) for Parts 1, 4, and 8; French Government Tourist Office, Part 2; Sovfoto, Part 3; Technical Cooperation Administration, U. S. Department of State, Part 5; British Information Services, Parts 6 and 7; and Price Brothers & Company Limited, Part 9.

The authors sincerely hope the new edition will be of service to college and university students of the 1960s as they attempt to gain perspective on the turbulent and varied world in which they find themselves.

J. H. W., Jr.
J. T. K.
R. S. T.

*Columbia, Mo.*
*February 1, 1961*

# Contents

# PART 1
## *Introductory Concepts*

# Some Introductory Concepts of Geography

The main reason for studying geography is to gain a better understanding and appreciation of the world in which we live. Of course, many other subjects besides geography contribute to this end. In fact, most school subjects are concerned in one way or another with enhancing our understanding and appreciation of the world about us. Geography, however, has one characteristic which tends to distinguish it from most other subjects, namely, that it centers attention on the study and interpretation of particular *areas* in the world. A well-known geographer, George B. Cressey, has stated this idea as follows: "It is the task of geography . . . to draw information from widely scattered sources, and to give it a new significance as applied to the understanding of specific areas." [1]

The term "area," as used by geographers,

[1] By permission from *Asia's Lands and Peoples*, by George B. Cressey. Copyright, 1944, 1951. New York: McGraw-Hill Book Company, Inc. Pp. 34–35.

The cotton truck in this view is part of a spreading net of modern transportation facilities that is gradually breaking down the isolation and self-sufficiency of underdeveloped lands and is bringing them, for better or worse, within the orbit of a world-wide exchange economy. The specific locale is Uganda in East Africa; the cotton, from small African farms, will be processed at a local gin and then will move to an overseas market. (Department of Information, Uganda Protectorate, by courtesy of *Foreign Agriculture*.)

may refer to any portion of the earth's surface. The largest of all areas is, of course, the entire world. However, in most respects the world is much too large and complicated to be readily comprehended all at once. For purposes of study it is generally necessary to subdivide it into areas of a smaller size. In this book primary attention is given to two kinds of areas, the *countries* as outlined on an ordinary political map and the *major world regions* in which the individual countries lie.

## THE MAJOR WORLD REGIONS

As customarily used by geographers, the term "region" refers to an area of considerable size which has a substantial degree of internal unity or homogeneity and which differs in significant respects from adjoining areas. A region may be wholly contained within a single country, or it may include several different countries or parts of countries. This book is organized in terms of eight major world regions: Europe, the Soviet Union, the Middle East, the Orient, the Pacific World, Africa, Latin America, and Anglo-America (map, facing page). Although these regions are commonly recognized as grand divisions of the world, authorities differ as to the precise area which should be included in each. In this book the eight world regions are delimited as blocks of countries, and thus their outer limits follow political boundary lines. This method of regional division has been adopted for convenience in using statistical materials and for sharpness in presenting regional concepts on an introductory level. However, the student should not assume that the political lines employed as regional boundaries necessarily represent sharp lines of cleavage in other respects. In physical, cultural, and economic terms the major world regions tend to be separated by zones of transition where the characteristics of one region change gradually to those of the next. This tendency to merge gradually rather than to be separated by sharp lines is also true of regions of a smaller order of size. Since regions are merely convenient devices useful in generalizing about the world, it is more important to grasp the particular set of features which characterizes the core of a region than it is to search for an exact line where the characteristics of one region end and the characteristics of another region begin.

The scheme of eight major world regions employed in this book is only one among various alternative methods of subdividing the world for purposes of study. However, it is believed to be especially well suited as an organizing device for accomplishing the major objective of the book, which is to assist the student in acquiring a fund of concepts about the geography of the contemporary world that any educated person might reasonably be expected to know. The regional names employed already have some familiarity for the student and are in common use. Thus the student can proceed from the known to the unknown in acquiring the new perspectives which a sound knowledge of world geography is able to give.

Each of the major world regions has certain well-defined characteristics which tend to give it a unity or personality of its own.

*Europe* is a diversified industrial, commercial, and agricultural region in middle latitudes.[2] It includes a larger number of individual countries than any other area of comparable size. These countries are small in area, being generally comparable to

---

[2] For the guidance of students who have had no previous course work in college or high-school geography, a limited number of important technical terms are explained in bracketed sections in the text following the paragraph in which they first appear.

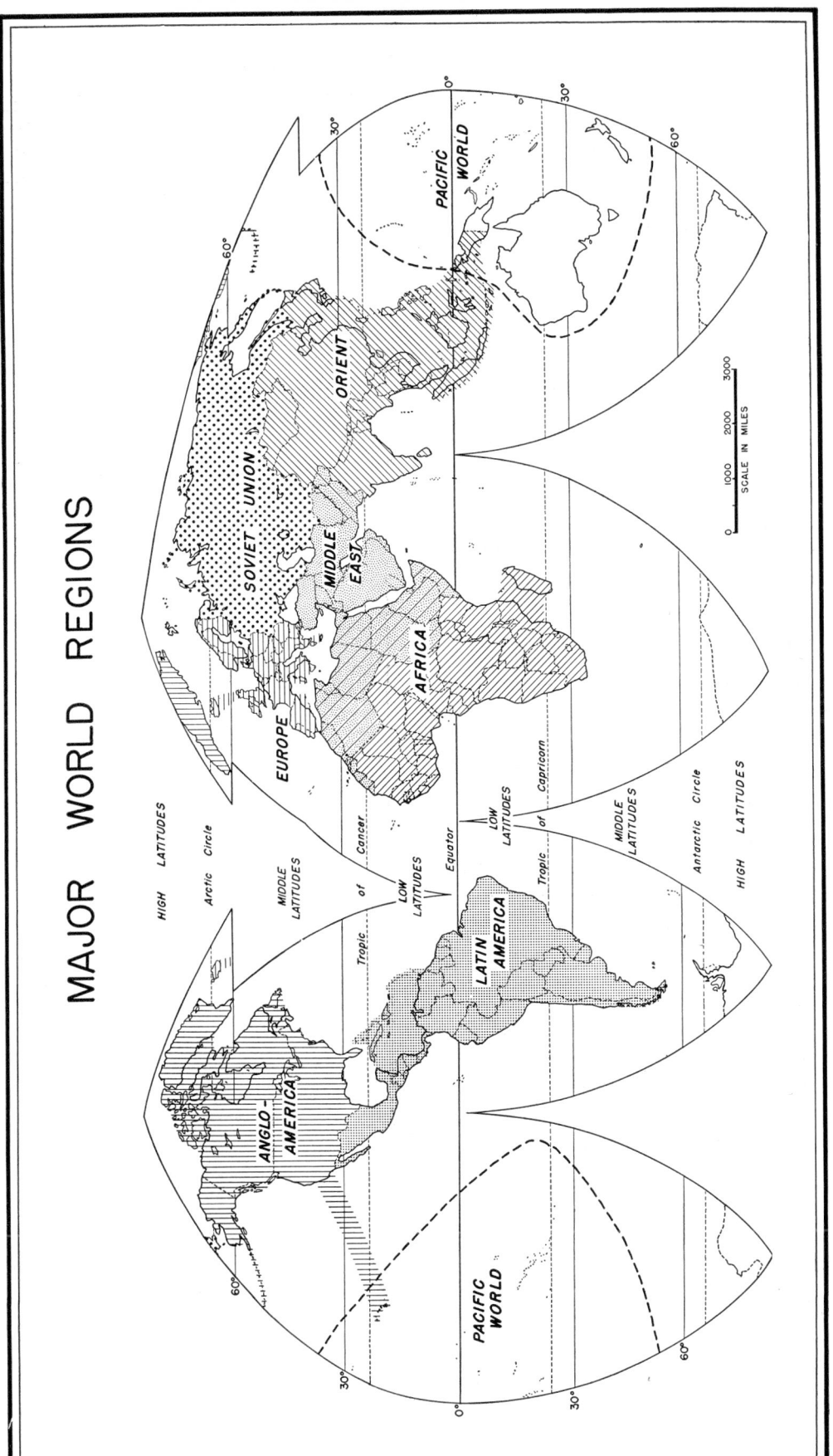

# MAJOR WORLD REGIONS

PACIFIC WORLD

ORIENT

SOVIET UNION

MIDDLE EAST

EUROPE

AFRICA

ANGLO-AMERICA

LATIN AMERICA

PACIFIC WORLD

HIGH LATITUDES

Arctic Circle

MIDDLE LATITUDES

Tropic of Cancer

LOW LATITUDES

Equator

LOW LATITUDES

Tropic of Capricorn

MIDDLE LATITUDES

Antarctic Circle

HIGH LATITUDES

SCALE IN MILES
0    1000    2000    3000

This map delineates the eight major world regions forming the basic framework of organization for this text. (Boggs Eumorphic Equal Area Projection, copyright A. J. Nystrom & Co.)

American states. However, many of them have relatively large and/or dense populations. Some European countries have overseas possessions acquired during an age of oceanic expansion which extended from the fifteenth century to the twentieth. During this period Europe became the dominant region in world affairs. Today this dominance has been lost as a result of profound world changes associated in part with World Wars I and II. Many European dependencies have recently gained independence, and others will become independent in the near future. The economic and military power which was once centered in Europe is now shared by other areas, notably Anglo-America and the Soviet Union. But despite the loss of its commanding position, Europe continues to be an important and influential region. Its impact on the rest of the world in recent centuries has been so great that a knowledge of Europe is a necessity for the understanding of any other major region.

[EDITORIAL COMMENT. The term *latitude* denotes position with respect to the equator. Latitude is measured in degrees, minutes, and seconds. The equator, which circles the globe midway between the poles, has a latitude of 0°. All other latitudinal lines are parallel to the equator and to each other. Hence all latitudinal lines are called "parallels." Places north of the equator are said to be in north latitude; places south of the equator, in south latitude. The highest latitude a place can have is 90°. Thus the latitude of the North Pole is 90°N., the South Pole, 90°S. Places near the equator are said to be in *low latitudes;* places near the poles, in *high latitudes* (map, p. 5). The Tropics of Cancer and Capricorn, at 23½°N. and 23½°S., and the Arctic and Antarctic Circles, at 66½°N. and 66½°S., form convenient and generally realistic boundaries for the low latitudes and high latitudes, respectively (although a more symmetrical arrangement would place the boundaries at 30°N. and S., and 60°N. and S.). Places occupying an intermediate position with respect to the poles and the equator are said to be in *middle latitudes*. In a general way the middle latitudes may be thought of as temperate or seasonal latitudes. They contrast strongly in yearly regimes of temperature with the relatively constant and monotonous heat of low latitude lowlands and with the extremes of cold which prevail for much of the year in the high latitudes. (For a definition of longitude, see page 231.)]

*The Soviet Union,* though a single country, is continental in size and resources. So vast, influential, and distinctive is this Communist state that one seems justified in regarding it as a major region comparable in world importance to regions containing many different countries. It is by far the largest country in area on the globe, being more than twice as large as Canada, China, or the United States. However, its size as seen on a map is somewhat deceptive. Much of it is handicapped by a harsh physical environment which restricts the possibilities for human settlement and use, and large sections are almost empty of population. Most of the people live in a triangular coreland (map, p. 252) about half the size of the United States. One of the most significant distinguishing characteristics of the Soviet Union is its type of planned economy, instituted by the Communist Party since the Russian Revolution of 1917. Prior to the 1930s, the Soviet Union was very predominantly an agricultural country. Today it has become an industrial power ranking second only to the United States. Since World War II, Communist forms of society patterned in varying degrees after that of the Soviet Union have been established in various European and Asian "satellites" and in Communist China and Yugoslavia.

*The Middle East* is predominantly a region of deserts and semiarid grasslands. Authorities differ regarding the extent of this region; some would disavow the term "Middle East" altogether as being too vague and thus tending to create confusion. However, it now seems firmly established as a regional name. In this book the Middle East is considered to include an area stretching across northern Africa and southwestern Asia from Morocco and the Spanish Sahara to West Pakistan and Kashmir. In large sections of this region human settlement is discouraged by lack of moisture. Industrial resources are not outstanding, and modern types of manufacturing are poorly developed, though they are gradually expanding in the region's few large cities. Despite the rapid growth of scattered urban populations in recent years, the Middle East remains primarily a region of farmers and herdsmen. Crop growing is largely confined to irrigated oases along the major rivers and to limited areas, particularly around the Mediterranean Sea, where winter rains bring more moisture than is customary in the region. Although the Middle East is not well supplied with most types of natural resources, it has an abundance of one vital commodity, oil. The world's largest deposits are found in the vicinity of the Persian Gulf, and other sizable deposits, newly discovered, underlie the Sahara Desert of northern Africa. One of the most significant characteristics of the Middle East is the dominance in most countries of the Moslem religion. This region forms the heart of the Moslem world. Until recently a colonial region in large part, this area is today comprised mainly of independent states. In general, these states are poorly organized, militarily weak, and poverty-stricken.

*The Orient,* a region extending around the southern and eastern margins of Asia from India and Pakistan to Korea and Japan, is the home of about half of the human race. In most of its countries, two thirds or more of the inhabitants are farmers. But manufacturing and other sources of employment associated with growing urban areas are increasingly important; indeed, in Japan only two fifths of the employed population is agricultural. The majority of the region's inhabitants gain little more than subsistence from plots of land that seldom average larger than 3 to 5 acres per family and are often much smaller. In many parts of the Orient the pressure of population on resources is very severe. Most of the region's people live in tropical or subtropical climates, though large areas extend outside of these climatic zones. Agriculture in many areas is facilitated by monsoonal rains during the summer months. Many millions of people are vitally dependent on these rains; when the summer monsoon fails, or is weak, famine may result. Like the Middle East, the Orient is composed mainly of independent states that have only recently emerged from a colonial status. Today this region is gripped by profound changes and conflicts associated with the decline of Western colonialism, the emergence of Communism, with its powerful new stronghold in mainland China, and the drive of many impoverished and underdeveloped nations to modernize and improve their economic and political status.

*The Pacific World* embraces the island continent of Australia, together with a host of islands, large and small, scattered about in the vast reaches of the Pacific Ocean. This region is composed of dependent territories except for Australia and New Zealand, which are independent countries, and the new American state of Hawaii.[3] The Pacific World lies in the tropics, with the exception of New Zealand and southern Australia, which are in middle latitudes. Its island peoples long led a self-sufficient existence built around simple forms of agriculture, the utilization of the coconut palm, and fishing. But the coming of the

---

[3] The independent island nations of Indonesia, the Philippines, and Japan are considered in this text to lie within the Orient rather than the Pacific World.

white man and disturbances wrought by the two world wars have brought great changes, not always propitious, to the trade-wind isles of the "South Seas."

The massive continent of *Africa* is the largest in area of the major world regions considered in this book, though many of its vast expanses of desert, grassland, and forest are so sparsely inhabited that the continent's total population is less than three fifths that of Europe. It will be noted that "Africa" overlaps the "Middle East," since North Africa is included in both regions (map, p. 5). This should occasion no difficulty so long as one conceives of regions simply as useful tools designed to further geographic understanding and appreciation. For various reasons it seems desirable to consider North Africa in the context of both "Africa" and the "Middle East." This procedure appears clearly to enhance our understanding and appreciation of both world regions, and thus to be consistent with the aims of geographic study. Most of Africa is an underdeveloped tropical region inhabited by Negroid peoples, though in North Africa Arabs, Berbers, and related Semitic and Hamitic peoples are the main population elements. White men of European descent, primarily inhabitants of the rapidly growing cities, are found principally in the southern and northwestern reaches, where Africa extends into subtropical latitudes, and in some parts of the tropical highlands of the continent. Somewhat more than half of the total European population is found in the continent's most highly developed country, South Africa. In the world's economy, Africa is principally important as an exporter of minerals and tropical and subtropical agricultural commodities, as a market for European manufactured goods, and as a field for capital investment by European nations and the United States. Politically it is an area in rapid transition from European colonialism to independence. In the immediate past Africa has exerted little direct influence on world affairs, its destinies being mainly controlled by forces outside the region. But today a host of newly independent African countries are taking their place in the world's councils. These new governments are faced with massive problems as they attempt to organize their countries effectively and to improve the lot of the impoverished farmers and herdsmen who comprise the mass of the population.

Aside from giant Brazil, with its 3.3 million square miles and 65 million people, and the sizable republics of Argentina and Mexico, *Latin America* is predominantly a region of small independent nations, together with such holdings of overseas nations in the West Indian isles or on the nearby mainland as survived the revolutionary period of the nineteenth century. The independent countries of Latin America were originally colonies of Spain, Portugal, or France.[4] Today the predominance of Roman Catholicism and of European languages, primarily Spanish and (in Brazil) Portuguese, reflect the former importance of European colonial powers in this region. Like Africa, Latin America is mainly tropical or subtropical in climate, though in the south it extends far into the middle latitudes. Economically, this region is most important to the outside world as an exporter of minerals such as oil, copper, iron ore, and bauxite, and tropical agricultural commodities such as coffee and cane sugar, and as a market for manufactured goods and investment capital from the United States and Europe. Its people, who are most commonly *mestizos* (a mixture of European and native Indian), support themselves primarily by agriculture, often on a subsistence or near-subsistence level. Only in scattered areas, such as southeastern Brazil, Buenos Aires, central Mex-

---

[4] The West Indies, a federation of British colonies established in 1958, had not attained full independence at the time of writing.

ico, and central Chile, has much manufacturing developed. Rapid population increases are posing difficult problems for a region that is, for the most part, seriously underdeveloped and poor.

*Anglo-America* consists of the United States, Canada, and, as a marginal appendage, Greenland. Like Europe and the Soviet Union, this region lies in middle or high latitudes in the Northern Hemisphere. The two nations that compose it, drawn together by cultural similarities, and closely inter-locked both economically and militarily, are firm friends and allies. The territory they occupy is probably the richest in natural resources of all the major world regions. On this resource base the United States and Canada have developed an extraordinarily productive "triple economy" of industry, agriculture, and trade. These two nations lead all others in productivity per person and general prosperity. They exercise great influence in world affairs.

## KEY TOPICS IN GEOGRAPHIC STUDY

To the student embarking on a study of world geography, the mass of detail to be mastered may seem at first to be overwhelming. However, the observant student will note that certain topics tend to recur as different regions and countries are studied. These key topics include (1) Location, (2) Population, (3) Political Status, (4) Natural Environment, (5) Type of Economy, (6) Potentialities, and (7) Problems. In the following pages each of these topics will be introduced and briefly discussed.

### ▶ *Location*

One of the purposes for which one studies geography is to learn the location of important features on the earth's surface—in other words, to learn where things are in the world. One tries to acquire a mental map, on which countries, important cities, rivers, mountain ranges, climatic zones, and other features are plotted in their correct relation to each other. No person can claim to be truly educated who does not carry such a map in his head. However, it is not enough to simply know the *facts* of location; one also needs to develop an understanding and appreciation of the *significance* of location. To a considerable degree the geographic characteristics of any area are due, directly or indirectly, to its location. For the most part, location is a concept which must be discussed with regard to particular areas. There is relatively little of real significance which can be said about location in general. Each area has a different location and must be separately evaluated.

Perhaps an illustration will point up the foregoing remarks. Let us compare the location of Great Britain with that of New Zealand (map, p. 10). Each is an island area, Great Britain consisting of a single large island, while New Zealand has two main islands about equal in size. Both areas are located in the middle latitudes. Both come within the influence of westerly winds which, blowing off the surrounding seas, bring abundant rain and moderate temperatures throughout the year. The climates of Great Britain and New Zealand are remarkably similar, in spite of the fact that these areas are located in opposite hemispheres and are about as far from each other as it is possible for two places on the earth to be.

Thus in certain ways the locations of Great Britain and New Zealand are similar. In other respects, however, their locations are vastly different. Great Britain is located in the Northern Hemisphere, which contains the bulk of the world's land and all of the principal centers of population and industry; New Zealand is on the other side of the

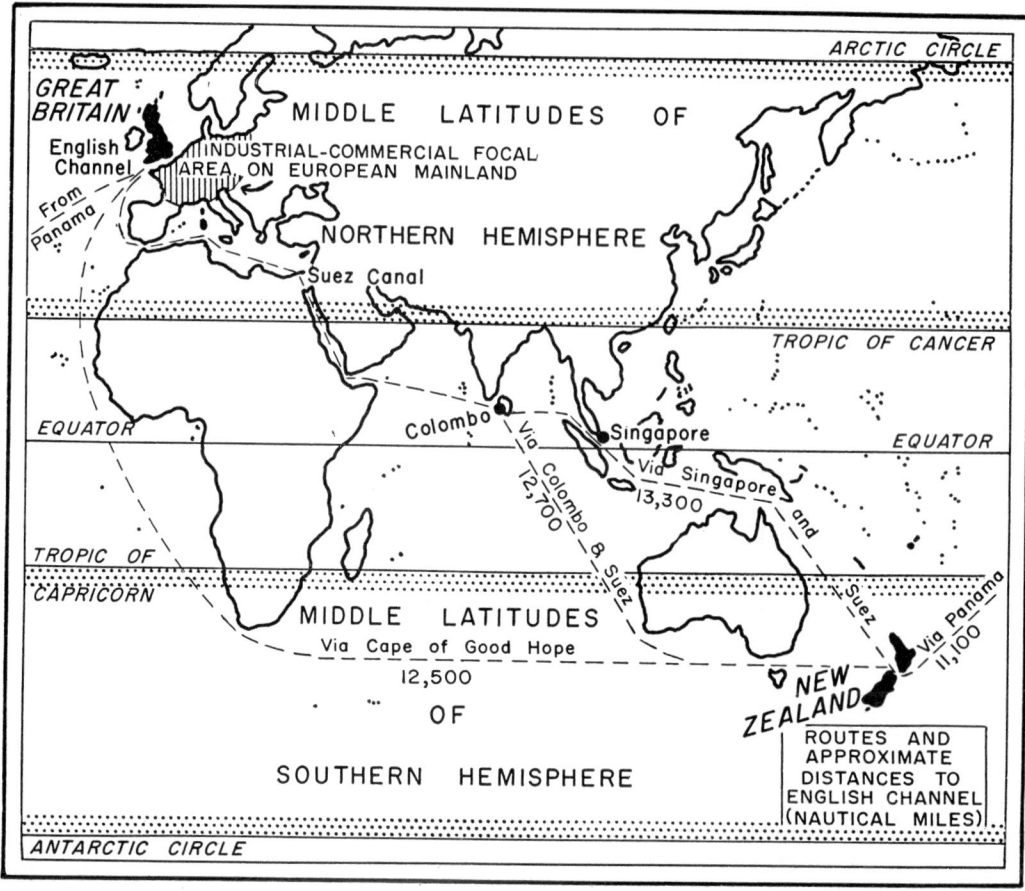

Great Britain and New Zealand compared in location. Most of the main industrial concentrations and seaports on the mainland of Europe (excluding the Soviet Union) are found in the area marked by the vertical line pattern. The middle latitudes are outlined by the dot pattern.

equator in the Southern Hemisphere. Great Britain is located near the center of the world's land masses (map, p. 64) and is separated by only a narrow channel from the densely populated industrial areas of western continental Europe; New Zealand is surrounded by vast expanses of ocean. Great Britain is located in the western seaboard area of Europe where many major ocean routes of the world converge; New Zealand is far away from the centers of world commerce. For more than four centuries Great Britain has shared in the development of northwestern Europe as a great organizing center for the world's economic and political life; New Zealand, meanwhile, has lived in comparative isolation. These differences of location help to account for the fact that Great Britain has become a densely populated industrial area and an important center of political and economic power, while New Zealand has remained a sparsely populated pastoral country of much less significance in world affairs.

The student should realize that factors of location are not constant, but are relative to the circumstances of a particular time. In other words, *the significance of location changes as circumstances change.* During the early centuries when the borderlands of the Mediterranean Sea con-

Excessive crowding in the lowlands of overpopulated regions leads to the tilling of steep slopes such as the Puerto Rican tobacco field shown in the above view. Erosion by heavy tropical downpours will soon destroy the soil and render this land worthless. (Government of Puerto Rico.)

altitudes, and (4) areas of tropical rain forest and tropical grassland or scrub, where excessive heat and moisture, dense forest growth or rank grasses, and infertile soils discourage fixed settlements. Of the four main types of "negative areas," the tropical forests and grasslands seem to offer the best possibilities for large future increases in population. Indeed, some areas of this type, particularly in the Orient, already support large and dense populations. However, areas as large or larger in Latin America, Africa, and the East Indies are still quite sparsely populated.

**Population Trends**

Various periods of history have witnessed great changes in the numbers, density, and distribution of people over the earth and in different countries and regions. Some of the most significant changes have occurred during the past three or four centuries. This period has seen an unparalleled increase in total population numbers. It is thought that since 1650 the world's population has more than quintupled, from an estimated 470–545 million to 2.9 billion. At the present time this increase is continuing at an estimated rate of 50 million or more a year. Fears are often expressed that mankind will outrun its food supply unless the increase in numbers is checked. However, some optimistic students of this problem believe that the earth could support several times its present population if all the available resources were more intensively and scientifically managed.

The tremendous increases in population during the past three centuries appear to be mainly the result of a declining death rate. The latter has resulted partly from improved medical and sanitary facilities and partly

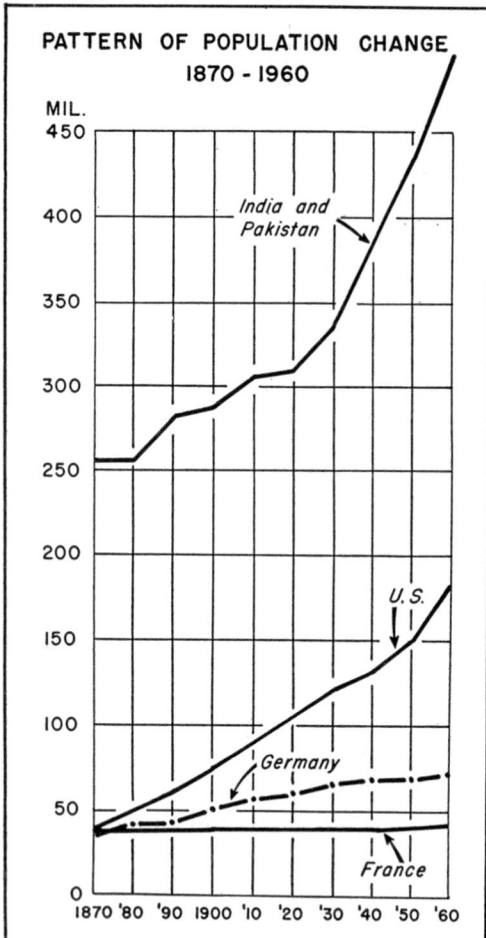

Note the population "explosion" in India-Pakistan since 1930. It is presenting those countries with grave problems of population support. (Modified from a graph by the Office of Foreign Agricultural Relations. The positions of France, Germany, and India-Pakistan in 1960 are based on United Nations population estimates; the United States position is based on the 1960 census.)

from the more abundant, varied, and dependable food supply made possible by improved agricultural techniques, better transportation facilities, and the opening of vast new lands for cultivation in the Americas and elsewhere.

At the present time population is increasing in nearly all of the world's countries,

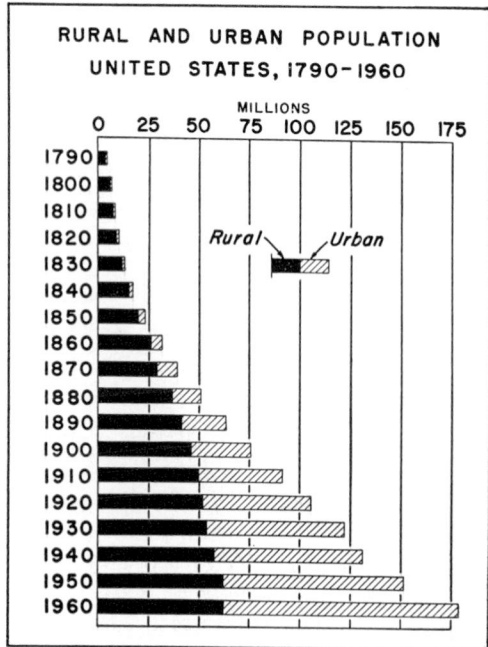

In the United States, as in the Soviet Union and many other countries, people are migrating in large numbers to cities. The rapid rise of urbanism is a highly significant and world-wide feature of our times. (Modified from a graph by the Office of Foreign Agricultural Relations.)

but the rate of increase is much greater in some countries than in others. Sharp upward trends of population in such countries as India and the United States contrast strikingly with the slow population growth of France (graph, left).

During the past three or four centuries the world pattern of population distribution has been altered considerably. This was brought about principally by two great movements of population: the migration of Europeans to new lands overseas and the migration of rural dwellers to cities (graph, above).

**Other Aspects of Population**

The general topic of population encompasses not only numbers, density, distribution, and movements or trends but also the

ple of the world does these things, it must be we who are queer and not the others.

Another way in which the uniqueness of America is apparent is illustrated by fences. In most parts of the world fences are built around houses, but there are no fences around the fields. With us the opposite is the case. There are few fences around houses, but practically all our fields are fenced. England and some of the neighboring regions of northwestern Europe have many hedges, but that condition prevails in only a relatively small area compared with the world as a whole. In most parts of the world the normal thing is to see field after field in unbroken succession covering all the land between the villages. The only thing to separate one field from another is a change in the crops or a little line, a foot or two wide, where an unsown strip separates one field of wheat, beets, or some other crop from another.

This lack of fences is symbolic of two far greater differences between America and the rest of the world. The first of these differences is that the size of land holdings is far smaller in most parts of the world than in the new lands in the temperate parts of North and South America and Australia. . . . [In most areas of the Old World] fences are a very expensive luxury. This is not only because the farms are so small, but also because as a general rule the farmers of the Old World do not have all of their land in one place. Each man usually owns several small separate parcels. If fences were built around every individual field, the cost would be prohibitive. Because our fields are so large it is relatively cheap to fence them.

The other thing illustrated by the absence of fences is that in the world as a whole materials are relatively more expensive than labor, but with us the reverse is the case. In [large] parts of the world . . . the place of fences is taken by people. A small boy or an old man or woman can be hired to herd the sheep or cattle far more cheaply than a fence can be made. . . .

Another of our queer habits is that even among our urban populations a vast number of us live in detached houses set among grass and green trees. It is hard for us to realize that there is anything strange about this, but the facts are clear. Even in our larger cities, like New York or Chicago, there are large areas where this type of detached dwelling prevails. Such houses sometimes contain two or three families but usually only one. In smaller cities, especially in those with less than 100,000 people, a large fraction of the population lives in

such houses. And of course this is also true of our millions of suburban people. This seems to us so much a matter of course that we fail to appreciate the fact that it is very uncommon when the world as a whole is considered. In Italy, India, China, and most other countries, such houses are practically unknown. In Germany, and the neighboring parts of Europe, only a very few people live in single houses surrounded by lawns. . . . In cities like Madrid, Rome, Vienna, and . . . Berlin, big apartment houses built up solidly on regular city streets often adjoin the fields. Almost the only important parts of the Old World where there are large numbers of detached suburban houses are Great Britain, Holland, and Scandinavia. Yet, even in England, the industrial worker who lives outside the central part of a town is usually housed in a little two-story house of brick or stone which forms part of a long monotonous row. He may have a bit of lawn as big as a tablecloth in front of his house, but the chances are that his house is part of a solid row. Even where such houses are separate from one another, they usually have merely a narrow paved walk between them.

An even more striking evidence of the queerness of the people of the United States is the fact that the vast majority of our farmers live on farms. This may seem absurd. It seems to us so natural and convenient for a farmer to live on his farm that we call anything else stupid. . . . In Canada, Australia, and New Zealand the same habits and opinions prevail. Yet, strange to say, in all the rest of the world there are probably not much more than another 30 or 40 million farming people who live in this isolated way. In Scandinavia, to be sure, and in mountainous regions in many parts of the world, the farmers do live by themselves on their own land. In England this is true to a slight degree, but even there the great majority of farmers live in villages and go out to their work each day. In other countries, such as Spain [and] Italy . . . the wealthier land owners may live in isolated houses on their own land, but the bulk of the agricultural population lives in compact villages. The hundreds of millions of farming people in India, China, Japan, and most other parts of the world practically all live in compact villages. . . .

In many ways such agricultural villages are the most characteristic feature of human geography. This is because they retain a stronger individuality than does either the land on which there are no houses or the land that is covered with houses in cities. Grain fields, pastures,

Village settlement in an intensively farmed section of the Old World. The farmers go out to the fields each day from their homes in the two villages shown in the view. The photo was taken in southern Luxembourg near Luxembourg city. (U. S. Air Force Photo.)

forests, and gardens have a strong family resemblance all over the world. Of course, a field of cabbages is very different from a field of potatoes, and an apple orchard is not at all like a banana patch. Nevertheless, cabbages look much the same everywhere no matter who raises them, and so do potatoes, apples, and bananas. Then, too, all over the world the cities tend gradually to become more and more alike. When Yokohama and Tokyo suffered from earthquake and fire, large sections were rebuilt in a purely Western style. . . . Electric lights, steel frames, modern processes of using concrete, and a thousand other new methods tend constantly to become standardized all over the world. Cotton factories and hotels in Bombay are almost like those in North Carolina. A railroad station or moving picture house is much the same thing in Jerusalem and in Montevideo. Cities like Constantinople, Cairo, Madras, and Hankow still possess a high degree of individuality, to be sure. Nevertheless, even in

those cities some sections are so thoroughly modernized that the mere appearance of the streets scarcely tells a stranger whether he is in America, Europe, Asia, or Africa. On the other hand, the farming villages all over the world still display a persistent individuality. The flat-roofed, mud villages near Smyrna in Turkey could never be confused with the palm-thatched huts near Madras or with the thatched houses of a wholly different type near Kyoto. Everywhere the farming villages, far more than almost any other feature of the surroundings, reflect the characteristics of the local geography. Since [the majority of] the world's people live in such villages, we may well say that they are one of the most fundamental features of human geography. Yet in this respect as well as in wealth, transportation, use of machinery, and the use of fences with all that they imply as to the size of land holdings and the value of labor, we are so unique that we well deserve to be called queer.

# PART 2
## *Europe*

# Introduction to Europe

For the purposes of this book, "Europe" is defined as the group of countries in Eurasia lying west of the Soviet Union and Turkey. This definition is at variance with traditional ideas. Europe has customarily been considered as one of the continents, separated from Asia by the Ural Mountains, Caspian Sea, Caucasus Mountains, Black Sea, Turkish Straits (Bosporus, Sea of Marmara, and Dardanelles), and Aegean Sea. Thus Europe has been considered to include parts of the Soviet Union and Turkey, often referred to as "European Russia" and "European Turkey," respectively. For various reasons, including important differences in culture and en-

vironment, it has been thought desirable to exclude the Soviet Union and Turkey from "Europe" as that region is conceived of and discussed in this book. To avoid confusion, a name such as "Europe Exclusive of the Soviet Union and Turkey" might have been employed. However, there seems no great need for this cumbersome title so long as the student keeps in mind the precise area to which the term "Europe" is meant to apply. There is actually an increasing tendency in current usage for the name to be employed in much the same sense as in this volume.

Essentially a great peninsula fringed by lesser peninsulas and islands, Europe is bounded on the west and north by the At-

The highly commercialized character of western Europe's economy and the region's dependence on food from overseas sources are reflected in this view of Rotterdam harbor in the Netherlands. Wheat from overseas producing areas is being transferred from the ocean vessels to Rhine barges, which will carry it inland to consuming areas such as West Germany's Ruhr industrial district. (*Foreign Agriculture.*)

25

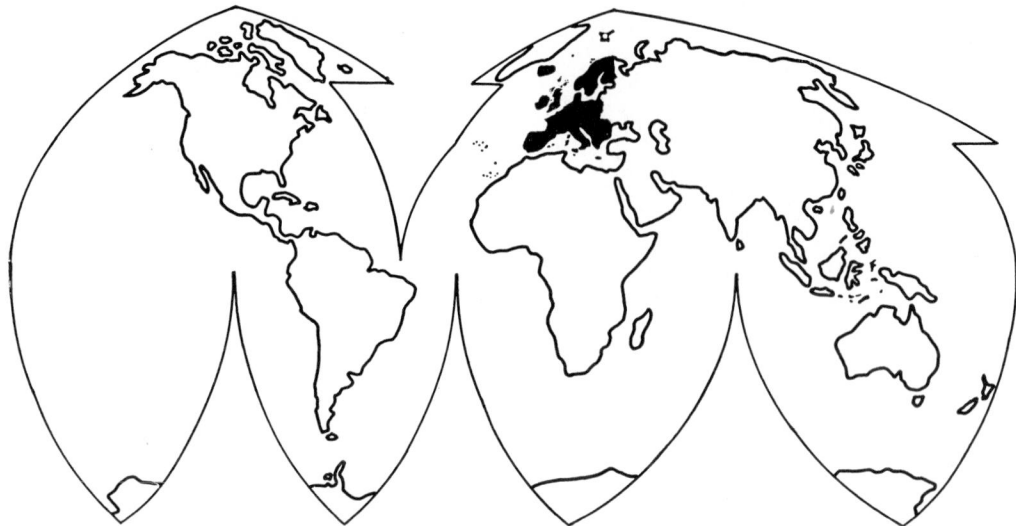

Location of Europe. (Boggs Equal Area Projection, copyright A. J. Nystrom and Co.)

lantic and Arctic oceans and on the south by the Mediterranean Sea. Eastward, Europe merges with the main continental mass of Eurasia. (See maps, facing page and p. 40.)

## REGIONAL GROUPS OF COUNTRIES IN EUROPE

The countries of Europe can be divided into a number of fairly distinct regional groups, as summarized below.

At the northwest, separated from the mainland by the English Channel and North Sea, are the *countries of the British Isles.* They include the United Kingdom of Great Britain and Northern Ireland, and the Republic of Ireland. These island countries are now entirely separate in a political sense. However, they have been closely associated historically and are still closely linked by trade.

The *countries of West Central Europe* lie on the mainland opposite the British Isles. Germany and France are the major countries in this group. Other countries include the small but highly important Benelux nations of Belgium, the Netherlands, and Luxembourg; the mountainous countries of Switzerland and Austria; and the tiny semi-independent political units of Liechtenstein, Andorra, and Monaco. The countries of West Central Europe, considered as a group, are dominantly industrial and commercial in their activities and outlook. Together with the United Kingdom, they constitute the industrial and commercial core of Europe. In these productive countries agriculture is by no means neglected, although its over-all importance is less than that of industry and trade. Indeed, large sections in some of these countries are dominantly agricultural. Generally speaking, the farmers of West Central Europe pursue a highly commercialized agriculture characterized by intensive and scientific methods and high yields. The countries of this area carry on a complex interchange of goods and services. They form a group to which the phrase "highly developed" may properly be applied.

The *countries of Northern Europe,* often referred to as the Scandinavian or Fenno-

Introductory place location map of Europe showing political units as of January 1, 1961. Note the fact that in most European countries the political capital is also the largest city. The micro-states of San Marino, Liechtenstein, and Monaco are shown in black. Vatican City state is contained within the city of Rome. In Italy, Rome has a larger population than Milan in the city proper but the estimated population of Milan's metropolitan area is somewhat larger than that of Rome.

scandic countries, include Denmark, Sweden, Norway, Finland, and Iceland. Relatively small in numbers, but industrious, thrifty, and progressive, the peoples of these lands have made skillful use of a restricted resource base in achieving general levels of health, education, and welfare which are exceeded by few nations. The different countries of this regional group have many environmental and cultural similarities and have had close historical ties with each other.

Very different from the cool, northerly countries just described are the warm and sunny *countries of Southern Europe,* often called the Mediterranean countries. This group includes Italy, Spain, Portugal, and Greece, together with the micro-states of San Marino and Vatican City state, and the British possessions of Gibraltar and Malta. These countries considered as a group are mountainous, generally poor in natural resources, and dominantly rural and agricultural rather than urban and industrial. In spite of a historic past and ancient cultures, they are today relatively poor and very undeveloped as compared with countries like the United Kingdom or the Netherlands. Extensive areas in Southern Europe have levels of living which are probably as low as any to be found in Europe. Some areas, however, are better off, the most notable example being northern Italy, where important industries exist and conditions for agriculture are more favorable than in most parts of Southern Europe.

Along or near the borders of the Soviet Union are the *countries of East Central Europe*—Poland, Czechoslovakia, Hungary, Romania, Bulgaria, Albania, and Yugoslavia. Germany and Austria have had close historical connections with the East Central European countries, but in other respects do not fit well with this group. Following World War II the countries of East Central Europe, with the exception of Yugoslavia, became political "satellites" of the Soviet Union. As this edition went to press, it seemed impossible to forecast how long the new Soviet-instituted political order was likely to last. Such uncertainty has long been characteristic of this region. Through the centuries political boundaries have fluctuated violently, and the various national groups have been repeatedly submerged by great powers bordering the region. The pattern of peoples, languages, religions, and cultures is more complicated than anywhere else in Europe. Most of the people speak Slavic languages, although Hungarian, Albanian, and certain other languages are significant exceptions. Taken as a whole, East Central Europe, like Southern Europe, is mainly agricultural, although a considerable amount of industry exists in certain areas and more is being developed. In many parts of this region the rural populations have been seriously retarded and poor. Since World War II the political, economic, and social life of the satellite countries has been remodeled along Communist lines. This fact is also true of Yugoslavia, although the latter nation has been pursuing an independent course, having broken away from Russian control in 1948. In 1956 an anti-Communist revolt in Hungary was suppressed, with considerable bloodshed, by Soviet military forces. But upheavals in Poland gained for that nation a larger measure of autonomy.

Combining countries into regional groups in the manner of the preceding paragraphs is a useful device for securing an introductory general picture of an area as complicated as Europe. However, it needs to be emphasized that each regional group is composed of countries having definite "personalities" of their own and worthy of study as individual units despite broad physical and cultural similarities.

Most European countries are different from their neighbors in language, and often in religion. In the following section, Europe's complex pattern of languages and religions is discussed, particularly with respect to its origins.

# LANGUAGES AND RELIGIONS

Europe emerged from prehistory as the homeland of many different tribal peoples. In classical and medieval times, certain peoples experienced periods of vigorous expansion, and their languages and cultures became widely diffused. First came the expansion of the Greeks and the Celtic peoples; later that of the Romans, the Germanic (Teutonic) peoples, and the Slavic peoples. As each expansion occurred, traditional languages persisted in some areas but were displaced in others. All of the important languages eventually developed many local dialects. With the rise of centralized national states in early modern times, particular dialects became the bases for standard national languages. Thus the dialect of Paris evolved as standard French and the dialect of London as standard English. But peasants in many localities continued to use their accustomed dialects and do so today. Europe's language pattern, then, is complex: with certain exceptions every country has its own national language, and many local dialects and minor languages persist in isolated or deeply rural areas or in zones along international frontiers.

## ▶ Expansion and Decline of the Greek and Celtic Languages

The first millennium B.C. witnessed a great expansion of the Greek and Celtic peoples. In peninsulas and islands bordering the Aegean and Ionian seas, the early Greeks evolved a civilization that reached unsurpassed heights of philosophical inquiry and literary and artistic expression. Greek traders and colonists spread the language and culture of their homeland to many parts of the Mediterranean world. In Roman times Latin became the principal language of administration and commerce in the Roman dominions, but Greek continued to be widely used, especially in areas bordering the eastern Mediterranean. The culture of ancient Greece forms one of the major foundations of Western civilization. But classical Greek has long since vanished as a vehicle of everyday speech. The Greek language is still predominant in Greece, but the various dialects of the modern spoken language differ greatly from the Greek of Sophocles, Herodotus, and Plato. However, the "pure" form of modern Greek taught in schools diverges less from the ancient language.

During the period from about 1200 to 400 B.C. a massive expansion of Celtic-speaking peoples took place from a nuclear area in the southwestern part of present-day Germany. This expansion affected a large part of continental Europe and the British Isles. But today Celtic languages survive in only a modest way on some far western peninsulas and islands: Breton in Brittany, Welsh in Wales, Irish Gaelic in Ireland, and Scottish Gaelic in northwestern Scotland. Few people speak a Celtic language exclusively; in nearly all cases English or (in Brittany) French is spoken as a second language.

## ▶ Romance, Germanic, and Slavic Languages

In present-day Europe the overwhelming majority of the people speak Romance, Germanic, or Slavic languages. The Romance languages are descended from Latin, originally the language of ancient Rome and a small district around it. As the Roman Empire expanded, Latin was spread to a vast area in southern and western Europe, southwestern Asia, and northern Africa. It did not necessarily displace the languages of conquered peoples (though often it did), but the upper classes in each Roman province were encouraged to learn it, and it became increasingly common as the language of administration, commerce, and education. Over a long period, regional dialects of Latin evolved into the Romance languages of today: Italian, French, Spanish, Portuguese, and others.

Today each Romance language is centered in a particular national state, but often the language frontier does not coincide with the political frontier. For example, Italian is the principal language not only of Italy itself, but also of Corsica and the city of Nice in France and of some parts of southern Switzerland. The French language extends beyond the borders of France to western Switzerland and also to southern Belgium, where it is known as Walloon. The Romance dialect of northwestern Spain called Galician is closely related to the neighboring Portuguese language.

In northeastern Spain, Andorra, and the Balearic Islands, the Romance language known as Catalan is spoken. It is distinctly different from the Castilian Spanish that is the standard language in most of Spain. Catalan is very similar to the language of southern France called Provençal. The latter has been largely superseded by standard French, though it is still spoken by many peasants and some attempt is made to keep it alive as a literary language. Minor Romance dialects survive in some mountain valleys of southeastern Switzerland. The Romanian language is generally considered a Romance language, though it has acquired many Slavic words and expressions.

In the middle centuries of the first millennium A.D., the power of Rome declined and a prolonged expansion by Germanic and Slavic peoples began. Germanic peoples first appear in history as a group of tribes inhabiting the coasts of Germany and much of Scandinavia. Their incursions overthrew the Western Roman Empire in the fifth century, but left little permanent impress on the languages of many areas that were overrun. However, German became established as the language of present-day Germany, Austria, Luxembourg, Liechtenstein, and most

of Switzerland, and it is widely spoken in Alsace and eastern Lorraine in France. In the Netherlands Dutch developed as a language closely related to the Low German dialects of northern Germany, while Flemish, almost identical to Dutch, became the language of northern Belgium. The Frisian language, once widespread along the North Sea coast, is today confined to the Frisian Islands and small districts on the adjoining mainland.

Except for Finnish, an Asiatic language belonging to an entirely different language family, the present languages of Northern Europe are descended from the same ancient Germanic tongue. Modern Icelandic has evolved least from the parent language and would be largely unintelligible to a speaker of Danish or Swedish. The dialect of the Faeroe Islands is very similar to Icelandic. From the fourteenth century to the nineteenth, Norway was ruled by the Danish crown, and Danish, in a slightly modified form, became its standard language. Many peasants, however, continue to speak the older, more purely Norwegian dialects known as *Landsmål,* and there is a desire in some quarters to use them as the basis of a national language to replace the Danish-inspired *Riksmål.* The Danish and Swedish languages are, in general, mutually intelligible. Swedish is the main language in parts of western Finland, though most of that country's population speaks Finnish. Danish is spoken in a small section of northern Germany adjoining Denmark.

English is basically a Germanic language, though it has many words and expressions derived from French, Latin, Greek, and other languages. Originally it was the language of the Angles and Saxons who invaded England in the fifth and sixth centuries A.D. The Norman conquest of the eleventh century established French as the language of the court and the upper classes. Modern English retains the Anglo-Saxon grammatical structure, but it has borrowed great numbers of words from French, as well as smaller numbers from many other languages. English is the principal language in most parts of the British Isles.

Slavic languages are dominant in most parts of East Central Europe. They were originally spread by migrations of Slavic peoples in the Middle Ages. The major languages today include Russian and Ukrainian, Polish, Czech, Slovak, Serbian, Croatian, and Bulgarian. As a result of postwar territorial changes and population transfers, few speakers of Russian and Ukrainian are found outside the Soviet Union. Czech and Slovak, spoken respectively, in western and eastern Czechoslovakia, are closely related to each other. The same is true of Serbian and Croatian, the principal languages of Yugoslavia. Though they are nearly identical in spoken form, Serbian is written in the Cyrillic alphabet, while Croatian utilizes the Latin alphabet.

In the Middle Ages Europe was invaded periodically by nomadic peoples from the grasslands of Asia and southern Russia. Most of their conquests were transitory. But the Magyar invasion of the ninth century established modern Hungary as an enclave of non-Slavic speech in the midst of a predominantly Slavic region. A sizable Hungarian minority exists in Romania. The Hungarian (Magyar) language is distantly related to Finnish. Originally the Bulgarians were Asian nomads, but after settling in their present homeland they adopted a Slavic language.

Survivals of very ancient languages persist in mountainous or isolated corners of Europe. Basque, a language apparently unrelated to any known tongue, is spoken in the western Pyrenees Mountains of France and Spain. The Albanian language is a survival of an ancient group of languages that was once widespread in the Balkan Peninsula.

## ▶ Religious Divisions

Since Roman times Europe has been a major stronghold of Christianity, and modern European civilization owes much to Christian influence. In the Middle Ages most Europeans belonged to the Roman Catholic Church, except for the Greeks, Serbians, Bulgarians, and Romanians, who adhered to the Orthodox Eastern Church, as they do today. But the pattern of religions was complicated by two developments that occurred in early modern times: the Turkish invasions of southeastern Europe and the Protestant Reformation. In the sixteenth and seventeenth centuries the Ottoman Turks spread the Moslem faith widely in the Balkan Peninsula, where it endures today as the principal religion of Albania and as a minor faith in Yugoslavia and Bulgaria. As a result of the sixteenth century Reformation, Protestant sects became dominant in northern Germany, Denmark, Norway, Sweden, Finland, Iceland, the Netherlands, and Great Britain. All of these areas have remained dominantly Protestant to the present day. Important Protestant groups are found in Czechoslovakia and Switzerland, and smaller groups in various other European countries. In total number of adherents, however, the Roman Catholic Church is Europe's largest religious division, as it has been since the Christian church was first established. Areas that are predominantly Roman Catholic include Italy, Spain, Portugal, France, rural Switzerland, Belgium, the Republic of Ireland, southern Germany and the German Rhineland, Austria, Poland, Hungary, much of Czechoslovakia, and the Croatian and Slovenian areas in northwestern Yugoslavia. Large Roman Catholic minorities are found in the United Kingdom and other European countries. Jewish minorities exist in many countries, although Jewish populations were decimated by persecution in Nazi Germany, Poland, and other areas formerly controlled by the Nazis. Hundreds of thousands of European Jews have emigrated to Israel. The effects of the official Communist philosophy of atheism in East Central Europe and East Germany are difficult to determine with any degree of precision.

## THE IMPORTANCE OF EUROPE

In recent centuries the peoples of Europe have exerted a profound influence on the rest of mankind. In fact, these centuries have been in many ways a European Age, characterized by great migrations of Europeans to overseas areas, establishment of European political control over vast territories peopled by non-Europeans, and penetration of European trade and cultural influence into all quarters of the globe. "For centuries Europe was at the root of every important world trend: modern civilization stemmed from it; science, art, trade, and migrations fanned out of it and imposed European supremacy on the other parts of the world; standards were set according to European normality." [1]

The interaction of European and non-European peoples and cultures resulting from European expansion has been one of the most significant developments, not only of modern times, but of all human history. Multitudes of people outside of Europe have had their ways of living profoundly altered by the spread of European goods, institutions, languages, customs, beliefs, ideas, and ideals, and the Europeans themselves have been deeply affected by their contacts with other lands.

Modern European expansion had its principal beginnings in the fifteenth and sixteenth centuries, when a series of great voyages of discovery and exploration opened the way to vast new areas previously unknown or only dimly realized. By the nineteenth century Europe stood unchallenged as the dominant region in world affairs. Most areas outside of Europe became dependent on it in either a political or an economic sense, or both. Europe served as a great focus, or center of organization, for the world's economic and political life. From the European core, lines of trade and political influence extended to outlying territories in all parts of the world. This world-wide economic and political system was mainly designed to facilitate the exchange of European manufactured goods for foodstuffs and industrial raw materials (as well as certain manufactures of a luxury character) produced in other parts of the world. Modern techniques of manufacturing were first developed in Europe, and for many decades the manufacturers of Europe had little effective competition in world markets. Most of the world's people depended primarily on Europe for such factory-made items as they were able to afford. Europe, in turn, became dependent on other areas for a considerable part of its food supply and for minerals, fibers, and other materials not produced in Europe, or produced in insufficient quantities to meet the needs of European industry.

In the twentieth century Europe has lost its former predominance. The reasons for this turn of events are complicated, but certain relevant factors can be cited. Among these are: (1) the weakening effects of two world wars, both of which were initiated and mainly fought in Europe; (2) the emergence of the United States and the Soviet Union as world powers; (3) the rise of nationalist movements in the colonial world; and (4) an increasing decentralization in the world of modern types of manufacturing, hence a lessening of the former dependence on Europe for manufactured goods.

Whatever the causes, there can be no doubt that the relative importance of Europe has declined. However, this should not be taken to mean that Europe is now unimportant, for this region is still tremendously significant. Essentially, the continuing importance of Europe seems mainly connected with four factors: (1) its large, dense, and highly skilled population; (2) its large annual production of goods and services; (3) the political, economic, and cultural ties

---

[1] Jean Gottmann, *A Geography of Europe*, rev. ed. New York: Holt, Rinehart and Winston, 1954. P. 1. Used by permission of the author and the publisher.

which it still retains with various overseas areas; and (4) its great potentialities for future development.

## ▶ The Population of Europe

Although Europe is the smallest in area of the major world regions considered in this book, it is the second largest in population, being exceeded only by the Orient. In a space little more than half as large as the United States is concentrated a population more than double that of the United States and Canada combined. Despite the reverses of recent decades, Europe's 420 million people, often highly skilled and long accustomed to political, economic, and cultural leadership, must still be reckoned with as a highly significant factor in world affairs.

Except for most of the Scandinavian Peninsula, most of Finland, and Iceland and the higher mountains, all large sections of Europe have an over-all population density that exceeds the world average. However, the greatest congestion is found along two major population axes—an east-west axis extending from Great Britain across northeastern France, Belgium, the Netherlands, Germany, and western Czechoslovakia to southern Poland; and a north-south axis—broken by the Alps—that extends from Great Britain to northern Italy (map, right). These axes of population correspond to the major axes of European industry. In Europe the densest populations are found in or near the principal industrial districts and depend mainly on manufacturing and associated activities for a livelihood.

## ▶ Productivity of Europe

One of the most significant reasons for the continuing importance of Europe is its immense yearly production of goods and services. Over the centuries the peoples of Europe have developed a complex array of farms, fisheries, mines, and factories, capable of producing a tremendous volume of foodstuffs, raw materials, and manufactures. At present Europe, exclusive of the Soviet Union, produces about one fourth of the

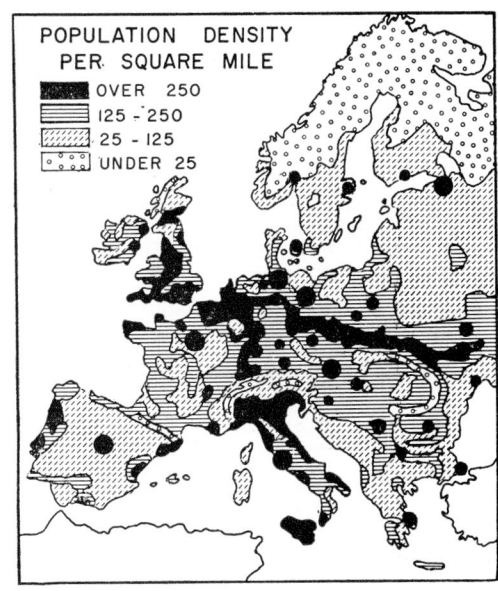

Generalized pattern of population densities in Europe. Black dots represent major urban agglomerations outside the main belts of maximum density. Largest dots represent metropolitan areas of 1,800,000 or over; second largest dots mark areas of 1,000,000 to 1,-800,000; smallest dots mark areas of 500,000 to 1,000,000. Most European urban areas of 500,000 or over lie within the belts of maximum density shown as continuous strips of black. The large dot at upper right marks Leningrad in the Soviet Union. (Modified from a map in Jean Gottmann, *A Geography of Europe,* Holt, Rinehart and Winston, 1954.)

world's wheat, one third of its oats and barley and one half of its rye, two fifths of its coal, one third of its iron ore and steel, and large amounts of many other important commodities.

Especially significant on a world scale is Europe's production of manufactured goods. Although the relative importance of European manufacturing has declined, this region still represents one of the three greatest concentrations of industry on the globe. Only Anglo-America and the Soviet Union are in a class with Europe as manufacturing regions. Since World War II, most European countries have greatly expanded their total output of manufactured goods over prewar levels.

European production is not confined merely to production of commodities. In a broad sense the term production also includes services of various kinds, such as transport and communication services, banking, insurance, and investment services, and others. Europe has long been the center of a world-wide network of service facilities, and still retains great importance in this regard, although the United States has offered increasing competition in recent decades, especially in financial services.

### ► Continuing Ties with Overseas Areas

Although their influence in overseas areas has declined, many European countries continue to have strong political, economic, and cultural ties with countries outside of Europe. For example, the United Kingdom, which has been historically the most important of the colonizing and imperial powers, still forms the center of a Commonwealth of Nations embracing about a fourth of the world's land and people (see pp. 85–87). In recent years many colonial possessions of European nations have secured independence (map, right). However, some of them have retained at least a nominal political tie with the home country. Such ties are exemplified by voluntary "commonwealth" bonds connecting India, Pakistan, Nigeria, and other Asian and African countries with the United Kingdom, and by ties between France and the independent units of the French Community (see p. 94).

Many countries outside of Europe, whether associated politically with European nations or not, still look to Europe as a market for their surplus foodstuffs and industrial raw materials and as a supplier of manufactured goods which they do not produce in sufficient quantities to meet their needs. The bulk of the world's seaborne commerce still moves in European ships, and the world-wide European network of communication, insurance, and banking facilities is still vitally important to the transaction of the world's business.

Less tangible than political and economic ties, but nevertheless important, are cultural ties between European nations and overseas countries. Such ties are especially well exemplified by the close cultural bonds between Great Britain and its former colonies of Australia, New Zealand, and Canada. Although the latter nations are entirely self-governing, their cultures reflect many affiliations with the home country.

### ► Potentialities of Europe

The potentialities of Europe, like those of almost any region, are difficult to assess. Much will depend on events and trends in the rest of the world. But there is no doubt that Europe, given peacetime conditions and favorable trading relationships with other regions, has the necessary manpower, skills, experience, resources, productive plant, and world-wide commercial and political connections to achieve much higher levels of productivity and a better life for its citizens. Perhaps it can even regain a measure of its lost influence in world affairs. Realization of these goals will depend partly on the ultimate success of current efforts to bring about a greater degree of economic and political unity, or at least cooperation, among the European nations. This movement, essentially a post-World War II phenomenon, is described in the following section.

## INTERNATIONAL COOPERATION IN POSTWAR EUROPE

In the years immediately following World War II, the peoples and countries of Europe were in difficult straits. Communist expansion, backed by the military power of the Soviet Union, threatened their liberties and way of life. Communist parties took control

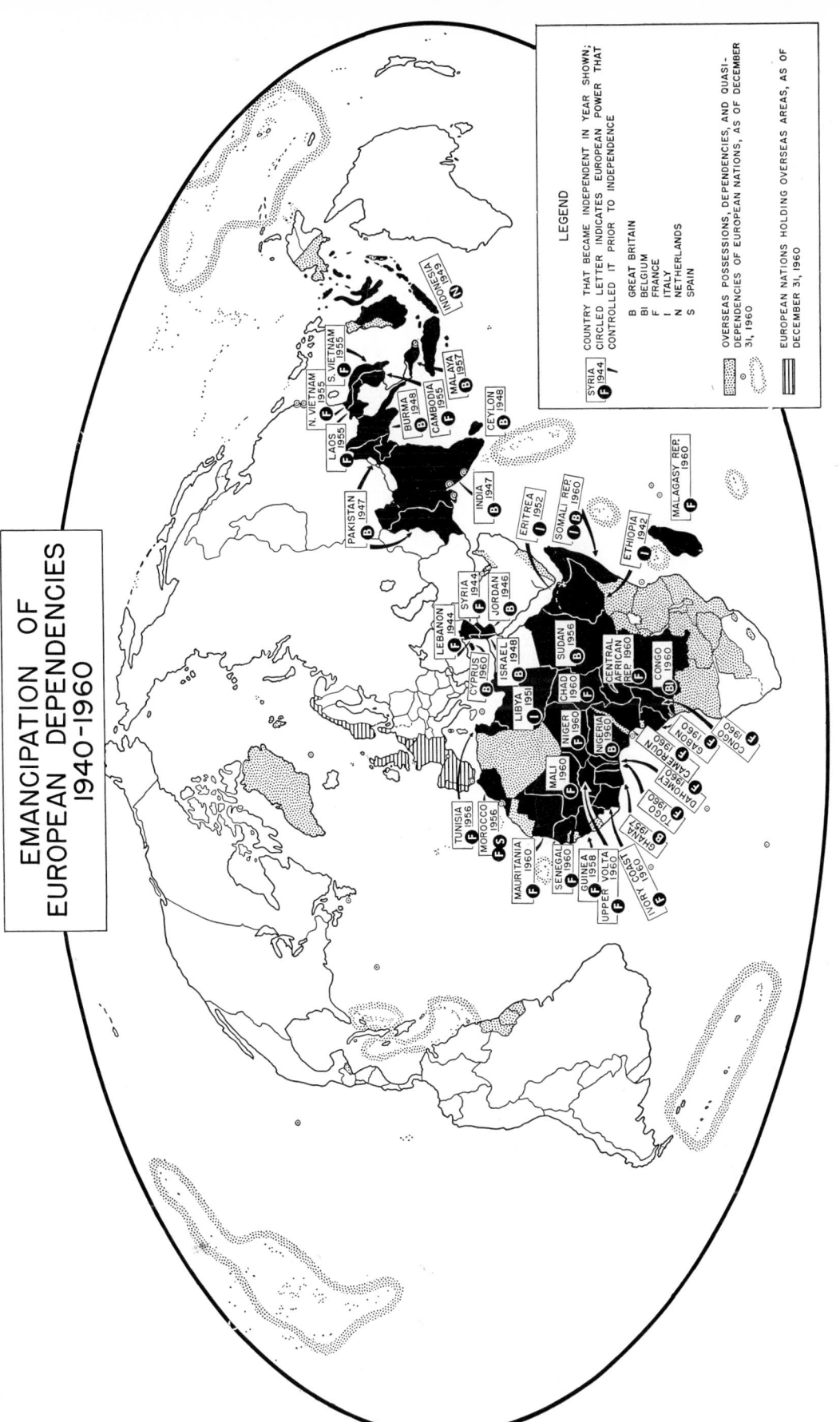

# EMANCIPATION OF EUROPEAN DEPENDENCIES 1940-1960

The period 1940–1960 saw great changes in the political map of the world, resulting in considerable part from the emancipation of overseas areas held by European nations. Dotted bands in the oceans surround general areas within which the included islands were still held by European nations (nearly all by the United Kingdom or France) at the end of 1960. The circled dot in the Arctic Ocean east of Greenland marks Jan Mayen Island, a possession of Norway. Five small units of former French India which were ceded to India by France in the early 1950s are not indicated on the map. Some uninhabited island possessions of European nations, as well as Antarctic claims, are not shown. (Briesemeister Elliptical Equal Area Projection, courtesy of the American Geographical Society.)

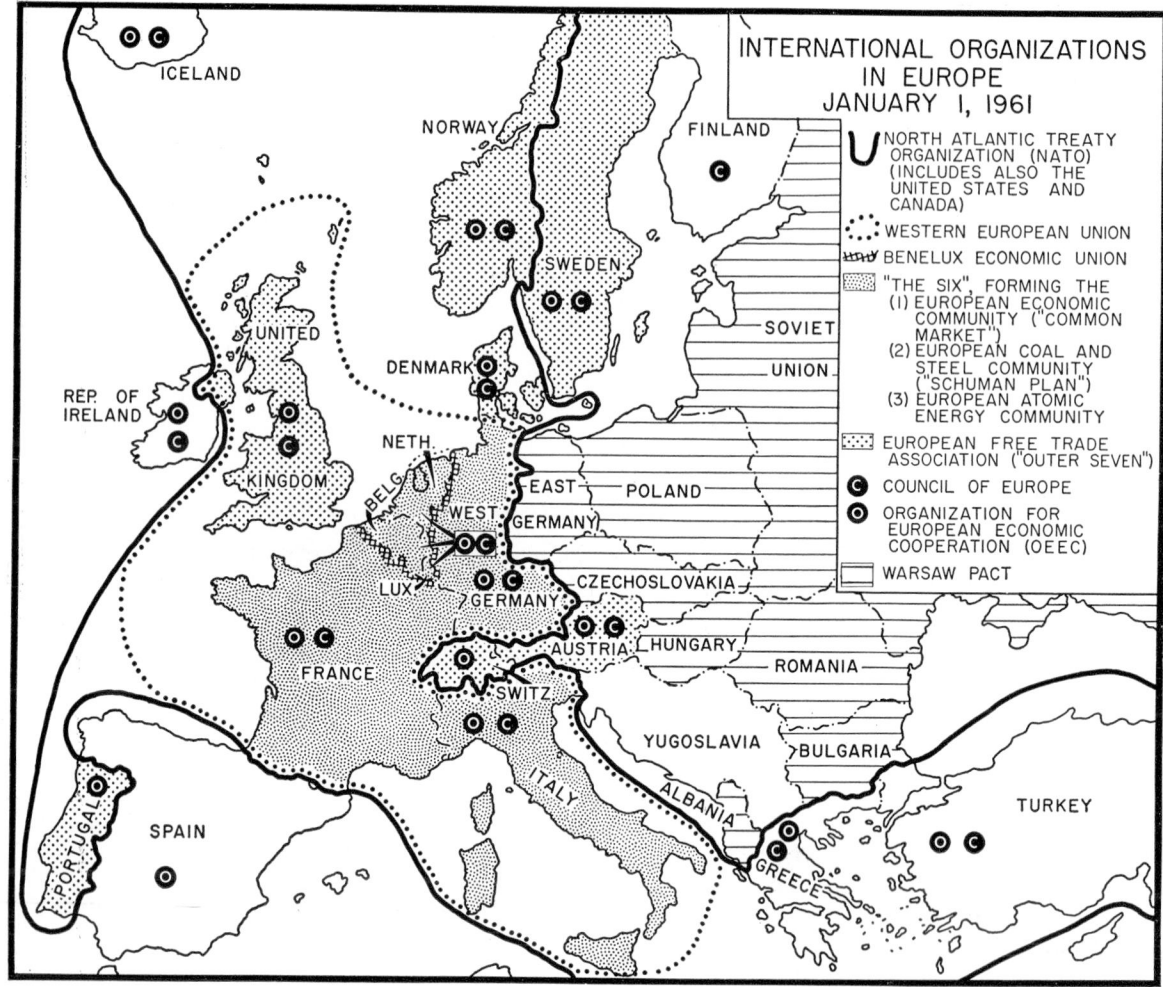

International economic, political, and military organizations in Europe, as of January 1, 1961. A formal military alliance of the Soviet Union and its European satellites was formed under the Warsaw Pact in 1956. Late in 1960 a convention was signed to change the name of OEEC to Organization for Economic Cooperation and Development (OECD) and to include the United States and Canada in its membership. The move was subject to ratification by the national legislatures of the countries concerned.

in the countries of East Central Europe and in East Germany, and seemed on the verge of doing so in Italy and France. In the overseas possessions of the European colonial powers there was increasing pressure for independence. Great Britain and France were faced with revolts and widespread disorder in their Middle Eastern, African, and Asian possessions. The Netherlands, driven from its East Indian empire by Japan in World War II, was unable to regain effective con-

trol after Japan's defeat. Meanwhile the economies of most European nations labored under a severe strain. Financial reserves had been drained by six years of fighting, and a normal peacetime pattern of production and trade was slow to emerge after the war. Serious economic crises were experienced by several countries in 1946 and 1947.

A saving factor, American economic and military aid, now entered the situation. In 1948 the United States, faced with an urgent need to bolster the nations of western and southern Europe against Communism, began sending them financial aid under the Marshall Plan to stimulate economic recovery. In the military sphere the North Atlantic Treaty Organization (NATO), a defensive alliance, was formed in 1949. Comprised of the United States, Canada, and the majority of European nations outside the "iron curtain" (map, left), it provided a vehicle for funneling American military aid to Europe.

The European countries receiving American aid responded vigorously, and after 1948 the trend of economic recovery and military preparedness was steadily upward. Meanwhile a significant movement toward greater cooperation and unity, especially in the economic sphere, was developing. It grew out of a feeling on the part of many Europeans, including important leaders in several countries, that the security and development of their countries required their combination into larger economic and political units, though opinions varied as to the proper degree and form of combination. The result was a series of new "communities" and other intra-European organizations designed to foster unity (map, left). These efforts were actively encouraged by the United States, but the principal initiative came from Europe itself. One of the earliest organizations to be formed was the Council of Europe, a deliberative "parliament" composed of political and intellectual leaders from the participating states. It held its first session in 1949 at Strasbourg on the French-German boundary. Some idealists viewed it as the beginning of a federated "United States of Europe," but so far it has been only a useful forum to promote the general cause of greater European unity.

It is in the economic sphere that the most notable progress has been made. Many European leaders, feeling that schemes for political federation were impracticable or premature, have bent their primary efforts toward establishing economic unification, often with the hope that political unification would follow. In 1948 the Organization for European Economic Cooperation (OEEC) (map, left) was formed to plan and coordinate the use of Marshall Plan funds and otherwise to promote recovery and economic advance. The Marshall Plan was terminated in 1952, but OEEC continued to function (see caption to map, left).

A much publicized and highly significant aspect of the movement for greater economic unity has been the effort of six OEEC members—France, West Germany, Italy, Belgium, the Netherlands, and Luxembourg—to fuse their economies through progressive removal of trade barriers among themselves and establishment of a common tariff against outside nations. In 1948 Belgium, the Netherlands, and Luxembourg inaugurated the Benelux Economic Union. Five years later the European Coal and Steel Community, formed in 1951 under the Schuman Plan, began to operate. Comprised of "the Six," its purpose was to expand and integrate the production and lower the unit costs of coal, iron ore, steel, and scrap, thus laying a foundation for general economic advance. The six nations pledged themselves to remove restrictions on the flow of these commodities across their respective frontiers. Hindrances to the flow of labor and investment capital in the coal, iron, and steel industries were also to be removed. A supranational High Authority was created as the Community's administrative arm, and legislative and judicial organs also were provided. In effect, each member state has surrendered a little of its sovereignty to the supranational government of the Community, which is charged with regulating and developing the coal, iron, and steel industries as if no frontiers between them existed.

## ▶ The Common Market and the "Outer Seven"

In 1958, after several years of negotiation, the six Schuman Plan nations inaugurated the European Economic Community or "Common Market." Its scope was much broader than that of the Coal and Steel Community. Tariffs and other trade restrictions were to be progressively removed on a wide range of industrial and agricultural commodities over a period of 12 to 15 years. Restrictions on the movement of workers and capital from one country to another were also to be removed. Thus the six nations would become, in most economic respects, one unit, with a standardized set of tariffs, quotas, and other regulations governing their trade with the outside world.

In creating the European Economic Community, the six countries are trying to secure the benefits of large-scale production by pooling their resources and furnishing a larger assured market for efficient producers. They anticipate that investment in mass-production enterprises will be stimulated and that increased specialization will develop, with each part of the Community expanding lines of goods that it is best fitted to produce. Trusts and cartels, which have long restricted competition within and among the six nations, are to be eliminated or discouraged. By merging their economies, the six countries hope to achieve greater production, larger exports, lower costs to consumers, higher wages, and a higher level of living than any one of them could achieve on its own.

Collectively, the six members of the European Economic Community comprise a unit that is impressively large in total population and that is equipped with substantial resources and great numbers of highly skilled workers. Its population is only about 10 million smaller than that of the United States. Its trade is of the first order of importance (map, right). But the estimated total consumption of goods and services by its people, measured by value, was only a third as great as United States consumption in the mid-1950s. The nations of the Community anticipate that their new organization will provide a means for narrowing this gap in consumption.

The negotiations that led to the signing of the Common Market treaties in 1957 also produced the European Atomic Energy Community (Euratom). In forming this organization, the six nations agreed to pool their atomic resources and to proceed cooperatively in the development of atomic energy. The Common Market and Euratom are governed by supranational authorities in the same general manner as the European Coal and Steel Community.

The United Kingdom, though it is ranged with "the Six" in a military alliance called the Western European Union (organized within the framework of the North Atlantic Treaty Organization to permit the rearmament of West Germany), has remained outside the European Coal and Steel Community, Common Market, and Atomic Energy Community. It has feared that membership in these organizations would jeopardize its economic and political relationships with the Commonwealth of Nations and the United States. In 1959 the United Kingdom was the leader in a movement to create a seven-nation "outer" free-trade area in which the members would eliminate trade restrictions among themselves but would maintain separate tariff schedules against outside nations. This arrangement would permit the United Kingdom to continue operating within the system of tariff preferences in the Commonwealth of Nations. An agreement to establish the free-trade area was signed in the summer of 1959, and the new organization, officially the European Free Trade Association, commenced to operate in 1960. Its members, often called the "Outer Seven," include the United Kingdom, Sweden, Denmark, Norway, Switzerland, Austria, and Portugal. Fears were current during and after its formation that the existence of two trading blocs—the "Inner Six" (Common Market) and the "Outer Seven"—would harm the over-all cause of European unity. At the time of writing, attempts were being made to harmonize the interests of the two groups of nations and thus to forestall possible friction and discord between them.

# A TRADE VIEW OF THE WORLD

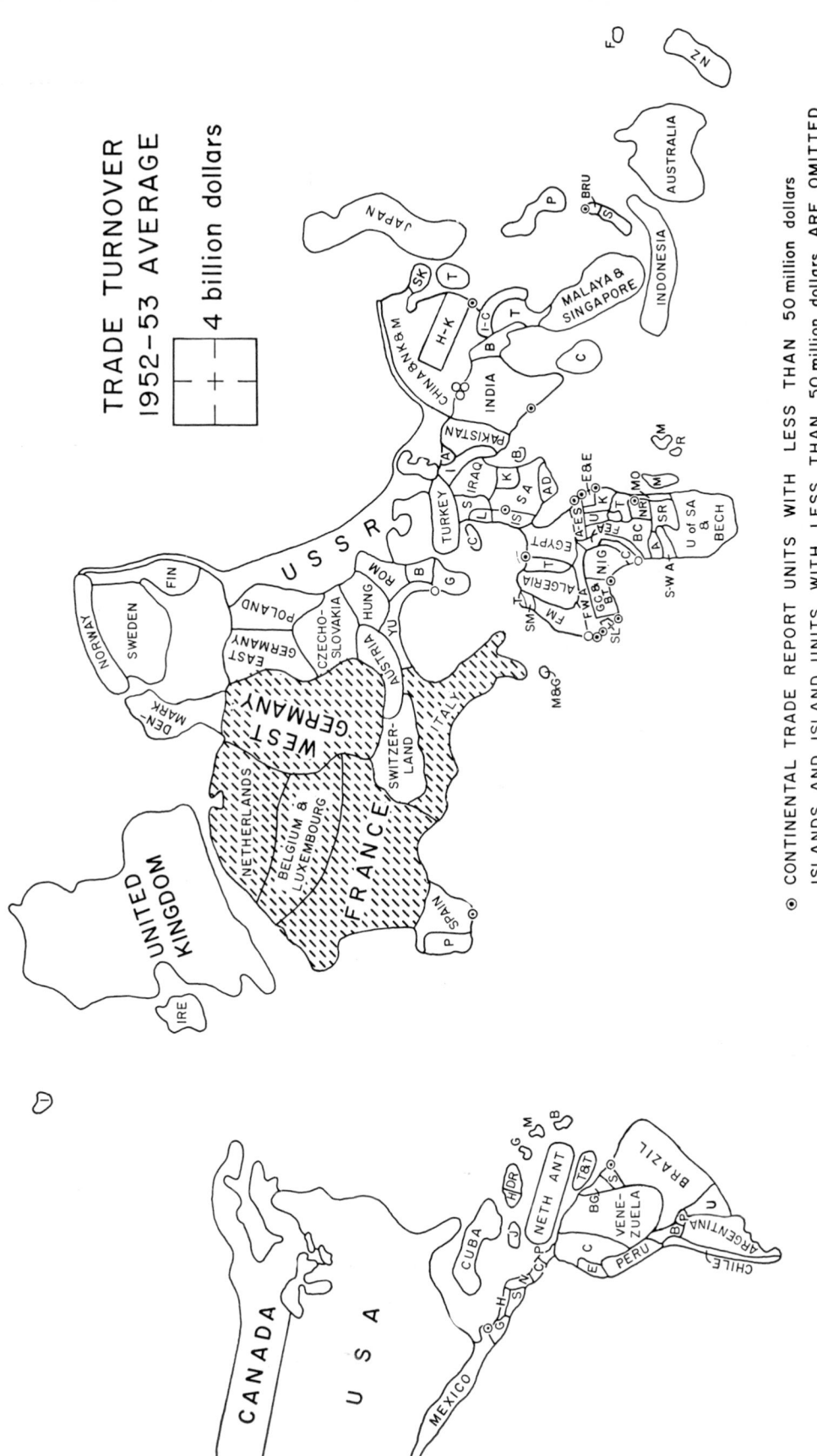

## TRADE TURNOVER
### 1952–53 AVERAGE

4 billion dollars

⊙ CONTINENTAL TRADE REPORT UNITS WITH LESS THAN 50 million dollars

ISLANDS AND ISLAND UNITS WITH LESS THAN 50 million dollars ARE OMITTED

○ UNITS FOR WHICH COMPARABLE DATA ARE NOT AVAILABLE

The size of political units as shown on the above map is proportional to their trade turnover (*i.e.*, their imports plus their exports). The dash pattern showing the six countries of the Common Market has been added to the original map. (From Andreas and Lois Grotewold, "Some Geographical Aspects of International Trade," *Economic Geography*, v. 33, 1957, p. 258. Used by permission of the authors and *Economic Geography*.)

The main islands, seas, peninsulas, and rivers of Europe.

## MAJOR FEATURES OF THE EUROPEAN ENVIRONMENT

The diversity of Europe is not limited to cultural diversity. The natural environment also is diverse. Probably no area of equal size in the entire world exhibits such a variety of natural conditions and resources. On the whole, this environment has proved favorable for human settlement and use. No other world region contains such a small proportion of unproductive land. In the following paragraphs certain significant features of the European environment are briefly discussed.

### ► Irregular Outline

One of the most noticeable characteristics of Europe as seen on a map is its extremely irregular outline. The main peninsula of Europe is fringed by numerous smaller peninsulas, including the Scandinavian, Iberian, Italian, and Balkan peninsulas of the second order of size, the still smaller peninsulas of Jutland, Brittany, and Cornwall, and many others (map, left). Offshore are a multitude of islands, including such large and well-known islands as Great Britain, Ireland, Iceland, Sicily, Sardinia, Corsica, and Crete. Around the indented shores of Europe arms of the sea penetrate the land and countless harbors offer a protection for shipping. The complex mingling of land and water has created an environment which provides many opportunities for maritime activity, and almost every European nation possessing a stretch of coast has turned extensively to the sea for a part of its livelihood. Excluding a few of the semi-independent micro-states, only four European countries—Switzerland, Austria, Czechoslovakia, and Hungary—lack direct access to the sea. Even these countries, however, are connected with the sea by rivers navigable for barges.

### ► Northerly Location

A circumstance of European geography which is not always appreciated is the northerly location of this world region. Much of Europe, including some of the most densely populated areas, lies north of continental United States. We are so accustomed to thinking of these northern lands as bleak and forbidding that it comes as a surprise to realize that Scotland lies in the same general lat-

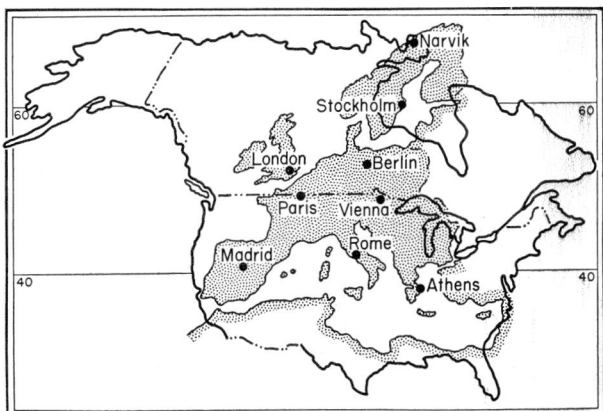

Europe and the Mediterranean Sea compared in latitude and area with the United States and Canada. Most islands have been omitted. (Goode's Homolosine Equal Area Projection, copyright University of Chicago Press.)

itude as Hudson Bay and that Norway has many communities located as far north as the northern mainland of Canada. The British Isles, the Scandinavian countries, Belgium, the Netherlands, and most of Germany and Poland lie north of continental United States (map, above). Only in Spain, Italy, and Greece do European latitudes reach as far south as North Carolina or Tennessee.

### ► Temperate Climate

As might be inferred from the presence of some of the world's most densely populated

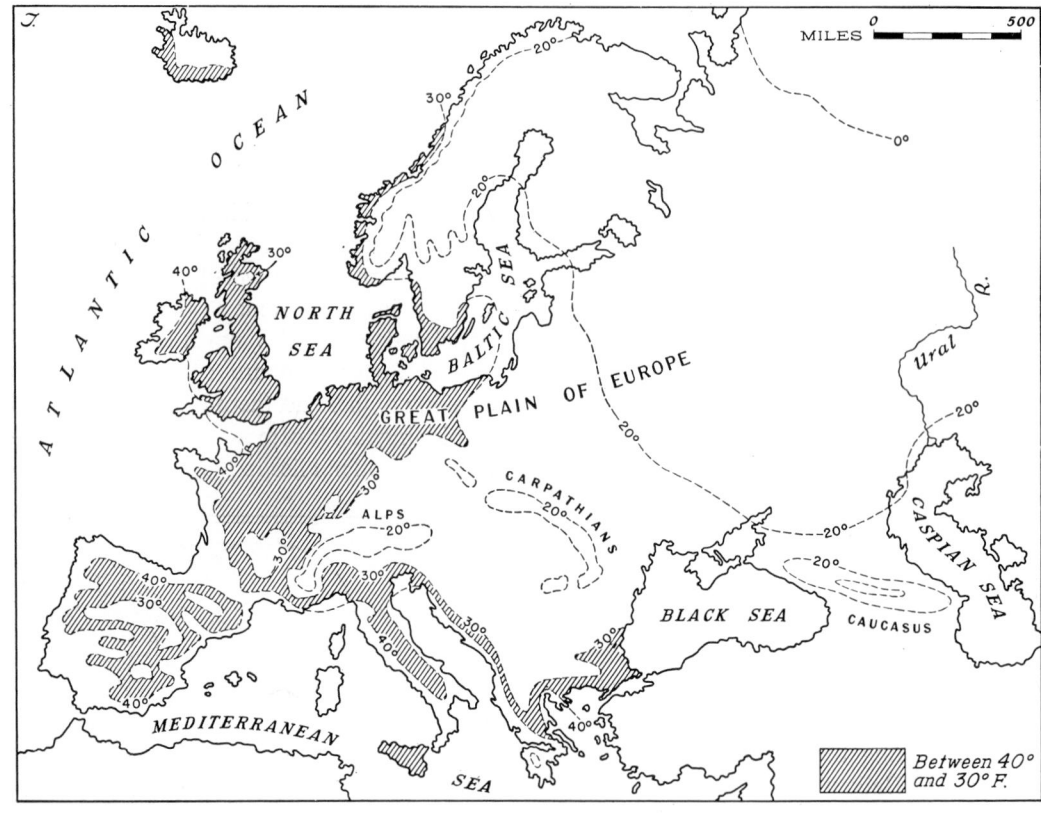

Actual temperatures in Europe in January in degrees Fahrenheit. The dashed lines, known as isotherms, connect places having the same average January temperature. (From Jean Gottmann, *A Geography of Europe*, rev. ed., New York: Holt, Rinehart and Winston, 1954.)

areas in latitudes corresponding to those of Canada, the climate of Europe is more temperate than the northerly location would suggest. Winter temperatures, in particular, are very mild for the latitude. For example, London, England, has approximately the same average temperature in January as Richmond, Virginia, which is 950 miles farther south. Reykjavik, the capital of Iceland, is nearly as warm in January as St. Louis, 1750 miles to the south, and Tromsö, located on the coast of Norway 3° north of the Arctic Circle, has a slightly higher January average than Chicago, which is 1900 miles farther south. (In the preceding comparisons, distances given are approximate and the places named lie at generally comparable elevations above sea level.) Such anomalies of temperature are largely due to

the influence of relatively warm currents of ocean water which wash the western shores of Europe during the winter. These currents, originating in tropical parts of the Atlantic Ocean, drift to the north and east, and make the waters around Europe in winter much warmer than the latitude would warrant. Westerly winds, blowing across these waters, bring considerable amounts of warmth to the land, making temperatures abnormally high, even in midwinter. Such effects are naturally most striking in places on or near the sea, although the moderating influence of the westerly winds and warm ocean waters is felt to some degree in all parts of Europe. In summer the ocean tends to have a cooling effect so that the seaward parts of Europe seldom experience excessively high summer temperatures.

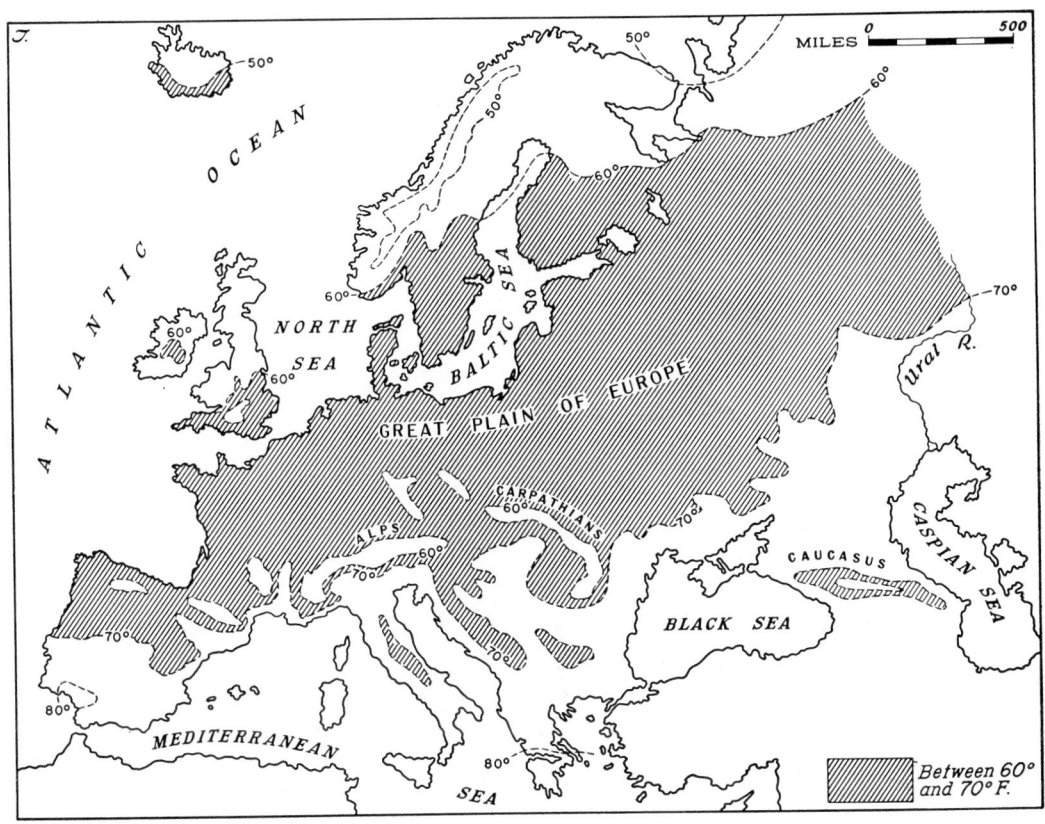

Actual temperatures in Europe in July. (From Jean Gottmann, *A Geography of Europe,* rev. ed., New York: Holt, Rinehart and Winston, 1954.)

Most large bodies of water temper the climate of adjoining land areas to some degree. Water gains and loses heat more slowly than land, and thus the oceans, seas, gulfs, and even large lakes have a moderating or stabilizing influence on the climate of lands which they border. The climate of Europe is affected not only by the open Atlantic, but also by the many arms of the Atlantic, such as the North Sea, Baltic Sea, and Mediterranean Sea, which penetrate deeply into the land. However, it is the Atlantic itself which has the most profound influence.

The same winds which bring warmth in winter and coolness in summer also bring abundant moisture to the land. Most of this falls in the form of rain, although the higher mountains and more northerly areas have considerable snow. Most European lowlands receive 20 inches or more of precipita-

tion a year (map, p. 44), and a few highland areas receive 100 inches or more. The general average of precipitation in the lowlands is 20 to 35 inches; few areas receive more than 40 inches a year. Although in some parts of the world 20 to 30 inches of precipitation would be distinctly marginal for agriculture, in western and northern Europe this amount is ample for a wide range of crops. The latter is essentially due to the effect of mild temperatures and high atmospheric humidity, which lessen the rate of evaporation and thus increase the effectiveness of the precipitation for crop growth. However, in Mediterranean Europe conditions are more unfavorable. In this area high summer temperatures cause excessive evaporation, and the yearly regime of rainfall concentrates most of the rain in the winter half-year. Thus moisture is most defi-

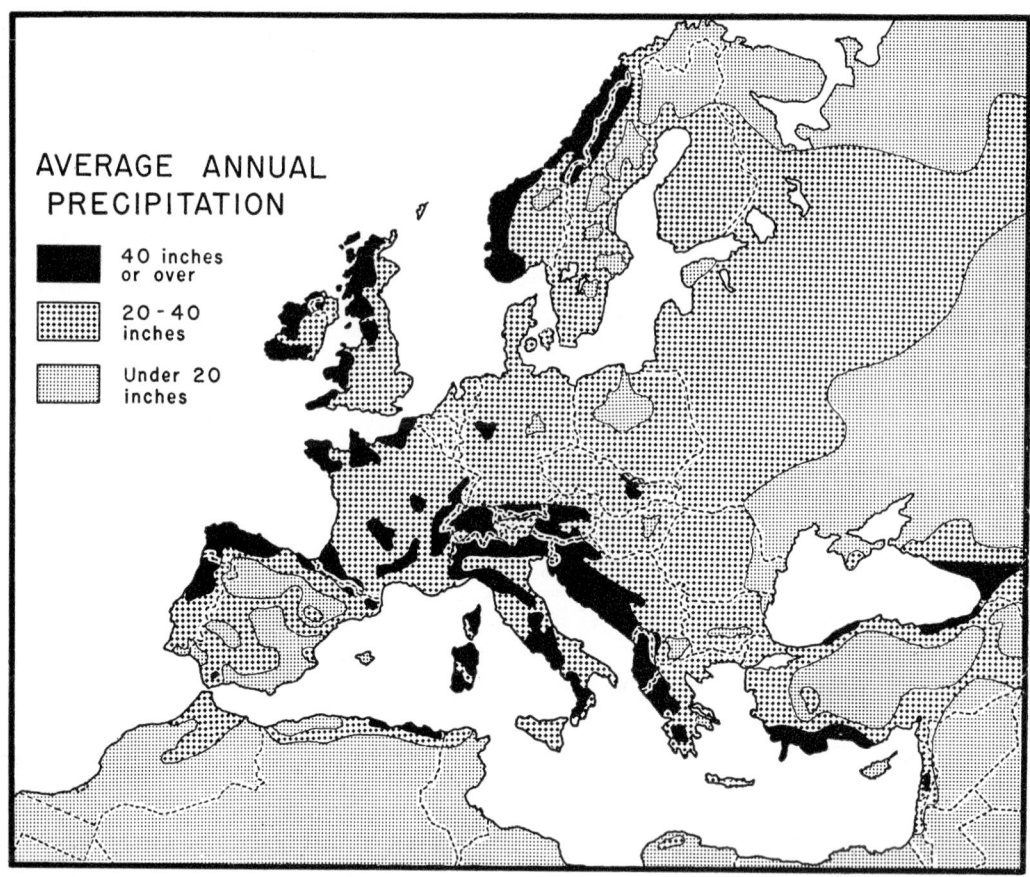

AVERAGE ANNUAL PRECIPITATION

40 inches or over

20-40 inches

Under 20 inches

Most parts of Europe receive sufficient total precipitation for crop production, although the utility of the rainfall in areas of mediterranean climate is lessened by its concentration in the colder half of the year. Highlands along windward coasts often receive excessively heavy precipitation. (After a map of the Office of Foreign Agricultural Relations, U. S. Department of Agriculture.)

cient during the summer season when it is needed most by growing crops.

### Types of Climate

Geographers and climatologists have observed, primarily on the basis of records kept by weather stations, that climate tends to be fairly uniform over considerable areas. Various systems have been devised for classifying climates into "types," to which descriptive names have often been applied, varying with the particular climatic system. Each climate type has certain characteristics of temperature, precipitation, wind behavior, and so forth, which tend to distinguish it from other types. In addition, each

type has certain associated features of vegetation, soil, and, to some degree, landforms, which tend to occur wherever the type is found. An area characterized by a particular climate type is known as a climatic region. Maps have been made showing the distribution of climatic types and regions on a world basis. Although such maps are somewhat inaccurate, due to lack of data for certain areas, they are extremely useful in geographic study. (See endpaper climatic map.)

*Marine West Coast Climate.* Climatic effects of the ocean are most pronounced in areas along the northwestern seaboard of Europe. The climate of these areas is often referred to as the *marine west coast* or *humid marine* climate. This type of climate is characterized by relatively mild winters and relatively cool summers, with ample precipitation for crops at all seasons, a high proportion of cloudy weather, especially in winter, and considerable fog. Throughout the year, changes of weather follow each other in rapid succession. Rainfall in the marine west coast climate tends to come in slow drizzles, often lasting for days. London has experienced as many as 72 successive rainy days. There are a large proportion of rainy days during the year. On the average London has 164 rainy days and Paris 188; parts of the Shetland Islands, north of Scotland, have 260 rainy days a year.[2] Winter days are characteristically short, cloudy, dull, and humid. In the lowlands winter snowfall is light, and the ground is seldom covered for more than a few days at a time. Summer days are longer, brighter, and more pleasant, but even in summer a good many chilly and overcast days occur. The frost-free season of 175 to 250 days is sufficiently long for most crops grown in the middle latitudes to mature. However, excessively cool and/or rainy summers in some areas are a handicap to certain crops such as corn and wheat. Regions of marine west coast climate are found in other parts of the world besides northwestern Europe, a notable example being the Pacific coast of Anglo-America from San Francisco northward to southern Alaska.

*Humid Continental Climate.* Inland from the coast in western and central Europe, the marine climate gradually changes. Winters become colder, summers hotter; the annual precipitation becomes somewhat less, with more precipitation in summer than in winter; and the percentage of cloudiness and fog decreases. At a considerable distance inland the climate becomes sufficiently different to be considered a separate type—the *humid continental* climate. This type of climate, which prevails in most of East Central Europe, is similar in many ways to the climate of east central United States.

*Mediterranean Climate.* Southern Europe has an unusually distinctive type of climate —the *dry-summer subtropical* or *mediterranean climate*. The most characteristic feature of this climate type is the occurrence of a pronounced autumn and winter maximum of precipitation. The total yearly precipitation is less, on the average, than in the marine west coast and humid continental climates, and very little precipitation occurs during the summer months, when temperatures are most advantageous for crop growth. Mediterranean summers are warm to hot, and winters are mild. In the lowlands snow is rare, although it may accumulate to considerable depths on adjacent mountains. The frost-free season is very long, lasting practically the entire year in some of the more southerly lowlands. Winters in this climatic region are famous for their mild, bright, sunny weather—a great attraction to tourists from the damper, cloudier, cooler regions to the north. In the United States a mediterranean type of climate occurs in parts of central and southern California.

*Subarctic, Tundra, and Highland Climates.* The greater part of Northern Europe has a *subarctic climate* characterized by long, severe winters and short, rather cool summers. Due to the shortness of the frost-free season, only the hardier crops can be grown. Most of the land in the subarctic areas is covered by coniferous forest.

The *tundra climate* is found in northerly areas where conditions are too severe for a normal stand of trees. In such areas the vegetation is composed of moss, lichens, grass, low bushes, and a scattering of stunted trees. Conditions are even less favorable for agriculture than in the subarctic zone. Frost is apt to occur at any time during the year. The principal areas of tundra climate in Europe are found along the Arctic shore of the

---

[2] Glenn T. Trewartha, *An Introduction to Climate.* New York: McGraw-Hill, 1954. P. 319.

European mainland and on the island of Iceland. Both the subarctic climate and the tundra climate of Europe are duplicated, on a much larger scale, in the Soviet Union and Canada. These climatic zones are among the most sparsely settled parts of Europe.

The higher mountains of Europe, like high mountains in other parts of the world, have a *highland climate* varying in character according to altitude. In parts of the Alps, for instance, a range of climates is found which varies from subtropical at the base of the mountains to tundra and ice-cap climates at the highest elevations.

## TABLE 2

### CLIMATIC DATA FOR SELECTED EUROPEAN STATIONS

| LATITUDE (TO NEAREST WHOLE DEGREE) | STATION | ELEVA- TION ABOVE SEA LEVEL (FEET) | TYPE OF CLIMATE | AVERAGE TEMPERATURE (DEGREES F TO NEAREST WHOLE DEGREE) | | | PRECIPITATION | |
|---|---|---|---|---|---|---|---|---|
| | | | | ANNUAL | JANU- ARY | JULY | ANNUAL AVER- AGE (TO NEAREST INCH) | PERCENT OCCUR- RING APRIL –SEPTEM- BER (TO NEAREST WHOLE PERCENT) |
| 53°N. | Dublin (Ireland) | 155 | Marine west coast | 48° | 41° | 59° | 28″ | 50% |
| 56°N. | Glasgow (Scotland) | 180 | Marine west coast | 47° | 39° | 58° | 37″ | 46% |
| 52°N. | London (England) | 18 | Marine west coast | 50° | 41° | 63° | 24″ | 48% |
| 49°N. | Paris (France) | 164 | Marine west coast | 50° | 37° | 65° | 22″ | 52% |
| 51°N. | Brussels (Belgium) | 328 | Marine west coast | 50° | 36° | 64° | 33″ | 51% |
| 56°N. | Copenhagen (Denmark) | 16 | Marine west coast | 46° | 31° | 63° | 21″ | 54% |
| 60°N. | Bergen (Norway) | 72 | Marine west coast | 45° | 34° | 58° | 84″ | 42% |
| 53°N. | Berlin (Germany) | 131 | Humid continental | 49° | 32° | 66° | 23″ | 56% |
| 52°N. | Warsaw (Poland) | 399 | Humid continental | 46° | 26° | 66° | 21″ | 61% |
| 45°N. | Belgrade (Yugoslavia) | 453 | Humid continental | 52° | 31° | 71° | 25″ | 58% |
| 43°N. | Marseilles (France) | 246 | Mediterranean | 57° | 43° | 72° | 23″ | 38% |
| 42°N. | Rome (Italy) | 208 | Mediterranean | 60° | 45° | 76° | 33″ | 32% |
| 38°N. | Athens (Greece) | 326 | Mediterranean | 63° | 48° | 80° | 16″ | 24% |
| 66°N. | Haparanda (Sweden) | 30 | Subarctic | 34° | 14° | 60° | 21″ | 51% |
| 70°N. | Vardö (Norway) | 33 | Tundra | 33° | 22° | 48° | 26″ | 42% |
| 47°N. | Santis (Switzerland) | 8202 | Highland | 27° | 16° | 41° | 96″ | 61% |

Temperature and precipitation data for selected European climatic stations are given in Table 2.

Taken as a whole, the climates of Europe are temperate, humid, seasonal climates which have proved favorable for human settlement. The general range of climates in Europe is duplicated in other parts of the world, most notably in Anglo-America. It is to overseas areas having climates generally similar to those of Europe that Europeans have migrated in the largest numbers.

## ▶ Varied Topography

The surface features of Europe are extremely diversified (map, p. 48). It is safe to say that no other area of equal size exhibits so much variety. Plains, plateaus, hill lands, and mountains form a complex pattern, and together with associated vegetation, water bodies, and works of man, produce a variegated and often highly scenic landscape.

[EDITORIAL COMMENT. Geographers are not in agreement regarding the precise meaning of plains, plateaus, hill lands, and mountains. In general, a *plain* is a relatively level area of slight elevation (although the "High Plains" of western United States reach elevations of 5000 feet above sea level). Some plains are flat, but most of them exhibit gentle to moderate slopes. However, it is the horizontal rather than the vertical dimension which predominates in plains country. Most of the world's people live on plains, so that consideration of plains and their significance becomes a highly important facet of geographic study. Geographers constantly speak of "land level enough" for farming, transportation, and the like.

To a degree, a *plateau* is simply an elevated plain. Most areas recognized as plateaus lie at elevations of 2000 feet or more, although some are considerably lower. To qualify as plateaus in the strictest sense, such areas should be terminated on at least one side by a steep edge, or *escarpment,* marking an abrupt transition from the plateau surface to areas at a lower elevation. However, the word "plateau" is often used loosely in referring to relatively level areas lying at considerable heights, whether terminated by a definite escarpment or not. Well-defined plateaus are often spoken of as "tablelands."

In *hill lands* and *mountains* the vertical dimension predominates. No sure way has been devised to distinguish between these two classes of landforms. In general, mountains are higher and more rugged than hill lands, are more of a barrier to movement, and offer fewer possibilities for human settlement and use. Whereas many areas of hill land support moderate to dense populations, most mountain areas are sparsely populated. Local usage of the term "mountain" varies greatly from place to place over the earth. In plains country, areas of a few hundred feet elevation which stand out conspicuously above their surroundings may be called "mountains" by the local inhabitants. However, the term is most commonly used in reference to comparatively rugged areas lying at least 2000 to 3000 feet above sea level.]

One of the most prominent surface features of Europe is a vast plain which extends from the Pyrenees Mountains across western and northern France, central and northern Belgium, the Netherlands, northern Germany, Denmark, and Poland, and stretches without a break far into the Soviet Union (map, p. 48). Outliers of this plain are found in Great Britain, in the southern part of the Scandinavian Peninsula, and in southern Finland. On this North European Plain are found the largest expanses of arable land in Europe. In addition, there are valuable deposits of coal, potash, salt, and other minerals. For many centuries this plain has been a major avenue of movement between east and west in Europe. Today it forms the

# NATURAL REGIONS of EUROPE

The meaning of the symbols in the legend at lower left is as follows: A—humid mid-latitude plains; B—humid mid-latitude hill lands (including small areas of low mountains and of plains); C—mediterranean (dry-summer) subtropical hills, tablelands, and small plains; D—glacially scoured subarctic plains and hills forested in conifers; E—Arctic tundra; F—mountains; G—approximate boundary between marine west coast climate (west of line) and humid continental climate (east of line) between the Alps and the Baltic Sea. Prominent cities are shown as reference points by a dot and capital letter.

A glaciated landscape in North Europe. The town in the view is Strängnäs, situated on the shore of Lake Mälaren in central Sweden. (Swedish National Travel Office.)

principal focus of European industrial, commercial, and agricultural activity. For the most part the North European Plain is not flat, except in certain areas, but contains great stretches of undulating or rolling land, with many gentle hills.

South of the northern plain, Europe is predominantly mountainous or hilly, although the mountains and hill masses enclose many relatively level areas. The mountains of southern Europe are mostly rugged alpine mountains, with many jagged peaks and snowcapped summits. The highest peaks are found in the Alps, a massive snowclad range containing many summits of 12,000 feet or higher. These mountains constitute a considerable barrier to traffic, though on the

whole a less formidable barrier than their appearance on a map would suggest, since they are cut through by many passes, river valleys, and tunnels. To the countries in which they lie, the mountains are valuable as sources of hydroelectric power, as tourist attractions, and as defensive ramparts in wartime. In some areas, particularly the Balkan Peninsula, they have tended to isolate small groups of people, and thus have aided in the development of many small, distinctive regions.

The hill lands of Europe are lower and less rugged than the mountains. Generally speaking, the hill lands are older than the mountains in point of geologic time. Having been formed earlier, they have been exposed to weathering and erosion for a longer period and thus have a smoother and more rounded aspect. Many of the important deposits of metals in Europe are found in the hill lands.

At the north the North European Plain is fringed by glaciated lowlands and hill lands in eastern Sweden and Finland, and by rugged, ice-scoured (though not very high) mountains in western Sweden and Norway. In the British Isles a few sizable areas of lowland are fringed by hill country and low mountains.

[EDITORIAL COMMENT. During the Great Ice Age, a massive continental ice sheet formed over the Scandinavian Peninsula and Scotland, from which it moved outward into Germany, Poland, the Netherlands, England, and Russia. Over a period of perhaps a million years ice sheets alternately advanced and retreated as glacial and interglacial ages succeeded each other. The latest retreat of the ice is thought to have begun at least 35,000 years ago. Continental ice sheets still cover about 10 percent of the earth's land surface in Greenland and Antarctica, as compared with an estimated 28 percent of the lands when the glaciers were at their maximum extent.

In some glaciated areas the ice sheets scoured deeply, removing most of the surface soil and gouging hollows which became lakes when the ice melted. Elsewhere the glaciers deposited the materials accumulated on their under side, either in the form of outwash carried by sheets of water issuing from under the ice, or else in the form of morainal materials dropped in place as the ice melted. In most of Norway and Finland, much of Sweden, parts of the British Isles, and Iceland (which had a local ice sheet of its own) scouring predominated over deposition. The present landscape of these areas is dominated by thin soil, bare rock, and a multitude of lakes (photo, p. 49). The ice sheets interfered with the pre-existing drain-age pattern so that the present streams tend to wander about aimlessly, with many rapids and waterfalls. Thus many natural sites for the development of hydroelectric power have been created. The latter is an important circumstance in Norway, Sweden, Finland, and Iceland, which are poor in mineral fuels and satisfy most of their power needs from hydroelectric stations.

Glacial deposits of varying thickness were laid down on the North European Plain. Unfortunately, many of the deposits were excessively sandy so that the present soils are not very fertile on the whole, although they have often been made productive by careful handling and large additions of fertilizer. Immediately south of the glaciated areas, deposits of a windblown material known as *loess* appear. This material appears to have been transported from the glaciated areas by winds after the surface was dry. A relatively continuous band of loess extends along the southern edge of the North European Plain, from northeastern France to southern Poland and southern Russia. Loess tends to weather into good soils, and the loess belt represents one of the most fertile and productive farming areas in Europe.]

► *River Systems*

[EDITORIAL COMMENT. Some terminology regarding rivers may be in order at this point. A *river system* is a river together with its tributaries. A *river basin* is the area drained by a river system. The *source* of a river is its place of origin; the *mouth* is the point where it empties into another body of water. As they near the sea, many rivers become rather sluggish, depositing great quantities of sediments to form *deltas,* and often dividing into a number of separate channels, known as *distributaries*. The Rhine divides in this manner, its two principal distributaries being the Lek and the Waal.]

In the mountains and hill lands of Europe many important rivers rise. Most of the rivers that are the chief transportation arteries empty into the seas which border Europe on the north and west. Among the most important of these commercial waterways are the Rhine, Scheldt, Seine, Thames, Mersey, Clyde, Weser, Elbe, Oder, and Vistula (map p. 40). Along the lower courses of many streams deep *estuaries* have been formed by the sinking of the river mouths. Such estuaries are often capable of admitting ocean vessels for considerable distances. The seaward portions of many rivers experience tides of considerable height. The daily ebb and flow of tidal waters helps to keep navigation channels scoured free of sediments, although the action of the tides must often be supplemented by dredging. Were it not for the tides, it would be very difficult for many of the smaller ports located some distance upstream to keep open. However, in certain rivers the range of tides is so great as to constitute a distinct handicap for the ports, requiring expensive installations to offset the rise and fall of the water level and thus permit continuous use of the wharves. The foregoing statements do not apply to the Mediterranean, Baltic, and Black seas, which are nearly tideless.

Many of the major seaports of Europe are located along the lower courses of rivers. Among the largest and most important of these ports are London, on the Thames; Rotterdam, on the Lek distributary of the Rhine; Antwerp, on the Scheldt; and Hamburg, on the Elbe.

The most important inland waterway of Europe is the Rhine. This river, together with tributary rivers and canals, is equaled or surpassed in economic significance only by the Great Lakes–St. Lawrence waterway of North America. The longest river of Europe, however, is the Danube. Although it is used considerably for navigation, it carries a much smaller volume of traffic than the Rhine. Flowing eastward to the Black Sea through regions which are primarily agricultural rather than industrial, the Danube is

largely lacking in the cargoes of coal, iron ore, steel, and other bulky industrial materials which constitute the major tonnage on the Rhine.

The rivers of Mediterranean Europe, in Italy, Iberia, extreme southern France, and the Balkans, are used very little for navigation. Flowing mostly through hilly or mountainous country, they are typically steep and swift with many rapids and waterfalls (the sluggish Po River in northern Italy is a conspicuous exception). Due to the unbalanced yearly distribution of rainfall in the mediterranean climate, these streams are less regular in flow than the rivers of northwestern Europe. They are often choked with water during periods of heavy rain in the autumn and winter, but may become mere trickles in the drought of midsummer.

The rivers of the Scandinavian Peninsula, Finland, and Iceland, like those of Mediterranean Europe, are mostly short, rock-strewn, and swift. However, they are more even in flow, partly as a consequence of the more balanced distribution of precipitation and partly as a result of the fact that many of these streams originate in lakes which serve as natural reservoirs and release water gradually throughout the year. These rivers, with their many rapids and waterfalls, are not very useful for navigation, except for the transportation of logs. However, many of them are harnessed for the production of hydroelectric power.

The usefulness of rivers emptying into the Baltic Sea is somewhat lessened by the fact that they are ordinarily frozen for a considerable period in midwinter. Parts of the Baltic Sea itself freeze in winter; indeed the Gulfs of Bothnia and Finland are normally frozen for 3 months or more. In some winters the extreme north of the Gulf of Bothnia is frozen for 7 months. The Baltic and its gulfs, being almost completely enclosed by land and continuously supplied with fresh water by a large number of rivers, are less saline than the ocean and so are especially susceptible to freezing. However, extensive use of icebreakers lessens the handicap to transportation.

In most other parts of Europe sea ice is uncommon. The shores of the North and Irish seas, the Bay of Biscay, and the Mediterranean are normally ice free throughout the winter.

# THE DIVERSIFIED ECONOMY OF EUROPE

Diversity is the keynote of the European economy, as it is of the European environment. Agriculture, fishing, manufacturing, mining, the forest industries, transportation, trade, and other forms of economic activity are highly developed. Much variety exists from one country and region to another, both in the relative emphasis given to each of the major pursuits and in the relative intensity of development.

## ▶ *Agriculture and Fisheries*

Agriculture finds its highest development in the countries bordering the North Sea. Scientific methods of farming are employed, and yields per acre and per man are high. However, the different countries vary considerably among themselves. Belgium, for example, consistently obtains higher yields than France, mainly as a result of more intensive methods. In the North Sea countries, agriculture is more highly commercialized than in other parts of Europe, a fact principally due to the close proximity of large and dependable urban markets for surplus foodstuffs.

### Types of Farming

Almost everywhere in Europe livestock are important in the farm economy. However, the emphasis on livestock raising is proportionately greatest in northwestern Europe. Two principal types or systems of farming are especially characteristic of the latter area—*dairy farming* and *commercial crop and livestock farming*. In dairy farming, cows are kept for the production of milk, butter, and cheese; calves not needed for the dairy herd are sold; and the income from dairying is often supplemented by produc-

tion of hogs and poultry. A high proportion of the available land is occupied by temporary or permanent pasture, and crop land is devoted principally to hay, feed grains, and root crops suitable for feed. In commercial crop and livestock farming, cattle and other animals, especially hogs, sheep, and poultry, are raised primarily for meat. The farm income results principally from the sale of livestock, although crop surpluses may be sold. The ratio of cropped land to pasture is higher than in dairy farming, with a good balance being maintained among grains, root crops, and hay.

In East Central Europe agriculture has been characterized in the past by poorer methods and lower yields than in the North Sea countries. Much of the farming has been of a semisubsistence nature, with a high proportion of the products being used at home rather than sold. Collective farming on the Russian model has been instituted in many parts of East Central Europe since the end of World War II.

In Southern Europe agriculture is both favored and hindered by the climate. Mild winters and a long growing season make possible the production of specialized subtropical crops, such as citrus fruits, olives, and early vegetables. However, lack of rain severely restricts the growing of crops in the summer, except for deep-rooted, drought-resistant perennials such as olives, grapes, dates, and figs, or crops grown by irrigation. Summer is the difficult season for most farmers in this part of Europe. Fall-sown grains (wheat, barley, or rye) are widely grown with the aid of fall and winter rains. In Southern Europe, as in East Central Europe, much of the agriculture is of a semisubsistence character. Farmers in this region are handicapped not only by a lack of summer rain, but also by a dearth of land sufficiently level to grow crops. The most important exception to these generalizations is the Po Valley, which has summer rain coupled with wide stretches of level land.

Generally speaking, agricultural methods in Europe are most backward and yields are lowest in areas where the largest proportion of the people depend directly on agriculture for a livelihood. Such areas, found mostly in Southern and East Central Europe, are frequently characterized by a serious degree of rural overpopulation.

### The Major Crops

Approximately half of the crop land in Europe is devoted to cereals. Wheat, the leading cereal, both in acreage and yield, is grown to some degree in nearly all parts of Europe, and tends to occupy the best soils. A map of wheat acreage probably comes closer to a map of general crop distribution than a map of any other single crop (maps, pp. 54–55).

On the sandy plains of northern Germany and Poland, rye is grown in larger quantities than wheat. It is the principal bread grain for the majority of rural people on the North European Plain east of the Elbe. Most of the world's rye is grown in Europe and the Soviet Union.

Growing of corn (maize) for grain is mainly restricted to areas having long, hot summers and a summer maximum of rainfall. Such conditions are found in the Danubian plains of Hungary, Romania, and Yugoslavia, and in the Po Valley of northern Italy. These four countries grow most of Europe's corn.

Considerable quantities of oats and barley are grown in various parts of Europe, both being used mainly for livestock feed. Irrigated rice is grown in a few districts in Italy, Spain, and a number of other countries. The Po Valley is the largest area of production.

Root crops are far more important in European agriculture than in the agriculture of the United States. Potatoes are grown in enormous quantities, particularly in Germany and Poland; they are used for human food, stock feed, and the production of alcohol. Sugar beets are extensively grown on the better soils; the beet tops are fed to stock, as are the residues after the juice has been extracted for the production of sugar. Turnips, mangels, rutabagas, carrots, and other root crops are very important for stock feed, especially in the North Sea countries.

Many important areas of market gardening and specialized horticulture are found in Europe, particularly in the zone of mediterranean climate and in the vicinity of the larger cities.

### European Fisheries

The products of European agriculture are supplemented by products of the fisheries. Europeans eat more fish per capita than do Americans, and fishing is intensively developed in a number of European countries. The most important fishing nations are the North Sea countries and Iceland. The shallow seas which border Europe on the northwest are rich in small marine organisms known collectively as *plankton*. Such organisms are the principal food for schools of cod, herring, and other fish of economic value. Many thousands of fishermen gain their principal livelihood from these waters. The Dogger Bank in the North Sea is famous as a fishing ground. Norway and the United Kingdom lead other European nations in total quantity of fish caught, although fishing is of greatest relative importance in the economy of Iceland, a country so notoriously poor in land resources that it must depend mainly on the sea for support.

### Dependence on Food Imports

In spite of its great production from agriculture and sea fisheries, Europe is not self-sufficient in most foodstuffs. In fact, among the principal foodstuffs it is 99–100 percent

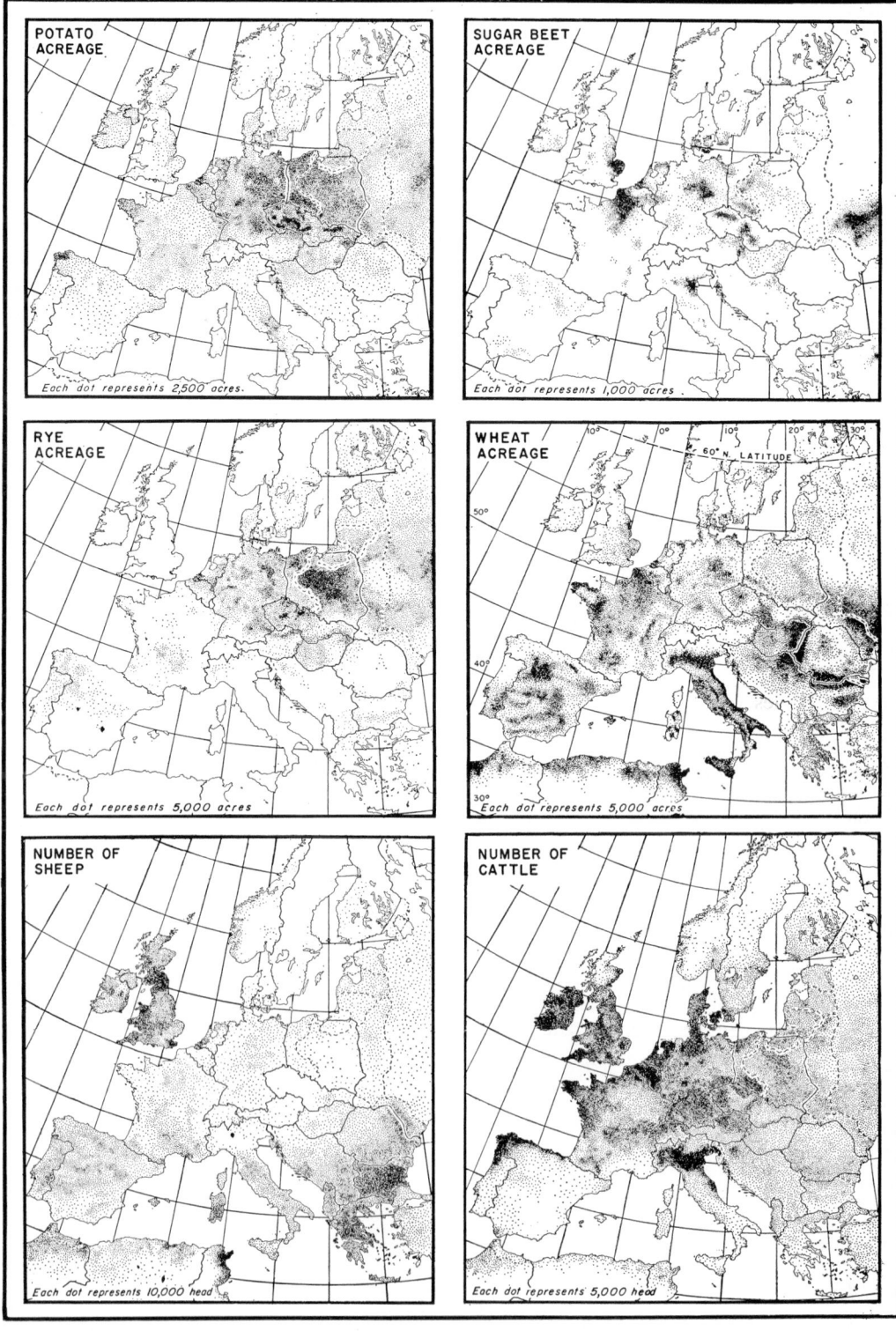

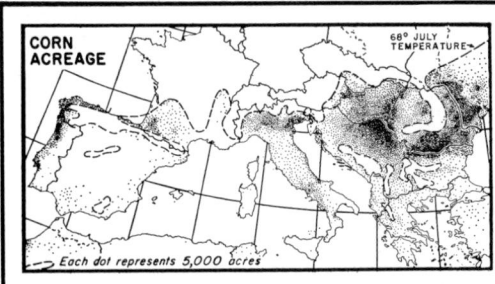 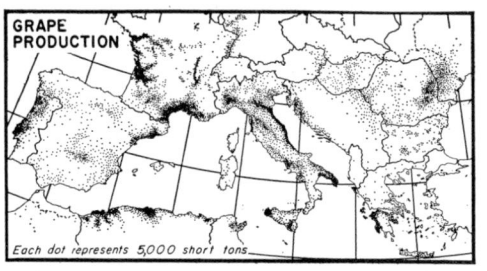

The short dashes on the maps on these pages indicate former political boundaries. Some of the boundaries shown by solid lines are not officially recognized by the United States government. (Modified from maps prepared by the Office of Foreign Agricultural Relations on the basis of pre-World War II data.)

self-sufficient only in whole milk, potatoes, and rye. Domestic production of the remaining foods must be supplemented by imports from other parts of the world. Among the more prominent food imports are wheat, corn, oil cake (for stock feed and fertilizer), animal and vegetable fats and oils, chilled and frozen meats, cane sugar, cocoa, tea, coffee, and tobacco. Europe also imports large quantities of fibers (cotton and wool predominantly) and natural rubber. As for many decades past, this region still remains the greatest market for the world's surplus agricultural commodities. However, the individual countries of Europe vary a great deal in their degree of dependence on agricultural imports. The United Kingdom is vitally dependent on such imports, but for such countries as Hungary, Romania, and Bulgaria they are relatively unimportant. There is a great deal of intra-European trade in foodstuffs, particularly in livestock products and fresh fruits and vegetables. Among the European nations, Denmark and the Netherlands are the largest exporters of food surpluses, while Great Britain and West Germany are the largest importers, both of surpluses originating within Europe and those originating outside of it.

## ▶ Manufacturing and Mining

The products of European factories run the gamut of industrial commodities, from pig iron and steel to the finest textiles, ceramics, optical goods, and metal wares.

### Metalworking

European industries produce three main types of commodities: metal goods, chemicals, and textiles. The most important of the metalworking industries is the iron and steel industry, which is mainly concentrated in a few major districts in Germany, the United Kingdom, France, Belgium, Luxembourg, Poland, and Czechoslovakia. These districts are located in close proximity to deposits of coal, iron ore, or both. Of the latter commodities, coal is the more abundant and widespread. It is tremendously significant, not only to the iron and steel industry, but also to many other European industries which depend on it as their principal source of fuel and power. However, in recent years it has been subject to increasing competition from other power sources, including (1) petroleum, most of which is imported, (2) hydroelectricity, and (3) natural gas, from deposits in Italy and a number of other European countries. The chief coal fields are found in an east-west line extending from the United Kingdom to southern Poland. This axis of coal deposits corresponds generally with the main axis of population and industry described earlier. In Europe, as in other industrialized parts of the world, there has been a pronounced tendency in past times for industrial plants and workers to gravitate to coal.

Iron ore is less plentiful than coal, and many of the smaller deposits have been exhausted. However, two major reserves of iron ore still remain—the deposits of Lorraine in eastern France and of the Kiruna district of nothern Sweden. The French ores are larger in amount, but the Swedish ores are of better quality. Smaller reserves of ore are found in Germany, the United Kingdom, Austria, Luxembourg, Czechoslovakia, northern Spain, and elsewhere.

The known deposits of nonferrous metals in Europe have been worked for a long period, some of them for thousands of years. Today these deposits can no longer supply the demand, and large quantities of copper, zinc, lead, bauxite, and tin must be imported. In addition, Europe requires large imports of the ferroalloys, including manganese, nickel, chromium, tungsten, cobalt, molybdenum, and vanadium. The latter are used to impart special qualities of hardness, toughness, resistance to heat, or other desirable properties to steel.

## The Manufacture of Chemicals

All industrial nations use large quantities of chemicals—acids, alkalis, dyes, and a host of others. This is due to the fact that many industrial processes require chemicals of some type. Fortunately, the chemicals needed in the largest amounts by modern industry can be manufactured from raw materials which are relatively abundant. Among the latter, salt, limestone, sulfur, and coal are especially important. Europe is well supplied with these materials, and it was in this region that the modern chemical industry was born, Great Britain and Germany being the early leaders in the industry.

The United States has now become the leading nation in chemical manufacture, but the European chemical industry remains significant. One of the most important branches of this industry is the manufacture of chemical fertilizers. Most European soils are not particularly fertile by nature, and it has taken large applications of commercial fertilizer (along with animal manures) to make them productive. The principal raw materials for fertilizer manufacture are available in Europe in large quantities: potash from huge natural deposits in Germany and France; phosphates from blast furnace wastes and from deposits of phosphatic rock in North Africa; and nitrates secured by the fixation of atmospheric nitrogen and also as a by-product of coke manufacture. Europe uses more chemical fertilizer than any other world region, with Anglo-America a close second.

## Textile Manufacture

The manufacture of textiles is the most widespread major branch of European industry. Although in many areas textile milling is the main industry, there is also an extensive development of textile manufacture employing chiefly women and girls in some areas where the male workers are principally employed in other enterprises—coal mining, steel milling, shipbuilding, and the like. Woolen and cotton textiles are mainly produced from imported fibers. Linen manufacture, particularly important in Northern Ireland, relies on European and Russian flax, and the synthetic fiber industry (rayon, nylon, etc.) mainly depends on European materials. The manufacture of silk is less important than formerly. Some raw silk is produced in the Po Valley and a few other areas.

Europe continues to lead other manufacturing regions in the production of highly finished goods requiring painstaking care and a high degree of skill in manufacture. Swiss watches, English woolens, German chinaware and cameras, Bohemian glassware, Irish linens, and the best French wines and liquers are famous, and unsurpassed in quality. Such products find a ready sale in export markets.

▶ *The Forest Industries*

The principal forest stands of commercial value are found in the Scandinavian Peninsula and Finland. Smaller commercial forest tracts are scattered throughout continental Europe, particularly in the mountains and hill lands. Despite an extensive development of lumbering in certain areas, the existing forests cannot fully supply the demand for timber products so that sizable imports from other world regions are required. A number of the European countries have developed scientific forestry to a high degree in an effort to conserve their remaining stands of timber. The present commercial forests are principally composed of softwood trees (spruce, fir, pine, etc.), although sizable stands of oak, beech, and other hardwoods occur in some areas. Among the European nations, Sweden, Finland, Norway, and Austria lead as exporters of lumber and wood pulp, the main types of forest exports. Most of these exports go to other European countries.

▶ *Internal Transportation*

Europe is equipped with an elaborate network of rail lines, water routes, highways, and airways over which flows a vast amount of freight and passenger traffic. Established long before the iron curtain separated Europe into rather distinct non-Communist and Communist realms of activity, this network is focused upon the industrial complexes and population concentrations to the northwest (map, p. 91). Most of the individual routes radiate out from the northwestern core of manufacturing and diversified agriculture to less populous and more agrarian places in the south, east, and northeast.

Europe's irregular coastline, together with numerous navigable rivers and man-made canals, is conducive to the movement by water of a sizable traffic. Like most coastwise and inland waterway traffic of technically advanced countries, this commerce consists largely of bulk goods—petroleum and its products, iron ore and concentrates, coal and coke, grain, cement, and even sand and gravel. Some general cargo, passengers, and mail also are carried. Large seagoing vessels tend to ply between major ports on regular schedules, and small coastwise shipping and river craft connect the large ports with smaller ports and receiving depots within their respective trading territories. In some places, coastwise or river transport is not ancillary to ocean shipping. Movement of coal from the German Ruhr to France via the Rhine River and connecting waterways is a good example.

Overland transportation, faster but more expensive than water transport, carries a higher percentage of passengers, mail, and general cargo. But it is also important in the movement of bulk goods; in the European Coal and Steel Community, for example, railroads account for about two thirds of the ton-mileage of a commodity movement consisting largely of coal, coke, iron ore and concentrates, and steel products, with waterways hauling approximately one fifth of this commerce and trucks carrying essentially all the rest. However, opening of the new Moselle waterway between the Rhine River and the Lorraine iron and steel district (see p. 103) may substantially increase the proportion of the Community's traffic that is carried by water.

Since World War II the motor truck has become an important long-distance freight carrier. As in the United States, the airplane is now a major carrier of passengers and mail, but is comparatively minor in freight movements.

# The British Isles

The British Isles lie off the northwest coast of Europe. There are approximately 5500 islands in the group, but most of them are small, and only two islands, Great Britain and Ireland, are of major consequence. The largest island, Great Britain, lies only 21 miles across the Strait of Dover from France, and the whole island group is generally considered part of Europe.

Two countries occupy the islands: the Republic of Ireland, with its capital at Dublin, and the United Kingdom of Great Britain and Northern Ireland, with its capital at London. The latter country is usually referred to by shorter names such as "United Kingdom," "UK," "Britain," or "Great Britain." It incorporates the island of Great Britain, plus the northeastern corner of Ireland and most of the smaller islands, including the Isle of Wight, Isle of Man, Hebrides, Orkneys, Shetlands, and Channel Islands (map, p. 61). Altogether the United Kingdom comprises about four fifths of the area and has about 95 percent of the population of the British Isles (Table 3).

---

The agriculture of Britain, closely geared to the requirements of the country's urban markets, reaches a peak of intensity in the famous glasshouse district of the Lea Valley, northeast of London. Over 1000 acres of cropland are enclosed by closely spaced greenhouses such as those shown in the above view of a portion of the district. Tomatoes, occupying about 700 acres, are the principal crop, but various other truck crops and flowers are grown. Produce from the district is disposed of at London's five vegetable markets. (British Information Services.)

# POLITICAL SUBDIVISIONS OF THE UNITED KINGDOM

The United Kingdom is sometimes incorrectly referred to as "England." However, England is merely the largest of four main subdivisions of the country, the others being Scotland, Wales, and Northern Ireland (map, right). These were originally independent territories. Wales was conquered by England in the Middle Ages, but preserves some cultural distinctiveness associated with the Welsh language, still spoken by over a quarter of its population. Northern Ireland, together with the rest of Ireland, was twice conquered by England. The earlier conquest in the Middle Ages was followed by a lapse of English control during the Wars of the Roses in the second half of the fifteenth century. A second conquest was completed in the seventeenth century. One of its outcomes was the settlement of Scottish and English Protestants in the North, where they became numerically and politically dominant. In 1921 when the Irish Free State (later the Republic of Ireland) was established in the Catholic part of the island, the Protestant North, for economic as well as religious reasons, elected to remain with the United Kingdom. Today Northern Ireland retains a certain amount of political autonomy within the United Kingdom. For example, it has its own parliament, which meets at Belfast and legislates in matters of local concern. However, like the other subdivisions of the

The two main islands and the major political divisions of the British Isles.

### TABLE 3

### BRITISH ISLES: AREA AND POPULATION DATA

| POLITICAL UNIT | AREA (THOUSAND SQUARE MILES) | | POPULATION (MILLIONS: 1959 ESTIMATES) | | DENSITY (PER SQUARE MILE: TO NEAREST MULTIPLE OF 5) | |
|---|---|---|---|---|---|---|
| United Kingdom | 94.5 | | 52.14 | | 550 | |
| England | | 50.3 | | 42.76 | | 850 |
| Wales | | 8.0 | | 2.63 | | 330 |
| Scotland | | 30.4 | | 5.19 | | 170 |
| Northern Ireland | | 5.5 | | 1.41 | | 260 |
| Isle of Man [a] | | 0.225 | | 0.054 | | 240 |
| Channel Islands [a] | | 0.075 | | 0.100 | | 1330 |
| Republic of Ireland | 27.1 | | 2.85 | | 105 | |
| British Isles [b] | 121.7 | | 55.00 | | 450 | |

[a] In a strict legalistic sense the Isle of Man and Channel Islands are not included in the United Kingdom, both being dependencies of the British crown. But in practical effect they are part of the United Kingdom and are so regarded in this chapter.
[b] Discrepancies in totals are due to rounding of figures.

United Kingdom it sends representatives to the Parliament at London. Scotland was first joined to England when a Scottish king inherited the English throne in 1603, and the two became one country under the Act of Union passed in 1707. Scotland has no separate parliament, but it does have special administrative agencies in Edinburgh which deal with Scottish affairs. It also has its own system of courts and law.

## SIZE AND WORLD IMPORTANCE OF THE UNITED KINGDOM

In area and, to a lesser extent, population, the United Kingdom is a relatively small country. Its area of slightly less than 95,000 square miles is about the same as the combined total for New York and Pennsylvania, and its population of about 52 million is less than a third that of the United States. In these respects it fits in a general class with the larger nations of continental Europe, but not with the larger nations of the world.

The international importance which this small country has attained is one of the more amazing aspects of the modern world. When British power and prestige were at their peak in the century between 1815 and 1914, the United Kingdom was generally considered the world's greatest power. Its overseas empire eventually covered a quarter of the earth, and the influence of its language and culture spread still farther. Until the late nineteenth century it was the world's foremost manufacturing nation. Its navy dominated the seas, and its merchant ships carried half or more of the world's ocean trade. It was the world's greatest trading nation, controlling about a fourth of all international trade in the middle of the nineteenth century and about a fifth at the turn of the twentieth century. Invested profits from its industries and commerce helped finance the development of much of the rest of the world. Its investments were especially large in the United States, Canada, Australia, India, South Africa, and Argentina, but they played a prominent role in dozens of other countries.

Since World War I the United Kingdom has experienced serious difficulties and it has definitely lost its pre-eminent position. But it is still an important nation. It operates the world's largest active merchant fleet, estimated to carry nearly a quarter of all international seaborne traffic. Its total international trade is second only to that of the United States. It still controls a large, if shrinking, colonial empire and forms the center of a vast Commonwealth of independent nations (see p. 85). It is one of four powers possessing atomic weapons (1960), and, as far as can be judged by steel output, is the fourth industrial nation in the world after the United States, the Soviet Union, and West Germany.

## THE ISLAND OF GREAT BRITAIN

Aside from minor islands and a small part of Ireland, the physical base of the United Kingdom is Great Britain, an island about 600 miles long by 50 to 300 miles wide. For its small size this island provides a homeland with a notable variety of landscapes and modes of life. Some of this variety can be attributed to a broad fundamental division of the island between two contrasting parts of the British Isles, *Highland Britain* and *Lowland Britain* (map, facing page).

### ▶ *Highland Britain*
Highland Britain embraces Scotland, Wales, Ireland, and parts of northern and southwestern England. It is predominantly an

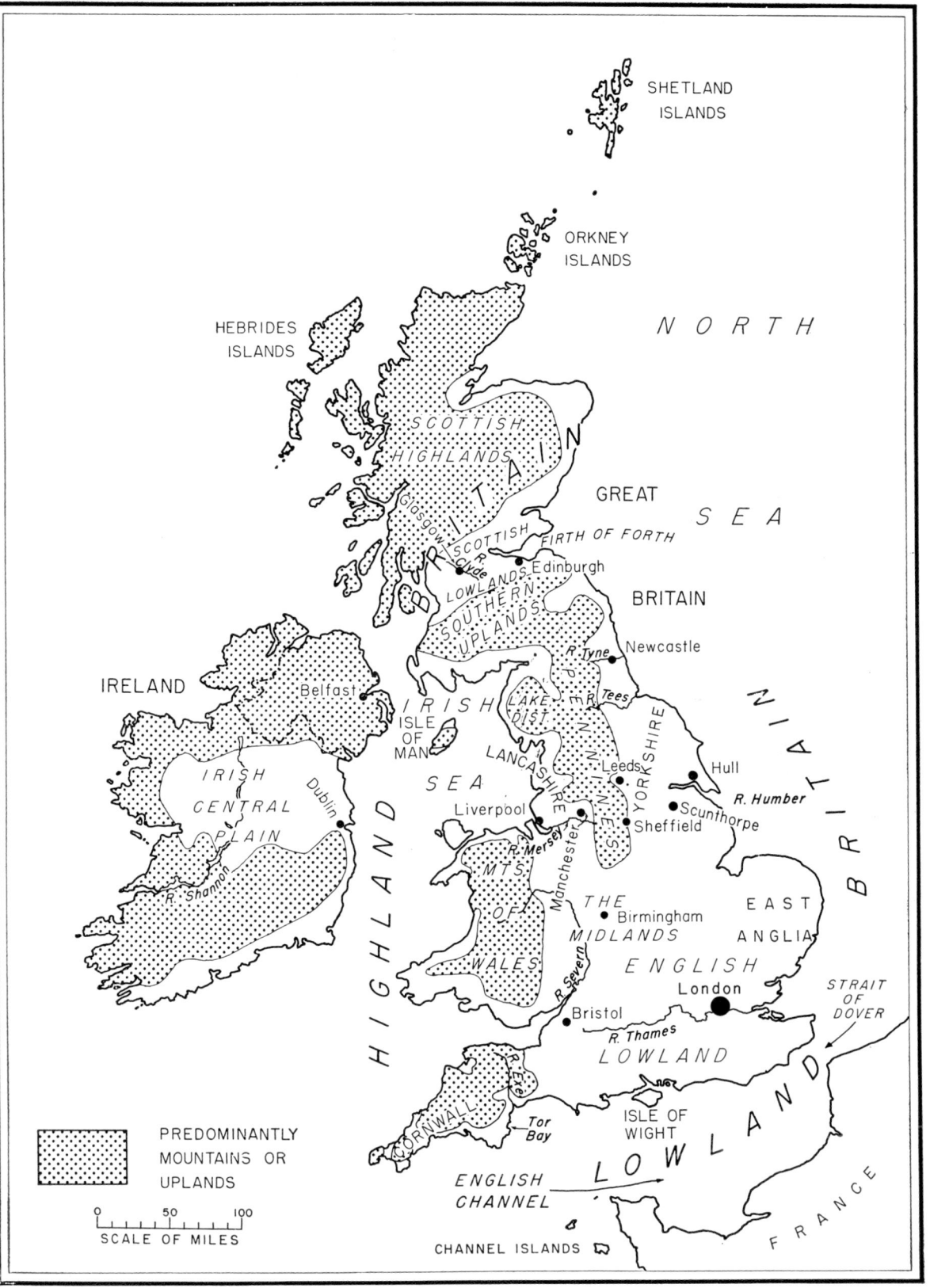

Highland and Lowland Britain. (Based in part on a map by L. Dudley Stamp.)

area of treeless hills, uplands, and low mountains, formed of rocks that are generally older and harder than those of Lowland Britain. All three of the major classes of rocks—igneous, metamorphic, and sedimentary—are well represented. Moors,[1] tenanted by sheep farmers or uninhabited, cover broad areas. The principal highlands, together with the maximum elevation of each, include (1) the Scottish Highlands (Ben Nevis, 4406 feet), (2) the Southern Uplands of Scotland (2764), (3) the Pennines (2930) and Lake District (3210) of northern England, (4) the mountains and uplands of Wales (3560), (5) the uplands of the Cornwall peninsula in southwestern England (2309), and (6) the mountainous and hilly rim of Ireland (3414).

[EDITORIAL COMMENT. *Sedimentary rocks* have been formed from sediments (sand, gravel, clay, or lime) deposited by running water, wind, or wave action either in bodies of water or on land, and consolidated into rock over a span of geologic time by pressure of the accumulated deposits or the cementing action of chemicals contained in waters percolating through the rock materials. The main classes of sedimentary rocks are sandstone, shale (formed principally of clay), and limestone. *Igneous,* or *volcanic, rocks* are formed by the cooling and solidifying of molten materials, either within the earth or poured out on the surface by volcanic action. Granite is a well-known type of igneous rock. *Metamorphic rocks* are formed from igneous or sedimentary rocks through changes occurring in the rock structure as a result of heat, pressure, or the chemical action of infiltrating waters. Marble, formed from pure limestone, is a common example of a metamorphic rock. Igneous and metamorphic rocks, being generally harder and more closely compacted than sedimentary rocks, are usually more resistant to weathering and erosion, and thus tend to form uplands or highlands in areas where the sedimentary rocks have been weathered into lowlands. (But in purely sedimentary areas, the more resistant sedimentaries form higher lands than the less resistant ones.) In general, sedimentary rocks weather into more fertile types of soil than igneous or metamorphic rocks, although certain types of volcanic rock break down into extremely fertile soils, and within the sedimentaries themselves there are great variations in this respect, with limestone usually forming soils of greater fertility than shale or sandstone. Sedimentary rocks are significantly different from igneous and metamorphic rocks with respect to associated economic minerals. Coal and petroleum, for example, are customarily found in sedimentary areas, whereas metal-bearing ores are found in igneous or metamorphic rocks, except for certain deposits (particularly of iron ore) formed of materials removed from these rocks by percolating waters and redeposited in sedimentary areas.]

Highland Britain includes two important lowlands: (1) the boggy, agricultural Central Plain of Ireland and (2) the Scottish Lowlands, a densely populated industrialized valley separating the rugged Scottish Highlands from the gentler, more fertile Southern Uplands of Scotland. The Scottish Lowlands comprise only a fifth of Scotland's area, but they incorporate more than four fifths of its population and its two main cities, Glasgow (1,897,000)[2] on the west and Edinburgh (596,000), Scotland's political capital, on the east.

---

[1] In its most common usage the term *moor* means a deforested upland, usually covered with grass or heather.

[2] Estimated population of metropolitan area (the total metropolitan aggregate, including Glasgow city plus suburban and satellite districts near by). Unless otherwise specified, population figures for cities in this text are metropolitan area estimates on a comparable basis from International Urban Research, *The World's Metropolitan Areas* (Berkeley and Los Angeles: University of California Press, 1959). Most estimates in this source are for the mid-1950s. See footnote on p. 594.

increasing productivity of labor in the coal industry and to increased use of petroleum.

Though coal remains the dominant source of power in Britain, other sources, notably petroleum and atomic energy, seem certain to grow in importance. A series of new or enlarged petroleum refineries in coastal locations (map, p. 66) has given Britain the greatest refinery capacity in Europe. The capacity of the refining industry increased 17-fold from 1938 to 1959. The leading concentration of refineries is on the Thames estuary downstream from London, but the largest single refinery is located at Fawley on the Channel coast near Southampton. In 1956 Britain opened at Calder Hall in northwestern England a nuclear-powered electric generating station—the first such establishment to supply power on a large scale to a national electricity network. Several other stations in widely dispersed coastal locations were under construction or planned at the time of writing.

## The Major Coal Fields

The United Kingdom's coal fields, which still supplied four fifths of the nation's power in 1960, lie, for the most part, around the edges of the highlands on the island of Great Britain. In England the Pennines are ringed on three sides by a series of fields. The *Lancashire fields* to the west and the smaller, scattered *Midlands fields* to the south of the Pennines (map, p. 66) provided fuel for the development of great industrial districts centering on Manchester and Birmingham. But more important than these fields today is the *Yorkshire-Derby-Nottingham field* in the lowland along the eastern flank of the Pennines. This field produces nearly half of the total British output and has the largest reserves of any field in the United Kingdom. Another major field, the Northumberland-Durham or *Northeast England field,* lies on the North Sea coast between the Tees River and the Scottish border. It ranks second in production among British fields. Coking coals from the southern part of this field are reputed to be the finest in Britain.

Coal makes up the largest tonnage of outbound cargo at ports on the Humber and Tyne estuaries and at most other ports along the northeast coast of England. This group of ports accounts for the bulk of the United Kingdom's waterborne coal shipments. Most shipments move coastwise to southern England, particularly to electric generating stations, industrial plants, and gas works in the London metropolitan area. The huge exports to foreign markets that made Newcastle-upon-Tyne a famous name in the world's coal trade have dwindled to a small fraction of their former size. In 1956, coal shipments from Newcastle and smaller ports on the Tyne amounted to only a third of the 1923 peak, and only 16 percent were for foreign markets, an exact reversal of 1923, when overseas shipments were 84 percent of the total.

The *South Wales field,* which ranks second among British fields in reserves and third in production, has been described as follows:

The South Wales coal field has a distinct "personality." It is the only coal field in this country set amid moorlands. Many parallel, deep, and steep-sided valleys have been carved into the sandstones of central Glamorganshire and western Monmouthshire, and shafts sunk in these valley floors tap the rich seams, which are present at some depth, and send out their coal by rail. Today many of the mines employ more than 1000 men, and some more than 2000.

This coal field is different from other British fields in another respect, for it includes the entire range of coals, from soft house-coals in the east, through steam, gas, and coking coals in the center, to hard, shiny anthracite in the west. While any one valley will usually contain coal of several types, the reputations of Newport and Cardiff have been built up on their almost smokeless steam coals, while the chief outlet for the anthracite coals is Swansea.[4]

---

[4] Henry Rees, *British Ports and Shipping* (London: Harrap, 1958, p. 176). Copyright by Henry Rees. Used by permission. This book, a concise survey, is highly recommended.

In former times steam coals exported from Cardiff were highly prized as ship fuel, but today the once enormous trade of the port in this "bunker coal" has almost disappeared.

The *Scottish Lowlands fields* stretch from sea to sea across the narrow waist of Scotland. The central field near Glasgow has contributed most to the industrial development of the Lowlands, but today the center of production is moving gradually eastward toward fields along the Firth of Forth.

Small coal fields exist in the vicinity of Dover and the important southwestern port of Bristol (610,000), as well as in northern Wales and along the coast of northwestern England, but their combined production amounts to little more than a twentieth of the United Kingdom total.

## ▶ *Iron and Steel*

Before the Industrial Revolution steel was a scarce and expensive metal. Iron, none too cheap or plentiful itself, was more commonly used. It was made in small blast furnaces by heating iron ore over a charcoal fire, with temperatures raised by an air blast from a primitive bellows. Supplies of iron ore in Great Britain were ample for the needs of the time, but the island was largely deforested by the eighteenth century, and by 1740 it was importing nearly two thirds of its iron from countries with better charcoal supplies, notably Sweden and Russia.

During the eighteenth century British ironmasters made revolutionary changes in iron production: replacement of charcoal by coke; improvement of the blast mechanism; invention and use of a refining process called puddling, to make the iron more malleable; and adoption of the rolling mill in place of the hammer for final processing. Thus the fuel shortage was solved, the scale and pace of production were expanded, and the island's general change-over to machine industry was promoted. Between 1720 and 1855 the output of iron in the United Kingdom expanded by something like 190

times; by the latter date the country was producing half the world's iron, much of which was exported.

Then in the 1850s British inventors developed the Bessemer converter and the open-hearth furnace. These allowed steel, a superior metal in strength and versatility, to be made on a large scale and cheaply for the first time. They are still the principal means of steel production today. In the Bessemer converter steel is made rapidly from molten iron by passing a blast of air through it to burn out impurities. In the open-hearth furnace it is made by heating iron with gas flames over a period of many hours and drawing off the impurities. In both processes quality is controlled by the addition of carbon and alloys, but it is controlled better in the slower open-hearth process. After these inventions iron became primarily a raw material for steel, though great quantities of iron are still consumed directly by fabricating industries.

Britain now had a head start in steel production; but British resources and markets could not support a position of leadership in the industry once better-endowed countries began to industrialize on a large scale. Steel production in both the United States and Germany surpassed that of the United Kingdom before 1900. Then in the 1930s the Soviet Union surpassed both Britain and Germany, leaving the United Kingdom today the fourth-ranking steel producer in the world. Britain still exports large quantities of steel, however, besides supplying her own metal-using industries.

Originally the iron industry in Great Britain relied entirely on domestic ores. A major problem in ironmaking is to bring together economically the industry's bulky raw materials, but in Britain suitable ores were often present in the coal fields. For a century after 1750 nearly all the ore used was "coal-measures" ore. Depletion of this ore led in 1850 to the start of large-scale iron mining outside the coal fields and in the 1870s to the first large imports of foreign ore. Since then the industry has depended mainly on low-grade domestic ores from the English Lowland (map, p. 66) and on high-grade imported ores. (In 1954 imported ore accounted for three fifths of the total iron content of all ore used.) In addition, pig iron and scrap metal are imported to supplement British supplies in feeding the steel furnaces.

## Major Iron and Steel Districts

In harmony with the widespread distribution of coal and ore deposits, British iron and steel plants have developed in widely scattered locations. With a few conspicuous exceptions in eastern England, most plants today are located in or near the major coal fields, and all of the coal-field industrial areas have a share of the industry. The principal districts may be summarized as follows (map, p. 66):

1. *Along the lower Tees River.* The plants in this district use coal from the Northeast England fields. Formerly they relied on low-grade iron ore from the Cleveland Hills area just south of the river. Now, however, the local ore is depleted and imported ore is mainly used. Sweden is the largest source, but ore is brought from areas as widely dispersed as North Africa, West Africa, Venezuela, and Canada. The principal city in this steel district is Middlesbrough (496,000), the greatest iron-ore port in the United Kingdom. In addition to steel, the district is an important producer of chemicals, based on local deposits of salt and anhydrite.

2. *A belt extending from the vicinity of Sheffield southward to Northamptonshire,* which is the principal center of British iron mining today. Plants in the northern part of this belt are located on the Yorkshire coal field, while those in the southern part are located in the ore fields. The main concentration is found in or near Sheffield (743,-000), a city famous for centuries for high-quality steels. A northeastern outlier of the belt is found around Scunthorpe, just south of the Humber estuary, where several large plants cluster on a local ore deposit.

3. *South Wales,* especially around Swansea (304,000) and in a belt extending northward from Cardiff (597,000 in Cardiff-Rhondda metropolitan area) to a large iron and steel plant at Ebbw Vale. This area, utilizing local ore in the South Wales coal field, was a major center of the early iron industry. Since the depletion of the coal-measures ore it has declined in relative importance as an iron producer (though its production on the basis of imported ore is sizable), but it has developed the greatest steel capacity of any district in Britain. Much of the steel is made from pig iron and scrap metal brought from other parts of England or from overseas. The Swansea area is the United Kingdom's largest producer of tin plate and is important for the smelting of zinc concentrates, mainly from Australia, and the refining of nickel-bearing ores from Canada.

4. *The Scottish Lowlands in the vicinity of Glasgow.* The development of the industry in this area has been broadly similar to that of South Wales: early iron manufacture from local coal-measures ores; then, after depletion of these ores, a concentration on steel production utilizing pig iron and scrap brought from elsewhere or pig iron produced locally from imported ore. This district relies on local pig iron to an even smaller degree than does South Wales.

5. A historically famous district lies around Birmingham (2,576,000), especially to the west and northwest of the city. This was the leading center for the British iron industry until the middle of the nineteenth century, and Birmingham was the first city to become world famous for large-scale iron production. But depletion of both iron ore and coking coal in the vicinity has reduced it to a center of only secondary importance today. Birmingham has developed a variety of engineering industries making secondary metal products. Its brass industry is the largest in Britain. Diversified engineering is the characteristic form of manufacturing in the English Midlands, though conspicuous exceptions are found in Stoke-on-Trent (499,-

000), which concentrates nearly the whole of the British chinaware and earthenware industries, and in the hosiery and boot-and-shoe industries of Leicester (440,000) and other cities in the east Midlands (map, p. 66).

## ▶ Cotton Milling in Lancashire

During the period of Britain's industrial and commercial ascendancy, cotton textiles were its leading export by a wide margin, amounting to almost a quarter of all exports by value in 1913. Though for a time it was rather scattered, the enormous cotton industry eventually became concentrated in Lancashire, in western England, with Manchester (2,499,000) the principal center (map, p. 66). Raw cotton was imported and manufactured textiles were exported through the Mersey River port of Liverpool (1,625,000), though Manchester itself became a supplementary port after completion of a ship canal to the Mersey estuary in 1894. Today Manchester remains the organizing, technological, and commercial center of the cotton industry, and a center of finishing industries (primarily bleaching, dyeing, and printing) and clothing manufacture, but most of the spinning of cotton yarns and weaving of cloth is carried on in other cities and towns of Lancashire.

A textile industry using imported materials, including cotton, and marketing a share of the product abroad long antedated the Industrial Revolution in Lancashire. In the Middle Ages hand workers spun and wove local wool and flax. Then in the seventeenth and eighteenth centuries the industry imported additional flax from Ireland, originated new fabrics using linen in combination with cotton, which was imported from the eastern Mediterranean, and sold part of the product in tropical markets in connection with the flourishing slave trade of Liverpool.

As it affected the Lancashire textile industry, the Industrial Revolution involved several lines of development. First a series of inventors, in good part Lancashire men, mechanized and thus speeded the spinning and weaving processes. Then inanimate power was applied to drive the machines, first falling water from Pennine streams, then steam raised by coal from the underlying Lancashire fields. Finally, in 1793, the American invention of the cotton gin provided a machine to separate the seeds from the raw cotton fibers economically, and thus made cotton a relatively cheap material from which inexpensive cloth could be manufactured.

The stage was now set for the spectacular rise of the Lancashire cotton industry and, incidentally, for the spread of cotton farming in the American South, which supplied most of the raw material. Liverpool merchants financed much of the industrial development of Lancashire, but the cotton factories were built inland on the streams and the coal. In addition to sources of power, the inland locations gave access to supplies of soft water from the Pennines for use in the finishing processes and in boilers. For over a century, until World War I, Lancashire dominated world trade in cotton and cotton textiles.

But 1913 saw the peak of British production, and since that time the decline of the industry has been about as spectacular as its former rise. This has presented the United Kingdom with one of its more serious economic problems of the recent difficult decades. The root of the trouble has been increasing foreign competition. In 1913 Lancashire exported almost 80 percent of its production, but most of the markets it served have since been lost. The cotton industry is peculiarly adaptable to areas that are commencing to industrialize, and it is often the first large-scale industry to be established in such areas. Among the reasons for this are (1) the relatively low level of skill required of the labor force in cotton mills, especially those manufacturing the cheaper grades of cloth, (2) the almost universal importance of the product, and

(3) the transportability of the raw material. Once the industry has been started in such an area, it often has important advantages of (1) cheap labor, connected with the nonindustrial country's lower level of living, (2) newer equipment, and (3) a protective tariff to keep out competition from older producers—such as Britain.

By World War I the United States cotton industry, serving mainly the domestic market behind a protective tariff, was a larger producer than Lancashire, and important cotton industries had been established in continental Europe, Russia, India, and Japan. During World War I, markets were lost to Japan and other competitors who were not so involved in the war and thus so commercially handicapped as the United Kingdom, and after the war these markets could not be regained. Between 1913 and the late 1930s, British cotton exports declined by approximately two thirds, and economic distress was prevalent in Lancashire during most of the interwar period. Since World War II the downward trend of the Lancashire industry has continued, though at a much slower pace. Production is now more concentrated on quality fabrics which competitors find more difficult to duplicate, and it is more geared to the home market. However, Lancashire's future as an industrial area seems to lie mainly with other industries, which have been growing as cotton production has declined. Important among these are engineering industries producing textile machinery and electrical equipment; the clothing industry; chemical industries based on massive salt deposits south of the Mersey River; and, at Liverpool, the processing of imported foodstuffs, particularly wheat, cane sugar, and oilseeds.

## ▶ The Woolen Textile Industry of Yorkshire

The United Kingdom is the world's largest exporter of woolen textiles, though it is now second in production to the United States.

Most of the British woolen industry is concentrated in western Yorkshire in Leeds-Bradford (1,901,000) and a large number of smaller textile towns and cities. This area on the east slope of the Pennines contains the largest single concentration of woolen and worsted textile plants in the world. Bradford is the largest producing center; Leeds, the main city in size, is a diversified manufacturing center in which engineering industries and clothing manufacture are more important than the woolen industry.

In the Middle Ages Great Britain, an island well supplied with grazing land, exported raw wool and then woolen cloth to continental Europe. Thus the Industrial Revolution, as it applied to woolen manufacture, involved the mechanization of an industry that had long been important, rather than, as in the case of cotton milling, the development of a new industry based on a fiber that had never been of prime importance. With the mechanization of the woolen industry, production expanded rapidly and soon outran Britain's output of raw wool. Thus the country became not only the leading exporter of woolen goods but also the leading importer of raw wool, a position it still occupies.

The west Yorkshire area was the leader among several important woolen-manufacturing districts in Great Britain before the Industrial Revolution. It was well suited for the industry through its resources of water from the Pennine streams, which supplied power and abundant soft water for cleaning wool and finishing cloth. With the coming of the Industrial Revolution, this was the quickest of the woolen-manufacturing areas to adopt the new machinery, first used in adjacent Lancashire, and it was the only such area that happened to be on a coal field. The industry largely died out in competing areas—except for some upland sections of Scotland, producing distinctive tweeds and tartans—and as it grew it became concentrated more and more into west Yorkshire.

The British woolen industry was less spectacular in its rise and has undergone a less drastic decline than the cotton industry. Although it did gain a position of world leadership, its growth was somewhat checked by the rapid rise of the cotton industry after the invention of the cotton gin, and by the fact that many countries already had woolen industries by the time of the Industrial Revolution. It neither exported as much nor was as dependent on the export market as the cotton industry, since Britain's home consumption of woolens has been large. But it, too, reached an export peak before World War I and has since declined. However, the decline has been greatly checked by the importance of the home market as compared with the market for cotton goods; by the greater labor skills required in its processes, which makes it more difficult to initiate in new industrial areas; and by its greater emphasis on quality, for which the British industry has long had a world-wide reputation. Nevertheless, Yorkshire now relies increasingly on industries that formerly were of secondary importance, including the production of textile and other machinery and clothing.

Yorkshire is served by a group of seaports along the Humber estuary, of which the most important is Hull (339,000), Britain's third port in tonnage handled, after London and Liverpool.

### ▶ *Shipbuilding*

When wood was the principal material in building ships, Great Britain, as a major seafaring and shipbuilding nation, was presented with increasingly serious difficulties due to deforestation. Large timber imports were brought from the Baltic area and from America; and the importation of completed ships from the American colonies, principally New England, was so great that an estimated one third of the British merchant marine was American-built by the time of the American Revolution. During the first half of the nineteenth century American

wooden ships posed a serious threat to Britain's commercial dominance on the seas.

But in the latter nineteenth century ocean transportation was transformed by iron and steel ships propelled by steam. Britain led the way, and by the 1890s was building four fifths of the world's seagoing tonnage. Two districts developed as the world's greatest centers of shipbuilding. These were (1) the Northeast England district, with a great concentration of shipyards along the lower Tyne River between Newcastle (1,137,000) and the North Sea, and with other yards along the rivers Wear and Tees; and (2) the western part of the Scottish Lowlands, with shipyards lining the River Clyde for miles downstream from Glasgow. Both districts had a seafaring tradition, Newcastle in the early coal trade and in fishing, and Glasgow in trade with America; both were immediately adjacent to centers of the iron and steel industry; and both had suitable waterways for location of the yards. Their ships were built mainly for the United Kingdom's own merchant marine—as they still are—but even the minority built for foreign shipowners were an important item in Britain's exports.

During the twentieth century Britain's share in world shipbuilding has declined steadily, except for short-term recoveries after both world wars. Its output represented about three fifths of the world total in 1913, one third of the total just before World War II, and is under one fifth today. Competition has come mainly from Japan, which displaced Britain as the world's leading shipbuilder in the 1950s, and from continental Europe, especially West Germany. Both of these competitors, particularly Japan, have had cheaper skilled labor than Britain, a factor which is quite important in shipbuilding and which has represented a long-time British advantage over the United States. These countries also possess the heavy industries and engineering skills upon which modern shipbuilding must be based, and they have recently appeared to adopt im-

A view of one of Britain's older industrial areas—the important seaport and shipbuilding center of Glasgow on the River Clyde. (British Information Services.)

proved techniques more readily than the older British industry. However, the total British output of ships has fallen much less since the years before World War I than has the country's share in an expanding world industry. The "Clydeside" and "Tyneside" yards are still among the world's greatest centers of the industry, and a multitude of activities originally subsidiary to shipbuilding make both districts important centers of metal and machinery manufacture.

## A LAND OF CITIES

The rise of the industries discussed in the preceding sections gave a powerful impetus to the growth of cities at the same time that the country's total population was increasing rapidly. The United Kingdom became the world's first predominantly urban nation, and by almost any measurement it is still more highly urbanized than any other nation. Only 4 percent of the employed population is supported by agriculture. The 1951 census showed that no less than 52 percent of the population lived in cities of over 50,000 inhabitants, and 43 percent in cities of over 100,000, while comparable figures for the United States, itself a highly urbanized country, in 1950 were 35 percent and 29 percent. Approximately nine tenths of the United Kingdom's people are classed as city or town dwellers.

Most of the large cities, with the notable exception of London, are on or very near the coal fields (map, p. 66). A tremendous cluster is found on or near the fields that flank the Pennines on the east, south, and west; that is, in the industrial districts of Yorkshire, the Midlands, and Lancashire respectively (map, p. 91). Here the metropolitan areas of two cities, Birmingham and Manchester, have over two million people each; two others, Leeds-Bradford and Liverpool, have between one and two million; three others—Sheffield, Nottingham (621,000), and Coventry (547,000)—have over half a million; and four smaller ones have over 200,000 each. Although this area is only about 100 miles long by 50 miles wide, its eleven major cities and their suburbs contain over 12 million people. Lesser urban clusters are apparent on and near the other major coal fields in the Scottish Lowlands, Northeast England, and South Wales.

In striking contrast, the largest metropolitan areas that lie at a considerable distance from the coal fields—aside from London—have well under half a million people. These are the English Channel cities of Portsmouth (397,000), a major naval base; Southampton (375,000), the main British terminal for large passenger liners; and Brighton-Worthing (372,000), a major resort center. For several decades, however, there has been a notable tendency for these and other cities away from the older industrial districts to grow especially fast. Electricity has freed many factories from the necessity of locating close to coal, and much of Britain's more recent industrial development has sought the relatively small, uncongested, and pleasant towns and cities of southern England.

## ▶ London

Britain's largest city is relatively far from the major coal fields and other big cities. The London metropolitan area sprawls over a considerable area in southeastern England and can be considered to include 10,491,-000 people, which makes it the third largest urban agglomeration of the world, after New York and Tokyo.

London is not only much larger than the other British cities, but differs from them economically and in historical background.

It was the country's leading city, and already a large city, before the Industrial Revolution, though its population has since multiplied many times over. In the late seventeenth century, when most of the present cities were little better than hamlets, it already had nearly 700,000 people. This was roughly a tenth of the population of Great Britain at that time, while metropolitan London today has about 20 percent of the total population of the United Kingdom. So London has more than held its own in population growth during the industrial age, despite its relative distance from the booming coal-field areas. But most of the major elements in its economy developed originally in the pre-industrial period and have only been expanded and supplemented during the past two centuries.

The first and most fundamental of these elements is *commerce*. The city became an important seaport as early as the Roman occupation of England in the first century A.D., and has continued so to the present. Several aspects of its location help to account for its early development as a trading center. (1) It is located in the corner of Great Britain which is nearest the continent. This section of the island was almost the only part of England which did much trading overseas in the long centuries before the age of overseas expansion, and it is still quite important in British trade. (2) It is located in the English Lowland, which was the most productive and populous part of Great Britain in the pre-industrial period, supplying most of the wool which England exported and most of the market for imports. (3) It is located on the Thames River, which allows comparatively deep penetration of ocean ships into the Lowland. A port set inland in such a manner allows more trading territory in the surrounding countryside to be served from it within a given radius than a port set on a comparatively straight stretch of coast or on a promontory. This principle can be easily illustrated by drawing an arc of 100 miles radius from the

Royal pageantry in the heart of London. The coronation procession of Queen Elizabeth II passing through Trafalgar Square. The Admiralty Arch, symbol of British sea power, is at the left center. (United Press.)

Channel port of Dover, which is closer to the continent, and another arc of 100 miles radius from London, and comparing the respective sizes of the areas falling within the two arcs (maps, p. 78). Inland location of a port tends to maximize the distance goods can be carried toward many destinations by relatively cheap water transportation and to minimize the more expensive land transport. This tends—other things being equal, which is a most important qualification—to give the inland port the advantage over the seaward port. (4) London is located where early conditions facilitated transport connections with much of the surrounding plain. One route, with branches, was provided by the Thames River and its tributaries. Before the age of the railroad and the motor truck, water transport had greater advantages over land transport than it has today; and these natural inland waterways were extensively used for transporting goods to and from London. Furthermore, London became a major junction of Roman roads, better than any Britain was to see for well over a thousand years. Again the location had advantages: the lower Thames was originally fringed by tidal marshes which

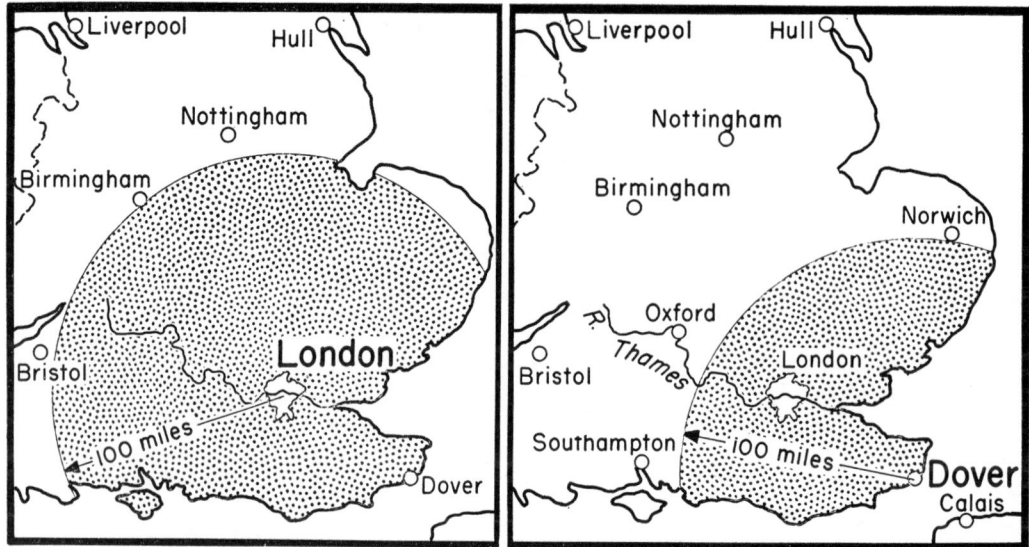

Stippled areas lie within a 100-mile radius of the center of London and of Dover, respectively.

were a major barrier to transportation, but at the original site of London firm ground penetrated these marshes and approached the river bank on both sides. By crossing the river at London highways could avoid the marshes.

In view of these advantages with respect to transportation and trade, it is not surprising that London became very early the principal port and metropolis of Great Britain, and handled as much as three quarters of the island's sea trade around 1700. In the industrial age it has faced strong competition from other British ports located closer to the rising industrial centers and some better located for access to the open Atlantic. But by the time this occurred London was too firmly established to lose its pre-eminence. It had a good harbor, which could be expanded by extending port facilities down the Thames. It had probably the world's greatest concentration of wealthy and well-established commercial and financial institutions for handling the enormously intricate operations and transactions of world-wide trade. The city itself was the country's single greatest market for many imported goods. It was well placed for trade

with Europe and developed a large entrepôt trade, a trade in which London merchants imported goods from overseas and then resold them to continental importers, thus acting as middlemen between foreign producers on the one hand and foreign consumers on the other. Distances between the main population centers of Great Britain are not really great, the Midlands industrial area, for instance, being only about 100 miles from London and Leeds about 200 miles. So London was not too badly handicapped by distance alone in its competition with ports such as Liverpool or Hull for the trade generated by the new industrial areas.

The result has been a proportionate decrease but a great absolute increase in London's trade during the industrial age. It now handles only about one third of the United Kingdom's total overseas trade, and is usually exceeded in value of exports by the second-ranking port of Liverpool; but as Britain's total trade has multiplied, so has that of London, despite the proportionate loss to other ports. One third of the trade of the world's second greatest trading nation places London among the top two or three ports in the world, after New York and pos-

ward extensions into parts of Wales and southern Cornwall (map, p. 81). Raising of beef cattle in the lowlands is so widespread that it is difficult to generalize; central and western England and northeastern Scotland are the most prominent large areas, while densities are comparatively light in eastern England and in most highland areas. Sheep are an element in the farm economy of most areas, both highland and lowland, but the densest concentrations are found in the Southern Uplands of Scotland and the uplands of Wales. Since the 1930s they have declined sharply on farms in southeastern England. Sheep are raised primarily for meat, the annual value of the wool clip being perhaps a fifth to a seventh the value of the annual output of mutton and lamb.

## TWENTIETH-CENTURY DIFFICULTIES AND TRENDS

Since World War I the United Kingdom has experienced an almost constant succession of economic difficulties, punctuated by military and political struggles which have tended to show the country's declining power and influence. The economic difficulties have been due largely—though by no means wholly—to declining exports in the principal industries upon which Britain's export trade was based before 1914. By the time these difficulties appeared there was no turning back from an economy heavily dependent on trade, since the swollen population required large food imports, and manufactures to pay for the food required imported raw materials.

Although the foundations for trouble had been laid previously, World War I was the turning point for the British economy. Depressed economic conditions characterized many areas of the country—especially those depending greatly on cotton textiles, coal, shipbuilding, and woolen textiles—during most of the period between the world wars. However, the rest of the world was also in a depression, at least during the 1930s, and Britain's position did not yet appear crucial despite the fall in commodity exports. A major reason was that exports of goods had not been sufficient to pay for imports, even before World War I. A very important role had always been played by "invisible exports." These included (1) capital from the formerly immense profits of British industry, which was invested on a large scale in the development of many other countries, (2) shipping services, which the huge British merchant marine supplied for much of the world, and (3) various other services, such as banking and insurance, which London provided on an international scale. Essentially, Britain's accumulated wealth was made to do various jobs in and for other countries; and the profits from these activities covered the deficit in the United Kingdom's trade in goods. In the late 1930s they paid for as much as 30 percent of the imports, but no longer quite made up for the excess of imports over exports.

World War II was disastrous to this system. Exports could not be maintained at substantial levels and the war fought at the same time. By 1944 exports stood at less than a third of the 1938 level. Consequently, to pay for imports overseas investments amounting to more than a billion pounds sterling were sold, and debts amounting to over three billion pounds were contracted to overseas suppliers. At the same time much of Britain's industrial equipment was overworked and not replaced when it normally would have been. So Britain emerged in 1945 a much impoverished, debt-ridden, and needy victor —though a justly proud one.

Crucially important was the fact that invisible exports were no longer available in quantities sufficient to pay for an excess of goods imports over exports. The export industries would now have to earn the nation's way back to solvency. Helped by massive American aid for a few years, they have done so. The volume of exports has been pushed up to a level about four fifths higher than before World War II; and this rather remarkable achievement has been combined with holding imports to a relatively small increase, in good part by providing more food from home soil. Britain has become self-supporting again at a relatively high level of living, although a really comfortable margin of solvency has not been attained.

### ▶ Major Export Industries

The post-World War II comeback has not been effected by the old export industries, however. Even in the interwar period the growth of a number of newer industries provided bright spots in the generally gloomy picture, and since World War II some of these have burgeoned into dominant places in the economy. At present the major export industries are: (1) *general engineering,* the production of machinery in great variety, of which textile machinery and tractors are examples prominent in the export trade, (2) *the automobile industry,* second or third largest in the world after that of the United States and possibly West Germany, (3) *the iron and steel industry,* which still produces large direct exports as well as metal for other industries, (4) *the chemical industry,* which exports products ranging from cosmetics and medicines to fertilizers, (5) *electrical engineering,* exporting generating equipment and many other products. Of these five, only iron and steel and general engineering were leading export industries in 1913, and the latter was much less important than today.

These newer industries—the aircraft industry is another that has been much publicized and may be mentioned—are generally types in which advanced scientific and production skills are highly important; and these are British assets, stemming from long experience and educational attainment, which cannot be so easily matched by many countries as Britain's resources of power, materials, or cheap labor. Thus Britain has a greater competitive advantage in them than in the older industries, at least for the time being.

Although many of the new plants have been established in the coal-field industrial districts, many others have located in London or other cities and towns in southern England. An example is the automobile industry (map, p. 66), which is centered especially in the Midlands at Birmingham and Coventry and, to a lesser extent, Derby (365,000) and Nottingham (621,000), but also is important in London and in the smaller cities of Oxford (188,000) and Luton (156,000) which lie within a 50-mile radius of London to the north. Thus there is a modern tendency for the old distinction between industrial highland margins and nonindustrial lowland to diminish somewhat.

### ▶ Postwar Rise in Level of Living

Along with industrial recovery and reorientation, Britain has achieved an over-all rise in its level of living since World War II. Prewar Britain was always a land of marked inequality. Some gained great wealth, and there was a substantial middle class, but large numbers of workers remained very poor. Many received better medical care, better food, and fared better in general in the armed services or under the government-controlled economy of the war years than they ever had before; and after the war a Labor (socialist) government was elected to provide the "new deal" in peace that had been glimpsed in war. It nationalized some basic industries, made full employment a basic aim of government, instituted a "cradle to the grave" system of social security, and imposed a very heavy progressive income tax to raise revenue and scale down economic inequality. To effect recovery it also imposed long years of "austerity," with reduced imports and little consumption of a luxury character. The Conservative party, since its return to power in 1951, has been able to relax austerity, but has retained most of the Labor measures. A major result appears to be that while many of the wealthy are not so well off as in 1939, a booming economy with full employment and extensive social security has brought about the highest plane of living that those on the lower rungs of the economic ladder have ever enjoyed. It should be noted too, that although the postwar situation has involved great extensions of governmental power, both Laborites and Conservatives have successfully maintained the traditions of responsible government and political liberty that have long been marked features of British life.

## THE COMMONWEALTH OF NATIONS

But a revived economy cannot make the United Kingdom a world power of first rank in the new age of giant powers. One result, and evidence, of Britain's declining power has been the rapid dissolution of the British Empire. During the twentieth century, and with increasing rapidity since World War II, one colony after another has been granted independence (map, p. 35). However, the newly independent ex-colonies have desired more often than not to maintain a special bond with the United Kingdom and with other ex-British colonies. Thus an association of independent countries, called the Commonwealth of Nations, has replaced much of the former empire (map, p. 87). Loss of empire may be a sign of weakness, but creation of the Commonwealth is a remarkable achievement which speaks well for Britain's over-all record as a colonial power.

The Commonwealth of Nations includes twelve independent states (1960), a number of which control dependent or semidependent territories. Five states—the United Kingdom, Canada, Australia, New Zealand, and South Africa—constitute an older group situated primarily in middle latitudes, though sparsely populated sections of some countries extend into low or high latitudes. The first four have populations and cultures that are predominantly British in origin, though other important European elements exist in Canada and, to a lesser extent, Australia. In South Africa a European minority, partly British, dominates a native African majority. The remaining states have all become independent since World War II. Six of them—India, Pakistan, Ceylon, and Malaya in Asia and Ghana and Nigeria in Africa—lie in tropical or subtropical latitudes and are European in neither population nor control. A seventh state, the island republic of Cyprus in the eastern Mediterranean, has a population that is Greek or Turkish in origin. Various units in Britain's remaining empire were moving rapidly toward full independence at the time of writing. It seemed likely that most of them would remain in the Commonwealth after independence.

The nations of the Commonwealth are held together by sentiment and self-interest. Feelings of relatedness based on common descent are strong among Britain, Australia, New Zealand, and, to a somewhat smaller degree, Canada. In South Africa such feelings principally affect the British element, which is a minority even among Europeans. Mutual trade preferences and other forms of economic cooperation, together with political and military support from other members, are important considerations for all Commonwealth states. The Commonwealth countries consult together and seek cooperative action on common problems, and participation in the Commonwealth magnifies the importance and influence of each member in the world at large. Such considerations have held the members together so far, and have made the Commonwealth a considerable element in world affairs, despite differences of opinion and even quarrels among some of its members.

# IRELAND

Ireland is a land of hills and lakes, marshes and peat bogs, cool dampness and verdant grassland. The island consists of a central plain surrounded on the north, south, and west by hills and low, rounded mountains (map, p. 61, and photo, p. 88). The climate is marine to an extreme, with average temperatures ranging from the low 40s in January to about 60 degrees in July, and rainfall from over 100 inches in western uplands to about 30 inches in eastern lowlands. Glaciation blocked drainage lines and has left many lakes connected by sluggish rivers, of which the most famous is the River Shannon. Marshes and waterlogged moorland are common, and peat bogs cover one seventh of the island. Nearly all of the natural forest is gone, but in the cool dampness luxuriant grass grows, giving the countryside its prevailing and proverbial green.

▶ *Industrial Development*

The island is almost completely lacking in important natural resources for industry. There are no mineral deposits or forests of much consequence, though government-sponsored programs of reforestation have had a limited success in small areas, as they have in Great Britain. In recent decades several small hydroelectric installations have been built, and since 1950 new techniques for utilizing peat have allowed construction of three electric generating stations using that material, with more planned. But peat is a very low-grade fuel, and much of it cannot be utilized economically by generating stations, often because of the small size of individual bogs. No situation of power abundance in the island can be foreseen, and generation of electricity still depends heavily on imported fuels, mainly coal from Great Britain.

But Ireland's comparative lack of industrial development is partly a consequence of its long subordinate relationship to England. After effective conquest of the whole island by the English in the seventeenth century, it was oppressed for two centuries under probably the harshest rule imposed on any British colonial territory. Most of the land was appropriated and divided among large estates held by English landlords, who were often absentees living in Britain; the Irish peasantry was reduced in many instances virtually to serfdom and the proceeds of its labor were drained off—and often out of Ireland—in extortionate rents and taxes. Irish trade and industry were penalized, restricted, and at times nearly destroyed by governmental measures designed to favor British competitors. All parts of Ireland were affected, but the Catholic South more than the Protestant North. (There was a strong element of religious persecution in British rule, Catholics being regarded as potentially disloyal to the Protestant crown.) Ireland, especially the Catholic part, became a land of deep poverty, sullen hostility, and periodic violence.

The North, somewhat less handicapped, did develop important industries despite the poverty of natural resources. Northern Ireland today has essentially an industrial economy, with more industrial employment than the whole of the larger Republic. Its major industries are textiles, especially the famous Irish linen, shipbuilding, and in recent years aircraft production. Belfast (537,000) is the principal industrial center as well as political capital and chief seaport. It is by far the leading center for all of the main industries. The only material Northern Ireland provides for its major industries is a minor portion of the flax used in making linen. Perhaps it is a reflection in part of Northern Ireland's precarious resource base

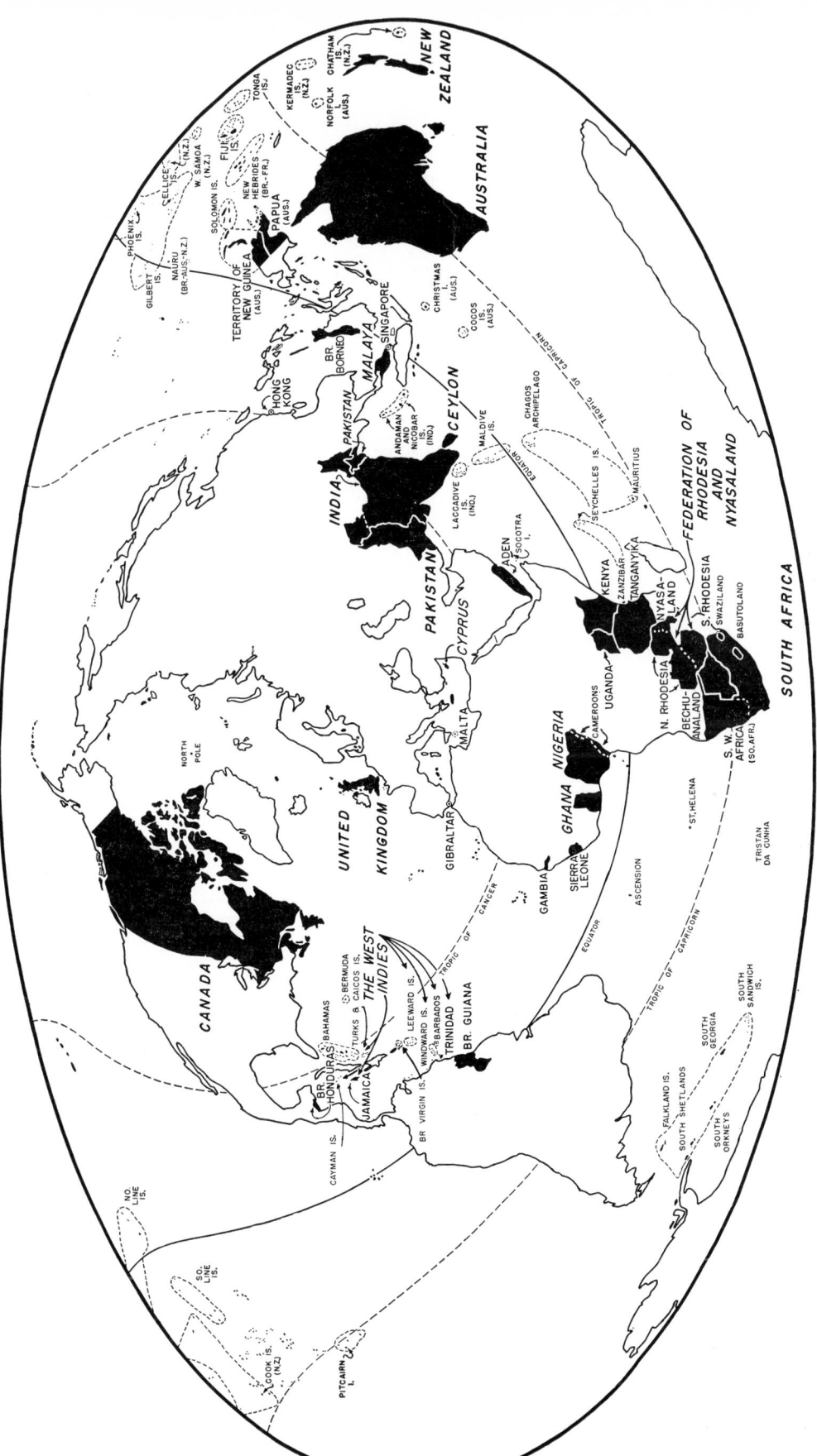

The Commonwealth of Nations. Areas in black are political units included in the Commonwealth as of January 1, 1961. Small island dependencies are encircled by dashes. Names in largest type indicate sovereign states, except for the Rhodesian and West Indian federations. Each of the latter has an elected parliament and prime minister, but is not completely self-governing. Dependencies not otherwise identified as to ownership are administered by the United Kingdom. Several Persian Gulf states under British protection do not belong officially to the Commonwealth and are not shown. (Briesemeister Elliptical Equal Area Projection, courtesy of the American Geographical Society.)

An Irish landscape—the village of Cahersiveen in southwestern Ireland. Rounded, treeless hills, such as those depicted, are characteristic of the British Isles. (Irish Tourist Bureau.)

that this has been the only part of the United Kingdom to have noteworthy unemployment since World War II, and that its plane of living is somewhat below that of Great Britain.

The Republic of Ireland has less industry, and most of what it does have makes only light consumer goods for the domestic market behind tariff protection. Well over half of the Republic's imports are manufactures in great variety. Dublin (680,000), situated on the Irish Sea at the eastern edge of the Central Plain, is the main industrial center, the leading seaport, and the political and cultural capital of the Republic. It is also the only large city. The southeastern port of Cork, next in size, has only 147,000 people in its metropolitan area.

### ▶ Agricultural Production and Trade of the Irish Republic

In the absence of large-scale industry, the Republic of Ireland is still very predomi-

nantly an agricultural country. The same physical and climatic handicaps to cultivation that affect Great Britain are present, but in even greater degree. Only about one fifth of the Republic is classed as arable land, one half is pasture, and most of the rest is waste land. Grazing is the main element in the agricultural economy (as it is in Northern Ireland), and much of the arable land is devoted to fodder crops. The country's largest export is live cattle for fattening and slaughter in Britain. Attempts are being made to expand home production of food, as large imports of grain are now necessary, and also to fatten and slaughter more animals at home and export the more valuable meat instead of the live animals.

There is a strong tendency in the modern world for agricultural areas and societies to be poorer, at least by quantitative measurements such as per capita income, than those with more industrial employment. The farmer's net output, measured by value, tends to be less than that of the worker in mechanized industries and his return smaller. The tendency is exemplified in Ireland, where the average per capita income of the Republic is less than half that of the United Kingdom, and noticeably below that of most of the industrialized countries of western and northern Europe. The estates of the period of English control are gone, and today the Irish farmer is usually a small owner rather than a "rack-rented" tenant; but farms are often neither large nor highly mechanized. There is marked rural poverty, especially in western Ireland, where a particularly rugged and poor agricultural environment is inhabited by an unusually dense peasant population, stemming originally from flight to the area to escape English exactions.

Another result of the Republic's agricultural economy is its very close economic relationship to the United Kingdom, contrasting strongly with continued political hostility toward that country. The United Kingdom is both the logical and historical market for Irish agricultural produce, and more than three quarters of the Republic's exports are sold there, essentially in return for British manufactures. Meanwhile the old political antagonism has been fired since Irish independence by the desire to unite Northern Ireland to the Republic and by terrorist activities of the underground Irish Republican Army in that cause. In World War II this antagonism was expressed in Ireland's cool official neutrality—though large numbers of Irish joined the British armed forces or worked in British war industries as individuals—and it has also been expressed in the attempt—thus far not very successful—to foster Irish Gaelic as a national language in place of English. In 1949 the Republic withdrew from the Commonwealth of Nations, and thus severed its last remaining political tie with the United Kingdom.

▶ *The Problem of Depopulation*

An almost unique distinction of Ireland is depopulation. Few sizable areas in the world have smaller populations today than a century ago, but the island of Ireland has just over half as many people as the 8.2 million it had in 1841. In the late eighteenth and early nineteenth centuries its population increased very rapidly on the precarious basis of one main subsistence crop, the potato. In the late 1840s this crop failed for several years in succession, and the potato famine which resulted claimed the lives of nearly a million people in five years, while another million and a half fled the island, mainly to the United States, in the decade following 1846. A pattern of emigration was established that has continued to the present day, though most emigrants now go to the United Kingdom. In addition a low birth rate was established, with birth control effected mainly by a social pattern in which marriage was generally postponed until the middle thirties or later in life. Between emigration and the low birth rate the downward trend of total population in the Republic has continued almost without interruption. In 1956 the country had over 60,000 (2 percent) fewer people than in 1940. Figures for 1951–1956 show that the natural increase during this 5-year period, 135,000, actually averaged to a higher annual rate of increase than for any previous year since 1881. But the net emigration during the period was about 200,000, the highest average yearly rate since before 1891. Though over-all density in the Republic remains fairly high for a basically agricultural country, there is a certain amount of alarm and talk of "national suicide."

# France

The west central portions of the European mainland across the English Channel and North Sea from the British Isles are occupied by a group of highly developed industrial nations which have long had close relations with each other. Germany and France are the largest nations in the group and the only ones which have ranked as great powers in the twentieth century. Four of the remaining countries—the Netherlands, Belgium, Luxembourg, and Switzerland—are found in a historic buffer zone separating the two major nations. Austria, though it is not in the buffer zone, may be included in the group because of its close relationships with Germany. Monaco and Andorra, adjoining France, and Liechtenstein, between Switzerland and Austria, are insignificant micro-states with a quasi-independent status; only proximity entitles them to be numbered with the countries of this group.

Topographic variety, economic interdependence, historical antagonism, and burgeoning cooperation are key phrases describing the countries of West Central Europe as a group. In physical terms the area they occupy may be thought of as consisting of three concentric and widely different arcs of land (maps, pp. 48 and 91): an outer arc of lowland plains bordering the Bay of Biscay, English Channel, and North and Baltic seas; a central arc of hills, low mountains, and small plains; and an inner arc consisting of the high Alps mountains, with another high range, the Pyrenees,

A large potash mine on the level plain of the Rhine in Alsace. (French Embassy Press and Information Division.)

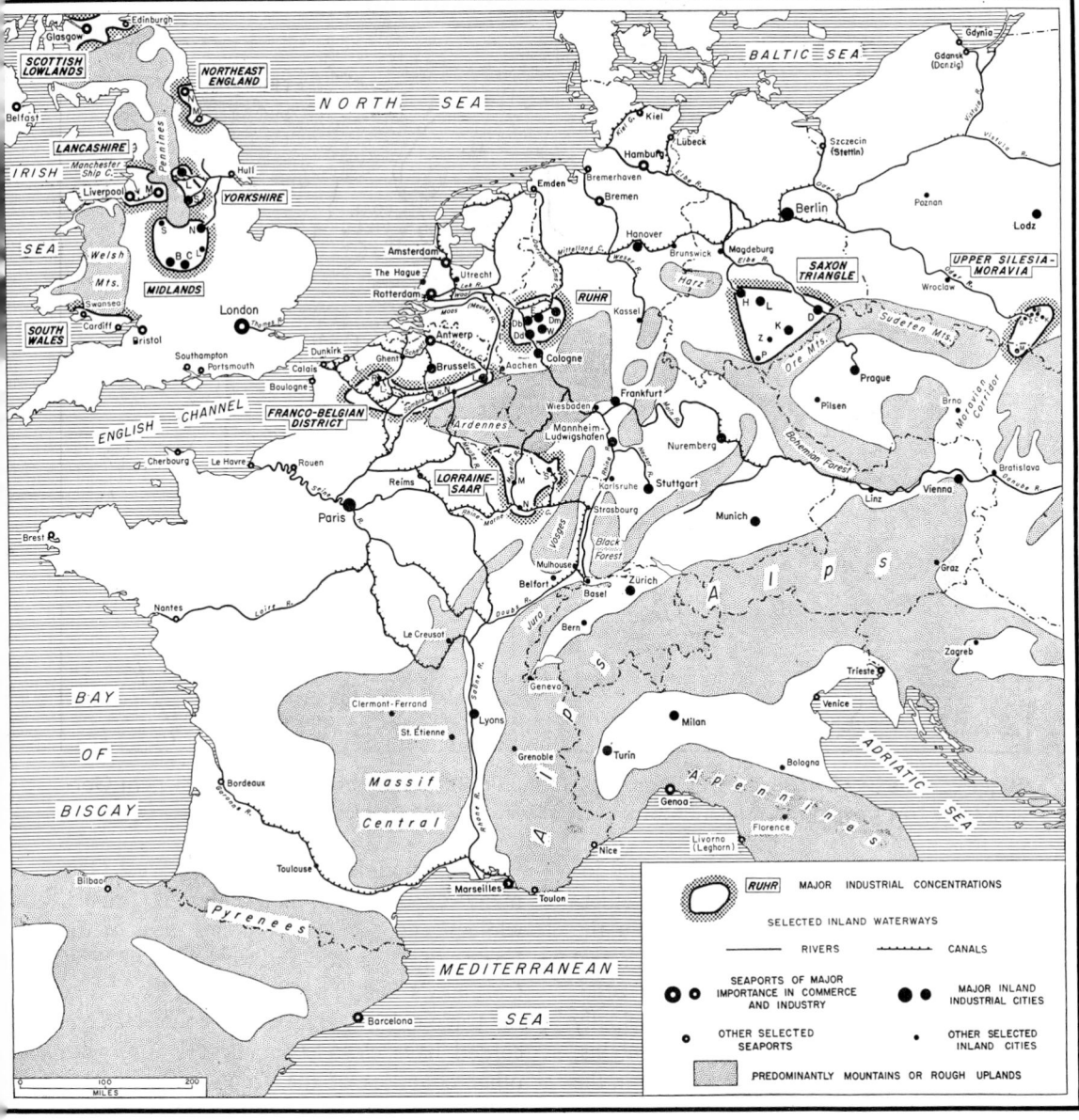

Cities, industrial concentrations, waterways, and highlands in West Central Europe and adjoining areas. Most sections of the internal waterways shown are navigable for barge traffic. The "major industrial concentrations" are relatively continuous industrialized areas. All of the industrial concentrations shown contain large deposits of bituminous coal, except the Saxon Triangle, which has large lignite deposits. Note the clustering of industrial concentrations in border zones between highlands and plains. Cities indicated by letter are as follows: Northeast England—N, Newcastle, M, Middlesbrough; Yorkshire—L, Leeds-Bradford, S, Sheffield; Lancashire—M, Manchester; Midlands—B, Birmingham, C, Coventry, L, Leicester, N, Nottingham, S, Stoke-on-Trent; Franco–Belgian District—L, Lille, R, Roubaix, C, Charleroi, N, Namur, L, Liège; Lorraine–Saar—M, Metz, N, Nancy, S, Saarbrücken; Ruhr—Db, Duisburg, Dd, Düsseldorf, E, Essen, Dm, Dortmund, W, Wuppertal; Saxon Triangle—H, Halle, L, Leipzig, D, Dresden, K, Karl-Marx-Stadt (Chemnitz), Z, Zwickau, P. Plauen; Upper Silesia–Moravia—K, Katowice, B, Bytom, C, Chorzow, Z, Zabrze, G, Gliwice, M, Moravska Ostrava. Dotted areas represent highlands offering some hindrance to transportation and being sufficiently steep, rugged, or infertile to discourage dense agricultural settlement.

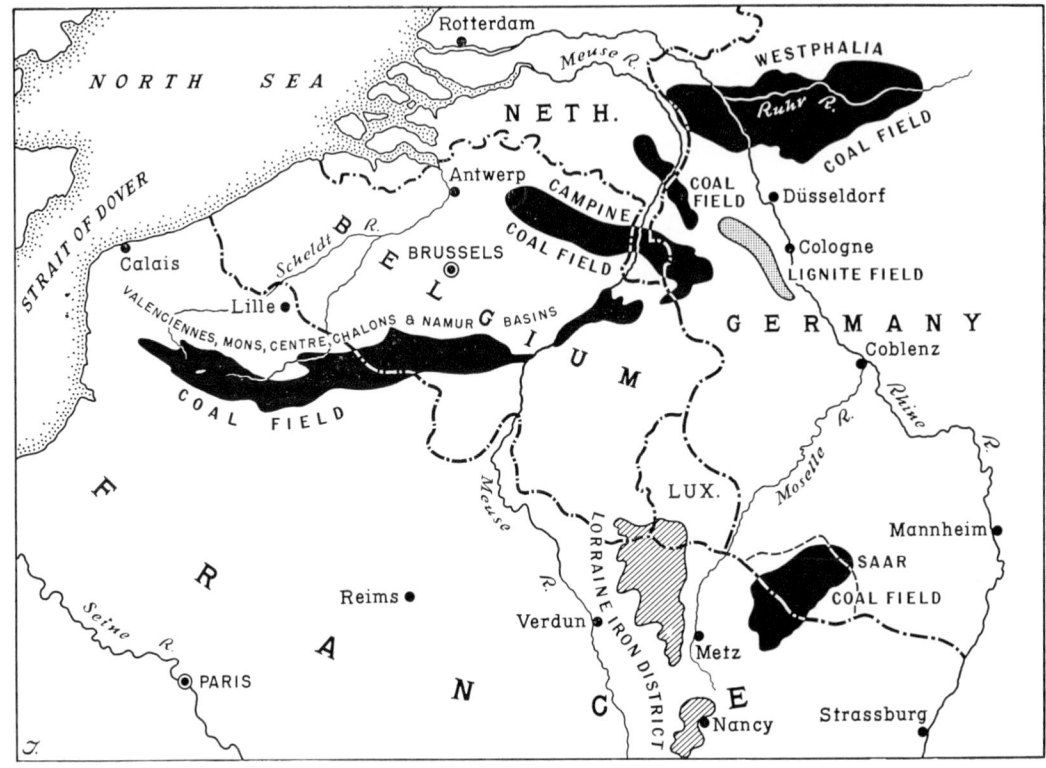

Major coal fields of West Central Europe. Note the line of fields stretching across western Germany, the Low Countries, and northeastern France. (U. S. Geological Survey.)

offset to the west. France and Germany include portions of all three arcs, the Netherlands and northern Belgium lie within the outer arc of plains, southern Belgium and Luxembourg are in the central hilly zone, and Switzerland and Austria lie principally within the inner arc of Alpine mountains, though their main populated areas are in the southern fringes of the central arc.

The largest deposits of coal and iron ore in Europe (map, above) provide basic resources for an industrial development of the first magnitude. A series of great industrial concentrations stretches across this area from northern France to southwestern Poland, following the main axis of coal deposits (map, p. 91). Other industrialized areas exist by the score. Coal and iron ore furnish an important basis for trade and cooperation among the countries of the group, most of which are deficient in one or both of these

vital commodities. For example, West Germany exports coal and coke to France, while France, in turn, supplies most of the iron ore for the iron and steel mills of West Germany's Saar district. Many other bases for trade exist, and all of the countries concerned have close economic relations with other countries of the group.

Political relations have been troubled, however, by antagonisms of long standing. The countries of this group have fought each other repeatedly in past wars. In the twentieth century the principal antagonists have been Germany and France, but most of the other countries have been drawn into their contention and strife. Today France and West Germany are making a strong effort to cooperate with each other, and they have joined with Belgium, the Netherlands, Luxembourg, and Italy in forming a number of important new supranational economic "communities" (pp. 34–38 and p. 102). These include the European Economic Community or Common Market, the European Coal and Steel Community, and the European Atomic Energy Community (Euratom). Switzerland and Austria, meanwhile, have become linked with the United Kingdom, three Scandinavian countries, and Portugal in yet another economic grouping, the European Free Trade Association (p. 38). But both Switzerland and Austria remain closely connected in a multitude of ways with their neighbors in West Central Europe and enjoy generally harmonious relations with them.

# THE INTERNATIONAL IMPORTANCE OF FRANCE

Of the two major countries in West Central Europe, Germany is much the larger in population, with an estimated 72 million people in 1959 as opposed to an estimated 45 million for France. Even West Germany, the part of the country outside the Soviet iron curtain, had an estimated 55 million people in 1959 (including 2.2 million in West Berlin) and thus was considerably larger in population than France. France, however, is much larger in area than postwar Germany: approximately 213,000 square miles (including the island of Corsica), as against 137,000 square miles for all Germany and 96,000 for West Germany alone. In fact, excluding the Soviet Union, France is the largest European country in area.

The importance of France, however, does not rest primarily on its size, though its population of 45 million is an element of very considerable significance. It is one of the world's more important industrial and trading nations and is an atomic power by virtue of independently manufacturing its own atomic weapons—one of only four powers to have done so (1960). In cultural prestige, at least in the Western world, France also stands very high—possibly at the top. Still other factors that add to the importance of France are its strategic geographical position in Europe and its central role in the French Community—a worldwide political association that includes France, its overseas departments and dependencies, and many former colonial possessions that have elected to remain in the Community after independence. France's industrial and commercial importance is discussed at some length in the latter part of the chapter. In the following paragraphs the country's cultural achievements, its strategic geographical position, and its relationships with the other units of the French Community are briefly surveyed.

► *Achievements of French Culture* France was conquered for Rome by Julius Caesar in the first century B.C. and thereafter became thoroughly Romanized. It has thus been a highly civilized land longer than any other European country except the peninsular countries of Southern Europe. During the Middle Ages Paris, the French capital, became the main center of Roman Catholic scholarship and culture. In modern times the French have made eminent contributions in all fields of scholarship and art, and Paris has generally been regarded as the world's foremost artistic and cultural center. Such names as Pasteur and Curie in science; Descartes, Pascal, Voltaire, Rousseau, and Bergson in philosophy; Molière, Racine, Hugo, Balzac, Zola, and Proust in literature; Matisse and Gauguin in art come readily to mind as evidence of France's contributions to civilization. Even to make such a short list is almost to falsify by selection. In addition, many illustrious foreigners have drawn their inspiration from and pursued their studies in France. The position of French as an international language, particularly as a major language of diplomacy, and the continued attraction of Paris for the world's artists, students, and tourists, as well as for important international conferences, are further evidences of the cultural prestige of France.

## ▶ Strategic Importance of the French Beachhead

During the twentieth century France's strategic position has been that of a beachhead. In two world wars a major path to the conquest of Germany has lain through France. In the event of still another great war involving land fighting on the European continent, it seems quite possible that France would again play a similar role. Location at the western end of Europe (except for Spain and Portugal, which have been militarily weak and relatively isolated behind the Pyrenees), sea frontage on three sides, proximity to Great Britain, and good communications with the continent to the east have combined to make France a critical area in the wars and hence a critical area in the politics of the twentieth century.

## ▶ The French Community

The world significance of France has been heightened by its importance as an imperial and colonial power. Before it began to dissolve in 1954 the French overseas empire totaled about 4½ million square miles (21 times the size of France itself) and had a population of over 70 million—a colonial aggregate second only to that of Great Britain in population and second to none in area. Actual settlement overseas by Frenchmen was seldom on a large scale—the principal exception being Algeria—but political control was often accompanied by a strong penetration of French culture. Today many of the leading figures in France's former possessions speak French, have received the same type of education that Frenchmen receive, often including higher education in French universities, and have had political or military training and experience in the service of the French government. In the Americas, areas of French-descended population and/or culture exist as survivals from an earlier empire that was lost before most of the more recent possessions were acquired.

France's colonial empire as such survives now in only a minor way, having practically disappeared in a few tumultuous years (map, p. 35). In 1954 military defeat by a Communist-led rebellion resulted in loss of control over Indochina, the major Far Eastern part of the empire; and in the same year the last French enclaves on the coast of India were ceded to that country. France's defeat in Indochina was a spur to nationalist movements, already strong, in her North African possessions—Morocco, Algeria, and Tunisia—and in 1956 independence was yielded to Morocco and Tunisia. Then in 1958 the units of the empire classed as "overseas territories" [1] were allowed to vote on the question of their continued political association with France. The African territory of French Guinea voted against further association and was granted immediate independence, but the other units all voted to remain as semi-independent republics in what is now called the French Community (map, right). In 1960 the units comprising former French West Africa, French Equatorial Africa, and Madagascar were granted full independence, but retained their membership in the Community (see Ch. 23). (The remaining units have kept their previous status as overseas territories.) In 1960 France also relinquished control of her African trust territories, French Togoland and

---

[1] In French West Africa the territories of Senegal, French Sudan, Mauritania, French Guinea, the Ivory Coast, Dahomey, Upper Volta, and Niger; in French Equatorial Africa the territories of Gabon, Middle Congo, Ubangi-Shari, and Chad; in or bordering the Indian Ocean the territories of Madagascar, the Comoro Islands, and French Somaliland; in the Pacific Ocean the territories of New Caledonia and French Polynesia; in the North Atlantic Ocean off Newfoundland, the territory of St. Pierre and Miquelon.

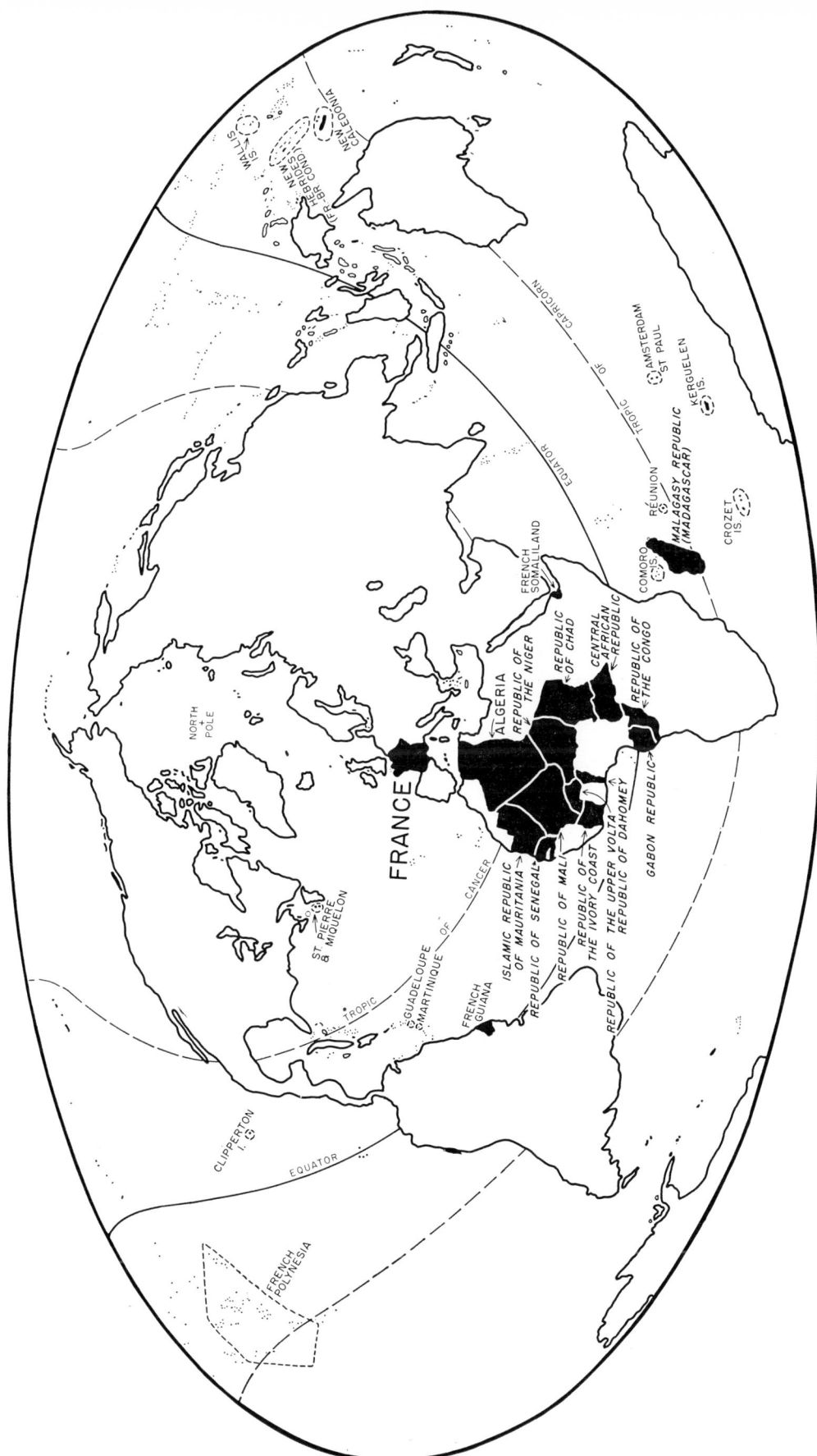

The French Community, January 1, 1961, shown in black. Small island units are encircled with dashes. Independent states other than France itself are labeled with slanted capital letters. (Briesemeister Elliptical Equal Area Projection, courtesy of the American Geographical Society.)

French Cameroons, which became independent republics outside the Community.

### The Algerian Conflict

While the foregoing events have been occurring, another important French possession, Algeria, has been racked by bitter warfare between nationalist rebels and the bulk of the French army (see pp. 308–310). The Algerian situation involves political problems that are more difficult to solve than are those of most colonial areas, due primarily to the fact that large numbers of Frenchmen have settled there and have become a favored and powerful minority in Algeria's predominantly Moslem population. Thus the question of Algeria's future involves the future of these French settlers and of the massive French economic interests they represent; and recently it has been complicated by the area's enhanced value due to the discovery of large deposits of oil and natural gas in the Algerian Sahara.

Actually the Algerian conflict represents a continuation of general circumstances that have afflicted France for two decades. Since 1939 the country has been almost continuously at war: with Germany between 1939 and 1945; in Indochina between 1946 and 1954; and in Algeria since 1954. No country in the world has been more continuously harried, distracted, and drained by military and political conflict during the years since 1939. The Indochinese war alone absorbed much larger resources than were made available by the United States to aid the internal recovery of France from the disaster of World War II. Such a background of conflict presents a rather startling contrast to France's many accomplishments in economic and other fields during the same period.

## A GREAT POWER IN DECLINE

France was once a very great power. In the seventeenth and eighteenth centuries its power was a primary factor in European politics, and in the early nineteenth century, under Napoleon I, it came near to subjugating the entire continent before it was checked by a continental coalition in alliance with Great Britain. France's power was based on the fact that the French kings unified a large and populous national territory at a relatively early date. Before Germany and Italy achieved political unification in the later nineteenth century, France was a larger country relative to its European neighbors than it is today.

### ▶ Physical and Cultural Unity of the French Hexagon

Modern France lies mostly within an irregular hexagon framed on five sides by seas and mountains (map, right): in the south the Mediterranean Sea and Pyrenees Mountains forming two sides of the hexagon; in the west and northwest the Bay of Biscay and the English Channel forming two sides; in the southeast and east a fifth side formed by the Alps and Jura mountains and, farther north, the Vosges Mountains with the Rhine River a short distance to the east. Part of the sixth or northeastern side of the hexagon is formed by the low Ardennes Upland, which lies mostly in Belgium and Luxembourg; but broad lowland passageways lead into France from Germany both north and south of the Ardennes. Aside from the large Massif Central in south central France, all of the country's major highlands are peripheral. Even the Massif Central, a hilly upland with low mountains in the east, is skirted by lowland corridors which connect the extensive plains of the north and west with the Mediterranean

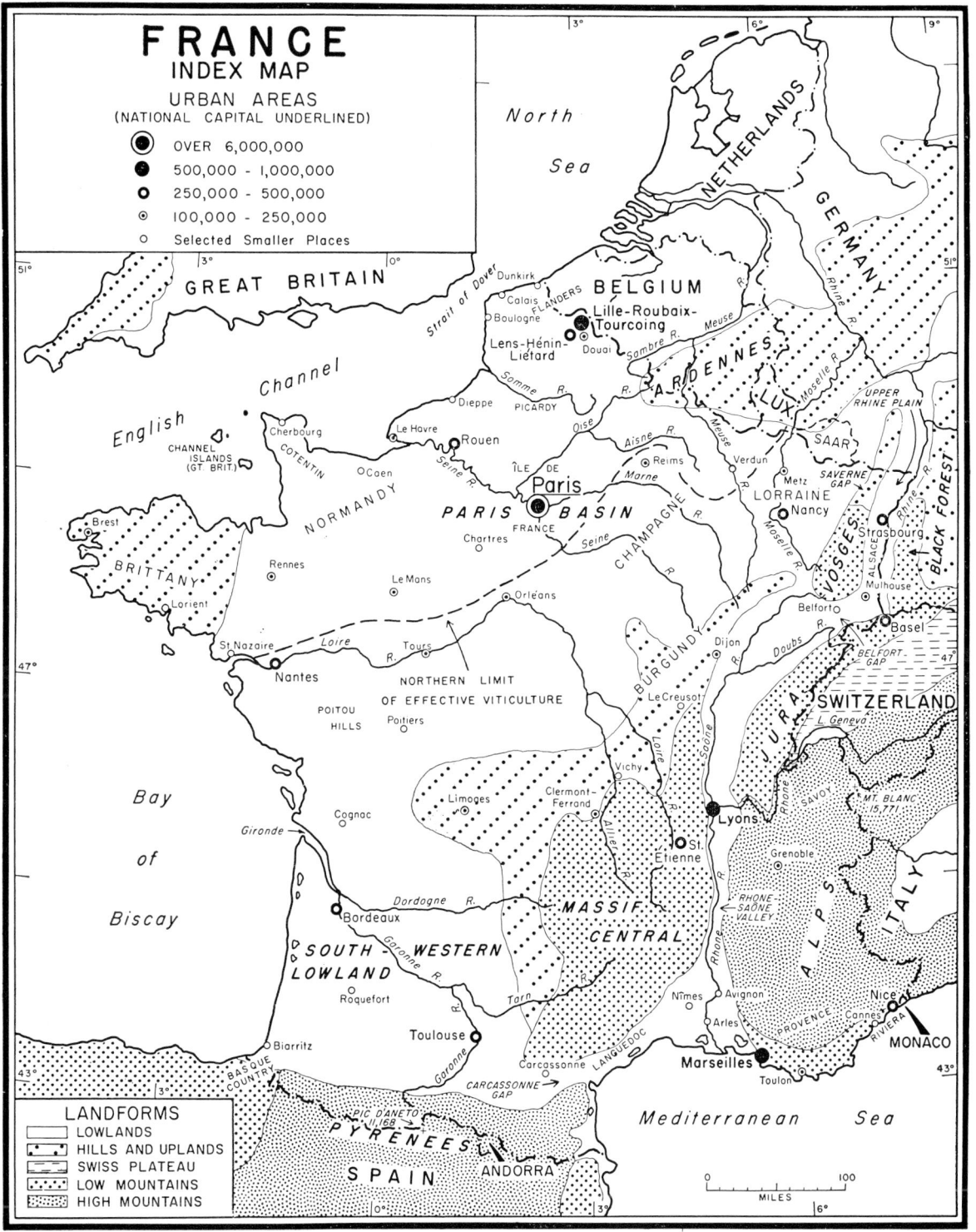

Index map of France. City-size symbols are based on metropolitan-area estimates.

coast. These corridors include the Rhone-Saône Valley between the Massif to the west and the Alps and Jura to the east; and the Carcassonne Gap between the Massif and the Pyrenees. Thus France is a country whose frontiers coincide, except in the northeast, with seas, mountains, or the Rhine, and which has no serious internal barriers to movement.

At a very early time the French hexagon began to form in some degree a recognizable political unit. It entered history as Roman Gaul, conquered mostly by Julius Caesar in the first century B.C. The Romans found a degree of cultural unity already established within it among the Gallic tribes. The Rhine was the frontier between these tribes and the Germans to the east, and, failing to conquer the Germans, the Romans established the Rhine as the frontier of the Empire. Five hundred years of Roman occupation and Latinization increased the unity of Gaul, and also increased the distinction between it and unoccupied Germany. During the Middle Ages the land within the hexagon was politically fragmented, like most of Europe, but Germanic invaders were absorbed and a considerable degree of unity was maintained in a culture now becoming French. An exception was the area nearest the Rhine, where Germanic languages and culture became established for some distance west of the river. In the later Middle Ages the physical character and underlying cultural unity of the territory within the hexagon were important factors aiding the French kings in their successful attempt to build a unified and centralized state extending over a broad area. This state emerged in the fifteenth, sixteenth, and seventeenth centuries, and attained in general the boundaries of ancient Gaul, except near the Rhine.

### Mountain Frontiers of the South and East

The state which emerged as modern France was to a considerable degree a natural fortress, as two of its three land frontiers lay in rugged mountain areas. The Pyrenees, along the border with Spain, are a formidable barrier with two peaks over 11,000 feet and only one pass lower than 5000 feet. Even today only a handful of highways and railroads connect France and Spain. The main routes skirt the ends of the range. Most roads through the mountains are blocked by snow for a considerable period in winter. The micro-state of Andorra lies on one of these routes in the eastern Pyrenees. In general, the lowest elevations in the Pyrenees are found in the west near the Bay of Biscay. Here the small linguistic group called the Basques—neither French nor Spanish in language—occupies an area extending into both France and Spain. Though mountain pastures in the Pyrenees are utilized by livestock graziers from both sides of the range, these mountains form a fairly effective zone of separation between the French and Spanish populations.

In southeastern France, the Alps and Jura mountains are followed by France's boundaries with Italy and Switzerland. The sparsely populated Alps frontier between France and Italy is even higher than the Pyrenees: Mont Blanc, the highest mountain in Europe, reaches 15,771 feet, and several other summits exceed 12,000 feet. The mountains are cut by several deep passes which have long been important as routes; and a highway tunnel under construction beneath the northern shoulder of Mont Blanc will provide an important new connection between France and Italy when it is opened in 1963. But the number of important routes through the mountains is limited, and the Alps have been an important defensive rampart throughout France's history. The Jura Mountains, on the French-Swiss frontier, are a very different kind of range, but also difficult to cross. Their rounded crests generally reach only 3000 to 5500 feet, but are arranged in a series of long ridges separated by deep valleys. Easy passes through the ridges are comparatively few.

### ▶ Territorial Components of France's Northeastern Frontier

France's northeastern frontier, extending from Switzerland to the North Sea, is less defensible than the mountain frontiers in the south, and unlike them, extends for long distances through well-populated areas where different cultures—the French and the Germanic—meet and interlock. It was France's misfortune that a stronger industrial and military power coalesced across this frontier during the nineteenth century. Though France's eventual decline from its position as a truly great power was probably inevitable when the United States and the Soviet Union began to emerge as giant, effectively organized powers, it has been most closely and directly associated with the rise of Germany.

Belgium and Luxembourg, although they lie between France and Germany, have not effectively separated them in times of conflict. Hence the French-German frontier may be thought of as a zone reaching to the North Sea and including these smaller countries. The border zone comprises six well-defined physical sections: the Belfort Gap, the Upper Rhine Plain, the Vosges Mountains, Lorraine, the Ardennes Upland, and the northern plains.

1. *The Belfort Gap, or Gate* (also known as the Burgundian Gate). This is a lowland corridor between the northern end of the Jura Mountains and the southern end of the Vosges Mountains. It forms an easy, though narrow, passageway for transportation and military movement between the Rhone-Saône Valley and interior of France to the west and the Rhine Valley and Germany to the east.

2. *The Upper Rhine Plain.* From the Rhine port of Basel, in Switzerland, to a point north of the French Rhine port of Strasbourg, the boundary between France and Germany follows the Rhine River. Here the river flows through a level-floored alluvial valley formed originally by the foundering of a section of the earth's crust. The valley, known technically as a rift valley or *graben,* lies between ranges of low mountains which are rather similar in physical character: the Vosges Mountains in France and the Black Forest in Germany. These mountains are remnants of a continuous structure which existed before the central section slipped downward to form the rift valley. The floor of the valley is often called the Upper Rhine Plain. The French section of the plain, about 10 to 20 miles wide, lies in the old province of Alsace.[2] The plain is outside France's strongest defense lines, and has long been an important pawn, and prize, in French-German struggles.

3. *The Vosges Mountains.* For about 70 miles this low, wooded range overlooks the flat Upper Rhine Plain. Lower uplands continue northward into Germany beyond the Saverne Gap at the north end of the mountains proper. Although the highest summit is below 4700 feet, the Vosges range presents a steep face to the east and has constituted a military barrier of considerable value.

4. *Lorraine.* Between the Vosges Mountains and the Ardennes Upland, a rolling lowland connects France and Germany across the old French province of Lorraine. It is sometimes called the Lorraine Gate. To the west it opens into France's largest lowland, which is centered on Paris and is often referred to as the Paris Basin. Between the German border and Paris, the terrain is interrupted at intervals by long escarpments facing eastward. These escarpments, formed

---

[2] At the time of the French Revolution, France's ancient provinces were abolished as administrative-territorial units, and the present structure of small, less autonomous units called departments was instituted. But many of the provincial names from pre-Revolutionary France (Alsace, Lorraine, Burgundy, Champagne, Brittany, Normandy, and so on) are still well-recognized, significant, and useful regional designations.

by the outcropping of resistant layers among the sedimentary rocks which underlie the Paris Basin, have proven useful military barriers in past wars when properly fortified. But the lowland gateway of Lorraine has nonetheless been an easier military route into France than the upland to the north or the mountains to the south.

5. *The Ardennes Upland.* This low plateau centers in southern Belgium and extends into adjacent Luxembourg and Germany, and for a very short distance into France. It is one of many remnants in western and southern Europe of an ancient mountain system often called the Hercynian system. Over a vast span of geologic time, the Hercynian mountains were planed off by erosion, and then the remnants were submerged for long ages beneath the sea, where great thicknesses of sediments accumulated and hardened into rock. Disturbances in the earth's crust uplifted some sections, and they appear today as comparatively low, discontinuous uplands or highlands. Long-continued erosion has removed much of the sedimentary covering, and the original igneous or metamorphic rocks underlie the surface in many areas. Some areas, such as parts of the Massif Central of France, show evidence of comparatively recent volcanic activity. Around the margins of these old highlands are found sedimentary formations that contain Europe's principal coal deposits. Besides the Ardennes and the Massif Central, the remnants of the Hercynian system include the uplands of Brittany, Cornwall, southern Wales, and southern Ireland; the Pennines of England; the Vosges Mountains and the Black Forest; the Rhine Uplands of Germany; the uplands and highlands of central Germany and western Czechoslovakia; and sizable areas in the Iberian and Balkan peninsulas.

Stream valleys deeply entrenched below a rolling, forested surface make the Ardennes a considerable barrier to transportation, especially to east-west transportation, as the major rivers flow from south to north. This area has generally been considered unfavorable terrain for military movement, although Germany launched two major offensives across it in World War II.

6. *The northern plains.* For about 80 miles, from the northern edge of the Ardennes to the North Sea, the French-Belgian frontier runs through low plains, which are a segment of the North European Plain and thus are continuous across Belgium and the Netherlands into northern Germany. In both world wars the plains of Belgium, forming a broad corridor equipped with excellent transportation facilities, were an important avenue of invasion from Germany into France. The seaward portion of these plains is the region of Flanders (map, p. 97), famous for the bitterly contested battles fought there between British and German armies in World War I.

## ▶ Major French-German Conflicts and Their Consequences

Thus the Franco-German border zone consists of three lowland passageways into France—the northern plains, Lorraine, and the Belfort Gap—separated by two upland barriers, the Ardennes and the Vosges, plus Alsace lying outside one of the barriers. This border zone is the arena in which France and Germany fought three major conflicts between 1870 and 1945. These conflicts were disastrous for France and, while hardly the basic causes of France's difficulties and relative decline, were certainly major milestones along the path.

The first conflict was the Franco-Prussian War of 1870–1871. In this war German forces broke into France through Lorraine, destroying French armies around Metz and farther north along the edge of the Ardennes. Paris was invested and France was compelled to surrender. This stunning German victory demonstrated that France was no longer the dominant military power in continental Europe; and one of its immediate outcomes, the establishment of a unified German state under Prussian leadership, augured ill for France's future.

At the end of the Franco-Prussian War,

France was compelled to cede to Germany Alsace and northeastern Lorraine, where a frontier was established which left Nancy and Verdun in France but placed Metz in Germany. Germany's claim to the ceded areas was based on the fact that they were, as they still are, predominantly German in language, having been acquired piecemeal by France in the seventeenth and eighteenth centuries. But there is considerable evidence that the majority of their population would have preferred to remain in France, and Germany refused to allow a plebiscite to determine their preference. Their annexation gave Germany strategic military advantages vis-à-vis France, and also gave it control of very considerable mineral resources. These included major potash deposits in southern Alsace (photo, p. 90) and salt deposits in Lorraine. But as it eventually turned out, the most valuable resource was the iron ore of Lorraine. The Lorraine deposits, extending from the vicinity of Nancy northward into southern Belgium and Luxembourg (map, p. 92) are the greatest source of iron ore in Europe. Control of them was probably not a major motive for annexation at the time, as they are low-grade ores with a high phosphorus content and hence were not highly valuable in 1871. (Phosphoric iron ores produced steel which broke easily under pressure or stress.) But in 1878 two British inventors, Thomas and Gilchrist, introduced a process to make good steel from such ores by lining the steel furnaces with refractory bricks made from crushed limestone to neutralize the phosphorus. Thus Germany found itself in possession of a most valuable resource, while only a minor part of the deposits were left in adjacent French Lorraine.

The second Franco-German conflict was the World War of 1914–1918. In 1914 German armies invaded France by the northern plains route. In a month Belgium was largely overrun, and northeastern France was penetrated to a point about 15 miles from Paris, but there the Germans were checked in the Battle of the Marne and fell back some miles. Four years of trench warfare followed, fought along various lines in northeastern France. During most of this time about a tenth of France was in German hands, and when the German armies were finally driven out in 1918, they added systematic destruction to the havoc wrought in this area by the fighting itself. Thus large and important parts of France were devastated by 1918. But even this disaster was overshadowed by the enormous toll of human lives. The French armies had borne the main brunt of the allied effort on the western front, and no less than 1.3 million men had died in service; close to half a million had perished in one battle—the six-month defense of Verdun in 1916. These losses amounted to over 3 percent of France's *total* population, and compared with a loss of just over 100,000 for the United States—a country with more than twice the population of France.

As a result of her "victory," France regained Alsace and the portion of Lorraine which had been lost in 1871. She also acquired control over the economy of the German industrial district called the Saar. This area, an important producer of coal and steel, lies just east of Lorraine and is closely tied to it economically. The Saar was not ceded to France, but was placed under an international political administration and attached to France economically, with the provision that the Saarlanders should eventually decide their own status in a plebiscite. When this plebiscite was held in 1935, the population voted overwhelmingly to be reunited with Germany.

The third French-German conflict came as part of World War II (1939–1945). Again France was invaded, in 1940, by the northern plains route. This time the Netherlands as well as Belgium was engulfed in the German assault. But the movement through Belgium proved to be only a powerful feint, and when large French and British forces had been drawn into northern Belgium to meet it, the main German thrust was delivered across the Ardennes Upland.

This section had always been considered too difficult for major military operations, and was only lightly defended. But it proved to be no longer a sufficient barrier in a new age of mechanized and motorized warfare. German armies broke across and out of the Ardennes, and then turned north to reach the English Channel, thus trapping the allied armies in the north in a huge pocket against the sea. These trapped armies were destroyed or captured, except for some 338,000 men who were evacuated to Britain through the Channel port of Dunkirk. The Germans were then able to brush aside the remaining French forces as they rapidly overran much of the country, sending it down to stunning defeat.

Four years later, in 1944, liberation from German occupation again made France a battlefield. After intensive preparatory bombing, which reached far into France, allied armies landed in Normandy and swept the German forces back across northern France. Their advance was stubbornly contested, especially in Normandy, and many French communities were reduced to ruins, although Paris was spared. A secondary invasion force landed on the Mediterranean coast and moved into Germany via the Rhone-Saône Valley and the Belfort Gap. Liberated France emerged from the war with most of its transportation equipment and one eighth of its housing destroyed, with wheat production at well under half of the prewar level, with most of its machine tools removed to Germany, and industrial production at about one fifth of the prewar output. About 600,000 men had died in service, compared to about 400,000 for the United States with a population over three times that of France.

### The New Era of Franco-German Cooperation

Thus for nearly a century much of Europe's destructive military history has been enacted in the French-German frontier zone, and especially on the French side of the border. But since World War II this old zone of conflict has become the scene of constructive efforts to substitute peaceful cooperation for strife and antagonism. France, Germany, Belgium, the Netherlands, and Luxembourg were leaders in the movement to create the deliberative assembly called the Council of Europe; and, with Italy, they have moved toward unification of their economies within the European Coal and Steel Community, the European Economic Community or Common Market, and the European Atomic Energy Community. These developments have been surveyed in some detail in Chapter 2 (pp. 34–38). It may be noted that all of the organizations named have their headquarters (1960) in cities lying in the old border zone of French-German conflict: the Council of Europe in Strasbourg, the European Economic Community and the Atomic Energy Community in Brussels, and the Coal and Steel Community in Luxembourg city. Most of the mines and factories within the jurisdiction of the Coal and Steel Community are within or near the border zone: in the German Ruhr and Saar; in Lorraine and northeastern France; and in central Belgium, Luxembourg, and the southern panhandle of the Netherlands.

Further results of French-German cooperation are to be seen in the amicable settlement of a dispute concerning the Saar which arose after World War II, and, as a part of the Saar settlement, in an agreement between the two nations to canalize the Moselle River. Following the collapse of Germany in World War II, control over the Saar's economy passed once more to France, and the area was given a quasi-independent political status. The resulting dispute between France and Germany was ended, however, in 1957 by return of the Saar to Germany following a plebiscite in which the Saar's population voted, as it had in 1935, to be reunited with the German state. Agreements concerning the Saar that were signed between France and West Germany in 1956 guaranteed France's right to purchase one third of the Saar's annual coal production, and West Germany agreed to assist France in canalizing the Moselle River. This stream, which flows through the Lorraine iron-mining and steel-milling district and connects it with the Rhine (map, p. 92), has long been canalized for barge traffic in Lorraine itself, but from Lorraine to the Rhine the river has been practically useless for through navigation by large barges due to frequent rapids and stretches of shallow water. Canalization of the lower river, scheduled for completion in 1963, is being accomplished by construction of 13 dams, which will not only deepen the river but will make possible the generation of large amounts of power at 10 hydroelectric stations attached to the dams. Opening of the Moselle waterway is expected to benefit greatly the industries of Lorraine by providing direct water transportation via the Rhine to Germany's Ruhr coal field and to the sea. It is anticipated that Ruhr coal and coke will provide the largest tonnages moving upstream, while iron and steel, phosphatic slag for fertilizer, and some iron ore will move downstream.

## ▶ France's Population Problem

The relative decline of France as a world power has been closely related to the failure of the country's population and economy to develop at rates comparable to those of a number of other nations during the past century. Especially critical was the failure of France to keep pace with her former arch enemy, Germany, in population growth. In 1870 these nations were approximately equal in population, each having about 38 million people. The loss to Germany of the 2 million inhabitants of Alsace-Lorraine following the Franco-Prussian War put France at a population disadvantage, and the lower French birth rate caused a further widening of the gap. By World War I the population of Germany had reached 68 million, as contrasted with only 40 million for France. Approximately the same difference in population obtained immediately prior to World War II. The growth of the French population since 1800, as compared with that of certain other countries, is shown in Table 4. Some of the figures given are estimates. This table goes a long way toward telling the story of France's decline in military power and security.

The immediate cause of France's relatively stable population is a low birth rate. Falling birth rates have been generally characteristic of countries as they have become industrialized and urbanized and as their standard of living has risen. But the falling birth rate affected France before other countries, and affected not only the urban but also the rural population to a greater degree than usual. In France, as in

TABLE 4

COMPARATIVE POPULATION DATA: FRANCE AND SELECTED COUNTRIES

| YEAR | APPROXIMATE POPULATION IN MILLIONS | | | | | |
|---|---|---|---|---|---|---|
| | FRANCE | GERMANY | UNITED KINGDOM | ITALY | RUSSIA | UNITED STATES |
| Circa 1800 | 27 | 25 | 11 | 18 | 39 | 5 |
| Circa 1850 | 36 | 35 | 27 | 23 | 62 | 23 |
| Circa 1900 | 38 | 56 | 37 | 32 | 129 | 76 |
| Pre-World War I (1910–1913) | 40 | 68 | 41 | 35 | 139 | 92 |
| Pre-World War II (1936–1940) | 41 | 70 | 46 | 43 | 171 | 132 |
| 1959 | 45 | 72 | 52 | 49 | 209 | 178 |
| Approximate increase, 1850–1959 (millions) | 9 | 37 | 25 | 26 | 147 | 155 |

other countries, the larger families are generally found on farms, but French farm families tend to be smaller than in most countries, and this tendency showed itself at a relatively early date. It was an important factor in the comparatively early slackening of France's population growth.

No one can say for certain what has caused the early and extreme decline in French natality, although many hypotheses have been advanced. Among the more plausible hypotheses are the following:

1. Since the French Revolution the law has required a farmer to divide most of his property evenly among his children when he made his will. The hypothesis is that French peasants, in order to avoid the enforced subdivision of their family farms, have limited themselves to small families.

2. French society has placed a premium on the education of children. This has increased their expensiveness and decreased their economic value to the parents, thus, it is asserted, leading to smaller families.

3. The French Revolution proclaimed the equality of all men and the right of all to rise socially and economically to the highest levels their talents could attain. It is asserted that emphasis on climbing the social ladder has led to limitation of families in order for the adults to be less burdened for the climb.

4. The family has exercised great control over the choice of the marriage partner in France. It is asserted that marriages which have often been little more than economic arrangements have not been conducive to large families.

5. Though nominally Catholic by 90 percent or more, much of the French population is "anticlerical" or nonreligious. It is asserted that weakening of religious ties has had much to do with the rise of birth control.

6. It is asserted that increasing urbanization has had an adverse effect on the birth rate, since children are less convenient in an urban environment. Although this is undoubtedly true, France has been much less urbanized than a number of other countries which began considerably later to follow the same path of population development.

Probably all of the aforementioned factors have been operative against the French birth rate, and none fully explains the matter. Another factor that might be mentioned is the failure of the French economy to develop new opportunities for employment as rapidly as the economies of a number of other industrialized countries. At any rate, the small population increases that did occur from the middle of the nineteenth century were largely due to immigration. After World War II the French birth rate took a sudden and unexpected upward spurt, with results reflected in Table 4. But expert opinion questions whether this will continue.

# THE NATIONAL ECONOMY OF FRANCE

## ▶ Characteristics of French Agriculture

Although France is one of the world's more important industrial nations, agriculture is almost as important as industry in terms of employment. In 1957, 26 percent of the labor force was employed in agriculture as against only 29 percent in manufacturing.

Agriculture is relatively more important as a source of employment in France than in any of the other nations bordering the North Sea.

France emerged from the French Revolution as a nation of small peasant farmers, most of whom owned their farms. The proverbial industry and thrift of the French peasant have been a great asset to the country, but his often narrow and unreasoning individualism and conservatism have been on occasion a provoking source of national weakness.

### Agricultural Advantages and Production

Compared to most European countries France has distinct agricultural advantages. Much of the country is composed of plains with soils that are at least reasonably fertile. Most of France lies within the mild and moist marine west-coast type of climate, but the country lacks the large areas of excessive precipitation that restrict cultivation in the British Isles. Southern France's strip of mediterranean climate affords environmental variety and makes it possible to produce subtropical crops, such as early vegetables and rice, that are not duplicated in other countries facing the North Sea.

About 39 percent of all French land is cultivated. This is the same proportion of cultivated land as in Germany, and is higher than the proportion in West Germany or any other country along the western seaboard of Europe except Denmark. France's total acreage of arable land is greater than that of any other European country; and, since its population growth has been retarded, the arable acreage per person is greater than in any of the other highly developed North Sea countries except Denmark. France is able to approach self-sufficiency in food, although there is regularly some net import.

Considering the comparatively small area of the country (it is smaller by a fifth than the state of Texas), France's agricultural output is marked by surprising variety and volume. Wheat, grapes, sugar beets, and potatoes can be distinguished as the crops receiving special emphasis, although many others are grown and are important in various localities. Wheat is the most important crop and is grown in every part of the country, occupying about two fifths of the total arable acreage. It is especially prominent, however, on the best lands of France, which occur in a belt extending from French Flanders to districts lying south of Paris. This area, located mainly within the Paris Basin, has exceptionally fertile soils, formed largely from limestone and loess (see p. 50). Large acreages and unusually high yields of wheat make the region the principal "breadbasket" of France. In addition, the region accounts for most of the country's production of sugar beets, which are like wheat in that they respond especially well to good soils. France is ordinarily the world's fifth-ranking wheat producer, after the Soviet Union, the United States, China, and Canada; and is the third-ranking producer of sugar beets, after the Soviet Union and the United States. (Production of sugar beets in West and East Germany combined exceeds that of France, but France produces more than either of them individually.)

The tolerance of the potato for poor soils and a cool, damp climate, plus the fact that it gives a very high yield of calories per unit of land, makes this crop particularly adapted to the circumstances of much of Europe and adjacent parts of the Soviet Union. The countries of this area account for the great bulk of the world's potato production. With better soils and more agricultural land per person, France does not rely so heavily on the potato as several other European countries, but the crop is cultivated in most parts of the country, and France is the fourth-ranking producer in the world, after the Soviet Union, Poland, and West Germany.

The grape is a very special element in French agriculture, as wine is in the country's diet and culture. France produces between 10 and 20 percent of the world's wine and consumes an even larger percentage. High-grade French wines, often identified with the name of the district or city from which they come, are exported in considerable quantities. The vineyards and wineries producing them are dominant economic elements in some districts as far north as the Loire Valley, Champagne, and Lorraine.

Especially important concentrations are found in the valleys of the Loire, Garonne, Rhone, and Saône rivers. But most of the wine consumed in France itself is lower-grade "ordinary wine," the production of which is especially concentrated in Languedoc, along the Mediterranean coast west of the Rhone. Domestic production has been supplemented by large imports from Algeria, although such imports have frequently glutted the market and resulted in the conversion of large quantities of wine to industrial alcohol. The exceptionally high rate of wine production and consumption in France can be attributed not only to cultural preferences and traditions of the population, but also to the influence of powerful economic interests on the government. The only country of the world which approaches France in its emphasis on wine is Italy.

Variety is a keynote in French agriculture, however, and the four major crops are supplemented, replaced, or overshadowed by others in many localities. Among the lesser crops apples deserve special mention, as France is the world's leading producer. The orchards are principally localized in the cool, wet, and hilly lands of Normandy and Brittany, and most of the production is for cider. In the Southwestern Lowland between the Massif Central and the Bay of Biscay, summers are warm enough for corn to be a major regional crop, though wheat exceeds it in acreage and production. Such feed crops as barley and oats are widely grown over the country.

Still to be discussed among major products of French agriculture are beef and milk. In meat production, consisting mainly of beef, France exceeds all other European countries and is actually one of the leading countries in the world—comparable to Argentina, for instance, and far outranking Canada. In milk production France is definitely surpassed only by the United States and possibly the Soviet Union. Cattle are an important element in the agriculture of most parts of France, but especially in northern coastal areas and in the Massif Central. The

northern coastal region, from Brittany to Flanders, is wetter and cooler than most of France; and Brittany and Normandy are very hilly. These conditions are favorable to hay and pasture and, in conjunction with the proximity of the Paris market, have led to the development of the principal dairy region of France. In the Massif Central poor soils and rugged topography discourage crop production, and this area depends mainly on a rather unproductive type of grazing agriculture. The same is true of the even more rugged Alps and Pyrenees.

**Weaknesses of French Agriculture**

The remarkable total output of agricultural products in France is achieved despite certain apparent and oft-noted agricultural weaknesses. One of these weaknesses is a maldistribution of land. Over two thirds of France's farmers have farms that are less than 25 acres in size; and a quarter of them have farms averaging less than 2½ acres. Three quarters of the land is controlled by the one quarter of the farmers that have the largest acreages. France's farm population includes a great many small farmers who make a relatively poor living and lack capital for the employment of modern methods. Under these circumstances it is not surprising that French agriculture is less efficient in its use of the land, on the average, than the agriculture of several neighboring countries. Yields per acre are generally lower than in any neighboring countries except Italy and Spain, which are much less favored by nature and much poorer in general than France.

Various circumstances have contributed to these weaknesses. Farming has been valued not just as an element in the economy, but as a way of life, and a large peasant class has been regarded as one of the foundations of a healthy society. Consequently, the agricultural policy of the French government has generally been directed toward maintaining the small farmer on the land, using tariff and quota protection from foreign competition and various subsidies as its instruments; and the size of the farm population has provided political backing for these policies. The relatively slow growth of France's urban and industrial economy has also been a factor of great importance. The urban and industrial sector of the economy has not drained labor from the countryside rapidly, has not provided the farmer with strong market incentives for increased efficiency and production, and has been small enough to allow France to meet its agricultural needs without any great drive for rapid agricultural progress.

Broadly speaking, France's agricultural weaknesses are least apparent in the north, and become progressively more marked in the part of the country that lies south of the Loire Valley. The north is in general a land of larger farms, more modern methods, and high productivity; the south a land of small and poor farms, more traditional methods, and low productivity, which pulls down national averages. The north may be somewhat more favored in the nature of its land and climate, but the contrast is probably more closely related to the slower and smaller development of urban markets in the south. In the country as a whole, the more dynamic growth of urban population and industry since World War II has been accompanied by a new rise in agricultural efficiency and output after decades of comparative stagnation.

## CITIES AND INDUSTRIES

### ▶ The Primacy of Paris

Paris is the greatest urban and industrial center of France, completely overshadowing all other cities in both population and manufacturing development. With an estimated metropolitan population of 6,737,000 it is by far the largest city on the mainland of Europe. Paris is located at a strategic point relative to natural lines of transportation, but it is especially the product of the growth and centralization of the French govern-

### ▶ Fisheries

France's food supply from agriculture is augmented by products of her fisheries, the third largest in Europe (after those of Norway and the United Kingdom). Boulogne (city proper, 94,000), located at the southern entrance to the Strait of Dover, is the most important fishing port, accounting for nearly a third of the total French catch. Its fishing fleet is dominated by large trawlers which fish primarily for cod in North Sea and North Atlantic waters. Some vessels operate as far afield as the banks off Newfoundland. Lorient (city proper, 47,000) in Brittany ranks second in total fish landings. It is the leader among many fishing ports scattered around the rugged and indented coasts of the Brittany peninsula. Much of the fishing here is concentrated in coastal waters of Brittany itself, fishing craft are of many sizes, and comparatively few vessels range much farther than the English Channel or Bay of Biscay. The catch includes a great variety of fish and shellfish. Brittany has long been famed as a nursery of sailors for the French navy and merchant marine, and many Bretons are employed in the fishing trawlers which operate from Boulogne. France's main Atlantic naval base, Brest (144,000), is located near the western end of the peninsula.

ment and of the transportation system created by that government. Like London, it has no major natural resources for industry in its immediate vicinity, yet is the greatest industrial center of its country.

The city began on an island in the Seine River (photo, p. 108), which offered a defensible site and facilitated crossing of the river. The early growth of Paris, which dates from Roman times if not before, must have been furthered by its location in a highly productive agricultural area and at a

Paris: the Seine and Notre Dame (left) on the Île de la Cité. (Standard Oil Company, N. J.)

focus of navigable streams as well as of land routes crossing the Seine. The rivers which come together in the vicinity of Paris include the Seine itself, which comes from the southeast and flows northwestward from Paris to the English Channel; the Marne, which comes from the east to join the Seine; and the Oise, which joins the Seine from the northeast (map, p. 97). In recent centuries these rivers have been improved and canals provided where necessary to give Paris waterway connections with seaports on the lower Seine, with the coal field of northeastern France, with Lorraine, and with the Saône and Loire rivers (map, p. 91).

In the Middle Ages Paris became the capital of the kings who gradually extended their effective control over all of France. As the rule of the French monarchs became progressively more absolute and centralized, their capital, housing the administrative bureaucracy and the court, grew in size and came to dominate the cultural as well as the political life of France. When, in relatively recent times, national road and rail systems were built, their trunk lines were laid out to connect Paris with the various outlying sections of the country. The result was a radial pattern with Paris at the hub where all major lines met. As the city grew in population and wealth, it became increasingly a large and rich market for goods.

The local market, plus transportational

advantages and proximity to the government, provided foundations upon which a huge industrial complex has developed. Speaking broadly, this development comprises two major classes of industries. On the one hand, Paris is the principal producer of the high-quality luxury items—fashions, perfumes, cosmetics, jewelry, and so on—for which France has long been famous. The trades that produce these items are very old. Their growth before the Revolution of 1789 was based in considerable part on the market provided by the royal court, and since the Revolution it has been favored by the continued concentration of wealth in the city. On the other hand, and more important now, Paris has become the country's leading center of engineering industries and secondary metal manufacturing. These industries are concentrated in a ring of industrial suburbs that has sprung up in the nineteenth and twentieth centuries. Automobile manufacturing is the most important single industry in this group, but a great variety of metal goods is produced. In addition, the city's highly diversified industrial structure includes chemical industries, the manufacture of rubber goods, printing and publishing, food processing, and many other industries.

**The Seine Ports**

Two ports near the mouth of the Seine handle much of the overseas trade of Paris. Rouen (335,000) is the ancient capital of Normandy and a major center of France's cotton textile industry. It is located at the head of navigation for ocean vessels using the Seine. However, with the increasing size of ships in recent centuries more and more of Rouen's port functions have been assumed by Le Havre (201,000), located at the entrance to the Seine estuary. Various port industries are located at Le Havre, and the lower Seine area in general has become the principal district for refining the oil which France imports in large quantities. Le Havre is the principal transatlantic passenger port of France by a wide margin

over Cherbourg (city proper, 40,000) on the Cotentin peninsula, and it vies with Marseilles for first place as a freight port.

### ▶ Urban and Industrial Districts Adjoining Belgium

France's second-ranking urban and industrial area is composed of cities clustered on or near the country's principal coal field, located in the north near the Belgian border (maps, pp. 92, 91, and 97). A bit north of the coal field several cities, of which Lille is the largest, form a metropolitan agglomeration of 899,000 people. On the coal field itself a number of mining and industrial centers in the vicinity of Lens and Douai aggregate over 500,000 people, and smaller centers are scattered over the field. The Lille metropolitan area is the leading textile center of France, with a linen industry dating from medieval times but overshadowed now by cotton and woolen production. Cities on the coal field manufacture iron and steel, chemicals, cement, heavy machinery, and miscellaneous metal goods. They also constitute France's leading center for the production of ceramics, glassware, and pottery.

The mines of the northern coal field account for approximately half of France's total coal production. But the coal is deep underground and lies in thin and broken seams, so that it has been difficult and expensive to mine; and it includes very little coal of coking quality. France's coal resources are much inferior to those of Germany or Great Britain, and her total production has generally been seriously inadequate for the country's needs. Since World War II the mining industry has been nationalized and extensively modernized and re-equipped, but France remains a sizable importer of coal and coke.

### ▶ Urban and Industrial Development in Southern France

France's third largest metropolitan center, Lyons (818,000), is located in the south, where the valleys of the Rhone and Saône rivers converge and provide routes through the mountains to the Mediterranean, Switzerland, and northern France. Lyons has long been an important city. It is the center of the leading silk-manufacturing district in Europe; but rayon textiles, increasingly important as a competitor of silk in the world's markets, also play a prominent role in the city's industrial output, as do chemicals and machinery. Abundant power resources are found in the surrounding area. Not far to the southwest the city of St. Étienne (368,000) mines coal from the most important of several small fields in the eastern margin of the Massif Central, and produces steel, machinery, and textiles. But the great power resource of the area is water power. To compensate for its inadequate deposits of mineral fuels, France has stressed the development of the hydroelectric potential of its mountain streams, and only four countries in the world—the United States, Canada, Japan, and Italy—surpass it in developed hydropower. Several large new projects have been completed since World War II on Rhone tributaries, and one on the Rhone itself south of Lyons. Not only is the increased power stimulating industrial development in Lyons and smaller cities of southeastern France, but additional dams on the Rhone will eventually bring the river under control and make it highly useful for navigation. At present the Rhone is of limited utility as a through waterway, due to the swift current, obstruction of the channel by alluvium deposited in spring floods, and water levels that fluctuate widely from season to season. It is a great contrast to its tributary, the Saône, which is a deeper and more placid river with a relatively even flow throughout the year. A considerable amount of barge traffic moves between Lyons and Paris via the Saône and connecting canals to the Seine (map, p. 91), but relatively little traffic of this kind moves from Lyons to the Mediterranean. However, the main rail and highway routes from Paris to the Mediterranean pass through Lyons and channel down the Rhone Valley to Marseilles.

France's principal Mediterranean cities—Marseilles, Toulon, and Nice—are strung along the coast east of the Rhone delta. Marseilles (798,000) is the country's fourth largest metropolitan center and in most years its leading seaport as measured by tonnage of seaborne freight. Marseilles is located on a good harbor far enough from the mouth of the Rhone to be free of the silt deposits which have clogged and closed the harbors of ports closer to the river which were once more important than Marseilles. Although it is a very old city, perhaps the oldest in France, Marseilles' rise to modern prominence was closely associated with the acquisition of France's trans-Mediterranean empire in North Africa and with the building of the Suez Canal, both in the nineteenth century. The French imperial system emphasized trade with the empire, especially with Algeria, and the Suez Canal made the Mediterranean a major world thoroughfare, while the Rhone-Saône trench provided an easy route between Marseilles and northern France. The city's industries process imported tropical foods, refine petroleum, build and repair ships, and manufacture various kinds of machinery.

Toulon (247,000), a short distance southeast of Marseilles, is France's principal Mediterranean naval base, while Nice (300,000), near the Italian border, is the principal city of the French Riviera, probably the most famous resort district in Europe. Along this easternmost section of the French coast the Alps come down to the sea to provide a spectacular shoreline dotted with beaches. The mountains also provide a slightly drier and warmer variety of mediterranean climate than is usual in these latitudes by affording some protection from northerly and westerly winds. A string of resort towns and cities along the coast includes, near Nice, the tiny principality of Monaco, which is nominally independent but is closely related to France economically and administratively.

Deposits of bauxite scattered along the Mediterranean littoral are among France's more important mineral resources. The largest deposit is a few miles inland from Toulon. Economical manufacture of aluminum from bauxite requires large quantities of low-cost electric power, and France's aluminum works are mostly located in Alpine valleys near hydroelectric installations. Surplus ore is exported through Toulon. France ranks first among the countries of Europe, and fourth in the world, as a producer of both bauxite and aluminum.

Southwestern France has less urban and industrial development than the north or the southeast. Its two main cities are on the Garonne River. Bordeaux (460,000), the principal seaport of the region, is located at the head of the Garonne estuary, which is called the Gironde. The port has given its name to the fine wines which are a major product of the surrounding region and have been exported through Bordeaux for centuries. Toulouse (300,000), a very old and historic city with modern machinery and chemical plants, developed on the Garonne at the point where the river comes closest to the Gate of Carcassonne, leading between the Pyrenees and the Massif Central to the Mediterranean coast.

In central and south-central France a considerable number of small to medium-sized cities are spaced at fairly regular intervals through the drainage basin of the Loire River. Besides St. Étienne, previously mentioned, the largest cities are the seaport of Nantes (275,000), located about 40 miles upstream from the mouth of the Loire, and the rubber-manufacturing center of Clermont-Ferrand (180,000) in the Massif Central.

### ▶ Mining and Heavy Industry in Alsace-Lorraine

In eastern France Alsace and Lorraine are important industrial areas, although their urban development is on a comparatively small scale. Lorraine mines more iron ore than any other mining district in the world except the Lake Superior section of the United States, and also produces about three quarters of France's iron and steel. The mines, blast furnaces, and steel works extend in a line northward from Nancy (279,000), past Metz (173,000), and into southern Luxembourg and Belgium (maps, pp. 91 and 92). Part of Germany's Saar coal field extends across the border into Lorraine, and coal is also brought from the Saar itself, from France's northern field, and from the German Ruhr. Coke must be brought in large quantities, principally from the Ruhr. Access to adequate and low-cost supplies of coal, and especially of coke, has always been a problem to the Lorraine iron and steel industry, but may now be on the way to solution. Production of coal from the Lorraine field itself has been rising, and French industrialists are making progress toward finding an economical method of coking this coal, which has previously been of noncoking quality. The industries of Lorraine have benefited from the elimination of trade barriers under the European Coal and Steel Community, and they will be further aided by lowered costs of bulk transportation for coal, coke, ore, and steel when canalization of the Moselle River is completed (p. 103). Even without these improved conditions, however, Lorraine has made France the world's sixth-ranking producer of steel, after the United States, the Soviet Union, West Germany, the United Kingdom, and Japan.

Other mineral and power resources have also furthered the industrial development of Lorraine and Alsace. Large deposits of salt near Nancy and of potash (photo, p. 90) near Mulhouse (202,000) in southern Alsace have provided raw materials for chemical plants located near the deposits. Streams of the Vosges Mountains have furnished water power, and Mulhouse as well as smaller cities around it have developed cotton textile and engineering industries. A major project is now under way to divert the Rhine through a canal running parallel to the river and to produce hydroelectric power at each of seven dams across the canal. The canal will leave the Rhine just downstream from Basel, Switzerland, and will re-enter it at Strasbourg (317,000), the Rhine port for both Alsace and Lorraine. In addition to hydroelectricity, the canal will furnish improved waterway connections southward for Strasbourg, which already is connected by a small canal with southern Alsace, the Belfort Gap, and the Saône River, and by a larger canal, the Rhine-Marne Canal, with Lorraine and the Seine River system.

### ▶ Some General Characteristics of French Urban and Industrial Development

From the foregoing discussion, it is apparent that few French cities are very large. Paris is a giant; but it is the only city with a metropolitan population of more than a million, and only three others—Lille, Lyons, and Marseilles—have over half a million. By contrast, the United Kingdom has twelve metropolitan areas of over half a million, including several of over a million; and West Germany has an even larger number. Even the small nearby countries of Belgium and the Netherlands have three metropolitan areas each numbering more than half a million—only one less than France in each case. Thus the scale and degree of urbanization are less in France than in most important industrial countries.

Relatively retarded and small-scale urban development reflects a comparable industrial development, though the relativity must be stressed, as France is a major industrial country. In proportion to total population, France is less industrialized than any neighboring country except Spain and Italy. Retarded industrial development is reflected in the fact that agricultural employment is still almost as large as that in manufacturing: 26 percent in agriculture in 1957 as against 29 percent in manufacturing.

A view of a characteristic French industry. Decorating chinaware by hand at Limoges. (French Embassy Press and Information Division.)

France's comparative lack of industrial development, especially in heavy industry and the engineering industries, has undoubtedly been partially responsible for the relative decline of French national power in the past century.

The small family-owned factory or shop has always been a prominent element in French manufacturing, and remains so today. Individual manufacturing establishments are more numerous in France than in the United States, which has a very much larger over-all industrial production. Thus the average scale of French enterprises is much smaller than in the United States, although there are, of course, many large manufacturing establishments in France. Small-scale establishments of the French type tend to be underequipped and thus to employ more hand labor and less mechanization than larger enterprises, with a resulting lower output per operative. They cannot take full advantage of the economies of mass production. Their methods are often well adapted to light consumer goods of a luxury character which emphasize elegance, taste, and individual craftsmanship (photo, left), and there is an unusually high degree of emphasis on such goods in French manufacturing. But a high development of such specialties cannot compensate for retarded growth of the larger and more basic metal and machine-building industries— not generally so well adapted to small-scale enterprise—in the strenuous international economic and military competition of the twentieth century.

### Factors in the Slow Growth of Large-scale Industries

No definitive explanation can be given for the slower growth of large-scale industry in France than in a number of other important manufacturing nations. The following factors, however, have apparently been operative, have often been cited, and are worthy of note:

1. Due to the slow growth of population, French industry has not had the stimulation of a rapidly expanding domestic market. Furthermore, there has not been a rapidly expanding labor force to man new industries as they arose. To say that slow industrial growth retarded population growth and that slow growth of population retarded industrial growth is to reason in a circle. But the reciprocal effects of two or more such factors on each other in either a "vicious circle" of stagnation or an upward spiral of development is a phenomenon that has often been noted in the world's industrial history.

2. The internal transportation system of France has been so strongly centered on Paris that, while the capital has excellent trunk-line connections with the various outlying regions of the country, connections between the regions themselves have often been inadequate. It is alleged that these regions have been handicapped with respect to efficient assembly of materials and distribution of products.

3. France's coal resources have been somewhat inadequate in both quantity and quality. Although other power sources have been steadily increasing in importance, the country's original industrialization in the nineteenth and early twentieth centuries was based heavily on power furnished by coal. During this period France was handicapped by coal resources that were decidedly inferior to those of major industrial competitors.

4. Adequate capital for industrial investment has often been lacking. France's banking system has frequently been criticized for its reluctance to lend venture capital; and the corporate form of business organization has operated under certain legal and governmental handicaps. In addition, the small family-owned French company seems often to have been reluctant to borrow heavily or sell stock widely for fear of loosening family control over the enterprise, and has consequently remained small and underequipped. A final circumstance lessening the

amount of capital available for investment in new enterprises has been the necessity of directing large sums into the replacement of industrial facilities destroyed in war.

5. The governments of France, until after World War II, generally did little to promote large-scale industrialization. Instead, they generally condoned and even helped to create a situation in which small and inefficient industrial producers were protected from the threat of competition: from foreign competition by tariff and quota restrictions on imports, and from domestic competition by various subsidies, cartel arrangements, and other restrictive practices. Such governmental measures were often to the apparent advantage of, and taken at the behest of, the industrialists themselves, but though they afforded a measure of security to industrial concerns, they took away the spur to greater efficiency and larger scale which a more vigorous competition would have provided. Another circumstance that has tended to retard France's industrial development is the fact that it has not been necessary in the past for the country to make any really concentrated and intensive effort to develop domestic industry in order to capture foreign markets, due to France's relative self-sufficiency in food and its control over a valuable colonial empire whose trade could be directed toward the home country.

6. Certain underlying cultural attitudes of Frenchmen probably have been inimical to full-scale industrial development. For example, Frenchmen tend to be pronounced individualists and antagonistic toward the social regimentation and standardization which frequently accompanies large-scale industrialization. In addition, there has been a tendency to accord the businessman a smaller degree of prestige and social status than the large landowner, the professional man, or the higher civil servant. As a result, the family-owned business seems often to have been regarded primarily as a stepping stone toward better things: if the business prospered enough that the family could acquire land and give its sons a professional education, that was sufficient—expansion and improvement of the business itself was not an urgent matter. Generally speaking, French culture has tended to emphasize such values as a modest security and independence, leisure, and style in living somewhat more, and steadily expanding production and consumption of material goods somewhat less, than have the cultures of many Western countries.

Whatever the precise combination of reasons, the fact is that French production following the Industrial Revolution failed to climb at the pace set by a number of other countries that were industrializing. Probably there was much good in this pattern of development, with its higher degree of social stability. Certainly foreigners have been much attracted by French life and culture. But a price had to be paid in declining national power and in the notable poverty of some sections of the population, especially industrial workers and small farmers and merchants. Now, for better or worse, the old pattern seems finally to be breaking down. Since World War II French governments have sponsored massive efforts to modernize and expand industrial facilities and practices and bring about a new pattern of dynamic growth. If these efforts succeed they will probably be as revolutionary in effect as the loss of empire or resolution of the old quarrel with Germany—if the recent hopeful beginnings toward the latter achieve lasting success. Thus far, postwar France has experienced a striking success in changing old ways, attitudes, and arrangements, and industrial production and efficiency have been rising rapidly, as they have in most of western Europe. But the country still has far to go before the old pattern disappears or its effects cease to be felt.

# Germany

For many centuries German-speaking peoples have played a prominent role in the affairs of Europe. But a unified German national state did not emerge until after the middle of the nineteenth century, and up to the present it has failed to achieve territorial stability. Its boundaries have fluctuated a great deal in the twentieth century as a result of two world wars, and today it is divided by the Soviet-imposed iron curtain into Western and Eastern sections under separate governments. Serious questions raised by its partitioning are yet to be resolved, and its future remains one of the most critical issues of international politics.

## EMERGENCE OF MODERN GERMANY

Prior to the year 1866, "Germany" was little more than a territorial expression referring to a loosely connected group of independent or semi-independent states, mostly small, in central Europe. This group of states, a holdover from the fragmented political order of medieval times, possessed a certain amount of economic unity resulting from the gradual

The iron curtain. Soviet troops returning through the Brandenburg Gate after placing wreaths on a war memorial in the British-occupied sector of Berlin. This picture was taken several years ago, but the situation it depicts—that of a divided Berlin and a divided world—remains essentially unchanged. (U. S. Army Photograph.)

abolition of customs barriers after the Napoleonic wars. But political unity was not achieved until the period 1866–1871, when all of the states except Austria and Luxembourg were combined into a single country which shortly emerged as the most powerful nation on the mainland of Europe.

The historical background of German unification has been briefly sketched as follows:

In ancient and medieval times Germanic peoples overran large parts of Europe. Having invaded the ancient Roman Empire, they settled down in various parts of the conquered lands and were eventually absorbed by the native populace. Later conquests led in the ninth century to the creation of the Holy Roman Empire of the German Nation. This loose congeries of petty German states finally expired at the time of Napoleon (1806) because of internal weaknesses. Voltaire said it was "neither holy, nor Roman, nor an Empire," and despite its name it was certainly not a national state in the modern sense.

Except for Italy, Germany was the last [important European power] to achieve national unity. During the centuries from the close of the Middle Ages down to 1870, while Great Britain, France, and Russia were strong and united, Germany remained subdivided among petty states, and its people as a whole felt little national consciousness. In political loyalty they were Prussians or Bavarians or Saxons, and Germans only in speech and culture.

Unification was a slow process, accomplished under the leadership of Prussia, which from about 1740 on gradually extended its own territories to include the whole of northern Germany. In 1871 Bismarck's statesmanship brought South Germany also into a new state, over which the King of Prussia was crowned as Emperor William I. Thus was created the Second German Empire, a firmly knit federation under Prussian domination.[1]

## TERRITORIAL GAINS AND LOSSES

The Second German Empire was much larger in area than all-Germany today (map, right). It reached eastward to include East Prussia and a sizable part of Poland, which had been partitioned among Prussia, Russia, and Austria in the eighteenth century. On the west it included Alsace-Lorraine, taken from France following the Franco-Prussian War of 1870–1871. In the north it included the former duchies of Schleswig, Holstein, and Lauenburg, taken over by Prussia and Austria following a war with Denmark in 1864, and annexed by Prussia after the Austro-Prussian War of 1866.

The new nation grew rapidly in economic and military power. Large coal-mining, iron and steel, and chemical industries were developed as a basis for general economic expansion. Germany built a large navy and merchant marine and developed a sizable foreign trade, centered in Europe, but extending to many other parts of the world. Between 1884 and 1900 a colonial empire was acquired, mainly in Africa but also including island territories in the Pacific Ocean and certain holdings in China.

Tensions and rivalries among the great powers of Europe led to World War I (1914–1918), in which Germany and its allies (Austria-Hungary, Turkey, and Bulgaria) were defeated by a world-wide coalition of nations, eventually including the United States. As a result of the Versailles Treaty following the war, Germany was obliged to cede much of its territory to other nations. Alsace-Lorraine was returned to France and northern Schleswig was ceded to Denmark following a plebiscite. Poland was organized as an independent nation and was given a Baltic Sea outlet—the "Polish Corridor"—between East Prussia and the rest of Germany. Two small areas of German-speaking population bordering East Prussia

---

[1] *Geographical Foundations of National Power* (Army Service Forces Manual M 103–1). Washington: Government Printing Office, 1944. P. 63.

A winter scene in the Harz Mountains. (German Tourist Information Office.)

summer maximum toward the south and east.

The soils of Germany, while extremely varied in type, are rather acid and infertile by nature. Soils significantly higher than average in fertility are found mainly in a discontinuous belt along the southern margins of the North German Plain. Here a cover of loess (wind-blown silt) has provided parent material for the most productive large group of soils in Germany. Another region possessing soils of comparatively high natural fertility is the alluvial Upper Rhine Plain between the city of Mainz and the Swiss border. The remainder of the country has soils that tend to be, at best, of moderate quality; many, especially those of the hilly or mountainous sections, are poor.

The original virgin forest is thought to have been a mixture of coniferous and deciduous trees; today conifers predominate, although deciduous species are relatively abundant. Tracts of forest are distributed irregularly throughout the country on the rougher lands and the better-drained areas of poor soil. Germany has long been famous for its state-administered and rigidly controlled program of forest management.

▶ *Coal, Potash, and Other Minerals* Among Germany's mineral resources (map, p. 122), coal is by far the most abundant and vital to the country's economy. The reserves amount to much less than those of the United States or the Soviet Union, but are nevertheless extremely large. The largest and best deposits of bituminous coal, together with some anthracite, are found in the Ruhr coal basin. Other deposits of consequence exist in the Saar coal basin (bituminous) and the much smaller Aachen field (anthracite and bituminous). Lignite is mined extensively in the industrialized region of Saxony, located in East Germany adjoining Czechoslovakia. It is used primarily in thermal generating plants to produce electricity.

Potash, a vital material in the chemical industry, is another mineral which Germany

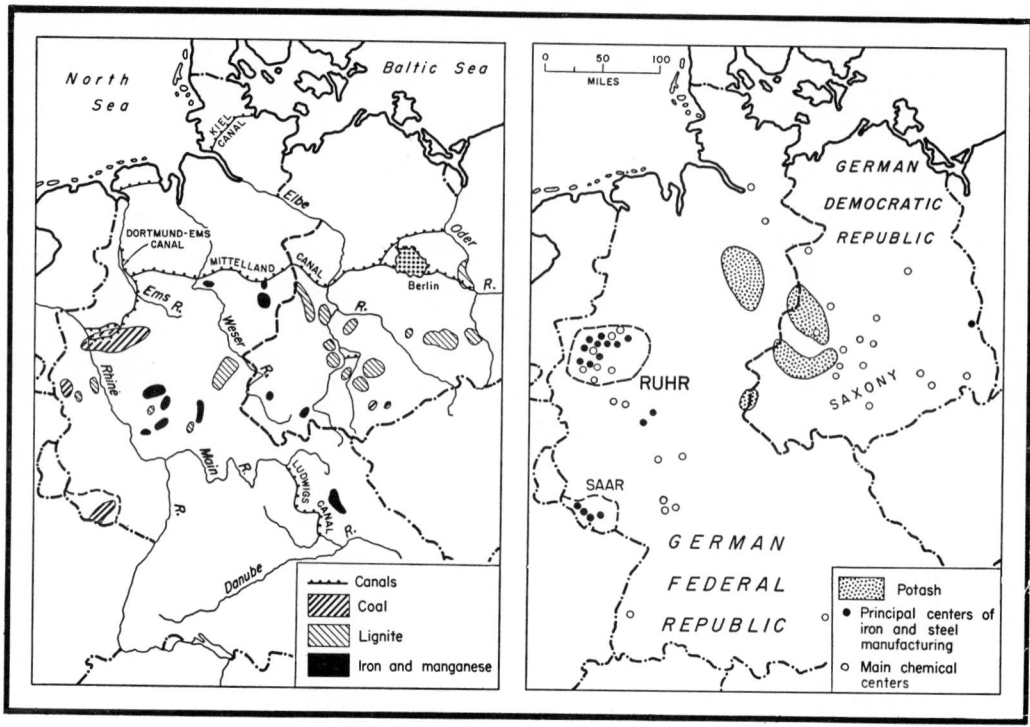

Major mineral resources and centers of iron and steel manufacturing and chemical manufacturing in Germany.

has in outstanding quantities. The deposits, situated mainly between the city of Hanover and the upper Elbe River, coincide in location rather closely with the principal area of fertile loess soils. The postwar division of the country has placed the bulk of German potash deposits within East Germany and thus within the economic orbit of the Soviet Union. West Germany, however, has sizable reserves, and its actual production of potash is somewhat greater than that of East Germany.

Aside from coal and potash, and substantial deposits of common salt worked in Saxony and the lower Rhineland, Germany is not well provided with minerals. Iron ore is mined at a number of places in West Germany, particularly in the vicinity of Salzgitter (102,000). But the production, though substantial, is mostly low grade, and must be supplemented by imported high-grade ores, primarily from Sweden. Small deposits of a number of other metals exist in both West and East Germany, but the reserves and production are far from adequate. The output from several small oil fields, principally in the southern part of the North German Plain, makes West Germany the second largest oil producer in Europe (after Romania), but it supplied only a third of the country's requirements in 1958. West Germany is also a small producer of natural gas.

## POPULATION AND ECONOMY OF GERMANY

Germany is one of the most densely populated countries in the world. Excluding a few of the micro-states, its over-all density of approximately 525 per square mile in 1959 was exceeded in Europe only by the Netherlands (900), Belgium (773), and the

United Kingdom (551). The German Federal Republic, with approximately 574 per square mile (including West Berlin), was somewhat more densely populated than the German Democratic Republic, with about 413 per square mile.

German is the household language of practically the entire population, though marked variations in dialect exist from place to place. With respect to religion, the population of West Germany is fairly evenly divided between Protestants (51 percent according to the 1950 census) and Roman Catholics (45 percent), but East Germany is overwhelmingly Protestant (82 percent, as opposed to 11 percent Roman Catholic). These figures reflect a traditional division between the North German Plain, which has been heavily Protestant, especially in the east and north, and southern Germany and the Rhineland, which have been the principal strongholds of the Roman Catholic faith.

### ▶ Distribution of Population and Cities

The distribution of rural population is fairly uniform throughout the country. The lightest densities are found in the more rugged parts of the central and southern uplands and highlands, and in some of the more infertile areas of the northern plain. The heaviest densities tend to occur in the zone of loess soils and in the southwestern depressions draining to the Rhine.

Germany is a highly urbanized country, though less so than the United Kingdom. The primary axis of city development tends to follow the border zone between the North German Plain and the southern uplands (map, p. 119). This axis is anchored on the west by a great cluster of industrial cities in the Ruhr and on the east by a smaller, less concentrated cluster of manufacturing cities in Saxony. The important cities of Hanover (868,000), Brunswick (448,000), and Magdeburg (478,000) are spaced along the central part of the urban axis. Berlin (4,245,000), the largest city of Germany, is situated slightly to the north of the axis at its eastern end. Other major German cities outside the main urban axis include (1) the North Sea ports of Hamburg (2,107,000) and Bremen (667,000), (2) the widely spaced cities along the Rhine and its tributaries, including (besides the Ruhr cities) Cologne (1,244,000), Bonn, the capital of West Germany (531,000), Mannheim-Ludwigshafen-Heidelberg (1,278,000), Frankfurt-on-the-Main (1,520,000), Stuttgart (1,337,000), and Wiesbaden-Mainz (425,000), and (3) the important, widely separated Bavarian cities of Munich (1,269,000) and Nuremberg (698,000).

### ▶ Germany's Premier Industrial District—The Ruhr

The urban dwellers of Germany, and many of the rural inhabitants as well, are primarily dependent upon manufacturing for a livelihood. As in all great manufacturing countries, industrial development rests primarily on three basic lines of goods: (1) metals, particularly iron and steel and products made from them, (2) textiles, and (3) chemicals. The largest single concentration of industry is found in the Ruhr, an industrial district so important as to have no real counterpart in all of Europe. The Ruhr is the principal seat of the German iron and steel and coal-mining industries, and has important metal-fabricating, chemical, and textile industries as well.

The Ruhr district takes its name from the Ruhr River, a small east-bank tributary of the Rhine (map, p. 124). Heavy industry has been attracted to the district by Europe's most important coal field, and particularly by the great reserves of coking coal. Some salient features of the Ruhr are sketched in the following selection: [3]

---

[3] Norman J. G. Pounds, "The Ruhr," *Focus,* v. 1, no. 3 (1950), pp. 1–2. A subhead and populations of cities have been added. Used by permission of the author and *Focus,* published by the American Geographical Society of New York.

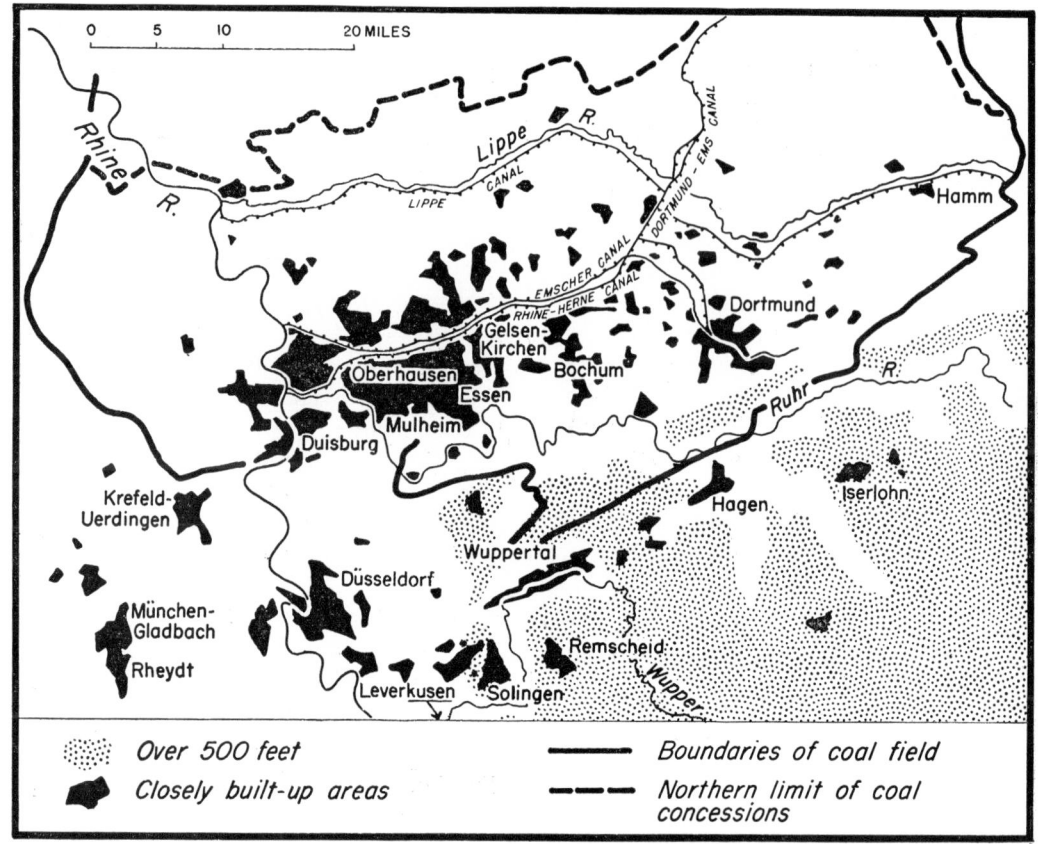

The Ruhr. (After two maps in *Focus*.)

[The Ruhr is located] in northwest Germany, close to the Belgian and Dutch frontiers. In the south the Ruhr is hilly, and large areas are forested. In the north it is low and rolling; movement is easy, and much of the land that has not been built upon is agricultural. Most of the cities and towns lie on the northern plain. . . .

Across the western edge of the Ruhr flows the Rhine, a great highway of trade between South Germany and the Netherlands. The industrial area is drained by the Ruhr, Emscher, and Lippe rivers. . . . Canals have been built along the Emscher and Lippe valleys and at their east ends are joined to the Dortmund-Ems Canal, by which they are linked with the German North Sea ports of Emden and Bremen.

The Ruhr industrial area has grown up within the last 100 years. Its origins lay in the primitive iron refining carried on in the hills, where there were small deposits of iron ore, as well as charcoal for the furnaces and running streams to power the machines and the hammers. It was not until after 1850 that industry spread on any considerable scale from this early center into the area that we now call the Ruhr. It was attracted by the beds of coal, much of which was suitable for coking and thus for the iron furnace. In the years 1850 to 1870 many steelworks were built. Local supplies of ore were soon exhausted and the Ruhr came to depend more and more on imports from foreign countries.

As industry developed in this area, so cities grew in size and importance. There are today three cities each with more than half a million inhabitants: Essen [702,000], Dortmund [611,000], and Düsseldorf [659,000].[4]

[4] *Editorial Note.* City populations in brackets are 1956 estimates for city proper from *United Nations Demographic Yearbook for 1957*. All other city populations cited in this chapter and other chapters, unless otherwise noted, are metropolitan area estimates from International Urban Research,

*The World's Metropolitan Areas* (see n. 2, p. 62). The latter source gives the metropolitan population of Düsseldorf as 883,000, while populations of Essen and Dortmund are subsumed in a metropolitan total for the inner Ruhr (see facing page).

There are [18] cities with more than 100,000 inhabitants.

## The Coal-Mining Industry

But without the coal field there would be no Ruhr as we know it today. The coal seams reach the surface along the valley of the Ruhr . . . and dip northward beneath the North German Plain. Mining began along the southern edge, but for more than a hundred years it has been spreading slowly northward, with the opening of mines of ever-increasing depth. The oldest mines are in the Ruhr Valley, which has thus given its name to the region; the newer are in the valleys of the Emscher and the Lippe. There seems to be no limit to this northward expansion except that set by the increasing depth and cost of mining.

The coal varies in quality. The lowermost seams, which come to the surface in the south, are anthracitic. Above them are, in order, coking, gas, and flame coals. Of these the coking coals, which are mined in the Emscher Valley, are of the greatest industrial importance.

Between the two wars the Germans concentrated production in a reduced number of larger mines. At many of these, coking furnaces were erected. Here the coal is pulverized, blended, and coked. The coke is sent to the blast furnaces, and the gas from the retorts is used for various heating purposes in the steelworks; the exhaust gases from the furnaces go to fire the retorts in the cokeries. Coal mining and steelworking have thus been integrated geographically, not merely in the balance sheets of the operating companies.

The abundance of coal has led to the erection of synthetic-fuel plants, whose production of fuel oil from coal was of vital importance to the German military machine during the last war.

## The Inner Ruhr

A distinction often is made between the "inner Ruhr," the area of concentrated coal mining, iron and steel manufacture, chemical manufacture, and urban development, and the "outer Ruhr," in which cities are more widely spaced. Extending for about 40 miles from the Rhine in the west to Dortmund in the east, and for about 15 miles from the Ruhr River northward (map, p.

A characteristic industrial landscape in the Ruhr. The view shows iron and steel mills and congested barge traffic along the Rhine in the vicinity of Duisburg. (Dr. Paul Wolff and Tritschler.)

124), the inner Ruhr incorporates many individual cities and comprises an estimated 5.4 million people—the largest urban agglomeration in Europe except the London and Paris metropolitan areas. Though steel-making and steel-using industries are spread through the area, most of the actual smelting of iron ore is done in large, integrated iron and steel mills located in or near Duisburg (city proper, 480,000) or Dortmund. The Ruhr's largest individual city, Essen, home of the famous Krupp works, is a major producer of high-grade steels, but does little smelting. Essen is the principal administrative center of the Ruhr.

### The Outer Ruhr

In the "outer Ruhr," cities are more scattered, though still numerous, and their manufactures consist primarily of a great variety of secondary metal products and textiles. The agglomeration of Krefeld-München Gladbach-Rheydt (669,000), west of the Rhine, is predominantly a textile-milling area. South of the Ruhr Valley, the cities of Wuppertal, Solingen, and Remscheid form an urban agglomeration of 850,000. Wuppertal is a textile center, but Solingen and Remscheid make a variety of highly finished metalwares, including hardware, tools, and the high-grade cutlery for which Solingen is world famous. The large Düsseldorf metropolitan area (883,000), located on the Rhine some distance south of Duisburg, has a variety of engineering industries and some steel production. Cologne, still farther south, is not generally considered a part of the Ruhr.

### ▶ Industrial Districts Outside the Ruhr

### The Saxon Triangle

The industrial district which ranks second in importance to the Ruhr is found in Saxony, immediately to the northwest of Czechoslovakia. The production of this district is very diversified, although somewhat lacking in the heavier types of industry. The district is particularly noted for types of goods requiring a high degree of skill in manufacture—precision machinery, electronic equipment, optical equipment, and so on. Textile manufacture leads in employment, but the manufacture of machinery and chemical manufacture are highly significant. The main industrialized area of Saxony is shaped like a triangle (map, p. 91). At the northwestern apex is the city of Halle (536,000), the principal urban center of an important potash, salt, and lignite-mining and chemical-manufacturing area. Near by is the largest city of Saxony, the diversified industrial center of Leipzig (801,000), especially noted for its printing and publishing industry before World War II. At the southeastern corner of the triangle is another diversified industrial city, Dresden (741,000) on the Elbe River. Westward from Dresden a line of manufacturing towns and cities—including the major textile center of Karl-Marx-Stadt, formerly Chemnitz (495,000) and Zwickau (351,000)—extends along the northern foothills of the Ore Mountains to Plauen (city proper, 82,000) at the southwestern corner of the triangle. The Saxon Triangle lies entirely within East Germany. With its varied range of production and skilled labor force, this industrialized area represents one of the richest prizes to fall within the orbit of the Soviet Union as a result of World War II.

No brief résumé can do justice to the great variety and complexity of industrial production in Germany. The range of production extends from the basic lines of metals, textiles, and chemicals, through many types of machinery, motor vehicles, ships, electrical equipment, optical equipment, processed foods, and products made from wood, paper, leather, and tobacco, to such specialty items as toys, high-grade chinaware, and musical instruments. Manufacturing is by no means confined to the Ruhr and the Saxon Triangle, but is spread through a multitude of other cities and towns outside these major industrial foci.

## Berlin and Hamburg

Berlin was the most important single manufacturing city before World War II, with Hamburg probably ranking second. Like Paris, Berlin is situated in a locality that lacks significant natural resources for manufacturing. But like Paris, the city was able to develop important industries as an indirect result of political centralization. Most of this development began after 1871, and Berlin is thus much younger as a major manufacturing city than Paris or London. As the political capital of a large, new, and strongly centralized state, Berlin quickly attracted great numbers of people, and its population grew from half a million in 1865 to over 2 million at the turn of the century and to 4 million by 1925. Thus its developing industries could rely on a large market in the immediate vicinity, and they had good connections with other areas via the impressive network of transportation lines which was focused on the capital by the government. Berlin became one of the world's more important centers for the manufacture of electrical equipment, and this remains the city's leading industry in both employment and value of production. But a wide variety of other industries exist, mainly secondary consumer-type industries such as food processing, clothing manufacture, light engineering, and the manufacture of pharmaceuticals. Hamburg also has diversified industries, but its industrial structure tends to be dominated by a group of industries appropriate to a major seaport. Prominent among these are shipbuilding, petroleum refining, the processing of imported vegetable oils and oilseeds, tobacco, and rubber; and the smelting of imported copper and other nonferrous ores and concentrates.

## Other Industrial Areas

Special mention should also be made of the important group of diversified industrial cities located along the Rhine and its tributaries south of the Ruhr—particularly Cologne and Mannheim-Ludwigshafen on the Rhine, Frankfurt-on-the-Main, and Stuttgart on the Neckar. Each of these cities has a metropolitan population of over a million and each is a major center of engineering industries. The first three are prominent centers of chemical manufacture.

The Saar district contains Germany's second most important concentration of coal mines and iron and steel plants, though its output is far overshadowed by the enormous production of the Ruhr. For iron and steel manufacture the Saar depends mostly on Lorraine iron ore. Some coke and high-grade coking coal are brought from the Ruhr to be mixed with the Saar's own lower-grade production. The largest urban center of the district, Saarbrücken, is a city of 123,000, but its metropolitan area comprises an estimated 374,000 people.

## ▶ The Scientific Agriculture of Germany

The fact that Germany is predominantly a manufacturing country should not be allowed to obscure its agricultural productivity. Though it is not so self-sufficient in foodstuffs as France, West Germany is estimated to supply from its own production more than three fourths of its requirements for bread grains, sugar, and vegetables; more than nine tenths of its requirements for meat and butter; and practically all its requirements for potatoes and fluid milk. East Germany also attains a high degree of self-sufficiency in these foods. This high output from soils which are, in the main, only moderately fertile is a tribute to German enterprise and skill. The art of soil improvement through careful use of natural and artificial fertilizers, crop rotation, and other scientific land-management practices has been developed to a high degree, and the average crop yields secured by German farmers are among the highest in the world. Only the much smaller, intensively cultivated neighboring countries of Belgium, the Netherlands, and Denmark definitely surpass Germany in all-around per-acre yields. The highly developed chemical industry of Germany has aided the farmer by providing large quantities of chemical fertilizers. Germany is exceeded only by Japan, the Netherlands, Belgium, and New Zealand in total consumption of commercial plant food per acre of arable land. But despite the productivity of German agriculture, both West and East Germany must import sizable quantities of foodstuffs, fibers, and other agricultural products. In 1958 such items represented about 36 percent by value of all imports entering the German Federal Republic.

Rye, oats, and potatoes are the staple crops of the North German Plain except along the southern margin in the zone of fertile loess soils, where wheat and sugar beets are more important in many localities. The depressions in the central and southern upland country grow rye, wheat, oats, and barley in fairly equal proportions; potatoes and sugar beets, also, are important, though somewhat less so than on the northern plain. In West Germany the two bread grains of wheat and rye are approximately equal in production, though rye occupies a somewhat greater acreage, but in East Germany the production of rye is nearly double that of wheat. The great importance of potatoes in German agriculture is shown by the fact that in West Germany potatoes occupy an acreage approximately the same size as the acreage occupied by wheat, and in East Germany an acreage twice as large as that occupied by wheat. Among the world's countries West Germany and East Germany rank third and fourth, respectively, as producers of rye, after the Soviet Union and Poland (each of which produces more than the two Germanies combined). In potato production, only the Soviet Union surpasses the two Germanies combined; if considered individually, West Germany ranks third, after the Soviet Union and Poland, and East Germany ranks fifth, after the foregoing countries and France. In sugar-beet production the Soviet Union again leads, and the two Germanies combined are second, but if they are considered individually, West Germany ranks with France in third or fourth position after the United States, while East Germany ranks no better than eighth.

In the southwestern part of West Germany, orchards and vineyards are major specialties in the sheltered valleys of the Rhine and its tributaries, particularly the lower Main, Neckar, and Moselle.

Livestock production is an important branch of agriculture in all parts of Germany. In West Germany, livestock and livestock products account for an estimated three fourths of the value of all products marketed from farms. Major emphasis is placed on the growing of cattle and hogs: Germany raises more hogs than any other European country (excluding the USSR) and more cattle than any European country except France. In fact, West Germany by itself achieves these rankings. Sheep are of minor importance. In the cooler, more infertile, and poorly drained portions of the North German Plain, large sections are given over principally to the grazing of livestock, and the same is true of the rougher areas in central and southern Germany. Dairying is especially prominent in two areas: (1) the German Alpine Foreland and German Alps, south of the Danube, and (2) the reclaimed coastal marshes bordering the North Sea. It should be noted, however, that cattle in Germany consist primarily of dairy varieties. There is no well-developed beef animal, and thus, although certain districts may specialize in fattening steers for slaughter, there is not the sharp difference between the beef and dairy industries that one finds in the United States. Some hogs, cattle, and, of course, poultry, are present on nearly all German farms. These livestock provide cash products which are readily salable in nearby urban markets; supply quantities of manure for enriching the soil; consume kitchen wastes and crop residues such as the tops and pulp left over from sugar-beet processing; and generally fit well in the intensive, careful agriculture of such a densely populated, urbanized country as Germany.

## ► Transportation Facilities

The complex economies of the two Germanies are served by highly developed transportation facilities. The largest seaports are Hamburg on the Elbe and Bremen on the Weser, both in West Germany. These ports are located well upstream on the estuaries of their respective rivers, but both are served by outports at which fast liners call. Bremen's outport, Bremerhaven (131,-000), handles most of Bremen's passenger traffic; but in the case of Hamburg many passenger vessels make the journey up the Elbe to the main port, instead of discharging their passengers at the outport of Cuxhaven (city proper, 44,000). The great Dutch seaport of Rotterdam on the lower Rhine handles large tonnages of West German trade (including a portion of the Ruhr's iron-ore imports) and in a functional sense may be counted as one of the major German ports. In the harbors of Rotterdam and Hamburg a major specialty is the direct transfer of goods between ocean ships and river or canal barges (photo, p. 25). The Rhine River, navigable for barges from the Swiss port of Basel to the sea, is the largest German carrier of barge traffic, and the city of Duisburg, located on the Rhine near the western end of the Ruhr industrial district, is one of the most important river ports in the world (most of the traffic is actually handled by the suburb of Ruhrort). Canalization of the Moselle tributary from its junction with the Rhine to the Lorraine iron-mining and steel-milling district (p. 102) and completion of a new canal between the Main River and the Danube River will considerably increase traffic on the Rhine. Outstanding among the other inland waterways of Germany (maps, pp. 91 and 119) are (1) the Elbe River, navigable for barge traffic from Czechoslovakia to the North Sea, (2) the Mittelland Canal System connecting the Rhine and the Ruhr district with the Weser, Elbe, and, via Berlin, the Oder, (3) the Dortmund-Ems Canal connecting the Ruhr with the North Sea via the Ems River and the port of Emden (city proper, 43,000), which is the most important receiving port for Swedish iron ore en route to the Ruhr, and (4) the North Sea–Baltic Canal or Kiel Canal, a ship canal which crosses the base of the Danish peninsula and thus eliminates the sea journey around Denmark for many vessels plying between the Baltic and the German North Sea ports.

Fast inland transportation is provided by an effective system of railways and superhighways (*autobahns*), focusing on the larger cities, especially Berlin. An important postwar development has been the emergence of the truck as a major freight carrier. As in the United States, many trucking fleets are owned by manufacturing companies, while other serve as public carriers. Unfortunately, however, most German roads were not built to accommodate heavy truck traffic, and the *autobahn* system, which is capable of bearing heavy loads, converges on Berlin and hence cannot be used to full capacity because of the existence of the iron curtain. However, the system is being enlarged, especially in West Germany, to meet current needs.

Large-scale transfer of passengers and freight by air is still in an immature stage of development, though it is growing rapidly. One of the most significant contributions of air transportation at present is the quick and sure access it provides from the German Federal Republic to West Berlin. A spectacular demonstration of the latter was the famous Berlin airlift of 1948–1949, in which the Western occupying powers, through ferrying necessary supplies to West Berlin by air over a period of more than a year, succeeded in overcoming a Russian blockade of surface transportation into the city.

A current transportational development of significance is the construction of large pipelines to carry petroleum from ocean terminals to inland refining centers located along or near the Rhine. New pipelines from the Weser estuary and Rotterdam already are moving oil to refineries in the Ruhr and near Cologne; and projected lines may bring oil to a refinery at Karlsruhe (484,000) from Marseilles via Strasbourg and from Genoa, Italy via Switzerland. In 1960 East Germany was reported to be planning a refinery on the Oder River which would utilize oil brought by pipeline from the Soviet Union.

## AFTERMATH OF PARTITION AND POSSIBILITY OF REUNIFICATION

### ▶ *Economic Dissection: The Example of Hamburg*

As a consequence of defeat in World War II, Germany underwent not only a political but also a severe economic dissection. The country lost control of important coal-mining and steel-milling districts in Silesia (map, p. 117) and (temporarily) the Saar, as well as agricultural lands east of the Oder-Neisse line which normally had produced a considerable surplus of foodstuffs in prewar times. Probably the most damaging aspect of the postwar situation, however, was the disruption of normal trading relationships between East and West Germany. Some of the effects of this disruption are illustrated in the following concrete example.

During the late 1930s the port of Hamburg was one of the leading seaports of Europe and of the world. World War II brought great destruction to the city and particularly to the harbor. When peace came, the over-all capacity of the port had been reduced to about one fifth of its prewar level. Embarking upon an energetic rebuilding program, the port quickly restored its facilities and by 1955 had surpassed its 1936 tonnage of seaborne commerce. However, much of its prewar hinterland, notably the portion upriver on the Elbe, is now behind the iron curtain, and traffic to and from this territory stands at little more than half of the prewar volume. At present the port's primary hinterland is the northern section of the German Federal Republic, especially the city-state of Hamburg itself. Hamburg is still the leading German seaport, but its postwar rate of recovery was slower than that of its principal German competitor, Bremen, whose hinterland was not intersected by the iron curtain. Moreover, the composition of Hamburg's commerce has changed since the war. It is now made up more predominantly of bulk goods, particularly coal, petroleum, and their products, than it was in the 1930s. A sizable portion of this traffic moves to industrial and household consumers in Hamburg itself or other places near by.

The postwar severance of the German Democratic Republic has required extensive readjustments not only in Hamburg but in many other centers of industry and trade in both republics. Each of the two Germanies needs the trade of the other in order to function most effectively. There appears to be little evidence, however, that the political and economic cleavage represented by the Russian-imposed iron curtain will be fundamentally altered within the foreseeable future.

### ▶ *Absorption of Political and Ethnic Expellees*

German recovery from World War II was also hindered initially by the necessity of caring for a great number of expellees and other displaced persons. By 1950 the German Federal Republic had accepted nearly 8 million and the German Democratic Republic nearly 4½ million newcomers, most of them either political or ethnic expellees from Communist-held areas. The political expellees were former occupants of German national territory transferred to Polish or Russian administration following the war. The ethnic expellees were people of German descent who lived in countries outside of

Germany before the war, but were alleged to have had strong pro-German leanings. The latter group came mainly from Czechoslovakia, Poland, the former Free City of Danzig (now Gdansk), Hungary, Romania, and Yugoslavia. Nearly a fifth of Germany's total population is now comprised of the two categories of expellees and their families. Further complexity has been added by the voluntary migration of over 3 million persons from Communist to non-Communist Germany and by a much smaller movement in the opposite direction.

It was feared initially that the task of absorbing so many millions of homeless people into the economy of a defeated nation would prove insuperable. Yet West Germany had largely accomplished the task by 1954, and it appears to be no longer a serious problem in East Germany. The success of the two republics in coping with it reflects their resurgence from the debacle of World War II, and particularly the dramatic resurgence of West Germany.

► *Resurgence of the Two Germanies*
For over three years following defeat in 1945, Germany was in ruins. The war had cost her an estimated 5.6 million lives, including 3.8 million in the armed forces. Much of her machinery had been carried off as reparations. Her merchant fleet was gone. She had practically no credit. Industrial production at the end of the war stood at less than one tenth of the prewar level. Approximately one third of all housing had been bombed out; in the major cities the proportion was nearly twice as high. Unemployment, inflation, and hunger existed everywhere.

Beginning in 1949, however, the Western zones began rebuilding at a frenzied pace, and since that time the German Federal Republic has amazed the world with its rapid economic recovery. Aided initially by the United States and other nations, its economy soon acquired its own momentum, and it has emerged as one of the most dynamic in Europe. Between 1948 and 1958 its total economic production expanded more than 250 percent. A measure of the achievement is seen in the fact that in 1959 West Germany was not only Europe's largest producer of coal and steel (excluding the Soviet Union), but it led the United Kingdom in the production of both automobiles and ships. In its rebuilding program, attention was initially focused on the restoration of capital equipment, but consumer necessities were not overlooked: over 4.2 million dwelling units were constructed in the 1949–1958 decade, and as a result one in three of West Germany's families moved into new quarters. Despite an expanding population, there is no longer a pressing housing shortage in the country. The factories, commercial establishments, and other components of the country's large cities also have been essentially rebuilt, though in some cities, notably Berlin, little attempt has been made to reconstruct the devastated "dead heart" of the city, and new development has taken place primarily in the suburbs. Today the German Federal Republic figures prominently in any economic, political, or military program involving western Europe, and it is increasingly a factor of significance in the affairs of the world at large.

The German Democratic Republic, smaller in area and population, less well endowed naturally, linked politically and economically with war-ravaged nations, handicapped by rigid initial adherence to Marxist dogma, and burdened with heavy reparations demands by the Soviet Union, recovered more slowly than its western neighbor. But it, too, has been experiencing a marked resurgence, especially since reparations ceased in 1957. Its population, however, declined by about 2 million between 1953 and 1960.

► *Prospect of Reunification*
Although prediction is hazardous in the present era of rapid political changes, there seems to be little prospect that Germany can

recover its territories lost to Poland and the Soviet Union, or that the country can look forward to a reunification of the two German republics in the immediate future. Nor does the problem of Berlin seem near a solution, though an unexpected change for the better in relations between the Soviet Union and the Western powers might produce a formula that would end the Western occupation of West Berlin without surrendering its inhabitants to the Communist state which surrounds them. Poland and the Soviet Union have now established firm control over the former German territories east of the Oder-Neisse line. Most German residents have been evacuated to either West or East Germany, their places have been taken by Poles or Russians, and the territories have been reorganized functionally to mesh into the economies of the governing nations. Meanwhile the two German republics have drawn apart in their economic and political relationships. The German Federal Republic, recognized as a fully sovereign entity by the Western nations since 1955, has become more and more interlocked with them in political, economic, and military affairs. But the German Democratic Republic now looks largely to other Communist nations in political and economic relationships. The Soviet Union has become by far its most important trading partner, being both the largest supplier of its imports and the largest market for its exports. Nearly half of its total trade is now with the Soviet Union. Meanwhile its internal political and economic organization, including the organization of its agriculture, has been remodeled along Communist lines.

Thus Germany is now fragmented in political and economic fact, as well as in name. Probably most Germans would like to see their country reunified. But as months become years and years become decades, the possibility of reunification seems to be fading more and more into the indefinite future.

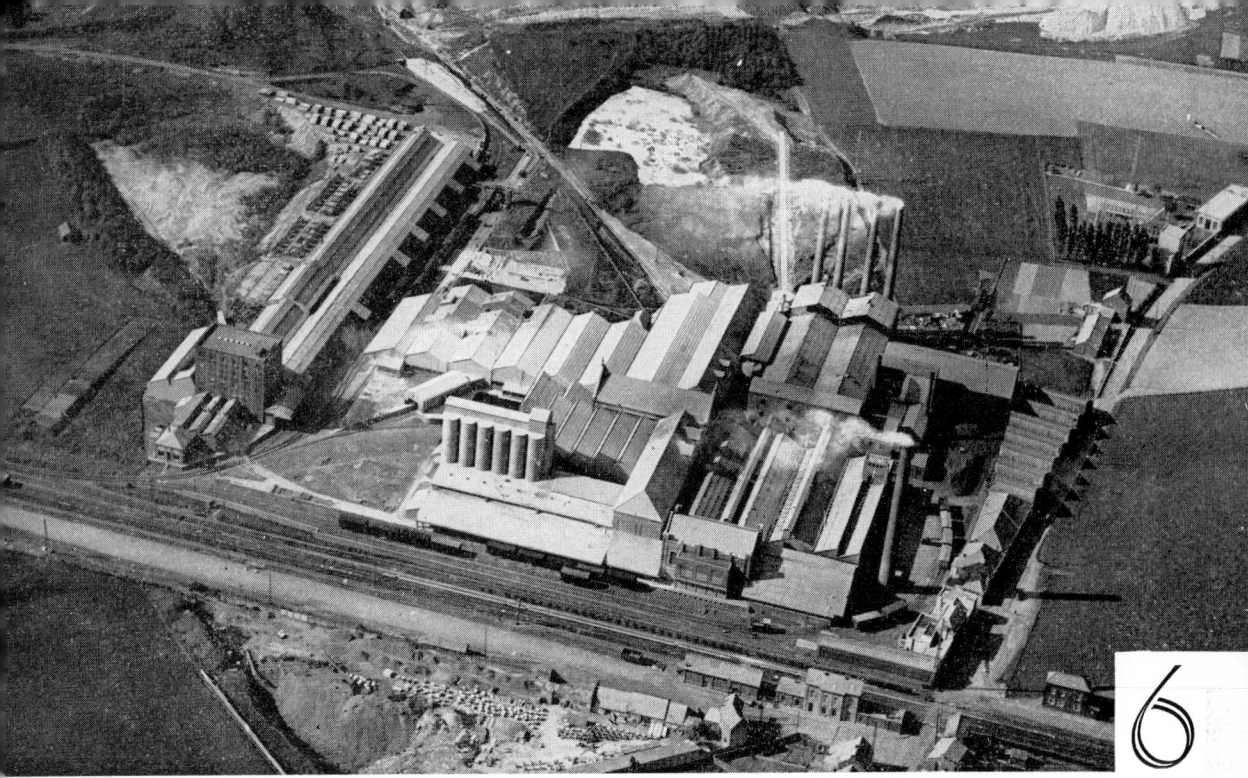

# The Benelux Countries

The three small countries of Belgium, the Netherlands, and Luxembourg have been closely associated with each other throughout their long histories. During some periods they have been included in a single political unit, although they have been politically separated during the greater part of the past four centuries. Since World War II they have been attempting to strengthen their mutual relations and to weld themselves into an economic union, while maintaining their respective political sovereignties. The new economic union has been designated Benelux, from the first syllable of each country's name, and the three nations are now often referred to collectively as "the Benelux Countries."

An older name often applied to the three is "the Low Countries." In its strictest sense, however, this term is properly applied only to the two larger countries, Belgium and the Netherlands, and will be so used in this chapter; while "Benelux" will be reserved for all three countries.

## LANDS OF LOW RELIEF

"Low Countries" is very descriptive of Belgium and the Netherlands, since approximately the northern two thirds of the former and practically all of the latter consists of a very low plain facing the North Sea. This plain is the narrowest section of the great

Manufacturing is highly developed in the densely populated Benelux nations. Pictured above is an extensive cement works in the environs of Mons, Belgium. (Sabena Belgian Airlines.)

plain of northern Europe which extends from France into the Soviet Union. In the Low Countries the plain seldom reaches as much as 300 feet above sea level. Large sections near the coast, especially in the Netherlands, are actually below sea level. They are protected from flooding only by a coastal belt of sand dunes, by man-made dikes, and by constant artificial drainage.

The only land in the Low Countries with even a moderate elevation lies mainly in Belgium, south of the line formed by the Sambre and Meuse rivers (map, right). Here the Ardennes Upland rises in some places above 2000 feet, although its surface is more commonly around 1200 feet above sea level. Much of the Ardennes is an area of little relief, though in places intrenched rivers produce a more rugged terrain. The term "Ardennes," as used in this chapter, includes the lower northern foreland or Condroz, located between the Ardennes proper and the Sambre-Meuse Valley. The edges of the Ardennes overlap Belgium's frontiers, extending without a break into the Rhine Uplands of the German Federal Republic on the east and for a short distance into France on the west. To the south the Ardennes includes the northern half of the tiny country of Luxembourg. Southern Luxembourg and a small adjoining tip of Belgium have a lower, rolling terrain similar to that of neighboring French Lorraine.

## POPULATIONS AND STANDARDS OF LIVING

High population densities are an outstanding characteristic of the Benelux nations, and especially of the Netherlands and Belgium. In fact, no sovereign nation in the entire world can match either of the latter two countries in over-all population density. The density of population in the Benelux area as a whole is greater than that of the most densely populated American state, New Jersey. New York, which has the largest population of any state, is about twice as large in area as Benelux, but has only four fifths as many people. Areas, populations, and population densities of the Benelux countries are given in Table 5.

In many countries of the world an unusually high density of population is associated with a low standard of living. In the Benelux countries, however, the reverse is true. By effective utilization of such opportunities and resources as their small and crowded national territories afford, the peoples of these countries are able to maintain standards of living which are equaled or surpassed by few nations. Estimates of per capita income rank the Benelux countries tenth,

TABLE 5

BENELUX: AREA AND POPULATION DATA

| COUNTRY | AREA (THOUSAND SQUARE MILES) | POPULATION (MILLIONS: 1959 ESTIMATES) | DENSITY (PER SQUARE MILE: TO NEAREST WHOLE NUMBER[b] |
|---|---|---|---|
| Netherlands | 12.6 [a] | 11.35 | 900 |
| Belgium | 11.8 | 9.10 | 773 |
| Luxembourg | 1.0 | .32 | 325 |
| Totals | 25.4 | 20.78 [b] | 818 |

[a] Not including waterways and sheets of water larger than 185 acres.
[b] Apparent discrepancies due to rounding of figures.

Index map of the Benelux countries. City-size symbols are based on metropolitan-area estimates. The East Flevoland polder is the latest area to be reclaimed from the Zuider Zee. Its surface was dry by the spring of 1957, and it is expected to be under full cultivation by 1965. See F. J. Monkhouse, *A Regional Geography of Western Europe* (London: Longmans, Green, 1959), pp. 48–55.

eleventh, and twelfth in the world, with Belgium highest and the Netherlands lowest among the three. The only countries that rank higher are the United States, Canada, Australia, and New Zealand, ranking first through fourth, and the European countries of Switzerland, the United Kingdom, Swe-den, Denmark, and Norway, ranking fifth through ninth.[1] While income level is not exactly equivalent to standard of living, the relationship is sufficiently close to indicate the high position of the Benelux units among the world's countries.

## THE SIGNIFICANCE OF TRADE

The economic life of the Benelux countries is characterized by an intensive development of three interrelated activities—industry, agriculture, and trade. An especially distinctive and significant feature of their economies is an unusually high development of, and dependence on, international trade. In total value of foreign trade (imports plus exports), the Netherlands and Belgium-Luxembourg ranked fourth and fifth, respectively, among the countries of Europe in 1959, being exceeded only by three much larger nations, the United Kingdom, West Germany, and France. (Since 1922 Belgium and Luxembourg have maintained a customs union, and trade figures for the two countries are reported as a unit.) In per capita trade, Belgium-Luxembourg ranked second, after Iceland, and the Netherlands ranked fourth, after Iceland, Belgium-Luxembourg, and Switzerland.

Several factors help to explain the unusual development of foreign commerce in the Benelux countries:

1. Trade is essential to such small countries, if they are to make maximum use of a limited variety of internal resources. Such resources as Luxembourg's iron ore or Belgium's coal must either be left in the ground or exported for comparatively small returns unless complementary materials needed for manufacturing can be imported.

2. The need of these countries to trade is matched by their ability to trade. Specializing in activities which offer the greatest possibilities for effective use of limited resources, the Benelux nations are able to export large surpluses of certain manufactures and, in the case of the Netherlands, livestock products, vegetables, and flower bulbs.

3. The position of the Benelux countries is highly favorable for trade. These countries lie in the heart of the most highly developed part of Europe. Their nearest neighbors, Germany, France, and the United Kingdom, are among the world's foremost producing, consuming, and trading nations. The resulting commercial opportunities are reflected in the fact that between 40 and 50 percent of Benelux foreign trade is accounted for by trade between Belgium-Luxembourg and the Netherlands or between these countries and their three larger neighbors. A second significant aspect of position lies in the location of the Netherlands and Belgium at or near the mouth of the Rhine. This river is the greatest inland waterway of Europe, and one of the greatest in the world. Location where the Rhine meets the sea permits the Low Countries to handle in transit much of the foreign trade of Switzerland, eastern France, and, especially, West Germany with its Ruhr industrial district.

[1] "National and Per Capita Incomes, Seventy Countries—1949." *Statistical Papers*, Series E, No. 1. New York: Statistical Office of the United Nations, October 1950. Also a paper by M. L. Watkins, Center for International Studies, Massachusetts Institute of Technology, quoted in C. P. Kindleberger, *Economic Development*. New York: McGraw-Hill Book Company, 1958, p. 6.

4. The trade of the Low Countries has profited somewhat from the fact that both the Netherlands and Belgium have held large colonial empires in the tropics. Before they became independent, the Netherlands East Indies and the Belgian Congo offered assured markets for goods and capital, and allowed the home countries to act as European entrepôts for tropical agricultural products and certain minerals, particularly nonferrous metals. Today, industrial and trading specialties connected originally with this former colonial trade continue to function in the Low Countries, though only a tiny fraction of their present foreign trade is with their former colonies.

# IMPORTANCE OF THE DUTCH AND BELGIAN PORTS

Exploitation of their commercial opportunities by the Low Countries is reflected in the presence of three of the world's major port cities within a distance of about 80 miles: Rotterdam and Amsterdam in the Netherlands, and Antwerp in Belgium (map, p. 135). During the twentieth century Rotterdam has normally ranked second only to New York among the world's seaports on the basis of total tonnage of goods handled. By the same criterion Antwerp has ordinarily been exceeded only by Rotterdam, London, and Hamburg among European ports; since World War II the slow recovery of Hamburg has enabled Antwerp to surpass this German port and rank second only to Rotterdam on the continent. The larger city of Amsterdam is a considerably less important port than Rotterdam or Antwerp, though its trade is large, nonetheless. The commercial activities of the three major ports are supplemented by those of numerous smaller ports in the Low Countries, particularly Ghent in Belgium.

### ▶ Amsterdam—The "Colonial" Port of the Netherlands

Amsterdam (1,017,000) is the largest city and the constitutional capital of the Netherlands, although the government is actually located at The Hague (767,000). As a port, Amsterdam handles mainly the trade of the Netherlands itself, plus a considerable entrepôt traffic in tropical products. The latter specialty stems from the fact that Amsterdam was the main port of the Netherlands during the centuries when the country's colonial empire was being acquired and organized, before the rapid rise of Rotterdam in the later nineteenth and twentieth centuries. Although the East Indian empire has been lost, Amsterdam has retained business connections and specialized marketing facilities built up during the colonial period, and so it has been able to keep a considerable amount of its "colonial" trade. In addition, the profits accumulated during several centuries of the East Indian trade have been used to finance industrial development in Amsterdam, and, by supplying capital for the large foreign investments of the Netherlands, have helped to make Amsterdam a center of international finance. Although the Eastern trade no longer appears to be a really major element in the economy of the Netherlands, it is still far from negligible, and has been of great importance in the historical development of the country, and particularly of Amsterdam.

In modern times Amsterdam has experienced considerable difficulties as a port. The original approach from the sea by way of the Zuider Zee eventually proved too shallow for modern shipping. This problem was solved in 1876 with the opening of the North Sea Canal, through which ships now enter the harbor. More recently, location away from the mouth of the Rhine has proved a disadvantage, and the city has been attempting to attract a larger share of

Rhine traffic by providing better canal connections with the river.

### ▶ Rotterdam—The Major Port for Rhine Traffic

Rotterdam (936,000) is better situated with respect to Rhine shipping than either Amsterdam or Antwerp, being located directly on one of the navigable distributaries of the river rather than to one side. Accordingly, Rotterdam controls and profits from the major portion of the river's transit trade, receiving goods by sea and dispatching them upstream by barge (photo, p. 25), and receiving goods downstream by barge and dispatching them by sea. Two developments have been mainly responsible for the port's tremendous expansion in recent times. First was the opening in 1872 of the New Waterway, an artificial channel to the sea far superior to the shallow and treacherous natural mouths of the Rhine, and superior also to the sea connections of either Amsterdam or Antwerp. Second, and more fundamental, has been the increasing industrialization of areas near the Rhine, particularly the Ruhr district, for which Rotterdam has become the main sea outlet. The need of the inland industrial districts for imports of ores, cereals, and other bulky commodities, coupled with their exports of such heavy goods as coal, steel, and chemicals, accounts for the huge tonnage of Rotterdam's trade.

### ▶ The Scheldt Port of Antwerp

Antwerp (833,000), located about 50 miles up the Scheldt River, is primarily a port for Belgium itself, but also handles an important share of the Rhine transit trade. Belgium's coast is straight and its rivers shallow, so that the deep estuary of the Scheldt gives Antwerp the best harbor in the country, even though it must be reached through the Netherlands. The city has become a major focus in Belgium's dense railway net, and has river and canal connections to Ghent, Brussels, and Liège. Transit trade is facilitated by Antwerp's position in relation to the major inland industrial areas of northwestern continental Europe. It is slightly closer than either Rotterdam or Amsterdam to these areas (map, p. 91), and it has somewhat shorter and more direct rail connections. Thus Antwerp ordinarily handles a large share of the transit trade in goods of a type which can move more profitably by the relatively expensive but faster rail lines than by the cheaper but slower barge.

Competition between Antwerp and the Dutch ports has provided a fertile field for controversy between the Low Countries in the past. Throughout the seventeenth and eighteenth centuries the Dutch were able to keep the lower Scheldt, which runs through their territory, closed to traffic, and thus to throttle Antwerp almost completely. Later disputes have arisen over the maintenance of the river's shipping channel, over Belgium's desire for a canal through Dutch territory to connect Antwerp directly with the Rhine, and over Belgium's payment of special subsidies to attract Rhine barges through the southwestern part of the Netherlands to Antwerp in preference to the more convenient Rotterdam. One of the tasks confronting the Benelux Economic Union is to resolve problems arising from the strenuous competition among the Belgian and Dutch ports, particularly between Antwerp and Rotterdam.

## MANUFACTURING IN THE BENELUX COUNTRIES

Despite the basic importance of international trade, it is manufacturing which forms the greatest source of employment in each of the Benelux countries. Belgium and Luxembourg, better endowed with mineral resources, are somewhat more industrialized than the Netherlands and have a far greater development of the heavier types of industry. Belgium, best endowed with coal, is the most important manufacturing nation of the three.

### ▶ Heavy Industry in the Sambre-Meuse District

One of Europe's major coal fields crosses Belgium in a narrow east-west belt about a hundred miles long (map, p. 92). It follows roughly the valleys of the Sambre and Meuse rivers, and extends into France on the west and Germany on the east. Liège (598,000), Charleroi (461,000), and smaller industrial cities strung along this Sambre-Meuse field account for most of Belgium's metallurgical and other heavy industrial production. The iron and steel industry is the most important, and its production is sufficient to place Belgium fifth among the steel-producing nations of Europe after West Germany, the United Kingdom, France, and Italy. The industry imports its ores, mainly from Luxembourg, France, and Sweden, and sells a great part of its production outside of the relatively small home market. Liège, the largest manufacturing center on the coal field, has metallurgical industries dating back to handicraft days, and was the first city in continental Europe to develop modern, large-scale iron and steel manufacture following the Industrial Revolution.

Small deposits of iron ore and zinc in the Ardennes originally furnished raw material for the Sambre-Meuse metallurgical industries. Although the zinc, like the iron ore, has long been exhausted, it started Belgian industry toward what has now become a remarkable specialty in nonferrous smelting. Belgium produces about 8 percent of the world's smelter zinc, a production exceeded only by that of the United States, the Soviet Union, and, in some years, Canada. In addition, the little country has become Europe's third greatest smelter of tin (after the United Kingdom and the Netherlands) and second greatest of lead, after West Germany. The nonferrous ores and concentrates for the smelting industry are now entirely imported,

and the bulk of the production is exported to other European nations in one form or another. Belgium thus acts as a processing middleman between the overseas ore producers and the European industrial consumers of these metals. Certain other specialties have also developed in the Sambre-Meuse district, notably the production of cement (photo, p. 133), glass, and nitrogenous chemicals. These products, which require much coal in manufacture, are principally made from local raw materials.

### ▶ The Light, Diversified Industries of Brussels

Throughout Belgium even the smaller towns are generally characterized by some industrial development. Away from the coal fields there is a tendency to specialize in lighter types of industry having smaller power requirements than the industries located near to coal. In these industries labor is often of great importance as a factor in the total cost of production. The Belgian capital, Brussels, is the outstanding center of such industries. Like most European political capitals, it is the largest city in the country, with a metropolitan population of 1,372,000, and is primarily a product of political and cultural centralization. The labor force, transport facilities, and local market it provides, however, have led to the development of a great variety of light industries, including textiles and clothing, skilled metalwork, printing, food processing, and luxury crafts. Antwerp, also, is an important center of diversified industries, particularly those that are generally found in a major seaport.

### ▶ The Belgian Textile Industry

As in most countries, textile manufacturing is the leading branch of Belgium's lighter industries. As far back as the twelfth century, Flanders (roughly the part of Belgium north of the Scheldt and west of Antwerp) was a center of commercial cloth production, importing raw wool (mainly from England) and selling woolen cloth in various parts of

Europe. The same area is now the center of Belgium's cotton, linen, and jute industries. It still imports its raw materials and exports a large part of the finished product. Flanders readily adapted its long textile tradition to machine production during the early nineteenth century simply by concentrating the former cottage workers into factory cities. The greatest of these cities today is the ancient commercial center of the industry, Ghent (452,000).

Flanders lost its leadership in Belgium's woolen industry to Verviers (city proper, 37,400), in the edge of the Ardennes, by the eighteenth century at the latest. The pure and soft water flowing from the Ardennes gave this place a considerable advantage in washing the wool preparatory to spinning. Its value can still be seen in the fact that Verviers not only produces a major share of Belgium's woolen goods, but also specializes in cleaning raw wool for distant mills, both in Belgium and in neighboring countries.

### ▶ Belgium's Export Trade

Belgium's export trade closely reflects the industrial emphases brought out in the preceding discussion. Processed metals (iron and steel, copper, zinc, tin, aluminum, lead) are by far the largest single category of exports by value. Other leading categories include textile yarns, fabrics, and fibers; machinery and vehicles; chemical fertilizers; miscellaneous metal manufactures; petroleum products from refineries at Antwerp; cut diamonds from Antwerp; and glass.

### ▶ Manufacturing in Luxembourg

Luxembourg's simple industrial structure presents a picture of dependence on foreign trade proportionately equal to, or greater than, that of Belgium. About 40 percent of the country's entire working population is employed in the iron and steel industry, which is carried on in several small centers near the southern border, where the Lorraine iron-ore deposits of France overlap into Luxembourg. Annual production of both pig

iron and steel ranges upward from 3½ million tons. The tiny country ranks eighth among the steel producers of Europe, and not lower than thirteenth or fourteenth in the world. The very small home market both necessitates and permits export of most of the production. In return, Luxembourg buys fuel (mainly coal and coke from West Germany), alloy metals, and many other products.

### ▶ Industries of the Netherlands

The Netherlands differs from Belgium and Luxembourg in the smaller part which domestic mineral resources have played in the rise of its industries. It resembles Belgium-Luxembourg, however, in the dependence of its industries on international trade. Basic factors in the rise of Dutch industrial production have been (1) the ability of Dutch industries to import both fuel and raw materials cheaply and (2) the availability of an abundant, skilled, and relatively low-priced labor force. Generally speaking, in their location the industries of the Netherlands are transportation and labor oriented rather than materials or market oriented.

Amsterdam and Rotterdam are the main seats of industry as well as of commerce. Prominent among the diversified industries of both these ports are shipbuilding and associated engineering industries. For a brief time in the seventeenth century the Netherlands was probably the world's greatest sea power, and a strong maritime tradition has survived. A disproportionately large merchant marine is an important factor in the Dutch economy, and ships are a prominent export. The ports of the Netherlands are the locale for a variety of industries which process overseas materials for sale in European markets. Industries that process foodstuffs of tropical origin, notably oilseeds, sugar, and cocoa, play a substantial role. But in value of exports they are overshadowed by industries that process imported minerals. The most important of the latter is the oil-refining industry. A huge concentration of refineries, especially at Rotterdam, is in good part an expression of the Netherlands' important financial and managerial interest in the world-wide operations of the Royal Dutch Shell Company. Among the nations of Europe the Netherlands ranks fifth in oil refining, after the United Kingdom, France, Italy, and West Germany. Petroleum products are by a wide margin the country's leading export among processed minerals. Iron and steel manufactured from imported iron ore (primarily Swedish ore) rank second, though the Netherlands' imports of iron and steel are somewhat larger than its exports, and its small steel industry, less than half the size of Luxembourg's, produces primarily for the domestic market. The largest producing unit is an integrated iron and steel plant located on the North Sea Canal near its seaward entrance. Also to be mentioned among mineral-processing industries is the smelting of tin. Indonesian tin, channeled into Europe through the Netherlands, has made the country the world's third or fourth nation in tin smelting, after Malaya, the United Kingdom, and possibly China. This industry is centered at Arnhem (181,000) on the Rhine rather than in one of the major port areas.

Away from the ports, and especially in some of the poorer agricultural districts, surplus labor and good transportation have led to the development of numerous small industrial cities. Textiles, light machinery, and consumer goods of various kinds are their major products. The industries of these cities rely heavily on imported raw materials and export a large part of the finished product. The only really important manufacturing industry which is based primarily on domestic raw materials is the widespread food-processing industry, which prepares for the domestic market and export the meat, milk, butter, cheese, and other products of the Netherlands' specialized agriculture.

## THE INTENSIVE AGRICULTURE OF BENELUX

Through manufacturing and trade the Benelux nations are able to support considerably larger populations than their agriculture can feed under present conditions. Like the United Kingdom, these nations import large quantities of food, together with feed for livestock and fertilizers to help increase their domestic agricultural production. Domestic production is particularly inadequate in the case of grains. Only limited areas in the Benelux countries are really well suited to the production of grains, particularly wheat, the grain consumed in the largest quantities for human food. Imported wheat has proved able to undersell the domestic product on the Benelux market, and thus farmers in the Benelux nations have usually concentrated their main efforts on farm commodities other than wheat. This is especially true of the Netherlands.

The extremely high density of population makes domestic food production insufficient despite the fact that crop yields in the Low Countries are among the highest in the world. Wheat, for example, ordinarily gives an average yield of 50 to 60 bushels per acre. This compares with a world average of perhaps 17 bushels per acre, and is exceeded by the average yield in only one other country, Denmark. However, such yields are only obtained through large expenditures of both labor and capital. So intensive is the labor expended on the cultivation of each acre that agriculture often resembles gardening. This type of farming is made both possible and necessary by the density of rural population and the small size of most farms. More than half of all Dutch farms and nine tenths of all Belgian farms are smaller than 12½ acres. Most Belgian farms are actually closer to 2 acres. Along with labor, capital is applied to the

The intricate canal network of the Dutch polders. Windmills, such as those in this photo, have largely been replaced by motor-driven pumps. (Netherlands Information Service.)

soil abundantly, mainly in the form of fertilizer. The Netherlands uses more fertilizer per acre than any other country in the world except Japan, and Belgium is not far behind.

A close adaptation of agriculture to climatic and soil conditions helps the Low Countries to obtain the maximum output from their restricted acreages of farm land. Since climatic conditions tend to be relatively uniform over both countries, differences in type of agriculture are mainly related to differences in type of land. Although in detail the picture is intricate, three main types of land, each with its associated types of agriculture, may be identified. These are the *polder lands,* the *loess lands,* and the *infertile lands.*

▶ *Dairy Farming in the Polder Lands*
Polder lands are those which have been surrounded by dikes and artificially drained. The process of turning former swamps, lakes, and shallow seas into agricultural

land has been going on for over seven centuries. An individual polder, of which there are a great many of various sizes, is an area enclosed within dikes and kept dry by constant pumping (photo, above) into the drainage canals which surround it. About 40 percent of the Netherlands now consists of an intricate patchwork of polders and canals, while Belgium has a narrow strip of such lands behind its coastal sand dunes (map, p. 135). The polder lands of the Netherlands extend for about 180 miles between the Belgian and German borders, in a belt which is seldom more than 40 miles wide and usually much less. The belt is roughly parallel to the seacoast, and is separated from the sea by dunes, swamps, or dikes.

The polders are the best lands in the Netherlands, and their production is the heart of Dutch agriculture. The reclaimed soil is very rich, water supply is subject to considerable control, and the canals form a complete transport network. The drier polders are often used for crop farming, and produce huge harvests. Most polders, however, are kept in grass, and dairy farming is the main type of agriculture. It thrives so well that large quantities of dairy products are exported, mainly to nearby industrial areas in Germany, Belgium, and the United Kingdom. Pork production is ordinarily a part of dairy farming, since the necessary feed for the hogs can largely be supplied by skim milk left over from butter making. The production of vegetables, fruits, and horticultural specialties such as the famous Dutch flower bulbs is also of considerable importance in the polder zone. Dairying and other specialized types of agriculture supply about a fourth of the total exports of the Netherlands, and more than compensate, in value at least, for the necessary food imports. The main categories of food exports from the Netherlands include: (1) evaporated, condensed, and dry milk, and cheese and butter, (2) fresh and processed meat (beef, pork, and poultry), (3) vegetables, and (4) eggs.

### ► The Fertile Loess Lands

A second section of outstanding fertility and agricultural production is found in Belgium. In central Belgium a gently rolling topography was mantled in glacial times by a blanket of loess, a fine dust picked up by the wind from glacial debris. This material has formed soils of exceptional fertility in Belgium, as in many other places. These soils are found in a belt across the country between the Sambre-Meuse Valley on the south and a line just beyond Brussels on the north.

Three characteristics distinguish the agriculture of the loess belt. One is an emphasis on wheat, which has been able to survive foreign competition on these good lands. Another is the production of sugar beets, a crop requiring an exceptionally fertile soil. Third is the production of fodder crops, which give very high yields and permit the loess area to specialize in the production of beef cattle, often brought in for fattening from poorer areas. This combination of food, feed, and livestock production supports the largest and most prosperous farms in Belgium.

### ► The Infertile Lands

The remaining lands of the Low Countries, and most of Luxembourg as well, can be described as relatively infertile, though small areas sometimes contradict this generalization. Sandy soils are dominant in northern Belgium and practically all of the Netherlands outside of the polder areas, though the sands are often interspersed with peat bogs and patches of clay, both of which can be made into good soil if properly managed. The soil of the sandy areas is generally lacking in humus, lime, and plant nutrients. That of the Ardennes is no better.

The agriculture of these areas is generally centered about livestock production (photo, p. 144), and crops are grown primarily for feed. The most common crops are rye, potatoes, oats, turnips, and hay. All are well adapted to the climate, and all except hay suffer relatively little, or actually grow better, in light and infertile soils. Rye and potatoes are used in these areas for human food as well as stock feed. Potatoes and turnips give especially good returns per acre, provided the necessary labor is available for harvesting. In addition, these root crops fit well with rye in that they give a crop during the summer on the same land that produced rye during the winter and spring. Livestock grown may be either beef cattle or dairy cattle, often both. Besides providing a cash income, they supply an important part of the large quantities of fertilizer necessary in farming such lands.

Although the density of population and intensity of agricultural production on the poorer lands are generally less than on the polders or the loess, they are often surprisingly great. In one sandy area, Flanders, the average production per acre is almost as large as on the naturally better lands, and

A cattle market in an open street of the old Flemish city of Bruges. This view reflects the importance of livestock in the intensive, prosperous agriculture of the Low Countries. (Belgian Information Center.)

the density of population is even greater. Here intensive agriculture and systematic improvement of the land have a continuous history dating back at least to the eleventh century. The precocious urban, commercial, and industrial development of Flanders stimulated Flemish agriculture during these early times. A garden type of agriculture has developed, especially centered on livestock, dairy, and vegetable production, but making some use of almost every crop that can be grown in the Low Countries and using soils almost completely transformed by centuries of improvement. Few of the world's farming areas are more skillfully handled.

## MAJOR PROBLEMS OF THE BENELUX NATIONS

The Benelux countries share the general problems of the modern world. Like many other countries, they are concerned with achieving and maintaining international peace and cooperation, national security, and internal unity, freedom, and economic well-being. However, due to peculiarities of position, resources, population, and economic development, the Benelux countries are faced with certain types of problems which present themselves in distinctive form or with particular urgency.

### ▶ The Belgian Problem of National Unity

Belgium has had the most difficulty among the Benelux nations in securing and maintaining internal unity and cooperation. Division of the population into two major language groups has been at the root of the difficulty. If one draws an east-west line across Belgium just south of Brussels, it will approximate a line of sharp linguistic division (map, p. 135). To the north Flemish, a slight variant of Dutch, is the dominant language except in Brussels. To the south live the French-speaking Belgians known as Walloons. Rivalries and antagonisms have sometimes arisen between the two groups. The Flemish people, until recently the minority group, have occasionally shown separatist tendencies. Differential birth rates have now given the Flemish group a majority, however, and Walloon uneasiness has appeared. There is always a latent danger that political issues will be fought primarily along language lines. How explosive such a situation can be was shown in 1950 when violent disturbances threatened over the question of the return of an exiled king. In the face of this language division constant care must be exercised to maintain national unity.

### ▶ Problems of National Security

At present, however, all three of the Benelux nations find problems of national security and economic welfare more pressing than others. The two types of problems are closely related due to the heavy costs involved in war and in peacetime provision of armaments against possible attack.

The position of the Benelux countries between Germany, France, and the United Kingdom, and their inability to defend themselves against these more powerful neighbors, have tended to involve them in every general European war, usually as a battleground. The low plains of Belgium offer a short and easy route between Germany and Paris, and even the Ardennes is no longer very effective as a military barrier, as was demonstrated by the German offensive through this upland area in the spring of 1940. Both world wars of the twentieth century have added to Belgium's long history as an international battlefield.

The Netherlands has offered a valuable base for operations from the continent against England and, conversely, an approach to the industrial heart of Germany. Flooding of the polders is no longer the effective defense against invading armies that it has been in times past. Thus, although the Netherlands escaped invasion in World War I, the country was conquered by the Germans early in World War II after five days of savage fighting in May 1940, and it was again a battlefield as the German tide was rolled back by the Allies in the latter part of the war. Few nations endured comparable destruction.

Luxembourg, also, suffered German invasion and occupation from May 1940 until liberation by the Allies in September 1944. In December 1944 and early January 1945 about a third of Luxembourg was laid waste in the Battle of the Ardennes, which represented the last major offensive effort by Germany on the western front.

### ▶ Trade Problems

The resulting concern of the Benelux countries for international peace has been paralleled by a concern with international trade which is proportional to their heavy dependence on importing and exporting. Since 1945 they have had to face particular problems in this field associated with (1) the loss of the East Indian empire by the Netherlands and of the Congo by Belgium, (2) restriction of trade with European areas behind the iron curtain, (3) postwar restrictions on imports by the United Kingdom and France, together with the temporarily depressed state of the German Ruhr for several years after the war, and (4) the necessity for trading more with the United States.

Most of these recent trade difficulties have been overcome, largely in connection with western Europe's general recovery from the devastation and dislocations of the war and its subsequent economic boom. Much has been achieved by the Benelux countries through their participation in various international projects to secure freer trade among the European nations. Since the Benelux countries are so very dependent on favorable political and economic circumstances for doing business with other countries, it is understandable that they have generally been ardent supporters of international organization. In the field of economic cooperation they have provided an example for the European Common Market in their own Benelux Economic Union, which was begun earlier and has moved a long way toward its goal of eradicating trade barriers between the Netherlands and Belgium-Luxembourg.

### ► Population Problems

Internally, the main problem of both Belgium and the Netherlands seems to be the expansion of agriculture and industry, already intensively developed, to support still increasing populations. The situation is particularly acute in the Netherlands, which has one of the highest rates of natural increase in Europe and has witnessed the addition of over 4 million people to the population of an already crowded country in the last four decades. In such a small, densely populated country as the Netherlands, such an increase may be disastrous if long continued—a fact that is reflected in the nation's very unusual policy of officially encouraging and assisting emigration.

### ► Reclamation of New Land for Agriculture

Land reclamation has been one response to increasing populations in both countries. Cultivation of the infertile lands has been greatly expanded in recent times, and the process continues. In Belgium such effort has centered in the Ardennes and, especially, in the Campine, the sandy area south and east of Antwerp. In the Netherlands special attention has been directed toward bringing into productivity some of the vast peat bogs which are interspersed with the sandy areas of the eastern part of the country, and also toward an extension of dairy farming into the poorer lands.

The most important and celebrated reclamation work currently going on in the Neth-

erlands, however, is the formation of new polders from the former Zuider Zee (map, p. 135). A massive 18-mile-long dike was completed across the entrance of the Zuider Zee in the early 1930s, and a sizable area of sea bottom has now been reclaimed. At present, two of the five large polders planned are under cultivation, and a third polder has been drained and is expected to be fully cultivated by 1965. Meanwhile the remainder of the Zuider Zee has become a fresh water lake, the Ijsselmeer. The completed project will add about 7 percent, all excellent farm land, to the land area of the Netherlands.

Another massive and much-publicized project of the Netherlands, called the Delta Plan, is aimed primarily at flood control and only incidentally at land reclamation. Its purpose is to prevent a recurrence of the devastating flood of February 1953, when the sea broke through the dikes in the southwestern part of the country during a storm, taking 1800 lives and causing property damage estimated at nearly 400 million dollars. The heart of the Delta Plan is the construction of dikes connecting the islands in the triple delta of the Rhine, Maas, and Scheldt with each other and with the adjoining mainland. The New Waterway, giving Rotterdam access to the sea, and the Scheldt River outlet for Antwerp will remain unobstructed, but the other channels through the delta will be closed by huge dikes. It is estimated that it will take at least until 1980 to complete the entire scheme, which involves various engineering works besides the major dikes referred to above.

### ► Coal as a Factor in Industrial Expansion

Agricultural expansion alone cannot maintain the present high standard of living in the Low Countries. The governments of both Belgium and the Netherlands, especially the latter, regard increased industrialization as essential. This is in spite of the fact that both are already among the most highly industrialized countries in the world: of all the world's countries only the United Kingdom has a higher proportion of its employed population in manufacturing industries than Belgium, and only these and two or three other countries in northwestern Europe have a higher proportion than the Netherlands.

A reasonably favorable situation with regard to power has characterized past industrial development in the Low Countries and seems likely to continue. Belgium's exceptional degree of industrialization is associated in part with unusually early utilization of coal resources. The Sambre-Meuse field was the first major coal field on the continent to be intensively developed. Its history has paralleled that of most of the British fields, with output reaching a peak in 1913 and then declining as thin, broken, and inclined seams have had to be worked at increasing depths. In Belgium, however, the situation was alleviated by the discovery in 1898, and development after 1917, of a new field, located in the Campine (map, p. 92). The coal lies from 1500 to 3000 feet or more below the surface, but thick seams, large reserves, and high quality have resulted in relatively efficient production, and a certain amount of heavy industry has already been drawn to the Campine in preference to the older Sambre-Meuse district. The field that underlies the Campine extends across the southernmost part of the Netherlands, known as South Limburg, and on to the vicinity of Aachen, Germany. Here the Netherlands, long considered to be essentially barren of domestic power resources, has developed since World War I an unusually efficient mining industry which supplies all but a minor share of the country's coal requirements. The South Limburg field yields varied types of coal, including much high-grade coking coal and some anthracite. Both of the Low Countries, as well as Luxembourg, lie within relatively short distances of major foreign coal fields. They have long imported some coal and coke, especially from the German Ruhr, and are now favored in obtaining their requirements beyond domestic production by their membership in the European Coal and Steel Community.[2]

An astonishing record of past accomplishment in these small countries suggests that in so far as solutions to their present difficulties can be achieved by vigorous action within their own borders, such solutions are likely to be forthcoming. Problems wider in scope, however, can only be solved by international action on a regional or a world scale, and on such action the Benelux countries can exercise, at best, only a modest influence. They lie at the opposite pole from national self-sufficiency—in an age when even large and powerful countries are far from self-sufficient—and may only press forward within their own boundaries and hope for the best from the world on which they are so dependent.

---

[2] It should be noted that the Low Countries are both importers and exporters of coal and coke, though in both countries there is a net import. This situation is accounted for by differing requirements of particular industries with regard to types and grades of coal and by transportation and price differentials which often make it more economical for a user to buy from a foreign supplier than from one in some other part of the home country.

# Switzerland and Austria

The two small countries of Switzerland and Austria, located in the heart of Europe, have often been contrasted and otherwise compared. Despite certain environmental and cultural similarities, these neighbors have been remarkably different in their historical development. One of the two countries, Switzerland, represents perhaps the world's foremost example of the economic and political success of a small nation, whereas the other, Austria, has experienced great economic and political difficulties, although these have lessened markedly in recent years. The likenesses and differences of the two countries will form a major theme in the present chapter.

## PHYSICAL SIMILARITIES OF SWITZERLAND AND AUSTRIA

With respect to physical environment Switzerland and Austria have much in common. Over half of each country is occupied by the high and rugged Alps Mountains (map, p. 150). North of the Alps both countries include part of the rolling morainal foreland of the mountains. The Swiss section of the Alpine Foreland is often called the Swiss Plateau. It lies mostly between 1500 and 3000 feet in elevation and ex-

A tiny village in the Swiss Alps. Note the characteristic church tower, jagged skyline, and forested slope at right behind the small inn. (Standard Oil Company, N. J.)

tends between Lake Geneva, on the French border, to the southwest, and Lake Constance, on the German border, to the northeast. The Austrian section of the foreland is slightly lower in elevation and extends from the Alps to the Danube River between Salzburg on the west and Vienna on the east. The Swiss and Austrian sections are separated from each other by a third portion of the foreland which lies in southern Germany. North of the foreland both Switzerland and Austria include mountains or hills which are much lower in elevation and smaller in areal extent than the Alps. These highlands differ in character. The Jura Mountains, on the border between Switzerland and France, consist of parallel ridges formed of sedimentary rocks, while the Bohemian Hills of Austria, on the border with Czechoslovakia, represent the irregular, eroded southern edge of the extremely old Bohemian massif, and are formed of igneous and metamorphic rocks. North of the Jura in Switzerland the area around Basel opens onto the Upper Rhine Plain of Germany and France, while in eastern Austria the Vienna Basin and a strip of lowland to the south (Burgenland) adjoin the Little Hungarian Plain on the east and the Moravian Lowland of Czechoslovakia on the north. The Alps extend from Switzerland southward into Italy and southwestward into France, and from Austria southward into Italy and Yugoslavia.

## RELATIVE SUPERIORITY OF AUSTRIAN NATURAL RESOURCES

The physical similarities of Switzerland and Austria are not paralleled by an equal endowment of natural resources. The resources of Austria are, on the whole, superior to those of Switzerland, and in addition Austria is favored by a lower density of population. Some of these advantages of Austria appear in Table 6.

The more favorable situation of Austria with respect to land under cultivation is due primarily to its higher proportion of relatively level terrain. It reflects also to some degree Switzerland's greater specialization in dairy farming, which leads the Swiss to keep a larger percentage of potentially cultivable land in pasture. As might be expected from these circumstances, Switzerland is much more dependent than Austria on food

TABLE 6

SWITZERLAND AND AUSTRIA: AREA, POPULATION, AND LAND USE[a]

| ITEM | AUSTRIA | SWITZERLAND | SWITZERLAND AS APPROX. % OF AUSTRIA |
|---|---|---|---|
| Area (thousand square miles) | 32.4 | 15.9 | 49% |
| Population (millions; 1959 estimates) | 7.05 | 5.24 | 74% |
| Approximate population density (per square mile) | 218 | 329 | 150% |
| Cultivated land, including fallow and orchards (000 acres) | 4376 (21%) | 1100 (11%) | 25% |
| Permanent meadows and pastures (000 acres) | 5710 (28%) | 4267 (42%) | 75% |
| Forests and woodlands (000 acres) | 7719 (37%) | 2424 (24%) | 31% |
| Other land use, mostly waste (000 acres) | 2911 (14%) | 2413 (23%) | 83% |

[a] Land-use data from *FAO Yearbook of Food and Agricultural Statistics: Production*, 1958.

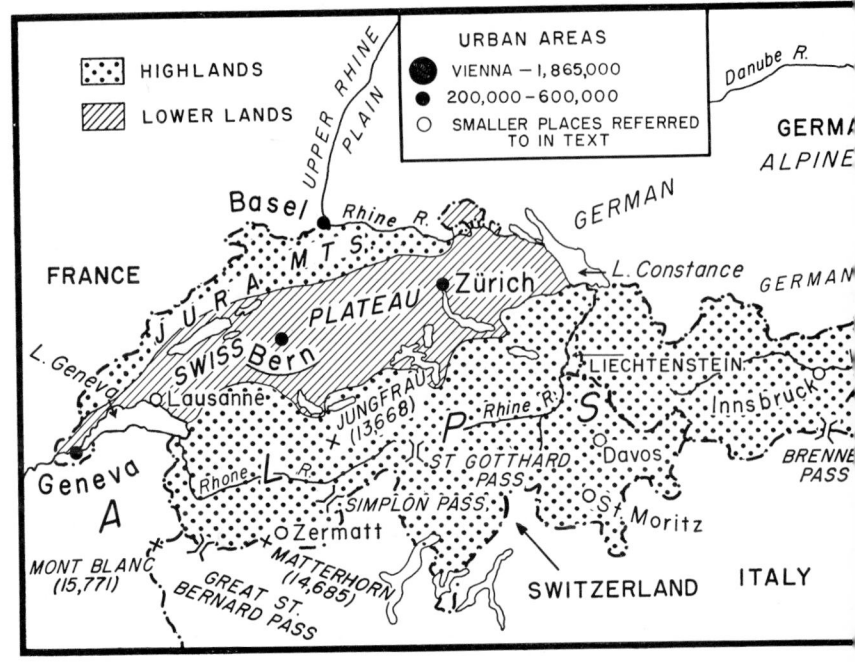

Index map of Switzerland and Austria. Political capitals are underlined.

imports. The greater proportion of forest land in Austria primarily reflects the fact that the Austrian Alps are in general lower and less rugged than the Swiss Alps, with a smaller percentage of their land above the tree line. Austria has important exports of forest products, whereas Switzerland is a considerable importer.

In addition, Austria has advantages with regard to mineral and power resources. Switzerland is almost devoid of important mineral resources, while Austria's mineral production is varied and valuable, although exhibiting on the whole more variety than quantity. Oil, primarily from deposits around Zistersdorf, northeast of Vienna (map, above), is extracted in sufficient quantities to place Austria third among European oil producers, after Romania and West Germany. However, production has been declining since 1955, and the annual output of oil is now much less than the country's consumption. Domestic iron ore produced for the most part in the Alps northwest of Graz supplies the greater part of Austria's needs, though substantial imports are necessary. There are scattered deposits of lignite, coal, bauxite, magnesite, and salt, as well as other minerals. Both Switzerland and Austria have large hydroelectric resources relative to their areas, but Austria's potential is greater.

## THE SUPERIOR SWISS STANDARD OF LIVING

The advantages of Austria with respect to natural resources have been overweighed by other factors in the historical development of the two countries so that the economic situation of Austria is today more adverse than that of Switzerland and the Austrian standard of living is much lower. Switzerland, in fact, is generally regarded as having one of the world's soundest and most successful economies, while Austria has been saved from economic collapse several times since World War I only by the ex-

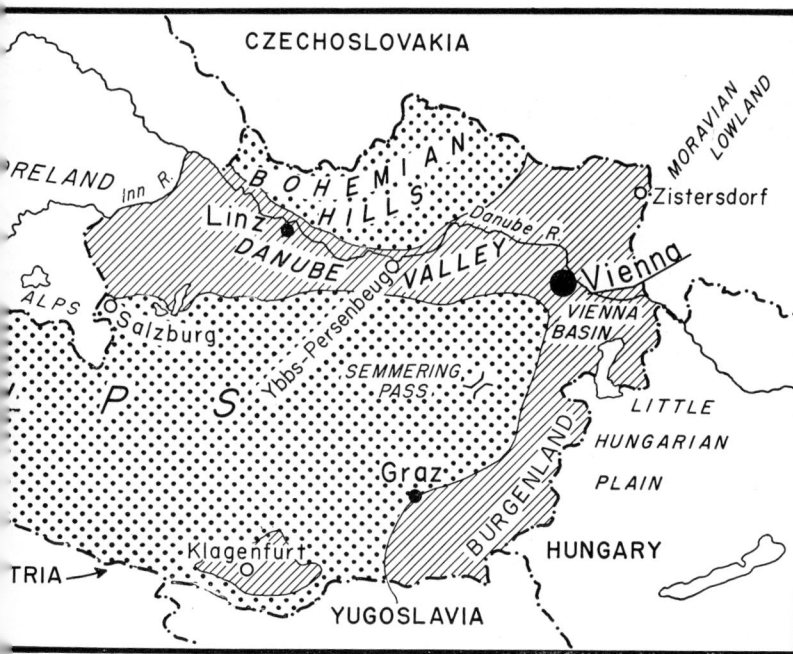

City-size symbols are based on metropolitan-area estimates.

tension of large amounts of foreign aid. The Swiss standard of living is certainly one of the highest in Europe and may well be the highest, while Austria's is closer to that of the underdeveloped countries of eastern and southern Europe. Austria's per capita income is only one third that of Switzerland. These contrasts between the two countries can be attributed primarily to a long period of peace enjoyed by Switzerland. During this time its citizens have been able to develop an economy finely adjusted to their country's potentialities and opportunities and supported by a stable and democratic government. Meanwhile the economy of Austria has been badly disoriented, warped, and hindered by a series of military and political calamities. Since the end of the post-World War II military occupation in 1955 (p. 156), Austria's economic and political situation has been relatively favorable and the country has made rapid economic progress. But it still has far to go to equal the prosperity of its more fortunate neighbor.

## ROLE OF SWITZERLAND AS A NEUTRAL BUFFER STATE

Except for some minor internal disturbances in the nineteenth century, Switzerland has been at peace inside stable boundaries since 1815. The basic factors underlying this long period of peace seem to have been (1) Switzerland's position as a buffer between larger powers, (2) the comparative defensibility of much of the country's terrain, (3) the relatively small value of Swiss economic production to an aggressive state, (4) the country's value as an intermediary between belligerents in wartime, and (5) Switzerland's own policy of strict and heavily armed neutrality. The difficulties which a great power might encounter in attempting to conquer Switzerland are often popularly exaggerated, since the Swiss Plateau, the heart of the country, lies open to Germany

Farms and wooded hills on the rolling Swiss Plateau near Lake Geneva. (Standard Oil Company, N. J.)

and France, and even the Alps have frequently been traversed by strong military forces in past times. On the other hand, resistance in the mountains might well be hard to thoroughly extinguish. In World War II Switzerland was able to hold a club over the head of Germany by mining the tunnels through which Swiss rail lines avoid the crests of the Alpine passes. Destruction of these tunnels would have been very costly to Germany, as well as to its military partner, Italy, since the Swiss railways were depended on to carry much traffic between them.

## THE PRODUCTIVE SWISS ECONOMY

The efficient and highly successful Swiss economy finds its greatest development in three lines of enterprise: (1) the production of highly finished, specialized manufactures for export, (2) dairy farming, and (3) the world's most renowned tourist industry.

### ▶ Industrial and Urban Development

In terms of employment and income Switzerland is primarily an industrial country, despite the fame of its picturesque resorts and Alpine dairy farms. Swiss industry is based on the country's two major industrial resources—hydroelectric power and the skill of Swiss workers. Most raw materials as well as supplementary fuels are imported. The country's industries are specialized along lines that minimize Switzerland's lack of bulky raw materials, while making full use of its power resources and traditions of workmanship that date back to handicraft days before the Industrial Revolution. The major products are (1) metal goods, including machinery (much of it designed to order—see photo, right) and, of course, the famous Swiss watches, (2) chemicals, especially pharmaceuticals, and (3) textiles, generally of very high quality and including silks, artificial silks, and embroideries in addition to more ordinary materials. In recent years chemicals and aluminum products have been gaining in importance. Most of Switzerland's export trade is comprised of the foregoing lines of goods. Major categories in 1958 included machinery (excluding vehicles), 24 percent; watches, clocks, and parts, 17 percent; chemicals, 17 percent; textiles, excluding apparel, 10 percent. Instruments and apparatus of various types comprised an additional 7 percent. Switzerland's export and import trade is world-wide, but in 1958 about two thirds of its total value was accounted for by trade with six units in western Europe and the United States—West Germany, 21 percent; Italy, 10 percent; France, 9 percent; United Kingdom, 6 percent; Netherlands, 4 percent; Belgium-Luxembourg, 4 percent; United States, 11 percent.

Reliance on hydroelectricity as the major source of power has facilitated the development of many small industrial centers throughout the country. The majority of these are located on the Swiss Plateau, but some are found in valleys of the Jura and Alps. Only five cities have metropolitan populations of more than 100,000: Zürich (588,000), Basel (326,000), Bern, the capital (221,000), Geneva (215,000), and Lausanne (151,000). Four of the five cities form virtually a straight line along the center of the Swiss Plateau, from Zürich on the northeast to Geneva on the southwest (map, p. 150). Basel, however, lies beyond the Jura at the point where the Rhine River turns northward between Germany and France. This city, located at the head of navigation for large barges on the Rhine, handles most of Switzerland's river-borne

A product of Swiss industry. This enormous turbine was manufactured by a Swiss firm for installation in one of Switzerland's many hydroelectric power stations. (Bell Engineering Works, Ltd., Kriens-Lucerne, Switzerland.)

commerce. In addition, it is the largest railway center in the country.

### ▶ Swiss Agriculture

An estimated 40 percent of Switzerland's food requirements must ordinarily be imported. The salability of Swiss exports has made such food imports possible and has enabled Swiss agriculture to become adjusted to lands which on the whole are better suited to pasture and hay than to cultivated crops. The result has been a high degree of specialization on dairy farming. The dairy industry is centered in small, intensively worked farms on the rolling to hilly lands of the central plateau (photo, left), although mountain pastures in the Alps are extensively used. The latter is an especially well-known aspect of Swiss agriculture. Dairy cattle and goats, accompanied by herdsmen or the entire farm family, are driven in the spring to pastures near the snow line, where they are kept throughout the summer. This seasonal migration of farm people and their livestock between the valley floors and high mountain pastures is known as *transhumance* and is practiced in many mountainous regions of the world. The high pastures of Switzerland, known as "alps," have given their name to the Alps Mountains. In recent times there has been an increasing tendency among Swiss farmers to pasture only the young cattle on the high meadows and to keep the main dairy herds at lower levels the year round. Switzerland has a limited export of cheeses, milk chocolate, and condensed milk. Recently the government has been encouraging greater self-sufficiency in foodstuffs, particularly wheat, in order to place the country less at the mercy of belligerents in time of war.

## ▶ *The Tourist Industry*

The total cost of Swiss imports is not ordinarily covered by exports of goods, but the deficit is more than made good by various "invisible" exports, of which services to tourists are the most important. Few countries have so much to offer the tourist, and probably no country has developed and organized the tourist trade so completely and successfully. Special training programs are made available to personnel in the tourist industry, and high standards are enforced. Alpine resorts such as Zermatt, Davos, and St. Moritz have become world famous, as has the name of a pioneer in the trade, Ritz. Switzerland, more than any other, is a country which exports its scenery. Other important sources of revenue from "invisible" exports include the return from foreign loans and investments and charges for international banking and insurance services, all of which Switzerland, as a relatively wealthy country and long-standing neutral, is in a good position to supply.

## THE NATIONAL UNITY OF SWITZERLAND

In their successful pursuit of economic goals, the Swiss have been aided by an effective national unity expressed in a stable, democratic, and competent government. The unity of the Swiss is the more remarkable in that it embraces a population divided in both language and religion. At present nearly three quarters of the Swiss speak German as a native tongue, about one fifth speak French, about one twentieth Italian, and about 1 percent Romansch, the latter an almost extinct descendant of Latin which has been preserved in the mountains of southeastern Switzerland. German, French, and Italian are dominant, respectively, in the sections of Switzerland adjoining Germany, France, and Italy. A religious division also exists, since approximately 56 percent of the Swiss are listed as Protestants and about 42 percent as Roman Catholics.

The internal political organization of Switzerland expresses and makes allowance for the ethnic diversity of the population. Originally the country was a loose alliance of small sovereign units known as cantons. When a stronger central authority became desirable in the nineteenth century, not only were the customary civil rights of a democracy guaranteed, but governmental autonomy was retained by the cantons except for limited functions specifically assigned to the central government. Although the functions allotted the central government have tended to increase with the passing of time, each of the local units (now 25 in

longs to a different language family, is entirely distinct from the other languages of Northern Europe. Even in Finland, however, about 10 percent of the population is of Swedish descent and speaks Swedish as a native tongue. Swedish is recognized as a second official language in Finland.

Among these countries there are no exceptions to the cultural unity embodied in a common religion. The Evangelical Lutheran Church is the dominant religious organization in each country, with over 95 percent of the respective populations reportedly adhering to it. It is a state church, supported by taxes levied by the respective governments, and is probably the most all-embracing organization outside of the state.

The countries of Northern Europe also exhibit basic similarities with respect to law and political institutions. These countries have very old traditions of individual rights, broad political participation, limited governmental powers, and democratic control. Thus old foundations have been available for building modern democracies, and the countries of Northern Europe are recognized as outstanding strongholds of democratic institutions. Iceland claims to have the world's oldest legislature, founded in 930 A.D. Today Iceland is a republic, as is Finland, while the other three states are constitutional monarchies. In all these countries real power rests with an elected parliament. In the twentieth century the countries of Northern Europe have consciously and actively worked to increase their similarities respecting legal codes and political institutions by coordinating their laws wherever feasible.

One other similarity not yet mentioned is the small size of these countries, especially in population. Comparative figures on area, population, and population density for the five countries are given in Table 7.

### ▶ Disadvantages of an "In-Between" Position

Small populations and limited resources have forced the countries of Northern Europe to give up imperial ambitions during recent times, though their armies and fleets were the scourge of much of Europe in times past. A policy of neutrality plus a relatively isolated position in one corner of Europe allowed them a long period of peace between the Napoleonic Wars and World War II. In the twentieth century, however, the increasing strategic importance of North Atlantic air and sea routes has jeopardized their safety. In the present world situation, these countries occupy an "in-between" position. They lie on the most direct routes between the United States and the western coreland of the Soviet Union. The coast of Norway, which adjoins the Soviet Union in the far north, offers some of the world's best

TABLE 7

NORTHERN EUROPE: AREA AND POPULATION DATA

| COUNTRY | AREA (THOUSAND SQUARE MILES) | POPULATION (MILLIONS: 1959 ESTIMATES) | DENSITY (PER SQUARE MILE: TO NEAREST WHOLE NUMBER) |
|---|---|---|---|
| Denmark [a] | 16.6 | 4.55 | 274 |
| Norway [b] | 125.1 | 3.56 | 28 |
| Sweden | 173.6 | 7.45 | 43 |
| Finland | 130.1 | 4.41 | 34 |
| Iceland | 39.8 | 0.172 | 4 |
| Totals | 485.2 | 20.14 | 42 |

[a] Excluding the Faeroe Islands and Greenland.
[b] Excluding Svalbard and Jan Mayen.

and most strategically located naval harbors in the famous fjords. This coast is especially suitable as a base for submarine operations against North Atlantic shipping and was so used by the German navy in World War II. Denmark, Norway's neighbor to the south, lies across the outlet from the Baltic Sea, on which some of the main Soviet seaports and naval bases are located. Finland lies between the Soviet Union and the Scandinavian Peninsula, and Sweden, the largest and most powerful country of Northern Europe, lies in the midst of these various positions. The changed significance of their position has presented the countries of Northern Europe with a common problem of national security, evidenced by the fact that only Sweden escaped involvement in World War II. It has also focused on them an increased degree of world attention and concern.

### ▶ Social and Cultural Achievements

Small size and resource limitations have made it necessary for each of the countries of Northern Europe to build a highly specialized economy in attempting to attain a high standard of living. Success in such endeavors has been so marked that these countries are probably known as much for high living standards as for any other characteristic. In general they are in the front rank of European countries, along with the United Kingdom and Switzerland, in this regard, although Finland and Iceland fall somewhat short of the other countries of the group. Their high standards of health, education, security for the individual and creative achievement are evidenced by impressive health statistics, long life expectancy, almost nonexistent illiteracy, disproportionately great achievements in art and science, and the reputation, particularly in Sweden, of having "abolished poverty."

In their attack on economic problems the countries of Northern Europe have employed a moderate socialism, consciously seeking a "middle way" between uncontrolled capitalism and Communism. They have attempted to put a floor under the living standard of every member of the community, while closely limiting the accumulation of wealth. Great emphasis on conservation of resources, the exercise and general acceptance of economic control and initiative by the state, and often the development of resources cooperatively by the state and private enterprise are prominent features of economic life in these countries. At the same time private business and ownership are fostered by the state in many lines of activity, as is trade unionism.

Parallel with the development of this "middle way," the countries of Northern Europe have experienced the world's greatest development of the private cooperative type of economic enterprise, reaching into almost every phase of production, distribution, and consumption. Cooperatives are particularly widespread and important in two countries of the group, Finland and Denmark. They are present, however, in all five countries.

## DENMARK

Denmark has the somewhat paradoxical distinction of possessing the largest city in Northern Europe, and of being at the same time the most dependent on agriculture of any country in the region. The Danish capital of Copenhagen (1,293,000) has well over a fourth of Denmark's population in its metropolitan area. Denmark has a much greater density of population than the other countries of Northern Europe, a fact accounted for by the presence of Copenhagen, the greater productivity of Danish agriculture, and the lack of any sparsely populated zone of frontier settlement.

and the location is better for utilization of the hydroelectric power which is one of Norway's primary resources. Norway already uses more electricity per capita than any other nation in the world, with less than two fifths of its estimated potential hydropower developed. Along the southwest coast a considerable electrometallurgical and electrochemical industry has come into being. The raw materials are imported for the most part and products exported. Among the more important products are aluminum, copper, ferroalloys (mainly nickel), zinc, carbide, and nitrogenous fertilizers.

▶ *The Southeastern Core Region*

More than half of the population of Norway lives in the southeast, which centers on the capital, Oslo (565,000). This is the core region of modern Norway. Here, where valleys are wider and the land is less rugged, are found the most extensive agricultural lands and the largest forests in the country. Streams coming down from the mountains to the west and north furnish power for sawmilling, pulp and paper production, metallurgy, electrochemical industries, and industries which process imported materials, such as woolen and cotton yarns, for Norwegian consumption. Near the mouth of Oslo Fjord the towns of Tönsberg and Sandefjord are the home ports of the world's largest whaling fleet, which operates mainly in Antarctic waters. Oslo lies at the head of the fjord where several valleys converge. It is the principal seaport and industrial, commercial, and cultural center of Norway as well as its capital and largest city.

▶ *Resources and National Economy*

Norway's basic natural resources are land, water power, fish, and forests. Although a variety of metalliferous ores are present, they are mostly of such low metallic content that they cannot be worked economically under present conditions. Some iron, copper, and molybdenum, and considerable

quantities of titanium ore are mined. Kirkenes, in the far northeast, is the largest center of iron mining. Most of its product is exported in the form of concentrates, largely to West Germany or Great Britain, though some of it moves to Norway's iron and steel plant at Mo i Rana.

Despite the meager amount of land that is usable for farming, agriculture is a basic element in the Norwegian economy, employing almost a quarter of the labor force. Most agricultural land grows feedstuffs for livestock—primarily grass, hay, barley, and oats—or potatoes, used both for livestock feed and for human food. The country has a small net export of meat and dairy products, though sizable imports of grains (primarily wheat), fruits and vegetables, sugar, and coffee are necessary. Many Norwegians combine farming with part-time fishing or forestry. Norway ranks first in Europe as a fishing nation. In 1957 the country's total catch—comprised largely of cod and herring—was exceeded by only four nations— Japan, the United States, the Soviet Union, and China. The forests of Norway, mainly composed of coniferous trees, are much less extensive than those of Sweden or Finland. Nevertheless, pulp, paper, and lumber account for a fifth of all Norwegian exports.

Manufacturing employs a larger number of workers than any other occupation. It is based mainly on domestic resources of hydroelectric power, forests, and fish. Electrically processed metals and chemicals, pulp and paper, some lumber and other timber products, and fish in various forms make up the great bulk of Norway's exports. Industries besides those indicated (for example, textile industries) serve mainly the domestic market. However, the latter industries account for about 80 percent of the total employment in manufacturing.

International earnings from the products of export industries are supplemented by those of the world's third largest merchant marine. Norway's merchant fleet is exceeded in size only by the merchant shipping of the United States and the United Kingdom, and it is by far the largest in the world on a per capita basis. It is a tangible expression of the country's intimate relation with the sea and long and distinguished seafaring traditions.

## SWEDEN

Sweden is the largest in area and population and the most diversified of the countries of Northern Europe. In the northwest it shares the mountains of the Scandinavian Peninsula with Norway; in the south it has rolling, fertile farm lands like those of Denmark; in the central area of the great lakes another relatively extensive area of good farm land occurs. To the north, between the mountains and the shores of the Baltic Sea and Gulf of Bothnia, Sweden consists mainly of ice-scoured, forested uplands similar to those which constitute the greater part of Finland. A smaller area of the latter type occurs south of Lake Vätter (map, p. 164).

### ▶ Agriculture

Swedish agriculture normally supplies about 90 percent of the country's food requirements. In addition, it provides limited exports, mainly of dairy products. Since Sweden has other important sources of exports, its agriculture has not had to be as specialized as that of Denmark. A major emphasis on fodder crops and livestock, representing a good adaptation to the soil and climate, is accompanied by a considerable production of bread grains. Though most grain production is for the home market, some wheat is regularly exported. Fruits and coffee are the largest food imports. About 9 percent of the country's land area is cultivated, most of this land being found in the two most favorable areas, *Skåne,* and the central lowland or lakes district. Skåne is a regional name for the southernmost tip of Sweden, an area with a surface largely morainal, like that of the adjoining Danish islands. It has always been the most productive agricultural area in Sweden, with soils of above average fertility and the country's mildest climate.

Skåne is the most densely populated part of Sweden, having about 10 percent of the national population on about 2 percent of the total area. The main urban center of the region, Malmö (220,000), is the third largest city of Sweden. It lies slightly to the southeast of Copenhagen on the opposite shore of the Sound.

The Central Swedish Lowland, extending between the important port cities of Stockholm and Göteborg, ranks second to Skåne in agricultural importance. However, agriculture in the Central Lowland is now subordinate to manufacturing in terms of employment and value of product. The average elevation of this part of Sweden is several hundred feet lower than in the granitic uplands to the north and south, and a considerable amount of glacial and marine deposition has provided the basis for fairly fertile soils. Patches of farm land are scattered through a forested terrain with many lakes. Farming in this area is built around dairying and associated fodder crops, leaving most of Sweden's substantial wheat production for the better soils and milder climate of Skåne.

Some farming is found in other parts of Sweden, but it is severely restricted by bare rock surfaces, thin and infertile soils, and, in the north, by a harsher climate. In these areas agricultural settlement is scattered, and farming is often combined with seasonal work in other occupations, especially logging.

### ▶ Forest Industries

Practically the whole of Sweden is naturally forested, with spruce and other conifers predominating north of the Central Swedish Lowland and mixed conifers and broadleaved deciduous hardwoods in the southern part of the country. In the extreme north the forest cover becomes sparser and the trees stunted.

As a group, the wood products industries based on these forests are the most important in Sweden from the standpoint of employment, value of product, and value of exports. This group of industries includes sawmilling, pulp milling, papermaking, the manufacture of wood chemicals and synthetic fabrics, and the production of fabricated articles such as plywood, window and door frames, furniture, and prefabricated houses. Pulp, paper, and lumber account for most of the value of production. While logging and wood industries are characteristic of most of Sweden, the main concentration is found in areas to the north of the Central Lowland. In these areas other economic opportunities are less abundant, large quantities of good timber are available, and logs can be transported with relative ease in winter by sled, or floated to mills in summer on the numerous rivers. Most of the sawmills

and pulp mills are located in industrial villages and towns which dot the coast of the Gulf of Bothnia at the mouths of the rivers (photo, below). From these mills huge quantities of wood products are exported to other countries by ship during the summer months when the Gulf of Bothnia is free of ice. Power for the milling operations is supplied by numerous hydroelectric stations, and much electricity is transmitted by high tension systems to the central and southern parts of the country where growing demands cannot be met by streams which are now almost completely developed for power.

### ▶ Mining and Manufacturing

It is the mineral wealth of Sweden and associated high development of metallurgical and mechanical industries which most distinguish the Swedish economy from that of the other individual countries of Northern Europe. Sweden is abundantly supplied with high-grade iron ore and mines some nonfer-

A large Swedish sawmill on the Gulf of Bothnia at the mouth of a river used for transporting logs from the interior. Logs from the millpond move up inclined trackways into the mill, where large circular saws cut them into the proper lengths and reciprocating band saws process them into boards. Note at the upper right the piles of lumber for export. (K. W. Gullers Studio, Stockholm.)

A trainload of iron ore en route from the Kiruna mines of northern Sweden to the ice-free Norwegian shipping port of Narvik. Note the electrified railway. (Swedish State Railways.)

rous and alloy metals as well. However, the utility of these minerals is somewhat lessened by a shortage of coal, a deficiency shared with the other countries of the region. A few hundred thousand tons of low-grade coal are produced each year from mines in Skåne, but this production is far from sufficient for the country's needs.

The largest and best known deposits of iron ore are located in the far north beyond the Arctic Circle. Here at Kiruna and Gällivare entire mountains of ore are being mined with power shovels and dumped into railway cars for export (photo, above). The iron ore of northern Sweden has a high content of phosphorus impurities but is very rich in metallic iron. Most of the production is marketed in West Germany, Great Britain, and Belgium. An electrified rail line connects the ore fields with the port of Luleå (25,000) on the Gulf of Bothnia, through which ore shipments move from May until the first of December, and with the ice-free Norwegian port of Narvik, which ships ore the year round. Total yearly shipments through Narvik are normally more than twice as large as shipments through Luleå.

Sweden itself is an important steel producer, but more in terms of quality than quantity. Though the country's largest iron and steel plant is a government-operated unit at Luleå, the domestic industry is mainly centered in an ore-producing district located in the edge of the uplands to the north of the Central Lowland. In this district some of the world's finest steels are made. The ores from which they are produced are extremely high grade and relatively free of phosphorus. These ores are smelted with charcoal and the steels are made in electric furnaces. The process is not adapted to really large-scale production, but the quality of the product is so high that "Swedish steel" has become practically a synonym for fine steel. It should be noted, however, that more than three fourths of Sweden's steel output, including much of that from central Sweden, is of a more ordinary quality and is made of iron from coke-fired blast furnaces. The mining area of central Sweden produces high-grade phosphoric iron ore in much greater quantity than the nonphosphoric ore referred to above. The greater part of this phosphoric ore is for export, but a portion is utilized by Swedish iron and steel plants.

The Swedish steel industry's emphasis on skill and quality carries over into the finishing and fabricating industries which use the steel. Among Swedish specialties which have acquired a world-wide reputation are such items as cutlery, tools and machine tools, surgical instruments, antiaircraft artillery, ball bearings, home appliances, business machines, and electrical equipment. Emphasis on skill in design and execution is also basic to the success of some Swedish industries outside the metal-goods field. The most noted of these is the glass industry of Småland, the infertile and rather sparsely populated plateau south of the Central Lowland.

Swedish manufacturing is principally carried on in numerous small industrial centers in the Central Lowland. These places, ranging in size from about 90,000 to mere villages, have grown up in an area favorably located with regard to minerals, forests, water power, labor, food supplies, and trading possibilities. The Central Lowland has been the historic core of Sweden and has long maintained an important agricultural development and a relatively dense population. At opposite ends of the lowland are Sweden's two major ports and major cities, Stockholm, on the Baltic Sea, and Göteborg, on the Kattegat.

### ► Stockholm and Göteborg

Stockholm (1,021,000) is the second largest city in Northern Europe. The location of the capital reflects the role of the Central Lowland as the early core of the Swedish state and the early orientation of that state toward the Baltic and trans-Baltic lands. Stockholm is the principal administrative, financial, and cultural center of the country and shares in many of the manufacturing activities typical of the Central Lowland. It is the country's most important single industrial center.

In the past century as Sweden has come to do more and more trading via the North Sea, Stockholm has been displaced by Göteborg (458,000) as the chief port of the country. Besides its advantage of position, the latter city has a harbor which is ice free the year round, whereas icebreakers are needed to keep open the harbor of Stockholm in midwinter. Göteborg combines the handling of nearly half of Sweden's foreign trade by volume with numerous manufacturing activities, among them an important shipbuilding industry.

### ► The Swedish Policy of Neutrality and Preparedness

In the Middle Ages and early modern times Sweden was a powerful and imperialistic country. Finland was conquered in the twelfth and thirteenth centuries, and in the seventeenth century the Baltic became almost a Swedish lake. During the eighteenth century, however, the rising power of Russia and to some extent of Prussia put an end to Swedish imperialism, aside from a brief campaign in 1814 through which Sweden won control of Norway from Denmark. Since 1814 Sweden has never been engaged in a war, and it has become known as one of Europe's most successful neutrals. A century and a half of peace has undoubtedly been partially responsible for the country's success in attaining a high level of economic welfare and a reputation for social advancement. At present, however, Sweden is carrying a heavy burden of armaments. As the strongest military power in Northern Europe, Sweden represents an important obstacle to possible Soviet domination of the Baltic area. Although the country escaped involvement in World War II, successful neutrality in another general war seems less likely. The dangers inherent in the international situation have led the Swedish government to build up strong armed forces while maintaining, at least formally, the nation's traditional policy of neutrality.

## FINLAND

Conquered and Christianized by the Swedes in the twelfth and thirteenth centuries, Finland was ceded in 1809 by Sweden to Russia, and it was controlled by the latter nation until 1917. Under both the Swedes and the Russians the country's status was that of a semiautonomous grand duchy, and its people developed their own culture and feelings of nationality to such an extent that the opportunity for independence provided by the collapse of Tsarist Russia toward the end of World War I was eagerly seized.

### ▶ Importance of Forestry and Livestock

Most of Finland is a sparsely populated, glaciated, subarctic wilderness of coniferous forest, ancient igneous and metamorphic rocks, and thousands upon thousands of lakes. Finland is primarily an agricultural country, and the majority of the population is concentrated in relatively fertile and warmer lowland districts scattered through the southern half of the country. Hay, oats, and barley are the main crops of an agriculture which is predominantly directed toward livestock production, especially dairying. Food crops—principally wheat, potatoes, and rye—occupy much smaller acreages. A pattern similar to that of Norway and Sweden results, with small surpluses of dairy products and heavy imports of other foods —although neither Norway nor Finland can duplicate Sweden's wheat exports. Coffee, wheat, sugar, fruits, and vegetable oils and fats are the major food items on Finland's import list.

To pay for food and many other imports, the nation depends primarily on exports of forest products. Almost three quarters of the country is forested, mainly in pine or spruce mixed with birch, and ordinarily over 75 percent of its total exports consist of lumber, wood pulp, paper, and other timber products of a type largely duplicating the forest exports of Sweden. Forest production is especially concentrated in the south central part of the country, often referred to as the Lake Plateau (map, p. 164). A poor and rocky soil discourages agriculture here, but the timber is of good quality and a multitude of lakes, connected by streams in interlocking systems, provide ready transportation for the logs.

### ▶ Problems of a Buffer State

For centuries Finland has been a buffer between Russia and Scandinavia. Since 1939 its position has been especially difficult. In that year, shortly after the outbreak of World War II, Finland refused to accede to Soviet demands for the cession of certain strategic frontier areas and, despite a valiant resistance, was overwhelmed by the Soviet Union in the "Winter War" of 1939–1940. Then, in an attempt to regain what had been lost, Finland fought with Germany against the Soviet Union from 1941 to 1944, and again was defeated as German power waned.

The peace settlement following the war left Finland still in existence as an independent country, although shorn of considerable areas in the east and north which were annexed by the USSR (map, p. 164). In the southeast the Karelian Isthmus between the Gulf of Finland and Lake Ladoga passed into Soviet control, and with it went the city of Viipuri, now Vyborg, which had been Finland's main timber port. More territory was lost along the central part of the eastern frontier, and in the north the area around the small port of Petsamo, now Pechenga, was ceded. The latter cession cut Finland off from access to the Arctic Ocean, and gave the Soviet Union rich nickel mines and smelting facilities, as well as a land frontier with Norway. The USSR also occupied the small Porkkala peninsula on the south coast of Finland, and established a military base there within easy artillery range of Helsinki. The peninsula was eventually evacuated and returned to Finnish control in 1955.

Besides territorial concessions the Soviet Union demanded large reparations payments, and it has insisted that Finland exhibit a reasonably friendly and cooperative attitude toward the USSR. In view of these events and circumstances, plus the steady growth of her huge neighbor's power, Finland has felt compelled to follow a very careful line of neutrality with respect to big-power quarrels. At the same time, however, the Finns have increasingly participated in inter-Scandinavian cooperation, both as a matter of practical interest and as an expression of their basically Western preference and orientation.

Following the war the economy of Finland was heavily burdened by (1) the necessity for rebuilding the northern third of the country, which was devastated by retreating German soldiers after Finland surrendered to Russia, (2) the necessity for resettling a tenth of the total population of the country after they fled as refugees from the areas ceded to Russia, (3) the loss of the ceded areas themselves, some portions of which were of disproportionate importance in the prewar economy of the country, and (4) the necessity for making large reparations payments to the Soviet Union. In spite of these various difficulties, however, the hard-working and thrifty Finns have made a rapid recovery from the war period. In the course of this recovery the economy of the country has been drastically changed in some respects. One of the most striking changes has been the rise of metalworking as the most important branch of industry, at least in terms of employment. This was made necessary by the fact that the Soviet Union required a large part of the reparations to be paid in metal goods. Several small steel plants and other metalworking

establishments were built to meet this demand. Despite the fact that Finland is deficient in high-grade metallic ores with the exception of copper, and also is deficient in coal, these plants have continued in operation after the end of reparations payments, serving mainly the domestic market.

### ▶ The Major Cities

The most important industrial center of the country, as well as its capital, largest city, main seaport, and principal commercial and cultural center, is Helsinki (514,000), located about in the center of the southern coast. This city has diversified food-processing, shipbuilding, mechanical, chemical, and other industries. Smaller industrial centers include Finland's second and third cities in population, Tampere (144,000), located in the southwestern interior, and, farther south, the port of Turku (127,000) at the southwestern corner of the country. Each is especially important for textile production. The industries of all these cities depend heavily on hydroelectricity, the main source of power in Finland, as in all the other countries of Northern Europe except Denmark.

Few countries today occupy a more precarious strategic position than Finland. The Finns struggle to get along as best they can with their powerful neighbor to the east, meanwhile striving to maintain democratic institutions and hoping that nothing causes the Soviet Union to move militarily toward Scandinavia or to regard Finnish independence as a threat.

## ICELAND

Iceland is a fairly large, mountainous island in the Atlantic Ocean just south of the Arctic Circle. Its rugged surface shows the effects of intense glaciation and vulcanism. Some upland glaciers and many active volcanoes and hot springs remain. The vegetation consists mostly of tundra, with considerable grass in some coastal areas and valleys.

Trees are few, being discouraged by summer temperatures averaging in the low fifties or below as well as by the prevalence of strong winds. The cool summers are also a great handicap to agriculture. Mineral resources are almost nonexistent.

Despite the deficiencies of its environment, however, Iceland has been continuously inhabited at least since the ninth century, and is now the home of a progressive and democratic republic which had an estimated population of 172,000 in 1959. Practically all of the population lives in coastal settlements, with the largest concentration in the vicinity of the capital, Reykjavik, which itself has about 67,000 people. Due to the proximity of the relatively warm North Atlantic Drift, the coasts of Iceland, and especially the southern coast where Reykjavik is located, have winter temperatures which are unusually mild for the latitude. Reykjavik has an average January temperature that is only 2° lower than the January average for New York City.

Agriculture and fishing are the main occupations of Iceland. Agriculture is centered around the raising of cattle and sheep. Farm land is used for hay and pasture, and a limited production of potatoes and hardy vegetables. Although some agricultural products are exported, the real backbone of the economy is fishing. Fish products supply about nine tenths of all exports by value, and thus pay for the many kinds of goods which must be imported. Manufacturing is confined mainly to food processing. It has been encouraged somewhat in recent years by the development of a small part of the island's considerable potential of hydroelectric power.

For centuries before 1918 Iceland was a colony of Denmark. In the latter year it became an independent country under the same king as Denmark, and in 1944 declared itself a republic. It has attracted much notice since the beginning of World War II because of its strategic position along major sea and air routes across the North Atlantic. The island was used by British and American forces as an air and sea base during the war. As a member of the North Atlantic Treaty Organization, Iceland at present is host to a small American military contingent which maintains base facilities at the important Keflavik international airport, 20 miles from Reykjavik.

## GREENLAND, THE FAEROES, AND SVALBARD

Two of the countries of Northern Europe, Denmark and Norway, possess outlying islands of some significance. Denmark holds Greenland, the world's largest island, off the coast of North America, and the Faeroe Islands between Norway and Iceland. Both of these areas are now considered integral parts of Denmark, and their peoples have equal political rights with other Danish citizens. Although the area of Greenland, approximately 840,000 square miles, is nearly a fourth that of the United States, about 85 percent is covered by an ice cap, and the population, mainly distributed along the west coast, amounts to only about 28,000 persons. The latter figure does not include American forces stationed at the large air base maintained at Thule in the extreme northwest of Greenland under the auspices of the North Atlantic Treaty Organization, to which Denmark belongs. Aside from approximately 2000 nonnative Danes and a small number of pure Eskimos in the remote northwest and other isolated places, the population of the island is of mixed Eskimo and Scandinavian descent. The principal means of livelihood are fishing, hunting, trapping, a limited amount of sheep grazing, and the mining of cryolite, a mineral used in the aluminum industry and certain other industries. A deposit at Ivigtut in southwestern Greenland has been quarried for more than a century and represents the only large commercial deposit in the world. Some of the world's cryolite is made artificially, however.

The Faeroes are a group of treeless islands where 34,000 people of Norwegian descent make a living by fishing and grazing sheep. They enjoy considerable autonomy under the Danish government.

Norway controls the island group of Svalbard, which is located in the Arctic Ocean and commonly known as Spitsbergen. Although largely covered by ice, the main island of West Spitsbergen contains the only substantial deposits of high-grade coal which are known to exist in Northern Europe. Mining operations are carried on by Norwegian and Soviet Russian companies, with the coal being shipped to Norway and the Soviet port of Murmansk. About 1500 Norwegians and 2700 Russians are employed in the mines. Norway also holds the volcanic island of Jan Mayen in the Arctic (see map and caption, p. 35), plus two small islands in the far South Atlantic, and claims a share of the Antarctic Continent.

# Countries of Southern Europe

On the south the continent of Europe is separated from Africa by the Mediterranean Sea, into which three large peninsulas extend (map, right). To the west, south of the Pyrenees Mountains, is the Iberian Peninsula, unequally divided between two countries, Spain and Portugal. In the center, south of the Alps, is the Italian Peninsula and its southern offshoot, the island of Sicily. To the east, between the Adriatic and Black seas, is the Balkan Peninsula, from which the Greek subpeninsula extends still farther south between the Ionian and Aegean seas. The countries which occupy the two western peninsulas and the Greek subpeninsula

—Portugal, Spain, Italy, and Greece—may be conveniently grouped as the countries of Southern Europe. Three of the four countries include islands in the Mediterranean, the largest of which are Sicily and Sardinia, held by Italy; Crete, held by Greece; and the Balearic Islands, held by Spain. These islands are governed as integral parts of their respective countries. Some Mediterranean islands are held by other countries, the most notable being Corsica, administered as a department of France; Cyprus, which is an independent republic; and Malta, which is a possession of the United Kingdom. Gibraltar, though not an island,

Ruined temples and a Roman road at Paestum bespeak the antiquity of civilization in Southern Europe and the ancient power of Rome. (Italian State Tourist Office.)

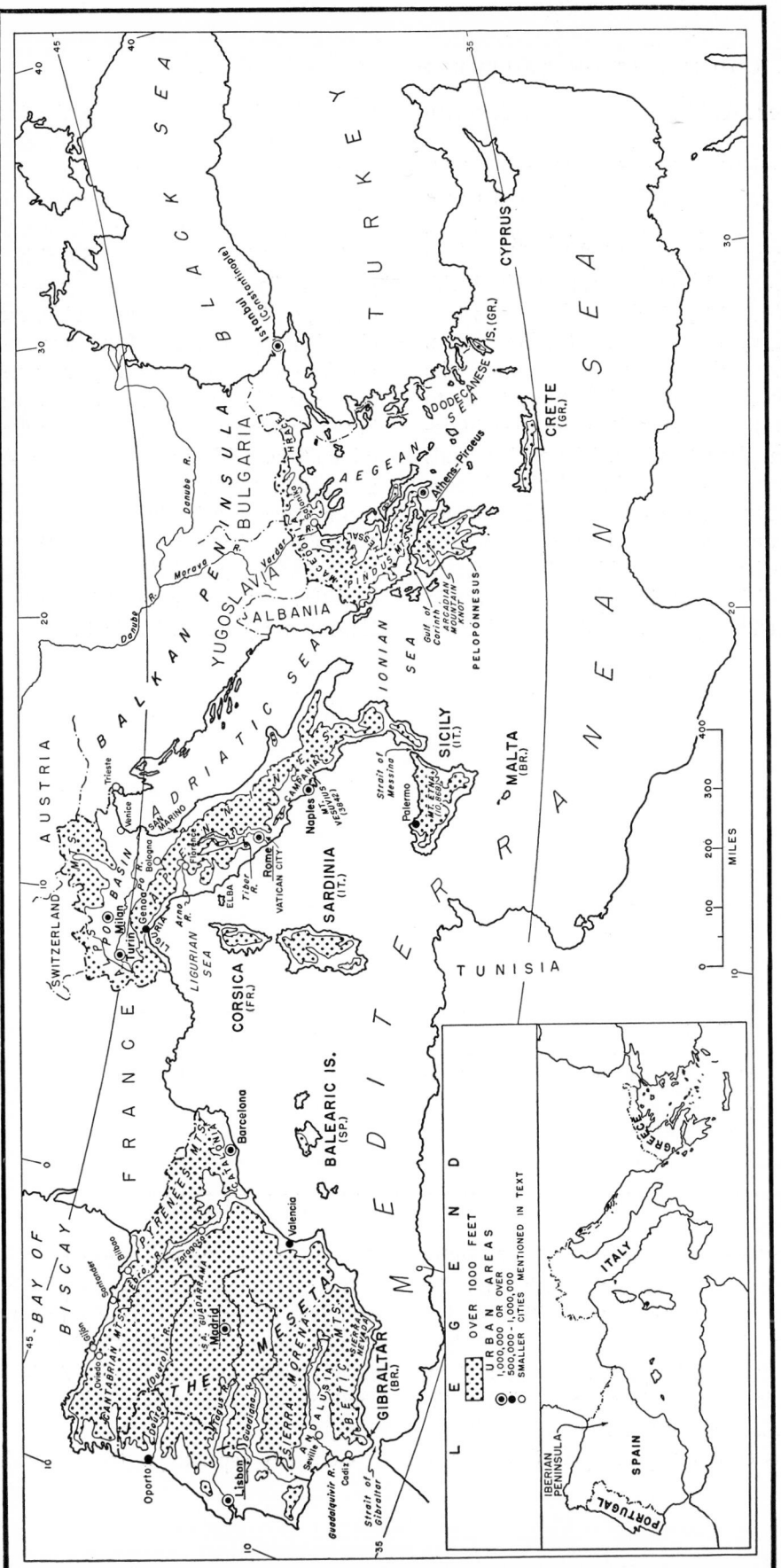

Index map of Southern Europe. Political capitals are underlined. City-size symbols are based on metropolitan-area estimates.

is a second British possession in Southern Europe.

The countries of Southern Europe exhibit many natural and cultural similarities as a group. Most of their natural characteristics, however, while tending to differentiate them from other parts of Europe, are shared with lands of northern Africa and southwestern Asia which front on the Mediterranean. Throughout the Mediterranean area the broad pattern of natural features tends to be much the same, despite differences in detail from place to place. There also tends to be a broad similarity in agricultural practices. However, the countries of Southern Europe are distinguished as a group from their Mediterranean neighbors by important cultural differences, including differences in religion and language. Most of the African and Asian lands fronting on the Mediterranean are predominantly Moslem in religion, whereas Roman Catholicism is the prevailing religious faith in Spain, Portugal, and Italy, and the Orthodox Eastern Church is dominant in Greece. The Spanish, Portuguese, Italian, and Greek languages are, of course, quite distinct from Arabic, the principal language in most of the non-European Mediterranean countries. Moreover, the countries of Southern Europe have shared in the development of Western or Occidental culture, whereas most of the African and Asian countries of the Mediterranean realm have principally been influenced by the culture of Islam (see pp. 291–293).

The areas, populations, and population densities of the four countries of Southern Europe are given in Table 8.

## TABLE 8
### SOUTHERN EUROPE: AREA AND POPULATION DATA

| COUNTRY | AREA (THOUSAND SQUARE MILES) | POPULATION (MILLIONS: 1959 ESTIMATES) | DENSITY (PER SQUARE MILE: TO NEAREST WHOLE NUMBER) |
|---|---|---|---|
| Italy | 116.3 | 49.06 | 422 |
| Spain [a] | 194.4 | 29.89 | 154 |
| Portugal [a] | 35.6 | 9.05 | 254 |
| Greece | 51.2 | 8.26 | 161 |
| Totals | 397.5 | 96.27 [b] | 242 |

[a] Figures for Spain include the Balearic and Canary Islands. Figures for Portugal include the Azores and the Madeira Islands. The island groups named are governed as integral parts of Spain and Portugal, respectively.
[b] Apparent discrepancy due to rounding of figures.

## THE DISTINCTIVE MEDITERRANEAN CLIMATE

A distinctive natural characteristic of Southern Europe is its climate, which typically combines mild, rainy winters with hot, dry summers. The Mediterranean area has given its name to this particular combination of climatic qualities. In systems of climatic classification a "mediterranean" type of climate is customarily recognized, although the designation "dry-summer subtropical," also in common use, is perhaps more descriptive. Other areas having this type of climate occur in southern California, central Chile, southwestern South Africa, and southern Australia (see end-paper climatic map).

Generally speaking, the countries of

Southern Europe experience temperatures averaging 40° to 50°F in the coldest month and 70° to 80°F in the warmest month. The total precipitation received during a year varies considerably from place to place, in response to differences in elevation and exposure to rain-bearing winds. The general average is between 15 and 35 inches per year, with most places falling in the lower half of this range. But regardless of total precipitation, most areas experience the characteristic seasonal regime of relatively moist winters and dry summers.

In Southern Europe the characteristics associated with the mediterranean climate become increasingly pronounced toward the south. The northern extremities of both Spain and Italy have atypical climatic characteristics. Except for a strip along the Mediterranean, northern Spain has a marine climate like that of northwestern Europe (see end-paper climatic map), cooler and wetter in summer than the typically mediterranean areas, while the basin of the Po River in northern Italy is distinguished by cold-month temperatures in the lowlands averaging just above freezing and a relatively wet summer. Much of the high interior plateau of Spain, the Meseta, cut off from rain-bearing winds by fringing mountains, has somewhat less precipitation and colder winters than is typical of the mediterranean climate, although the seasonal regime of precipitation is characteristically mediterranean. Table 9 illustrates some of the climatic characteristics of Southern Europe.

## TABLE 9
### CLIMATIC DATA FOR SELECTED SOUTHERN EUROPEAN STATIONS

| CLIMATIC TYPE OR AREA AND STATION | JANUARY AVERAGE TEMPERATURE (DEGREES F) | JULY AVERAGE TEMPERATURE (DEGREES F) | AVERAGE ANNUAL PRECIPITATION (INCHES) | AVERAGE PRECIPITATION JUNE–AUGUST (INCHES) |
|---|---|---|---|---|
| Typically mediterranean | | | | |
| Athens | 48° | 80° | 15.6″ | 1.3″ |
| Rome | 45° | 76° | 32.6″ | 3.2″ |
| Palermo | 50° | 76° | 25.3″ | 1.2″ |
| Valencia | 50° | 75° | 19.1″ | 1.6″ |
| Seville | 50° | 82° | 19.5″ | 0.6″ |
| Lisbon | 51° | 70° | 27.1″ | 1.1″ |
| Spanish Meseta | | | | |
| Madrid | 41° | 78° | 16.5″ | 2.1″ |
| Po Basin | | | | |
| Turin | 33° | 73° | 35.5″ | 9.3″ |
| Northern Spain (marine west coast climate) | | | | |
| Oviedo | 44° | 64° | 36.8″ | 6.3″ |

# MEDITERRANEAN AGRICULTURE

In the areas of mediterranean climate frosts are rare, the summers are hot and sunny, and thus the temperature regime is, in general, excellent for agriculture. But total precipitation is generally low, and a summer drought must be faced each year. Thus water is a critical factor. Where irrigation water is available during the summer months, a notable variety of crops can be produced. But in areas which are not irrigated—and they comprise the great majority—inadequate amounts or seasonal deficiencies of moisture limit the range of agricultural possibilities.

### ▶ The Basic Pattern of Agriculture

Agriculture in the Mediterranean Basin is principally based on crops that are naturally adapted to the prevailing climatic regime of winter rainfall and summer drought. Winter wheat is the single most important crop. It occupies more land in each of the Southern European countries than any other crop. Barley, a less prized but more adaptable grain, tends to supplant wheat in some particularly dry or infertile areas, such as the southern part of the interior plateau of Spain. Other typical crops are olives, grapes, and vegetables. The olive tree and the grapevine have extensive root systems and certain other adaptations which allow them to survive the summer droughts, and they yield for many years. Olive oil is the main source of fat in the typical Mediterranean diet, and virtually all of the world supply is produced in countries that touch or lie near the Mediterranean Sea. Spain, Italy, Greece, and Portugal, in that order, are the world's four largest producers of olive oil, normally accounting for four fifths or more of the world total. The principal use of grapes is for wine, a standard household beverage in Southern Europe. The countries surrounding the Mediterranean Sea, including Portugal, produce more than three fourths of the world's wine. Italy and France are the leaders by a wide margin, but Spain, Algeria, Portugal, Yugoslavia, Greece, Morocco, and Tunisia are significant producers. Where irrigation water is lacking, types of vegetables are grown which will mature during the wetter winter season or in the spring. Most important among the vegetables are several kinds of bean. These are a source of protein in an area where meat animals make only a limited contribution to the food supply. Feedstuffs are not available in sufficient quantities to fatten large numbers of animals, and parched summer pastures further inhibit the development of an adequate meat supply. Extensive areas which are too rough for cultivation are used for grazing, but their carrying capacity is generally low. Sheep and goats, which can survive on a sparser pasturage than cattle, are the favored animals. They are kept only partially for meat, and the total amount they supply is relatively small. In many places grazing depends on a system of transhumance utilizing lowland pastures during the wetter winter and mountain pastures during the summer. In some areas nonfood crops supplement the basic Mediterranean products. An example is the tobacco of Greece, which is grown on farms in most parts of the country and forms Greece's largest export.

Areas in which the supply of available moisture is either considerably above or considerably below average tend to diverge from the normal pattern of agriculture described above. The drier areas depend more on barley than wheat, and the very driest areas depend mainly on grazing of sheep and goats. Some wet and rough areas which have remained in forest are also grazed, particularly oak forests where pigs can feed on the fallen acorns or mast. The bark of one type of oak, the cork oak, supplies an important export for Portugal and a minor export for Spain. Portugal is the world's largest exporter of cork.

### ▶ The Intensive Agriculture of Irrigated Areas

Mediterranean agriculture comes to its peak of intensity and productivity in areas where the land is irrigated. In such areas relatively abundant and dependable supplies of moisture allow full exploitation of the subtropical temperatures, and the growing of a variety of fruits and vegetables, often with a large proportion destined for export, tends to supplement and sometimes to largely displace other types of production.

Although irrigation on a small scale is found in many parts of Southern Europe, a few irrigated areas stand out from the rest in size and importance. They are usually outstanding also for high population densities. Among these major areas of irrigation farming are northern Portugal; the Mediterranean and southwestern coasts of Spain, together with adjoining districts of Portugal; the northern coast of Sicily; the Italian coastal areas near the city of Naples; and the narrow Italian coastal plain fronting on the Ligurian Sea around the city of Genoa. The largest and most important irrigated area of all, the plain of the Po River in northern Italy, uses irrigation water to supplement year-round rainfall and is discussed separately.

In northern Portugal irrigation is used mainly to intensify a type of agriculture that does not differ radically from the normal Mediterranean type. In this area, however, irrigated corn replaces wheat as the major grain crop, and some cattle are raised on irrigated meadows. Grapes and sheep are the other agricultural mainstays.

In the coastal regions of Spain that front on the Mediterranean Sea, irrigation has made possible the development of extensive orchards. Oranges are the most important product, and Spain, though not the greatest producer, is the world's largest exporter of this fruit. The United States exceeds Spain about three or four to one as a producer of oranges, but Spain is the larger exporter, supplying from a fifth to nearly half of all world exports in recent years. The pre-eminent orange-growing district of Spain, around the city of Valencia, has given its name to a type of orange. Small acreages of irrigated rice in the coastal areas provide an important element in Spanish cookery and a minor export. Vegetables and in some places even tropical fruits like dates and bananas also are grown to supplement wheat, vines, and olives.

As an agricultural area, northern Sicily is mainly differentiated from ordinary Mediterranean areas by its concentration of irrigated citrus groves. Lemons are particularly important. Sicily is the largest producer of lemons in Europe and is second only to the United States in the world. The island normally produces around nine tenths of Italy's lemon crop and about three quarters of its oranges. Italy is the world's principal exporter of lemons and is one of the leading exporters of oranges.

The district around Naples, known as Campania, and the Ligurian Coast in the vicinity of Genoa are perhaps the most intensively developed and densely populated agricultural areas of Southern Europe. Vegetables and temperate fruits, especially peaches, supplement the olive and the vine in Liguria, while to vegetables, olives, and grapes Campania adds citrus fruits, tobacco, and hemp.

### ▶ Agriculture in Areas with Summer Rainfall

In the northern parts of the countries of Southern Europe sizable areas are found which do not have truly mediterranean climates, and these areas exhibit corresponding differences in agriculture. In northern Spain wheat becomes subordinate to corn and rye, and the summer rainfall permits a greater development of cattle raising than is customary in Southern Europe. Another large area that diverges from the normal pattern of climate and agriculture is the Po Basin in northern Italy. This area is of outstanding importance in Italian agriculture. A considerable amount of rain falls during the summer months on the level plain of the Po River, and the surrounding mountains provide superior water supplies for irrigation. In this area corn, grown both in irrigated and unirrigated fields, and irrigated rice become important cereal crops along with wheat. Vineyards are supplemented by orchards of peaches and other temperate fruits. In addition, the plain of the Po is the center of Italian production for such industrial crops as sugar beets and hemp, and for cattle, nourished on fodder crops and irrigated meadows. Crop yields and the general welfare of the peasants stand at considerably higher levels than in the more typically Mediterranean areas of central and southern Italy. The parts of northern Greece known as Macedonia and Thrace are distinguished agriculturally by a strong tendency to substitute cotton for grapes and olives to supplement grains and tobacco, which are the agricultural mainstays.

## RELIEF AND POPULATION DISTRIBUTION

In terrain and population distribution as well as in climate and agriculture the countries of Southern Europe present various points of similarity. Rugged terrain predominates in all four countries, and lowland plains occupy a relatively small part of the total land area. Individual plains tend to be small and to face the sea. They are separated from each other by the sea and by mountainous territory.

Population distribution corresponds in a general way with topography, with the lowland plains being densely populated and the mountainous areas much less so, although a number of comparatively rough areas attain surprisingly high densities. Thus on the whole the picture of population distribution is one of relatively isolated areas of dense population facing the sea and separated from one another by large areas of comparatively low population density.

In the Iberian Peninsula the greater part of the land consists of a plateau, the Meseta (photo, right), with a surface lying at a general elevation of between 2000 and 3000 feet. The plateau surface is interrupted at intervals by deep river valleys and ranges of mountains rising above the general level (map, p. 48). Population density is restricted, mainly by lack of rainfall, to figures ranging generally between 25 and 100 per square mile. For the most part the edges of the plateau are steep and rugged. The Pyrenees and Cantabrian mountains border it on the north, and the Betic Mountains, culminating in the Sierra Nevada, on the southeast. Most of the population of Spain and Portugal is distributed peripherally on discontinuous coastal lowlands which ring the peninsula. In the part of southern Spain known as Andalusia, the depression followed by the Guadalquivir River extends the coastal plain inland for more than 100 miles. In southern and central Portugal, also, the coastal plains are broader than in other parts of Iberia.

In Italy the Alps and the Apennines are the principal mountain ranges. Northern Italy includes the greater part of the southern slopes of the Alps. The Apennines form the backbone of the peninsula, extending from their junction with the southwestern end of the Alps to the toe of the Italian boot, and appearing again across the Strait of Messina in Sicily. The Apennines vary considerably in height and appearance from place to place. East of Rome the mountains reach more then 9000 feet elevation. In Sicily, Mount Etna, a volcanic cone, reaches 10,868 feet. This is the highest elevation in the entire mountain chain. Other cones tower above the general summit level in various places. Near Naples, Mount Vesuvius, which rises to 3842 feet, is one of the world's most famous volcanoes. West of the Apennines, most of the land between Florence on the north and Naples on the south is occupied by a tangled mass of lower hills and mountains, often of volcanic origin. Both Sicily and Sardinia, the two largest Italian islands, are predominantly mountainous or hilly.

Parts of the Italian highlands have population densities of more than 200 per square mile. Yet even these areas are sparsely populated as compared with most Italian lowlands. The largest lowland, the Po Plain, contains about two fifths of the

Grain fields (mostly wheat) and olive groves on the rolling upland surface of the Meseta in southeastern Spain. This view was taken about 100 miles southwest of Valencia. (Andreas Grotewold.)

entire Italian population, with densities in rural areas that are often over 500 and sometimes over 1000 per square mile. Other lowland areas with extremely high population densities are the narrow Ligurian Coast centering on Genoa, the plain of the Arno River as far inland as Florence, the Campania around Naples, much of the eastern coastal plain of the peninsula, and the northern and eastern coastal areas of Sicily.

In Greece most of the peninsula north of the Gulf of Corinth is occupied by the Pindus Range and the ranges which branch from it. Extensions of these ranges form islands in the Ionian and Aegean seas. Greece south of the Gulf of Corinth, commonly known as the Peloponnesus, is composed mainly of the Arcadian mountain knot. Along the coasts of Greece many small lowlands face the sea between mountain spurs and contain the majority of the people. Probably the best known of these lowlands, though far from the largest, is the Attic Plain, still dominated as in ancient times by Athens and its seaport, the Piraeus. Larger lowlands are found in Thessaly and to the north in Macedonia and Thrace.

## HISTORICAL CONTRASTS IN WEALTH AND POWER

In each of the countries of Southern Europe present conditions of poverty and national weakness offer a striking contrast to a past period of wealth and power. In Greece this period of past glory is the most remote, centering in the fifth and fourth centuries B.C., when Greek city-states were spreading the seeds of Western civilization through the Mediterranean area. To some degree there was a rebirth of Greek power and influence in the Middle Ages, when Constantinople was the capital of a Byzantine Empire which was largely Greek in population and control.

Italy's main period of former eminence was, of course, the centuries when the Roman Empire embraced the whole Mediterranean Basin and lands beyond. During the later Middle Ages, some centuries after the final collapse of the Roman Empire in the fifth century A.D., many of the Italian cities became independent centers of trade, wealth, and power. Venice became the center of a maritime empire within the Mediterranean area, as did Genoa to a lesser extent. Such inland cities as Milan, Bologna, and Florence also prospered and grew powerful on the basis of their trade with Europe north of the Alps. The growth of a hostile Turkish Empire astride routes to the East, the unification of powerful states such as France and Spain, and the discovery of sea routes to the East which bypassed the Mediterranean were factors contributing to the end of this second period of Italian preeminence. Following its appearance in the nineteenth century, the modern unified state of Italy made an attempt to emulate ancient Rome. A colonial empire was gradually acquired which included Libya, the Dodecanese Islands, Eritrea, Italian Somaliland, and Ethiopia. All of these colonial territories were lost as a result of World War II. Italy has been the only nation of Southern Europe to attempt the role of a great power during modern times. The futility and unreality of this attempt became manifest with the country's military collapse during World War II.

The main period of Spanish power and influence began in the Middle Ages when Spain stood as the bulwark of Christian Europe against Moslem civilization and in a struggle lasting for centuries eventually expelled the Moors from Europe. It was in the same year that this expulsion was finally accomplished, 1492, that Christopher Columbus, an Italian navigator in the pay of the Spanish court, crossed the Atlantic and discovered the lands that were eventually to be called the Americas. For a century thereafter Spain stood at its greatest peak of power and prestige. It was the greatest power not only in Europe, but in the entire world, and built one of the largest empires ever known, in areas as diverse and widely separated as Italy, the Netherlands, North and South America, Africa, and the Philippine Islands. This empire shrank in size with the gradual decline in the relative power of Spain. Today it consists of a few minor possessions along the coasts of equatorial and northwestern Africa (map, p. 466). The Spanish-held Canary Islands, off Morocco, are governed as an integral part of Spain.

Portugal, also, played a part in expelling the Moors from Iberia, and took the lead in the fifteenth century in seeking a sea route around Africa to the Orient. The first Portuguese expedition to succeed in the voyage, headed by Vasco de Gama, returned from India in 1499. For the better part of a century thereafter Portugal dominated European trade with the East, and built an empire there and across the Atlantic in Brazil. However, commencing in the latter part of the sixteenth century there was a rapid decline in Portuguese fortunes. This was associated in part with the conquest of the small Portuguese homeland by Spain, which held it from 1580 to 1640. Under Spanish rule, Portugal's interests were often neglected or subordinated to those of Spain. Meanwhile other European powers, particularly the Netherlands, offered increasingly successful competition in trade and colonization. By 1640 many of Portugal's possessions had fallen to the Dutch and could not subsequently be regained. However, the Portuguese held Brazil until the nineteenth century, when it gained independence, and Portugal still has a fairly large colonial empire today, mainly in Africa and its offshore Atlantic islands, but also including some minor possessions in Asia and the East Indies (maps, pp. 466 and 334). The Azores and Madeira Islands, lying, respectively, to the west and southwest of Portugal (map, p. 466), are administered with the home country.

Today the nations of Southern Europe have fallen far behind those of northwestern Europe in wealth and power. Greece is perhaps the most poverty-stricken country in Europe, although technical and financial assistance by the United States has helped it to improve its status in recent years. The other countries of Southern Europe are, on the whole, somewhat better off, but nevertheless stand far below such countries as the United Kingdom, Sweden, or Belgium in per capita income and general level of living. In all of the Southern European countries widespread poverty has caused a considerable amount of social unrest. This unrest has been aggravated by the fact that these countries exhibit great internal contrasts in wealth, between regions as well as between social classes.

## INDUSTRY AND ITS PROBLEMS

Many of the difficulties of the countries of Southern Europe in modern times have been closely related to retarded industrial development. Three of these countries—Greece, Portugal, and Spain—have remained essentially agricultural, though Spain has a fair amount of industry in the extreme north. Even Italy, which is by far the most industrialized country of Southern Europe and the largest producer of manufactured goods, has large-scale industrial development only in the northern third of the country. In most parts of Southern Europe agriculture has remained the principal means of livelihood, and industry has not developed sufficiently to be of much help in modifying conditions of poverty associated with too great a dependence on insufficient agricultural resources.

▶ *Shortage of Industrial Resources*
With the exception of Spain, the countries of Southern Europe are severely handicapped in industrial development by a lack of natural resources. Perhaps the most serious deficiency is in mineral fuels. Both Italy and Portugal mine small quantities of coal, and Greece and Italy mine small amounts of lignite. But deposits and production are inadequate in all three countries, and each is a considerable importer of coal. Indeed Italy, the largest and most industrialized of the three, is one of the world's principal coal importers. The situation with regard to petroleum is even less satisfactory. Minor deposits and a small production in Italy account for practically all of Southern Europe's known petroleum resources.

One exception to the paucity of mineral fuels is the natural gas of northern Italy. The output from a series of new fields in the Po Valley has lessened the country's dependence on imported coal and has provided a basis for enlarged chemical manufacture. Italy's natural gas production and the modest output of her oil wells—primarily wells in Sicily developed since 1955—have considerably improved the country's situation with respect to mineral fuels. But they compensate in only a limited way for the lack of coal and truly large petroleum deposits.

Most of the other important industrial materials are either absent or insufficient in quantity. Small quantities of iron ore are mined in Italy, and very minor amounts in Greece and Portugal, but in none of the three are the reserves or production of much importance. (As will be noted, Spain is an exception with respect to minerals, having sizable deposits of both coal and iron ore, as well as other valuable minerals.) The dry climate plus centuries of deforestation have made supplies of wood inadequate. Many "forested" areas are covered only with scrub, a vegetation so typical as to have special names, such as *maquis* or *garrigue* in French and *macchia* in Italian. True forests are quite restricted in area and are especially characteristic of areas not typically mediterranean in climate, such as northwestern Spain and Alpine Italy. The textile industry, developed to some extent in all four countries, depends mainly on imported raw materials, though some cotton is grown in Spain, Greece, and Italy and a considerable production of wool is secured from the sizable areas devoted to sheep grazing in all of the Southern European countries.

The mineral resources which are present might be of much greater use were it not for the lack of some of the critical materials already mentioned. Small deposits of a great many metals and other minerals do exist, and some are even abundant enough to make the Southern European countries important world suppliers. Outstanding among these is mercury. Italy and Spain together normally account for one half to three fourths of the total world production of this mineral. Other important minerals which are mined in considerable quantities include lead, zinc, sulfur (partially from pyrites), and bauxite in Italy; sulfur (from pyrites), tin, and tungsten in Portugal; and bauxite in Greece. In addition, a substantial production of some lesser known but important industrial minerals such as fluorspar comes from Southern Europe, especially from Italy and Spain. But the foregoing materials offer only a limited industrial advantage to a country when that country is lacking in such fundamental resources as coal, oil, iron ore, and wood.

### ▶ The More Favorable Position of Spain

Spain presents a somewhat different picture with regard to industrial resources than the other Southern European countries, largely because it possesses substantial deposits of both coal and iron ore. These deposits are located in the Cantabrian Mountains near the Bay of Biscay. Both coal and iron ore are found in the vicinity of Oviedo (120,-000) and Gijón (118,000), while iron ore is found near Bilbao (405,000) and Santander (118,000). In addition, Spain has important deposits and a considerable production of lead and zinc, wolframite (the ore of the important alloy metal, tungsten), potash, salt, mercury, pyrites for sulfur, and a number of other minerals. Yet Spain, much better endowed with mineral resources than many highly industrialized and prosperous nations, has never developed an important metallurgical or metal-fabricating industry. All but a small fraction of the iron ore mined in Spain is exported, and a comparable situation prevails with respect to most of the other mineral resources. Many of the mines are owned by foreign companies which draw the profits from the operations out of Spain as well as the materials mined. Spain does have a small iron and steel industry in the north near its iron ore and coal deposits, and some attempt is being made to expand it. But the country's best iron-ore deposits are nearing exhaustion, and the industry will have to depend increasingly on lower-grade ores, which still exist in quantity, or on better ores in less accessible locations. It should also be noted that while Spanish coal reserves are sizable, only a limited proportion are suitable for coking. Despite these negative aspects, however, Spain clearly possesses sufficient mineral wealth to support a much greater development of metallurgy than she has at present.

In the centuries since the period of Spanish world power in the sixteenth century, the social and economic order in Spain has tended to stagnate. During these centuries an ironclad conservatism on the part of the ruling classes has fastened on the country a system of society which is almost feudal in many aspects and is certainly out of harmony with modern ideas and trends in the

Western world. Spain's failure to develop economically and socially from a quasi-feudal condition contrasting a wealthy and privileged aristocracy with a poverty-ridden and repressed populace led to a series of bloody revolutions in the twentieth century and finally to the savage civil war of 1936 to 1939. In this war the fascist victory stabilized a Spanish society of privilege and repression. Other European nations, especially in the south and east, have also been marked by a persistence of feudal conditions in modern times, coupled with a failure to take full advantage of their resources in developing modern economies. But Spain is an outstanding example of this situation.

### ▶ Transportation Difficulties

Besides lack of resources, other hindrances to industrial development in Southern Europe have been the poverty of home markets in the various countries and, except in the case of Italy, the lack of a modern, efficient transportation system. Inability of consumers, especially peasants, to buy adequate quantities of industrial consumer goods and thereby to support needed industrial development is part of a vicious circle which often characterizes countries that are primarily rural and underdeveloped or overpopulated. Industry needs prosperous consumers to buy its products, but for the rural consumer to be prosperous one of the things most needed is for industry to develop sufficiently to draw surplus population out of the countryside. Modern industry also requires efficient transportation for large quantities of bulky materials. The railway and highway systems of the Southern European countries, excepting those of Italy, are inadequate to meet this need. The mountainous nature of much of the terrain is a considerable handicap to rail and road building, and the lack of coal and petroleum tends to hinder transportation just as it does manufacturing. A peripheral distribution of population in the various countries helps to alleviate the situation somewhat by allowing

extensive use of coastal steamers to handle traffic between the various populated sections, but cannot compensate in more than a limited way for retarded and expensive land transportation.

Among the Southern European nations only Italy has a reasonably good system of highway and rail transport. The Italians have been renowned road builders since Roman times. Many modern highways follow Roman roads laid out two thousand years ago. The Italian railway system is extensively electrified, especially in the north. It benefits from the continuing importance of old routes through the Alpine passes as major connecting links between the Mediterranean Basin and Europe north of the Alps. Other factors which have helped to make possible the development of a modern rail network have been the availability of electric power from extensive hydroelectric developments in the Alps and northern Apennines and an adequate freight traffic provided by the industrialized sections of northern Italy.

### ▶ Industrial Importance of the Po Basin

Lack of coal and many other important materials has forced industry in Southern Europe to depend mainly on two resources: hydroelectric power and cheap labor recruited from a poverty-stricken rural population. In the areas that are characteristically mediterranean in climate, the development of hydroelectricity has been hindered by the seasonality of the rainfall. During the summer most of the streams in such areas dry up to a trickle (in some cases completely), or become intermittent stagnant pools along a stream bed which may hold a torrent in the winter. This condition creates a major handicap which can be overcome only by construction of large and expensive reservoirs to equalize the flow of water between seasons, or by provision of steam-generating plants powered by coal, oil, natural gas, or atomic energy to maintain the flow of electricity in summer. Construction of adequate reservoirs in the Mediterranean area would in some cases require the flooding of densely populated valleys in places already short of farm land. Such difficulties plus a lack of capital for the execution of large projects have severely retarded hydroelectric development in many parts of Southern Europe.

The best possibilities for the generation of hydroelectric power are found in the northern areas which are not typically mediterranean in climate. Northern Italy has the most favorable situation for hydroelectric development and is by far the largest producer. Around the edges of the Po Plain, the Alps, and, to a lesser degree, the Apennines offer many excellent sites for generating stations. The possibilities offered by these mountain areas have been exploited so well that Italy is now Europe's leading producer of hydroelectricity, and northern Italy has become not only the most important industrialized area in Southern Europe, but one of the major industrial regions of all Europe. Two of Italy's four largest cities, Milan (2,154,000) and Turin (1,028,000), are the main centers of this industrial area. But many lesser centers, of which the largest is Bologna (402,000), share in the production, as does the port of Genoa (766,000), which dominates the overseas trade of the area. Genoa is Italy's most important seaport, and it ranks with Marseilles as one of the two leading ports of the entire Mediterranean. One of the outstanding characteristics of its trade is the heavy inbound tonnage of bulky fuels, industrial materials, and foods for north Italian industrial areas, including Genoa itself.[1] Major items include oil, coal, metals (including scrap), chemicals (including fertilizers), iron ore, salt, cotton, wool, timber products, and foods, especially grains. Manufactured goods constitute most of the port's outbound tonnage.

Milan, the industrial capital of northern Italy, is Italy's largest city as well as its most important center of manufacturing, finance, business administration, and railway transportation. It is also an important cultural center. Milan lies between Genoa and important railway tunnels through the Alps which give access to Switzerland and the North Sea countries. The famous seaport of Venice (367,000), located on the Adriatic Sea at the eastern edge of the Po Plain, is less favorably situated and more poorly equipped than Genoa to serve the present-day industrial centers of northern Italy, and it is much less important as a port than Genoa. But Venice's trade is sufficiently large to place the city third among Italian ports in tonnage of goods handled, after Genoa and Naples.

In both employment and value of production, metal-using industries represent the leading type of manufacturing in the Po Basin. Among these, automotive industries rank first. Turin is the leading center of automobile manufacturing, though Milan and other places are important. The metal industries secure the major part of their material from Italy's steel industry, which is heavily concentrated in the northern part of the country. Numerous small plants are found in the Po Basin. Some of these produce both pig iron and steel, but most of them produce steel only. Recent development financed by the national government has emphasized construction of integrated iron and steel plants in coastal locations. The largest plant is located in a suburb of Genoa. Italy produces some iron ore, mainly from the island of Elba, but the production falls far short of the country's needs. Sizable imports of iron ore and of iron and steel scrap are required. Since World War II the steel industry has been greatly expanded, and Italy has become Europe's fourth largest steel producer, after West Germany, the

[1] Allan L. Rodgers, "The Port of Genova: External and Internal Relations." *Annals of the Association of American Geographers,* v. 48 (1958), pp. 319–351.

United Kingdom, and France. However, its total output of steel amounts to less than a quarter of West German production, and ranks Italy in a general class with Belgium, Poland, and Czechoslovakia among European producers. Domestic production is supplemented by a net import of iron and steel. On the whole, steel has been a relatively scarce and expensive material in Italy, and this fact has encouraged the metal-using industries of the Po Basin to specialize in comparatively complex and expensive products which make full use of the region's abundant resources of cheap skilled labor, while at the same time minimizing the amount of metal required in proportion to the value of the finished product. The automobile industry, for example, tends somewhat toward the production of either expensive luxury or very light models. Typical products of other metal-using industries are typewriters, office machinery, and sewing machines. Textile industries experienced large-scale development earlier than metal industries in the Po Basin and are still nearly as important. Cotton, woolen, and artificial fiber industries account for most of the employment and production, but silk, linen, and hemp industries are of some importance.

Heavy dependence on imported raw materials and foreign markets, and an approaching saturation point in hydroelectric development, place obstacles in the path of further industrial expansion in northern Italy. An additional circumstance which would seem a barrier to further industrialization through exploitation of labor is the strength of the Communist party in the area. The Italian Communist party is the largest in free Europe, and its main centers of influence are in the northern industrial cities, although it has made some progress among the impoverished peasants of southern Italy. In northern Italy the party has profited from discontent among industrial workers growing out of the situation with regard to wages and employment. Although this part of Italy is in general much more prosperous than most parts of Southern Europe, the wages paid to workers have been comparatively low. Even so, the area has generally suffered from chronic unemployment in recent years.

### ▶ Industry in Northeastern Spain

The second most important seat of industry in Southern Europe is found in the northeastern corner of Spain. The city of Barcelona (1,655,000), second largest in Spain, forms, together with its environs, the major Spanish industrial district. In certain respects this district is quite similar to the Po Basin industrial area. Hydroelectric power is available in quantity, mainly from the Pyrenees; industrial labor is plentiful, sufficiently skilled, and cheap; and industrial raw materials are largely imported. Unlike the Po Basin, however, the Barcelona area is still primarily a textile producer, and it is not an important exporter of manufactured goods. Its products supply primarily the internal market of Spain and the Spanish colonial territories.

In both Spain and Italy there is a certain hostility to be observed between the industrialized and the rural sections. In Catalonia, the industrialized province of Spain in which Barcelona is located, this hostility has been reinforced by a jealous local patriotism and a distinct feeling of separateness from the rest of Spain. The Catalan language, spoken in the province, is distinct from Castilian Spanish, the major tongue of Spain. Other cultural, economic, and historical differences have helped to foster resentment against too close a control by the central government in Madrid, and repeated demands for a greater degree of local autonomy have occurred in the past. Since 1939, however, such aspirations have been rigidly suppressed by the fascist dictatorship, as have similar aspirations which exist with varying degrees of strength in certain other Spanish provinces.

## URBAN CENTERS OUTSIDE THE MAIN INDUSTRIAL AREAS

The Po Basin and Catalonia represent the only really important industrialized areas in Southern Europe. The general lack of industrial development is indicated by the character of large cities found outside these two areas. Most of these cities are either political capitals or ports serving especially productive agricultural areas, or both. They are, of course, not without industries appropriate to a port or to any large city, particularly one forming a reservoir of cheap labor, but their industrial functions are on the whole subordinate to government and trade.

The largest cities of Greece and Portugal, respectively, are their political capitals and main seaports, Athens (1,490,000, including the port of Piraeus) and Lisbon (1,130,-000). Madrid (1,840,000) is Spain's capital and largest city. In Italy, however, the capital city of Rome (1,959,000) has a slightly smaller metropolitan population than the Po Basin industrial city of Milan. Madrid and Rome are centrally located in their respective countries. Rome lies about halfway down the west coast of the Italian Peninsula, in a position to some extent intermediate between contrasting northern and southern sections of the country. The city profits in various ways from the fact that it is an important religious capital (the center of Roman Catholicism), as well as a political capital. Madrid was purposely chosen as the capital of Spain in the sixteenth century because of its location near the mathematical center of the Iberian Peninsula, approximately equidistant from the various peripheral areas of dense population. Located in a poor countryside, it has little economic excuse for existence, but its position as the capital has made it the center of the Spanish rail and road networks and thus has given it certain business advantages.

Most of the remaining large cities in Southern Europe are seaports. Salonika (305,000), in the north of Greece, is the second city of that country. It is the sea outlet for an important route through the mountains of southern Yugoslavia formed by the combined valleys of the Morava and Vardar rivers (map, p. 181). Naples (1,565,000) is the port for the Campania district and much of southern Italy, and is the third largest Italian city. Palermo (558,000) is the main city and port of Sicily. The largest inland city of Italy, apart from Rome and the industrial cities of Milan and Turin in the Po Basin, is Florence (493,000), at the head of the Arno Plain and at the southern end of an important route through the Apennines. It is a famous cultural as well as an industrial center. In Spain, the third city, after Madrid and Barcelona, is Valencia (640,000), the port for the main citrus-producing and exporting district. In Portugal, the only large city aside from Lisbon is Oporto (640,000), the principal port for the northern part of the country.

## AGRICULTURAL PROBLEMS OF SOUTHERN EUROPE

Retarded development of industry has thrown upon agriculture the burden of supporting the great majority of the people in Southern Europe. While agriculture has developed sufficiently to produce an export surplus of certain specialties, such as Greek tobacco, raisins, and cotton, Italian fruits and vegetables, Spanish oranges and olives, and Portuguese cork and wines, it has not supplied adequate quantities of cereals and animal products or a good living for most of the people engaged in agricultural occupations. An indication of the unsatisfactory agricultural situation lies in the fact that all of the Southern European countries must import some grain to supplement their home production. This is true despite the heavy emphasis on the production of grains in the agriculture of this region, and despite a low caloric intake per person as compared with northwestern Europe.

Until a few decades ago, the countries of Southern Europe were characterized by high rates of population increase. Rapid growth of population, coupled with retarded industrial development, required the absorption of an increasing number of people into agriculture. The result was an excessive subdivision of land, hence a decrease in the amount of land available for the support of each family. Today the rates of population growth in these countries are much lower than formerly, and the number of people supported by agriculture is declining in most areas. But the total farm population is still very large, and most farms are very small. In addition, they are often fragmented into numerous separate parcels, which may be miles apart. Such farms are difficult or impossible to operate efficiently.

Farms which are excessively small or fragmented may in themselves supply an adequate reason for rural poverty. This difficulty, however, has been augmented in Southern Europe by low crop yields, at least by European standards. For example, the Spanish farmer, on the average, gets only about half as much grain from each acre as does his neighbor in France, and less than a third as much as the Danish, Dutch, or Belgian farmer.

## ► Reasons for Low Agricultural Productivity

Many different factors underlie the generally low productivity of Southern European

A scene in the Mediterranean Basin. This villager on the island of Cyprus has collected a load of pine and cedar branches for household fuel. Securing an adequate supply of fuel is a constant problem in the deforested lands surrounding the Mediterranean. The widely spaced trees on the rocky hillside have extensive root systems and other special adaptations enabling them to survive the dry Mediterranean summers. (U. S. Department of Agriculture.)

farms. Pressure of population on the available land has led to the farming of some rather infertile areas, especially rugged areas where the growing of cultivated crops soon leads to soil erosion with consequent damage not only to hillside farms, but also to farms in the valley below. The lack of rainfall in summer, and sometimes in winter, is a hindrance. Some irrigated areas produce good yields, but only limited amounts of land have been or can be irrigated. In many areas a lack of adequate markets near at hand, or a lack of transportation giving access to distant markets, has prevented farmers from specializing in types of production that would bring higher returns and has obliged them to operate on a semisubsistence basis. Farmers in Southern Europe are ordinarily too poor to afford sufficient amounts of fertilizer, proper seeds, or satisfactory farm implements to make their fields productive. Comparatively few have access to adequate technical information on modern methods of farming, though such information is gradually spreading. The difficulty of accumulating a little capital, of getting ahead a little, is increased by the variability of the rainfall from year to year. Very often the earnings from sale of products in a year of adequate rain will be absorbed in the losses of a succeeding year of drought.

In recent years some agricultural gains have been made in Southern Europe. The amount of land under irrigation has been increased somewhat, especially in Greece and southern Italy. Average consumption of chemical fertilizers per acre has increased from 2½ to 6 times in the various countries of the region since the 1930s. Production of some export crops, notably irrigated cotton in Greece, has greatly expanded, and Greece has made considerable progress in raising crop yields on unirrigated land. But the generally depressed condition of agriculture in most parts of the region has not been affected in any fundamental way by these developments. On the whole Southern Europe remains far below northwestern Europe in agricultural productivity and prosperity.

### ► Problems of Landownership

In some areas of Southern Europe, rural poverty is partly the result of a system of landownership under which most of the land is held in large estates and the actual farmers are tenants or day laborers. Tenants on these estates are required to yield a considerable share of their meager produce to the landowner as rental for the land. Large estates are particularly characteristic of southern Italy and southern Spain. Estates in southern Italy may run to 30,000 acres, tenanted by as many or more people. Portions of such estates are often devoted to grazing or some type of commercial crop which is profitable to the landowner but is resented by the tenants, who would prefer to use the land for the production of food. Since World War II a number of peasant riots have occurred, resulting from the efforts of landowners to eject tenants from portions of large estates which they have simply occupied and begun to use without permission. Such happenings are a clear indication of intense land hunger among the peasants. The Italian government has indicated that it considers land reform in southern Italy to be of pressing importance for political stability in that area. Some progress has been made, but it has been slow because the government has also felt that it needed the support of the landowners. In Spain substantial reforms were instituted during a brief period of republican government in the early 1930s, but most of these were rescinded by the fascist regime which succeeded to power as a result of the civil war of 1936 to 1939.

### ► Rural Poverty—An Example from Macedonia

However, land tenure is not really at the root of Southern Europe's agricultural difficulties, though it is a contributing factor in some areas. This is clearly shown by the conditions of poverty which generally prevail even in those areas where the peasants customarily own their own land. Some idea of the situation and problems of the individual Southern European farmer, in this instance one almost certainly better off than the average, can be gained from the following selection: [2]

A farmer in Macedonia who had the reputation of being one of the most progressive in his village said when interviewed that he had not bought fertilizer for his fields, even though he knew very well that it would improve the harvest, simply because he could not afford the risk. In a good year, he calculated, fertilizer would pay off, for the increased yield meant more grain to sell and enough money to pay back the cost of the fertilizer. In a bad year, however, fertilizer would not make his fields produce enough grain for him to feed his family and at the same time pay the fertilizer debt. Consequently, rather than risk indebtedness, and be forced to sell some part of his small capital—half a dozen sheep, a pig, a donkey, and a mule—he preferred to do without the fertilizer, even though he knew that in the long run his fields would be impoverished and the task of feeding his family would become all the harder.

This man was both intelligent and hard-working. He had just returned to his little two-room house after cultivating his vines with a spade all day in the fields. He was dressed in carefully patched trousers and a tattered shirt, and on his feet he wore homemade moccasins. He owned about 15 acres of land, of which 5 were devoted to vines and fruit trees and the rest produced wheat and beans in alternate years. Each morning the village shepherd came and collected his six sheep and drove them out to the hill slope behind the village where they were pastured with the others from the community; in the evening they were returned to a fold made out of brushwood, where the farmer milked them. His donkey and mule were needed for plowing, and served the year round as beasts of burden. They were fed on straw from

the wheat through the winter, and picked up what they could along the paths and field margins of the village in summer. In all this, he was quite average.

He had four children, three sons and a daughter, between eleven and eighteen years of age. The problem which worried him most was not the hardship of day-to-day existence, real though it was, but rather the question of his children's future. With 15 acres to divide among four children, less than 4 acres could be given to each; and even though each child married someone who had an equivalent amount of land, there would be only 8 or 10 acres to support each of the new families. Life on his farm of 15 acres was a desperate struggle already; with less land, his children would face an impossible situation.

In this particular case, the peasant hoped to keep his farm intact for the eldest son. He was preparing to send his second son to the high school in Katerini, a town near by, where he could learn to be a clerk and with luck find a job. But the problem of supporting the boy away from home was serious, for he would have to buy both food and lodging. The farmer expected to sell his pig, although it was not full grown, in order to get the cash he needed to keep his son at school until the harvest, when, with a good season, he hoped to have a surplus of grain to sell for the same purpose. Looking ahead, he wondered how he would be able to manage when his eldest son was called up to serve in the army and his help on the farm would no longer be available. For the boy of eleven he had made no plans. The girl, he expected, would marry in the village.

Life for this peasant family was a grim and laborious business, a constant struggle to escape from sinking into still deeper poverty. With luck, good harvests and enormous hard work the farmer could hope to pass his farm down unimpaired to his eldest son, and open a way to a tolerable living for his other children. But he realized all too well that illness, bad weather, or accident could bring the whole structure of his plans and effort down in ruins and impose an apparently irremediable poverty on his children.

# THE STRATEGIC POSITION OF SOUTHERN EUROPE

The poverty and political impotence of the Southern European countries in modern

times have not made them politically unimportant. Rather, they have retained a con-

[2] Frank Smothers, William Hardy McNeill, and Elizabeth Darbishire McNeill, *Report on the Greeks*. New York: The Twentieth Century Fund,

Inc., 1948. Pp. 85–87. Used by permission of The Twentieth Century Fund, Inc.

siderable political significance deriving in part from a strategic position. The international political orientation of these countries has been a matter of grave concern to various outside nations, which have often vied with each other for power and influence in Southern Europe.

### ▶ Greece—A Mediterranean Gatekeeper

The international importance of modern Greece stems largely from the fact that the Greek peninsula lies between the Aegean Sea and the entrance to the Adriatic, and thus commands the routes of access to the Mediterranean from the Balkan Peninsula and Black Sea. In addition, the important route of sea trade running through the Mediterranean and Red seas can be effectively threatened from Greece. The strategic implications of its position has made Greece to some extent a pawn between land power and sea power in past times. Since its liberation from Turkey in the first half of the nineteenth century, Greece has customarily been under the influence and protection of Great Britain. As a major sea power vitally dependent on the Mediterranean–Red Sea route, the latter nation has naturally been anxious to keep strong land powers away from Mediterranean shores. Following World War II, Greece became the scene of a civil war between Communist and anti-Communist forces, and it seemed for a time that the country might be added to the list of Russian satellite nations. However, this threat was averted by assistance furnished the anti-Communist elements by the United States, taking over this responsibility from a weakened Britain. The position of Greece made such action feasible, since the country was easily accessible from the sea.

### ▶ The Italian Causeway to North Africa

Italy's position has made it a natural sea outlet for parts of central Europe, a potential threat to the security of the sea route through the Mediterranean, and a land bridge extending most of the way across the Mediterranean toward northern Africa. In World War II Italian participation on the side of Germany forced Britain to largely abandon the strategic Mediterranean–Red Sea route and to rely on the old pre-Suez route around Africa for traffic with areas surrounding the Indian Ocean. Separated from Africa only by the narrow stretch of water between Sicily and Tunisia, the Italian causeway also permitted German and Italian land forces to wage their African campaigns in relative security from Allied sea power.

The population of Italy, third largest in Europe, and the growing output of its industries add to the country's international importance. Several outside nations have been deeply involved or interested in Italian affairs during recent times. In the latter stages of World War II the country was the scene of a desperate and destructive struggle between Allied and German armies. Since the end of the war a struggle for influence in Italy has been carried on between the Soviet Union and the Western bloc of nations headed by the United States. This contest has been mainly fought in the arena of Italian internal politics, with Soviet influence being exerted through the powerful Italian Communist party and American support being given the anti-Communist elements of the country. Thus far the Communist party has failed to gain control, but the position of its opponents has seemed none too secure at times. Italy is closely linked with the Western nations in the North Atlantic Treaty Organization, the European Economic Community, and other international organizations of this type.

### ▶ The Spanish Base for Air Power

In Spain the civil war of 1936–1939 reflected the general tendency of internal political struggles in Southern Europe to be directly influenced by the action of outside powers. In this war the fascist or Insurgent faction eventually triumphed with the aid of an entire army provided by Fascist Italy and an air force and other special units largely provided by Nazi Germany. The losing republican or Loyalist side profited somewhat from aid by the Soviet Union, at that time a major antagonist of Germany and Italy on the European stage. In addition, a considerable number of volunteers from several nations fought in the Loyalist armies. The Insurgent victory was regarded as a considerable defeat for Britain and France, neither of which had intervened directly in the war, since it placed a hostile Spain on the flank of important British sea routes and left France almost surrounded by fascist countries. As it turned out, the new Spanish government refrained from entering World War II, though it maintained a generally hostile attitude toward the Allied nations.

Recently Spain has become more closely aligned with the Western nations, particularly the United States. In 1953 an agreement was signed to permit the establishment of American air and naval bases in Spain. The present Spanish government has been a bitter opponent of communism, and the country's position behind the Pyrenees, well removed from Soviet-held territory, provides some protection for bases. Thus strategic considerations have brought about an accord between Spain and the United States, despite strained official attitudes which have generally prevailed since the fascist victory in the Spanish Civil War. The principal American bases established in Spain thus far include three air bases near Madrid, Seville (430,000), and Zaragoza (279,-000), respectively, plus a supply base near Seville and a naval base near Cadiz (107,-000).

### ▶ The Smaller Strategic Significance of Portugal

Portugal has had a smaller degree of political and strategic significance during recent times than the other three nations of Southern Europe, and it has been less involved in international conflicts. The country's proximity to Atlantic sea routes passing near its coast has made it an object of British attention and support during most of its modern history, and the lack of any strong power in a position to challenge British influence has given Portugal a relatively peaceful existence.

Thus a common factor in the strategic geography of the Southern European nations has lain in their relation to the great sea route through the Mediterranean, or, in the case of Portugal, a position on the approaches to this route. The strategic importance of their position as viewed by outside powers has been manifest by a long history of outside interference in Southern European affairs. Great Britain, the leading sea power throughout most of modern history, has been especially active in this area. Concrete evidence of British interest and concern lies in the fact that Britain has retained political control over the colonies of Gibraltar and Malta, and continues to hold bases in its former colony of Cyprus.

# Countries of East Central Europe

The Soviet Union is bordered on the west by a belt of small nations extending from the Arctic Ocean to the Mediterranean Sea. In this book the part of the belt lying south of the Baltic Sea and north of Greece is referred to as East Central Europe. Seven different countries are included: Poland, Czechoslovakia, Hungary, Romania, Bulgaria, Albania, and Yugoslavia (map, p. 202). With an area of approximately 450,000 square miles, East Central Europe is a little smaller than the combined areas of Texas, California, and Maine. However, its population total is more impressive, amounting to an estimated 99 million people (1959) or well over half the population of the United States. The largest countries in area and population are Poland, Yugoslavia, and Romania; Czechoslovakia is intermediate in size; and Hungary, Bulgaria, and Albania are smaller. Areas, populations, and population densities of the various countries are given in Table 10.

In the period 1945–1948 these countries, and East Germany as well, fell under the control of the Soviet Union. Communist forms of political, economic, and social organization were instituted, and each country was brought within the economic and strategic orbit of the USSR. No country was

The Danube River at the Iron Gate. Boats are assisted upstream against the swift current by a railway on the bank. (Yugoslav Information Center.)

actually annexed, as the small Baltic republics of Estonia, Latvia, and Lithuania had been in 1940. But the Soviet Union, working through local Communist governments and using force or the threat of force where necessary, imposed a close supervision over each one. Thus was created a cordon of Communist satellite states in the border zone between the USSR and the non-Communist countries of western Europe.

In 1948 one of the satellites, Yugoslavia, successfully defied Soviet authority and has since pursued a separate course. It remains a Communist state, however, with many of the features and emphases generally associated with such states. Another satellite,

Poland, secured much freedom of action in 1956 after an uprising of factory workers in the city of Poznan (377,000). The incident symbolized the deep-seated resistance of the Polish people to tight Communist control and domination by the Soviet Union. Poland has remained within the Soviet sphere, but its relations with outside nations are broader, and its internal affairs are controlled less rigidly by its Communist government than is the case with its satellite neighbors. In 1956 an anti-Communist revolution in Hungary drew world-wide attention, but it was soon put down by the intervention of Soviet military forces.

### TABLE 10
### EAST CENTRAL EUROPE: AREA AND POPULATION DATA

| COUNTRY | AREA (THOUSAND SQUARE MILES) | POPULATION (MILLIONS: 1959 ESTIMATES) | DENSITY (PER SQUARE MILE: TO NEAREST WHOLE NUMBER) |
|---|---|---|---|
| Poland | 120.4 | 29.26 | 243 |
| Czechoslovakia | 49.4 | 13.56 | 275 |
| Hungary | 35.9 | 9.92 | 276 |
| Romania | 91.7 | 18.26 | 199 |
| Bulgaria | 42.7 | 7.79 | 182 |
| Albania | 11.1 | 1.56 | 140 |
| Totals,[a] Soviet satellites | 351.2 | 80.34 | 229 |
| Yugoslavia | 98.9 | 18.45 | 187 |
| Totals,[a] East Central Europe | 450.0 | 98.79 | 220 |

[a] Apparent discrepancies due to rounding of figures.

## POLITICAL INSTABILITY IN THE "SHATTER BELT"

East Central Europe is often spoken of as the "Shatter Belt," a term referring to the fragmented and unstable pattern of nationalities and political units which has characterized the region in past times. This pattern evolved from a complicated history of migrations, conquests, and reconquests involving many different peoples. In this region many empires have risen and dissolved, sometimes created by peoples within the

region, but more often imposed from without. The new Soviet empire is only the latest episode in a long history of control by outside powers. Over the centuries as the peoples of the region have quarreled and fought with each other and with intruders from outside, the political pattern has remained in a state of flux. Shifts in boundaries, revolts by subject peoples, and frequent reorganization of political units have evi-

Index map of East Central Europe. The "mountainous areas" are rather broadly generalized to bring out the major outlines of the topography. The Bakony Forest, separating the Great Hungarian and Little Hungarian Plains, and the narrow highland spur extending eastward from Slovenia in northern Yugoslavia are hilly rather than truly mountainous, and the same is true of certain other areas shown in the same pattern. Political capitals are underlined. See caption, page 91, for identification of cities shown by letter in the major industrial concentrations.

denced the political instability which has come to be recognized as an outstanding characteristic of this region.

### ► Origins of the Present Political Pattern

Several of the present countries in East Central Europe did not exist as separate political entities prior to World War I. At the end of the eighteenth century four large empires —the Turkish, Austro-Hungarian, Prussian (later German), and Russian—controlled most of the region. The present pattern of countries resulted from the disintegration of these empires in the nineteenth and early twentieth centuries. This process was hastened by World War I, in which Germany, Austria-Hungary, and Turkey were on the losing side. Russia, though on the side of the victors, withdrew from the war following the Bolshevik Revolution of 1917 and was not represented at the Paris Peace Conference of 1919. At this conference the political map of East Central Europe was rearranged to satisfy the aspirations of the various nationalities which had been included in the old empires.

Poland, which had been partitioned among Russia, Prussia, and Austria in the eighteenth century, was reconstituted as an independent country. Czechoslovakia, the homeland of two closely related Slavic peoples, the Czechs and Slovaks, was carved out of the Austro-Hungarian Empire as an entirely new country. Hungary, greatly reduced in size, was severed from Austria. The Kingdom of Serbia, which had won independence from Turkey in the nineteenth century, was joined with several districts taken from Austria-Hungary to form the new Kingdom of the Serbs, Croats, and Slovenes, later known as Yugoslavia. Romania, which had been independent of Turkish control since the mid-nineteenth century, was enlarged by territories taken from Austria-Hungary, Russia, and Bulgaria. Independence from Turkey had been achieved by Bulgaria in the second half of

the nineteenth century and by Albania immediately before the outbreak of World War I. The sovereignty of these nations was confirmed by the peace conference.

### ► Boundary Problems

The territorial settlement in East Central Europe following World War I left a number of important boundary issues unsolved. Such issues arose from the fact that several of the new states, as constituted by the Paris conference, included frontier areas that were claimed by neighboring countries on historical or ethnic grounds. At various times in past centuries a number of nationalities in East Central Europe had ruled over extensive territories outside the boundaries of their new political units. This became a basis for territorial claims on neighboring states. More important, however, were claims based on ethnic considerations. Due to intermixture of ethnic groups as well as to complex economic and strategic factors, the delimitation of political boundaries following the war left large ethnic minorities in Poland, Czechoslovakia, Yugoslavia, and Romania, and smaller but substantial minorities in Bulgaria and Hungary. Such groups, often localized in frontier zones, provided a basis for territorial demands by adjacent units regarding themselves as mother states for the minorities concerned.

Between World Wars I and II, boundary questions provided a fruitful source of bickering and dissension among the nations of East Central Europe, as well as between these nations and neighboring countries such as Germany, the Soviet Union, or Italy. Space will not permit a discussion of each individual dispute. A few of the more important disputed areas may be summarized as follows (map, left):

1. Transylvania, Bessarabia, and the southern Dobruja, acquired by Romania from Hungary, Russia, and Bulgaria, respectively, but still claimed by those nations.

2. Macedonia, divided between Yugoslavia and Greece, with parts of Yugoslav

Macedonia claimed by Bulgaria and Albania and Greek Macedonia claimed by Bulgaria and Yugoslavia.

3. The Banat, divided between Yugoslavia and Romania, with the Romanian Banat claimed by Hungary and the Yugoslav Banat claimed by Hungary and Romania.

4. Various border areas separating Yugoslavia from Italy and claimed by both nations.

5. Silesia, divided among Germany, Poland, and Czechoslovakia and subject to a complicated series of claims by them.

6. Portions of the Sudeten Mountains and Ore Mountains incorporated in Czechoslovakia but claimed by Germany.

7. The part of Poland known as the "Polish Corridor" and the Free City of Danzig, separating East Prussia from the remainder of Germany and claimed by Germany.

### ▶ Boundary Changes and Population Transfers since 1939

As a result of World War II, several shifts of territory occurred involving some of the disputed areas listed above. Romania was forced to cede Bessarabia and the northern part of adjoining Bukovina to the Soviet Union, and the southern Dobruja was returned to Bulgaria. The Soviet Union annexed a wide strip of territory in eastern Poland amounting to some 46 percent of the prewar area of that country. However, Poland was compensated for the loss when it took over large areas from Germany—areas included in the prewar German provinces of Pomerania and Silesia immediately east of the Oder and Neisse rivers and the southern half of East Prussia. Poland also took control of Danzig. The sum of these areas amounts to only half as much in square miles as the area taken by the Soviet Union from Poland. However, the industrial development, mineral wealth, and agricultural productivity of Poland's new territories (the "Recovered Territories" in Polish terminology) more than counterbalance her losses

to the USSR, at least in an economic sense. By far the most valuable area economically is the former German province of Silesia, with its coal and other mineral deposits, heavy industries, and fertile farm lands. The northern half of former East Prussia was taken over by the Soviet Union as a result of the war. Thus the Polish Corridor no longer exists, since Germany has lost the whole of East Prussia. Ruthenia, or Transcarpathian Ukraine, a mountainous, underdeveloped area at the extreme eastern end of prewar Czechoslovakia, was ceded by that country to the Soviet Union. A number of boundary changes benefiting Yugoslavia occurred along the Yugoslav-Italian frontier after the war. In 1947 the important seaport of Trieste (303,000), near the head of the Adriatic Sea, was included, together with adjoining areas, in the Free Territory of Trieste, under United Nations supervision. This enclave existed as a sore spot between Italy and Yugoslavia until 1954, when the two countries signed an agreement which placed the city of Trieste under Italian administration but made it a free port. Most of the remaining area comprising the Free Territory was transferred to Yugoslavia.

In addition to boundary adjustments, and often as a consequence of them, extensive population transfers have taken place in East Central Europe since the beginning of World War II. Such transfers, involving millions of people—Germans, Poles, Hungarians, Italians, and others—have notably simplified the ethnic pattern. Nearly a third of the prewar population of Poland and of Czechoslovakia was composed of minorities, but today these have largely disappeared. Ethnic minorities now comprise less than 2 percent of Poland's population and less than a tenth of Czechoslovakia's. The two countries have transferred most of their German population to Germany (p. 130), including nearly all of the Germans who lived in Poland's Recovered Territories. The Soviet Union has absorbed most of the Ukrainians and Belorussians (White Russians) of Poland and most of Czechoslovakia's Ruthenian minority, and Czechoslovakia has transferred part of its Hungarian minority to Hungary. The only countries in East Central Europe that still have truly large minorities are Yugoslavia (Albanians, Hungarians, Turks, Romanians, and others) and Romania (mostly Hungarians). Even in these countries, minorities comprise a smaller proportion of the population than before the war.

## DOMINANCE OF SLAVIC PEOPLES

The postwar expulsion of Germans from East Central Europe and the systematic extermination or flight of more than 3 million Jews during the period of Nazi control have intensified the Slavic character of the region. Slavic peoples are an overwhelming majority in every country except Hungary and Albania. The original homeland of these peoples is thought to have lain in the area between the Vistula and Dnieper rivers. In the early Middle Ages groups of Slavs began migrating into other parts of East Central Europe, as well as eastward into Russia. The Elbe River seems to have marked the limit of their penetration toward the west. Especially after 1100, an intermittent warfare was carried on between Slavs pushing westward and Germans moving in the opposite direction. Austria and Prussia originated as military "march states" on the German-Slav frontier. Persistent colonization by Germans in East Central Europe over a period of centuries resulted in the large German minorities found in several countries of this region prior to World War II.

### ▶ The Major Slavic Groups

The Slavic peoples are often grouped into three large divisions: (1) *East Slavs,* including Russians, Ukrainians, Belorussians (White Russians), and Ruthenians, (2) *West Slavs,* including Poles, Czechs, and Slovaks, and (3) *South Slavs,* including Serbs, Croats, and Slovenes. The Bulgarians and Macedonians are frequently included with the South Slavs, although each has been affected by important cultural influences other than Slavic. Another group, the Romanians, came under the influence of the later Roman Empire, and the Romanian language is often classed with the Romance languages derived from Latin. However, in most respects the Romanians have become Slavicized, especially in rural areas, and for practical purposes may be counted as a Slavic people.

Although the various Slavic peoples speak related languages, such languages are often not mutually intelligible. For example, the Polish language is not easily understood by a Czech, though Poles and Czechs are customarily grouped together as West Slavs. Other significant differences also exist. Although Serbian and Croatian, for example, are essentially one language in spoken form, the Serbs, like the Bulgarians and most of the East Slavs, use the Cyrillic alphabet, while the Croats use the Latin alphabet, as do the Slovenes and the West Slavs. A religious division exists between the West Slavs, Croats, and Slovenes, who are Roman Catholics for the most part, and the East Slavs, Romanians, Bulgarians, Serbs, and Macedonians, who adhere principally to various branches of the Orthodox Eastern Church.

### Non-Slavic Peoples

The principal non-Slavic population elements in East Central Europe, excluding the Romanians, are the Hungarians and the Albanians. The Hungarians, also known as Magyars, are the descendants of Asian nomads who settled in Hungary in the ninth century. They are distantly related to the

Finns and speak a language which is entirely distinct from the Slavic languages. Roman Catholicism has been the dominant religious faith in Hungary, though substantial Calvinist and Lutheran groups have long existed there. The Albanians speak an ancient Thraco-Illyrian language which is not related to the Slavic languages except in a very distant sense. Excluding Turkey, Albania is the only European country in which Moslems form a majority of the population. Substantial Orthodox and Roman Catholic minorities also exist there. Yugoslavia and Bulgaria have Moslem minorities that are estimated to comprise slightly more than a tenth of their respective populations. The Moslem element in the three countries reflects the long period of Turkish rule in the Balkan Peninsula, from the sixteenth century to the twentieth.

## MAJOR PHYSICAL DIVISIONS

The cultural and political complexity of East Central Europe is matched by physical diversity. Mountains, hill lands, plains, and plateaus form a pattern which is very complicated when viewed in detail. Considered in broad outline, however, a certain order can be discerned in the arrangement of surface features. These tend to group themselves into four major physical belts or zones: (1) the northern plain, (2) the central mountain zone, (3) the Danubian plains, and (4) the southern mountain zone.

### ▶ The Northern Plain

Most of Poland lies in the northern plain, between the Carpathian and Sudeten mountains on the south and the Baltic Sea on the north (map, p. 202). The plain is a segment of the North European Plain, which extends westward into Germany and eastward into the Soviet Union. The central and northern reaches of Poland are comprised of land that is rather sandy and infertile, with many swamps, marshes, and lakes, especially in the eastern Masurian Lakes district. The level expanses of plain are broken at intervals by terminal moraines, the low, regular hills created by the continental ice sheets which covered this area during the Ice Age. At the south the plain gradually rises to low, rolling uplands. Here a thick cover of loess has formed the most fertile soils of Poland.

Poland's largest rivers, the Vistula and the Oder, rise in the Carpathians and wind across the northern plain to the Baltic Sea. The Oder is the country's main internal waterway, carrying a considerable barge traffic between the important Upper Silesian industrial area (with which it is connected by a canal) and the Baltic. The principal seaports of Poland—Gdansk (formerly Danzig), Gdynia, and Szczecin (formerly Stettin)—are located at or near the mouths of these rivers. Danzig, located at the western edge of the Vistula delta, was created a Free City in 1919 because of its predominantly German population. Poland was given a privileged position in using the port, but decided to build Gdynia a short distance to the northwest as an additional all-Polish port. The two cities now form a metropolitan area with an estimated population of 437,000. Szczecin (238,000) is located about 50 miles inland on the west bank of the Oder. Formerly an all-German river except for its headwaters, the Oder is now controlled by Poland for most of its length. The lower river is shared with Germany for a considerable distance, although the part from just above Szczecin to the Baltic Sea is entirely within Polish territory.

### ▶ The Central Mountain Zone

The central mountain zone is formed by the Carpathian Mountains and lower ranges rimming the western part of Czechoslovakia. The plow-shaped Carpathians extend for a thousand miles from Slovakia and southern Poland to south central Romania. Geologically, these mountains are a continuation of the Alps. They are lower than the Alps, however, and are cut by a greater number of easy passes. Elevations of 8000 feet or more are reached only in the Tatra Mountains of Slovakia and Poland and in the Transylvanian Alps of Romania.

West of the Carpathians, lower mountains enclose the hilly basin of Bohemia, the industrial core of Czechoslovakia. On the north the Sudeten Mountains and Ore Mountains separate Czechoslovakia from Poland and Germany. Between these ranges at the Saxon Gate the valley of the Elbe River provides a lowland connection and a navigable waterway leading from the Bohemian Basin to the highly developed industrial region of Saxony in East Germany. To the southwest the Bohemian Forest occupies the frontier zone between Czechoslovakia and Germany and Austria. Lower highlands border Bohemia on the southeast. The mountainous rim of Bohemia has a general elevation of only 2000 to 5000 feet, while the floor of the Bohemian Basin lies generally at 1500 feet or less.

Between the mountain-rimmed upland basin of Bohemia and the Carpathians of Slovakia, a convenient and historic passageway is provided by the lowland corridor of Moravia. Through this corridor run major routes of transportation connecting Vienna and the Danube Valley with the plains of Poland. To the north, near the Polish frontier, the corridor narrows at the Moravian Gate between the Sudeten Mountains and the Carpathians. Just beyond this gateway, East Central Europe's most important concentration of coal mines and iron and steel plants has developed in the Upper Silesian-Moravian coal field of Poland and Czechoslovakia.

## ▶ The Danubian Plains

Two major lowlands, bordered by mountains and drained by the Danube River and its tributaries, comprise the Danubian plains. One of these, the Great Hungarian Plain, occupies two thirds of Hungary and smaller adjoining portions of Romania, Yugoslavia, and the Soviet Union. The Great Hungarian Plain is very level in most places, and contains much poorly drained land in the vicinity of its rivers. To the northwest an outlier, the Little Hungarian Plain, extends into the margins of Czechoslovakia and Austria. The second major lowland drained by the Danube is comprised of the plains of Wallachia and Moldavia in Romania, together with the northern lowland fringe of Bulgaria. Wallachia lies between the Carpathians and the Danube, while Moldavia is between the Carpathians and the Soviet Union. The Danubian plains represent the most fertile large agricultural region in East Central Europe. Broad expanses of level land with deep, rich soils, an average growing season of 190 days or more, and a summer maximum of rainfall provide good natural conditions for growing corn and wheat, which occupy the greater part of the arable land.

The Danube River, which supplies a navigable water connection between these lowlands and the outside world, is the longest river in Eurasia west of the Volga. It rises in the Black Forest of southwestern Germany and follows a winding course of some 1750 miles to the Black Sea, which it enters through three main channels. The Danube is customarily divided into three principal sections: Upper, Middle, and Lower. The Upper Danube, above Vienna, is principally fed by tributaries from the Alps. This section of the river is swift and difficult to navigate, though large barges use it as far upstream as Regensburg, Germany, and smaller craft as far as Ulm. Below Vienna the Middle Danube flows leisurely across the Little Hungarian and Great Hungarian plains past the Czechoslovak river port of Bratislava (city proper, 239,000) and the Hungarian and Yugoslav capital cities of Budapest and Belgrade. Three major tributaries enter the river between Budapest and

Belgrade: the Tisza from the Carpathians and the Drava and Sava from the Alps. In the border zone between Yugoslavia and Romania the Danube follows a series of gorges through a belt of mountains about 80 miles wide where the Carpathians reach southward to merge with the Balkan Mountains. At the eastern end of these gorges is the famous Iron Gate (photo, p. 200). Beyond the Iron Gate the Lower Danube marks the boundary for a long distance between the level plains of southern Romania and the low plateaus of northern Bulgaria. The river then turns northward into Romania and enters the Black Sea through a low, marshy delta with many lakes and swamps. The inland river ports of Braila (city proper, 102,000) and Galati (city proper, 96,000) in Romania are accessible to seagoing vessels. Constanta (city proper, 100,000) is the principal Romanian seaport on the Black Sea itself. No river in the world touches so many different countries as the Danube—eight in all, including Germany, Austria, Czechoslovakia, Hungary, Yugoslavia, Romania, Bulgaria, and the Soviet Union.

### ▶ The Southern Mountain Zone

The southern mountain zone occupies most of the Balkan Peninsula. Bulgaria, Yugoslavia, and Albania, the East Central European nations that share this zone, are very mountainous, though Yugoslavia and Bulgaria contain substantial areas of lowland, and Albania has small lowlands along the coast.

In Bulgaria the principal mountains are the Balkan Range, extending east-west across the center of the country, and the more extensive Rhodope Mountains in the southwest. These are rugged mountains that attain heights of 9000 feet in a few places. A peak in the western Rhodope rising to 9592 feet is the highest summit in East Central Europe. Between the Rhodope and the Balkan Range is the productive valley of the Maritsa River, constituting, together with the adjoining Sofia Basin, the agricultural and industrial core of Bulgaria. North of the Balkan Range a low, wheat-growing loess plateau slopes to the Danube.

In central and southern Yugoslavia a tangled mass of mountains constitutes a major barrier to travel. Through this difficult region a historic lowland passage connecting the Danube Valley with the Aegean Sea follows the trough of the Morava and Vardar rivers. An important east-west route linking the Morava-Vardar passageway with the Maritsa Valley leads through the high basin in which Sofia, the capital of Bulgaria, is located.

Along the rugged and picturesque Dalmatian Coast of southwestern Yugoslavia, mountains fringed by deep, canyonlike inlets rise steeply from the Adriatic Sea. Western Yugoslavia is continuously mountainous from the Italian and Austrian Alps in the extreme north to the mountains of Albania in the south (photo, opposite). The principal ranges run parallel to the Adriatic Coast and impose a succession of rocky heights crossed by only a few significant passes. The general range of elevations is 4000 to 6000 feet, but scattered summits reach 8000 to 9400 feet. Some of the most picturesque scenery is found in the heavily wooded Dinaric Alps, bordering the Dalmatian Coast. Much of the mountainous region of western Yugoslavia is characterized by karst or sinkhole topography caused by the solvent action of underground waters in limestone bedrock. The dry, inhospitable karst plateaus are among the most desolate and sparsely settled parts of Europe. Railroads crossing the mountains at the north, where they are narrowest, give access to Yugoslavia's seaports of Rijeka–Susak (75,000) and Split (city proper, 75,000), and to the Italian seaport of Trieste, which handles an important share of Yugoslavia's seaborne trade.

Nearly all of Albania is composed of rugged mountains, the main exception being a narrow, swampy coastal lowland. Perhaps best of all the Balkan countries Albania exemplifies Gottmann's assertion that "The Balkan highlands have lived as a tissue of

Barren karst highlands of western Yugoslavia tower above Cetinje in southwestern Montenegro. (Yugoslav Information Center.)

isolated cells, preserving archaic forms of life and resisting to the best of their abilities the multitude of influences and external interferences that have swirled across the peninsula throughout history." [1]

## THE CLIMATIC PATTERN

The climates of East Central Europe are transitional between the marine climate of northwestern Europe, the extreme continental climates of Russia, and the dry-summer subtropical or mediterranean climate of Southern Europe. In most areas winters are colder than in the British Isles, France, or the Low Countries, although not so cold as in Russia. The average January temperature is 29°F at Poznan, 26° at Warsaw, 30° at Prague, 32° at Budapest, 31° at Belgrade, 27° at Bucharest, and 28° at Sofia. Only in sheltered valleys and coastal lowlands of the extreme south do midwinter average temperatures rise significantly above freezing. An example is provided by the small seaport and resort city of Dubrovnik (city proper, 16,000), on the Dalmatian Coast of Yugoslavia, which has a January average of 48°. Summer temperatures are higher than in northwestern Europe, the average for July being 66° at Poznan and Warsaw, 67° at Prague, 70° at Budapest, 71° at Belgrade, 72° at Bucharest, 69° at Sofia, and 79° at Dubrovnik.

In most parts of East Central Europe the average annual precipitation is between 20 and 30 inches. The heaviest precipitation occurs in Yugoslavia along the Adriatic coast: Dubrovnik receives 60 inches a year, and some of the higher areas on windward slopes in the coastal mountains receive 180

[1] Jean Gottmann, *A Geography of Europe*, rev. ed. New York: Holt, Rinehart and Winston, 1954. P. 561. Used by permission of the author and the publisher.

inches or more—the greatest precipitation in Europe. Most areas in East Central Europe have a summer rainfall maximum except for the extreme south of Yugoslavia, the Dalmatian Coast, Albania, and extreme southern Bulgaria, which have the strong winter maximum that is characteristic of the Mediterranean region. Only a tenth of the annual rainfall at Dubrovnik comes in June, July, and August.

In the Danubian plains hot summers decrease the efficiency of the rainfall, and periods of drought make agriculture somewhat more hazardous than in the more dependable climate of northwestern Europe. But in most years moisture is sufficient for a good harvest. The humid continental long-summer climate of the Danubian plains is comparable in many respects to the climate of the United States Corn Belt, although Corn Belt summers are hotter and the annual precipitation of the Corn Belt is greater. The plains of Poland have a humid continental short-summer climate comparable to the climate of the American Great Lakes region.

## RURAL LIFE IN EAST CENTRAL EUROPE

In this region, climatic conditions are a matter of more direct importance to the majority of the people than in the industrialized lands of northwestern Europe. Large sections of East Central Europe, particularly in the south and east, are still predominantly rural and agricultural, though industrial and urban development is increasing rapidly in many areas. A substantial majority of the people in the region as a whole live in agricultural villages. In the 1930s agriculture supported an estimated 34 percent of the population in Czechoslovakia, 55 percent in Hungary, 63 percent in Poland, 75 percent in Yugoslavia, 78 percent in Romania, 80 percent in Bulgaria, and 91 percent in Albania. Today these percentages would be lower in all countries, and much lower in some. Czechoslovakia, Poland, and Hungary, in that order, are the most industrialized and urbanized countries, while Albania remains the most rural.

### ▶ Agricultural Characteristics

As an agricultural region, East Central Europe presents a great contrast to the North Sea lands. This region has borne many of the characteristics of an underdeveloped area: an excessive dependence on agriculture, much illiteracy among rural people, poorly developed transportation facilities, a lack of capital except at exorbitant rates of interest, and antiquated and inefficient farming methods with resultant low yields. As a result of rural overpopulation, relatively low crop yields, poor transportation, and a lack of urban markets, a large share of the farm production has been utilized at home. Before World War I, much of the best land was held in large estates worked by hired laborers or tenants, and rural life in many areas had an almost feudal cast. Such estates were especially common in Hungary, Romania, Poland, and Slovakia. Some land reform was initiated by governments in the nineteenth century, but progress was most rapid after World War I. The principal element in such reform was the breaking up of large holdings for sale to small landowners, though attempts—in the main unsuccessful—were also made to consolidate some of the scattered strip holdings of the peasants into more compact and efficient farm units. On the whole, redistribution of land was most successful in Czechoslovakia, especially in the more progressive western provinces of Bohemia and Moravia. Elsewhere, it was often frustrated by the opposition of politically powerful landowners. Even where programs of land reform succeeded, they were of limited usefulness in raising the standard of living in rural areas, though they did help to keep down discontent among the peasants, for whom ownership of land had an intense emotional significance. Many landless farm laborers were too poor to buy land, even under generous governmental credit arrangements, and farmers who did acquire land generally lacked the necessary capital, machinery, and knowledge to make effective use of it. Machinery would have been at a serious disadvantage in any case, due to the fragmented arrangement of most farms and the small size of individual strips of land.

Since 1945 the remaining large private holdings have been liquidated by the new Communist governments and programs of collectivized agriculture have been introduced. Collectivization has met with serious resistance on the part of the peasants, and in Yugoslavia and Poland—the countries that are freest of Soviet domination—it has not been pushed during recent years, though both countries are continuing their efforts to introduce it gradually and by noncoercive methods. Only about a tenth of the farm land in Yugoslavia and less than a fifth of that in Poland has been collectivized thus far. In the other countries, including East Germany, governments have pushed ahead with collectivization, though they have backtracked or slowed the pace from time to time. By 1960 nearly all of the farm land in Bulgaria was reported to be in collective or state farms,[2] while such farms were reported to comprise over four fifths of the farm land in Albania and Czechoslovakia, two thirds to three fourths of that in Romania and Hungary, and about half of that in East Germany.

Since World War II, agricultural production in East Central Europe and East Germany has tended to stagnate, in contrast to rapid increases in the production of manufactured goods and minerals. Yields per acre and total output of most crops have at best increased only moderately over prewar levels. Livestock herds, slow to recover from wartime decimation, have lagged even more. Resistance of peasants to collective farming and destruction of livestock during the war have undoubtedly been important factors underlying agriculture's failure to advance at faster rates. (Among other things, wartime livestock losses decreased supplies of manure to fertilize the land.) But another major factor has been the preoccupation of governmental planners with industrial development, which has led them to slight investment in agriculture in favor of investment in manufacturing and mining, and indeed to tax agriculture in various ways for the support of industry. Over large areas the dominant picture remains one of peasants working the land in more or less the traditional manner, unaided for the most part by

Harvesting sugar beets by machine on a collective farm in Bohemia. (Eastfoto.)

[2] *Collective farms* are worked jointly by peasant families, who share the proceeds after the operating expenses of the collective have been met. *State farms,* generally larger than collectives and operated directly by the government, are worked by employees who are paid cash wages. For a fuller discussion see pp. 226–229.

modern machines, adequate amounts of chemical fertilizer, high-quality seeds, adequate technical information, or sufficient financial incentives to produce. In some areas, particularly in Czechoslovakia and Poland, agriculture has been handicapped by a rapid draining of younger and more able workers for employment in expanding industries.

### ► The Pattern of Crops and Livestock

The principal crop-growing areas of East Central Europe are the extensive plains or low plateaus of Poland, Hungary, Romania, northern Yugoslavia, and northern Bulgaria; the uplands and valleys of western Czechoslovakia, and the Maritsa Valley of Bulgaria.

On the sandy plains of central and northern Poland rye and potatoes are the major crops, although wheat and sugar beets are important in the loess zone of southern Poland. More rye and potatoes are grown in Poland than in all the other countries of East Central Europe combined.

In the Danubian plains corn and wheat are the main crops. The long, hot, rainy summers make these plains one of the few areas in Europe suitable for growing corn on a large scale. Yugoslavia, Romania, and Hungary ordinarily produce about three fifths of Europe's corn. Wheat is an important crop in all of the East Central European countries, being more extensively grown through the area as a whole than any other grain. Rye, oats, barley, potatoes, and sugar beets are major crops in Poland and Czechoslovakia, but tend to be of minor importance in the other countries. The raising of cattle, hogs, horses, and associated fodder crops is a prominent feature of agriculture in all these countries. Sheep are most important in Romania, Yugoslavia, and Bulgaria. Throughout East Central Europe stock raising is the principal form of agriculture in the highlands. Transhumance, the seasonal movement of farm animals between the valleys and mountain pastures, is widely practiced.

The agriculture of East Central Europe reaches a climax of efficiency and productivity in western Czechoslovakia. Here in Bohemia and Moravia diversified crop and livestock farming is practiced which is more similar to the intensive agriculture of the North Sea countries than is true of other areas in East Central Europe.

### Subtropical Agriculture in Bulgaria and Yugoslavia

A relatively small but very distinctive agricultural region is found in the Maritsa Valley of Bulgaria, where subtropical temperatures coupled with summer rain permit the growing of tobacco, grapes, cotton, rice, and many varieties of fruits and vegetables. However, wheat occupies a larger acreage than any other crop. The Maritsa Valley is famous for its rose gardens, exporting attar of roses to the world's perfume industry. But rose scents can now be made synthetically, and the acreage and production of roses in Bulgaria have declined considerably in recent years.

Another distinctive area of subtropical farming is the Dalmatian Coast of Yugoslavia and adjoining districts of Albania, where citrus and olive groves and vineyards portray the characteristic agriculture associated with the mediterranean or dry-summer subtropical climate.

## URBAN DEVELOPMENT

The predominantly rural and agricultural character of most parts of East Central Europe is reflected in the small number of large cities. Only eight urban areas in the entire region have populations of over 500,000. (By comparison, the state of Ohio has six such areas.) The only country with more than one urban area of this size is Poland, which has three, including (1) the concentration of mining and heavy industrial centers in Upper Silesia (1,921,000), (2) the capital and leading center of diversified industries, Warsaw (1,595,000), and (3) the main textile center, Lodz (844,000). In all of the remaining countries of East Central Europe, the political capital is the largest city, and in all except Yugoslavia it is the principal industrial center as well. (In Yugoslavia, Zagreb vies with the capital, Belgrade, in industrial importance.) In all countries except Yugoslavia, the capital far overshadows any other city in size, as will be apparent from the following summation (population figures are estimates for city proper):

| Country | Largest City | Second City |
|---|---|---|
| Czechoslovakia | Prague (971,000) | Brno (304,000) |
| Hungary | Budapest (1,783,000) | Miskolc (135,000) |
| Romania | Bucharest (1,237,000) | Cluj (155,000) |
| Bulgaria | Sofia (644,000) | Plovdiv (163,000) |
| Yugoslavia | Belgrade (510,000) | Zagreb (368,000) |
| Albania | Tirana (108,000) | Scutari (39,000) |

In only two areas of East Central Europe do important clusters of industrial cities occur which are at all comparable to the great urban constellations found in the larger manufacturing districts of northwestern Europe. The most prominent cluster is found in southwestern Poland and adjoining areas of Czechoslovakia, in or near the important

Extensive rebuilding was necessary in many cities of East Central Europe after World War II. The view shows a group of apartment buildings built after the war in the Hungarian capital of Budapest. (Eastfoto.)

Upper Silesian-Moravian coal field. A second, less concentrated cluster exists in Bohemia; it includes Prague, Pilsen (city proper, 133,000), and smaller cities.

## INDUSTRIAL DEVELOPMENT AND RESOURCES

The industrialized areas of Bohemia, southwestern Poland, and northern Moravia, along with those of East Germany, have provided highly important nuclei for an extensive program of planned industrial development which has been undertaken in East Central Europe and East Germany under Communist direction since World War II. The economies of all countries in the area are being operated under national economic plans patterned after the famous five-year plans of the Soviet Union (see pp. 225–230). Yugoslavia's planning is done on a separate basis from that of the satellite countries, but its emphases are generally similar to theirs. The major aim of these plans is a great increase in industrialization. As in the Soviet Union, major stress has been placed on the nationalization of industries, expansion of mining, and expanded production of iron and steel, machinery, chemicals, construction materials, and electric power. Development of a strong base of heavy industries and sources of power has been viewed as an essential prerequisite for over-all industrial development, and investment in this type of development has been favored at the expense of consumer industries and agriculture. Stress has also been placed on improvement of transportation, especially the double-tracking of existing railroads. Most long-distance freight traffic in East Central Europe moves by rail. Water transportation is poorly developed as compared with western Europe, though some efforts are being made to improve it.

The planned expansion of mining and industry in the satellite countries and Yugoslavia has produced notable increases in the total output of minerals, manufactured goods, and power. Over-all production of iron and steel, for example, has more than tripled. The largest absolute increases in output have occurred in the countries that were already the most industrialized: Czechoslovakia, Poland, and, of course, East Germany. But the most spectacular percentage increases have occurred in the other countries, which began their postwar industrialization from a much smaller base.

Czechoslovakia and Poland are by far the largest producers of manufactured goods, minerals, and electric power among the countries of East Central Europe, although they share this lead with East Germany among the European satellites as a whole. These countries lead in the production of iron, steel, machine tools, machinery, textiles, chemicals, and many other lines of manufactured goods. Steel production in Communist Europe is heavily concentrated in Poland and Czechoslovakia. The two are approximately equal in total production. Together they account for about two thirds of the steel produced in the satellite area (including East Germany but excluding Yugoslavia) or three fourths of the production in East Central Europe (including Yugoslavia but excluding East Germany).

Hungary probably ranks third in East Central Europe in total industrial development and engineering industries, after Czechoslovakia and Poland. It is known particularly for the manufacture of trucks. In Romania, Yugoslavia, Bulgaria, and Albania, employment in agriculture still exceeds employment in manufacturing by a considerable margin, indeed in Albania and Bulgaria by a very large margin. Hungary, Romania, Yugoslavia, and Bulgaria have all shown large percentage increases in their output of metals, machinery, chemicals, and electric power since World War II. But light consumer industries such as food processing and textile manufacture are still a very prominent component of their industrial structures. In Albania such industries account for most of the meager industrial production.

A significant feature of postwar industrial development in East Central Europe and East Germany has been the construction of a number of large new iron and steel plants. The most publicized and probably the most important of these is located at Nowa Huta, a suburb of Cracow in southwestern Poland. Others are located at Czestochowa, Poland, where a small existing mill has been greatly expanded; at Moravska Ostrava, the main city in the Czech part of the Upper Silesian-Moravian coal field; in Hungary at Dunapentele on the Danube River south of Budapest; and in East Germany at Fürstenberg on the Oder River. Another plant, still unfinished at the time of writing, has been under construction near Kosice in Slovakia.

## ▶ Industrial Resources

### Minerals

Mineral resources to support industrial development in East Central Europe and East Germany seem, on the whole, less adequate than those available in non-Communist Europe, but a number of notable resources do exist, and gaps in the resource structure can often be filled by imports from the Soviet Union. The major resources may be summarized as follows:

1. *Coal.* The Upper Silesian-Moravian field in Poland and Czechoslovakia ranks with West Germany's Ruhr in total coal reserves, and possibly exceeds it. However, a much smaller proportion of its coal can be used for coking and much of the coke is lower in quality than that made from Ruhr coal. Nevertheless, substantial reserves of coking coal exist in this field (the best coal is in the Czechoslovak part) and in the much smaller Walbrzych (Waldenburg) field in Lower Silesia. In production of bituminous coal (exclusive of lignite and brown coal), Poland and Czechoslovakia rank sixth and seventh, respectively, among the countries of the world, being exceeded by the Soviet Union, the United States, West Germany, the United Kingdom, and China. If lignite is included, East Germany exceeds Czechoslovakia in total tonnage. All of the remaining countries in East Central Europe have coal deposits, but they are generally small and consist overwhelmingly of lignite and brown coal. Production has greatly increased since World War II, primarily for use in thermal stations to produce electricity. Most electricity in East Central Europe and East Germany is produced by coal, though in Yugoslavia hydroelectric power accounted for 58 percent of all production in 1959.

2. *Oil and Natural Gas.* Romania is the only oil producer of consequence, though several other countries have a very minor production, and Yugoslavia is known to have fairly sizable reserves. Romania's production, the largest in Europe (excluding the Soviet Union), comes from fields around Ploesti in the southern foothills of the Carpathian Mountains and from smaller fields in Moldavia. The country's known reserves are quite modest in size compared to those of the world's major oil producers. Recently Romania has commenced to exploit large reserves of natural gas, found mainly in the Transylvanian Basin between the Bihor Mountains and the Carpathians.

In 1959 agreements were concluded under which the Soviet Union will export crude petroleum via pipelines to East Germany, Poland, Czechoslovakia, and Hungary.

3. *Salt and Potash.* Chemical production in East Central Europe and East Germany is based in considerable part on large salt deposits in East Germany, Poland, and Romania and large potash deposits in East Germany. Yugoslavia also has substantial salt deposits and is a minor producer.

4. *Bauxite.* Reserves of bauxite in Hungary and Yugoslavia are very large, particularly those of Hungary, which according to one estimate has one eighth of the world's

total reserves. These two countries rank second and third, respectively, among European bauxite producers (after France). Most of their production is exported. However, both Hungary and Yugoslavia produce aluminum on a small scale, as do East Germany, Poland, Czechoslovakia, and Romania.

5. *Lead and Zinc.* Poland, Yugoslavia, and Bulgaria are the main producers. Yugoslavia is the largest producer of lead in Europe, and Poland is the largest zinc producer. Poland's main deposits of zinc and lead are found in Upper Silesia, in close proximity to the country's principal coal deposits.

*Other Minerals.* The area is generally weak in ferroalloys and nonferrous metals except lead and zinc. Yugoslavia shares leadership with Finland among European producers of copper, but its production is not really very large. Various countries in the region produce small quantities of bauxite, copper, manganese, tin, tungsten, and chromium. Phosphates and native sulfur are absent, though some sulfur is obtained from pyrites in several countries. Uranium is produced in the Ore Mountains of East Germany and Czechoslovakia, and in Hungary and Bulgaria. Undoubtedly the most critical mineral deficiency within the region as a whole is a shortage of iron ore. Yugoslavia

has probably the largest deposits, but even they are very minor as compared with those of France or Sweden. Several other countries have iron-ore deposits, but they are generally small and/or low grade. The iron and steel industries of the satellite countries depend heavily on imported ores, primarily from the Krivoy Rog deposits of the Soviet Union. Some ore is imported from Sweden.

**Forest and Fiber Resources**

Industry in East Central Europe can draw upon substantial forest resources. Nearly a third of the entire region is wooded, and every country except Hungary has sizable reserves of timber. Conifers predominate at the higher elevations and in the plains of Poland, although beech, oak, and other deciduous hardwoods make up a considerable part of the forest growth on the lower lands in many areas.

The cotton textile industries of the region depend heavily on imported cotton, though a minor production of cotton exists in the more southerly countries, particularly Bulgaria. Most countries have a substantial production of wool, but woolen industries in all countries depend partially on imported wool. Poland is Europe's largest producer of flax and has a substantial linen industry.

## MAJOR INDUSTRIAL REGIONS

Before the Communist era in East Central Europe, most of the area's coal mining and associated iron and steel production was concentrated in the Upper Silesian-Moravian coal field or in the Bohemian Basin. Today these areas still comprise the major concentrations of mining and heavy industry. In addition, the Bohemian Basin is East Central Europe's leading area of diversified industries, particularly those based

on highly skilled labor and long industrial experience. Within the satellite area as a whole, however, it stands second to East Germany in industries of this kind.

### ► *Coal and Steel in Upper Silesia-Moravia* [3]

The Upper Silesian-Moravian coal field, situated mainly in Poland but extending for a short distance into northern Czechoslo-

[3] The discussion under this heading is based on articles by Norman J. G. Pounds, particularly "The Spread of Mining in the Coal Basin of Upper Silesia and Northern Moravia," *Annals of the Association of American Geographers,* v. 48 (1958), pp. 149–163, and "The Industrial Geography of Modern Poland," *Economic Geography,* v. 36 (1960), pp. 231–253.

# PART 3
## *The Soviet Union*

# Introduction to the Soviet Union

The Union of Soviet Socialist Republics [1] emerged from World War II as a major center of world power. Such a development would have been difficult to foresee before the war. In the prewar period there was a pronounced tendency in the outside world to undervalue the political, economic, and military strength of the USSR. Russia was defeated by the Central Powers in World War I, after suffering possibly a greater toll of military casualties than any other participant. Between 1917 and 1921 the country experienced a destructive period of revolution, foreign intervention, and civil war. The October Revolution of 1917 and success of the Red Army in the subsequent civil war gave control of the government to the radical Bolshevik faction of the Communist Party. During the 1920s and 1930s a series of major internal crises occurred as

[1] Union of Soviet Socialist Republics, frequently shortened to USSR or Soviet Union, is the present official name of the Russian state. The USSR is the successor to the Russian Empire of tsarist (czarist) times. It came into existence following the overthrow of the last of the Romanov tsars in 1917. Pre-Revolutionary Russia is often spoken of as Old Russia, Tsarist Russia, or Imperial Russia. Post-Revolutionary Russia is often referred to as Soviet Russia. The name Russia is used loosely to refer to the country either before or after the Revolution. The part of the country west of the Ural Mountains and north of the Caucasus Mountains is often referred to as European Russia. The part east of the Urals and north of Soviet Middle Asia is called Siberia (map, p. 252).

**The main street of a collective farm village in the Moscow region. (Sovfoto.)**

the Communist leaders attempted to fasten a program of Marxian socialism on an exhausted and partly unwilling country, and in the meantime carried on a struggle for power among themselves.

## EMERGENCE OF THE USSR AS A MAJOR WORLD POWER

When Germany attacked the Soviet Union in June 1941, it was freely predicted in outside countries that the USSR would prove too weak and disunited to withstand the German assault for more than a few weeks or months. The Russians, however, showed an unexpected ability to resist. After suffering tremendous casualties and losses of territory in the early part of the war, their forces eventually rallied. Late in 1942 the German invasion was checked in a decisive battle at Stalingrad, on the Volga River. Thereafter the Germans were gradually pushed back, and by early 1945 Russian armies were besieging Germany itself. The end of the war found the Russians in possession of the eastern third of Germany, which became a postwar Russian zone of occupation.

Russian success in World War II was due in part to economic and military assistance furnished by outside nations, especially the United States, United Kingdom, and Canada. These allies sent large shipments of munitions and other supplies to Russia, and their military campaigns in North Africa, Italy, and northwestern Europe diverted sizable German forces from the Russian front. Mismanagement of the Russian campaigns by the German dictator, Adolf Hitler, may also have worked in favor of Russia. Nevertheless, the failure of Germany to conquer Russia was a clear indication that the strength of the USSR had been badly underrated. The end of World War II found the Soviet Union established as a world power ranking second in importance only to the United States.

▶ *Soviet Territorial Gains*

Following the war the actions of the Soviet Union created a state of profound uneasiness among the non-Communist nations of the world. Beginning in 1939 the Soviet government had considerably enlarged the national territory of the USSR by successive annexations of areas taken from neighboring countries. Most of these annexations took place in the western frontier zone of the Soviet Union between the Black Sea and the Arctic Ocean. The three Baltic republics of Lithuania, Latvia, and Estonia were absorbed in 1940. Other European nations losing territory to the USSR included Poland, Finland, Romania, Czechoslovakia, and Germany (maps, pp. 202 and 164). The greater part of the annexed lands had been Russian-held territory prior to World War I, but some areas were acquired for the first time. In the Far East the Soviet Union took the southern half of Sakhalin Island and the Kuril Islands from Japan. Both of these had been ceded to Japan by Tsarist Russia. In addition, the small semi-independent Asian country of Tannu Tuva was absorbed. All of the foregoing annexations were complete by the end of 1945. They added to the national domain of the USSR a total area of approximately 287,000 square miles (20,000 square miles larger than Texas), with an estimated population of 20 to 25 million.

After 1945 the political influence of the Soviet Union was extended still further through its dominance over the European satellite nations of Poland, Czechoslovakia, Romania, Hungary, Bulgaria, Albania, and East Germany. In the Far East Communist governments took power in North Korea, in mainland China, and in North Vietnam. (A Communist state already existed in Mongolia—see p. 391.) Thus was created a Communist political system embracing

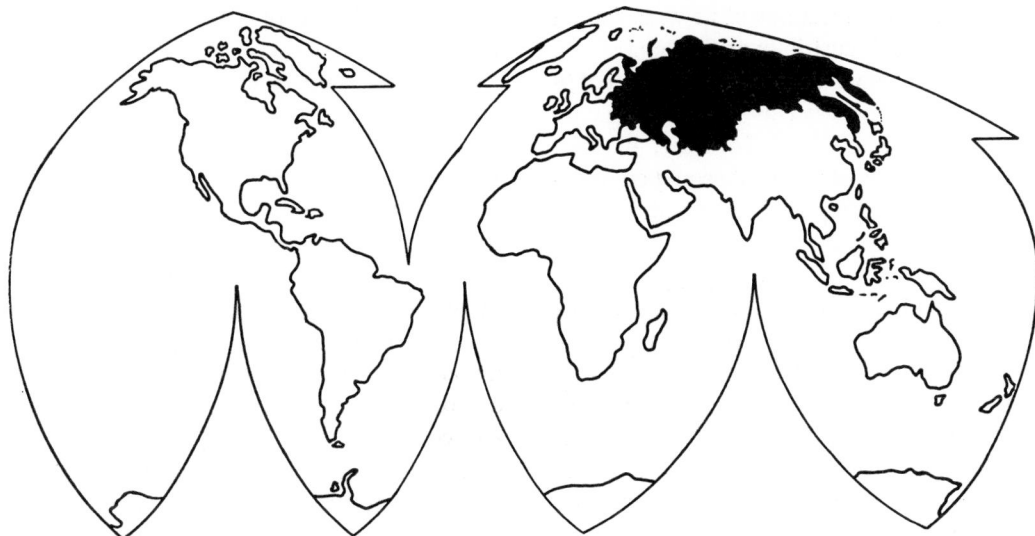

Location of the Soviet Union. (Boggs Equal Area Projection, copyright A. J. Nystrom and Co.)

about a fourth of the world's lands (excluding Antarctica) and about a third of its people.

### ▶ The Cold War

Although the United States and Britain had rapidly demobilized after World War II, the USSR was slow to follow suit. Large military forces continued to be maintained, and the production of armaments was kept at a high level. Meanwhile, agitation by local Communist groups was carried on in many countries outside of the Soviet orbit. Actual fighting between Communist and anti-Communist forces broke out in Greece, Indochina, Korea, and a number of other countries. Such events gradually created a state of alarm in the non-Communist world. Many nations outside the Soviet iron curtain began reluctantly to rearm and to form

defensive alliances against possible Communist aggression. In the period of cold war which developed, it became increasingly clear that the world had divided into two opposing groups of nations. One group was dominated by the Soviet Union and Communist China, the other looked to the United States for leadership and aid. A third group of countries, mainly in southern Asia and in Africa, maintained a precarious neutrality.

Thus the Soviet Union by success in war, economic and territorial expansion, military threat, and political intrigue has gained a position of immense importance in world affairs. Soviet technical and scientific progress was highlighted in 1957 by the first successful launching of an artificial earth satellite and again in 1959 by the firing of the first rocket to the moon.

## THE PLANNED ECONOMY OF THE SOVIET UNION

One of the characteristics for which the Soviet Union is best known is its tightly controlled, socialized type of planned economy. Since 1928 the economy of the USSR has been operated under a series of Five-Year Plans touching every major sector of eco-

nomic life. These plans prescribe the goals of production for the entire nation. They specify the types and quantities of minerals, manufactured goods, and agricultural commodities to be produced, the factories, rail lines, highways, canals, and dams to be built or improved, the locations of new residential areas to house industrial workers, and so on. To a considerable degree the Soviet economy may be regarded as a single gigantic enterprise directed from Moscow, in spite of recent attempts to delegate some administrative power to regional "Councils of National Economy." [2]

The Soviet state exercises a monopolistic control over the whole economic structure and resources of the country. It owns and operates large-scale industry, mines, power plants, railways, shipping, and other means of communication. It engages in farming on its own account through the institution of state farms, and it largely controls peasant agriculture through the organization of collective farming. It has an exclusive monopoly of banking, foreign trade, and exchange operations. It controls the domestic channels of distribution in its capacity as a manufacturer, farmer, merchant, shipper, and banker. Moreover, by administrative measures it can suppress such private competition as still exists.

All these branches of economic life are subject to the system of economic planning by the state; they are within the orbit of "planned economy" as it is understood and practiced in the Soviet Union.

It is true that the private market, however diminished or limited in scope, has never become entirely extinct, at any rate so far as petty trade is concerned. Although the Soviet policy toward private enterprise has generally been unmistakably restrictive, it has occasionally relaxed in the direction of greater liberality, at least in the realm of trade. But whatever its concessions to private enterprise, the Soviet state has maintained, unaltered, its dominance in the economic sphere. From the fields of large-scale industry and foreign trade, over which the Soviet state early asserted a monopoly, it extended its dominance to domestic trade and finally to agriculture. Since the early 1930s collectivization of agriculture has been an achieved fact. [3]

The economic system described above was initiated by stages following the Bol-shevik Revolution of 1917. Essentially the aim of the revolutionary leaders was twofold. They meant to abolish the old aristocratic and capitalist institutions of Tsarist Russia and to develop a strong socialist state able to stand on an equal footing with the major industrial nations of the West. For the first decade they were mainly occupied in consolidating their hold on the country and in putting a limited part of their program into effect. Large-scale industry, banking, and foreign trade were nationalized, but a certain amount of private trading, together with private ownership of small industries and agricultural land, was permitted under the New Economic Policy announced in 1921. This compromise policy was the result of a near breakdown in the newly instituted Communist economy during the difficult period of civil war and foreign intervention following the Revolution. However, it was intended only as a temporary expedient.

## ► *The Five-Year Plans*

In 1928 the first of the Five-Year Plans was announced, and succeeding plans have covered the period up to the present. [4] The two most prominent outcomes of these plans have been (1) the collectivization of agriculture and (2) a rapid expansion of large-scale industry.

### Collectivization of Agriculture

Between 1929 and 1933 about two thirds of all peasant households in the Soviet Union were collectivized. By 1940 this figure had risen to 97 percent. Today the number of independent peasant cultivators is insignificant. Collectivization was fiercely resisted by the land-hungry peasants, and drastic measures were necessary to put the government decrees into effect. Millions of

---

[2] Philip E. Mosely, "Khrushchev's New Economic Gambit." *Foreign Affairs,* v. 36 (1958), pp. 557–568.

[3] Lazar Volin, *A Survey of Soviet Russian Agriculture.* U. S. Department of Agriculture Monograph No. 5 (1951), p. 10.

[4] Though Soviet planning has been more or less on a five-year basis, irregularities have occurred from time to time. For example, the 1956–1960 plan was scrapped in 1957, and after two years of planning on an annual basis, a Seven-Year Plan for 1959–1965 was instituted.

livestock were slaughtered by the peasants, and crops were burned to avoid turning them over to the new collectives. Two main types of farm unit now exist: the collective farm (*kolkhoz*) and the large factory-type state farm (*sovkhoz*). They are described in the following selection.

Farming in the Soviet Union is organized into large-scale collective and state-operated farms. On January 1, 1958, there were 76,500 collective farms averaging 4200 acres of land in crops, with about 250 households per farm. There were also 5900 farms operated by the state. These averaged 25,200 acres in crops and nearly 400 full-time workers to each farm.

On the state-operated farms, the workers are paid cash wages, with bonus payments for high performance. In addition, they have small garden allotments and the privilege of keeping a cow, a pig or two, chickens, geese, and sometimes a couple of sheep or goats. On the collective farms, the workers share in the net income from operations in accordance with the days worked [and types of work done]; and they frequently receive bonus rewards for special efforts. Workers on collective farms also have garden allotments and the privilege of keeping individually owned livestock.

The farm people live in villages, with their individual allotments of land usually extending back of each house. Consequently, there are no individual farmsteads dotting the countryside as there are in the United States.

In the process of organizing the large collective and state farms, the land was consolidated into huge fields wherever the terrain would permit. The first impression one gets of the major grain areas is of a vast expanse of wheat, with some sprinkling of corn, sunflowers, and other minor crops. In some areas, shelterbelts of trees have been planted to break the force of the wind and to hold the snow cover. In the naturally forested areas of the north, the fields are smaller, and the terrain is broken up by streams, ponds, and wooded hills; the farms also tend to be smaller. . . .

Almost always, several villages are included within the boundaries of one collective or state farm.[5]

As originally conceived, the system of collectivized agriculture was supposed to result in the following major advantages:

1. The old arrangement of small, fragmented individual holdings separated by uncultivated boundary strips would be replaced by a system of larger fields incorporating the boundary strips, thus increasing the amount of cultivated land and giving scope for mechanized farming.

2. Increased mechanization would release surplus farm labor for employment in factories and mines, thus facilitating industrialization and bringing into existence the large urban working class looked to as the principal support for the Communist system.

3. Mechanization, improved methods of farming, and reclamation of new land under state supervision would result in greater over-all production.

4. Increased production, plus easier collection of surpluses from a greatly reduced number of farm units, would result in larger and more dependable food supplies for the growing urban populations.

5. Liquidation of individual peasant farming would remove the most important capitalist element still remaining in the USSR.

### Recent Changes in Soviet Farming

Soviet agriculture experienced many setbacks in the first quarter-century of collectivization, and over-all production was slow to expand. Various factors have been cited as contributing to the stagnation of farm production. They include: (1) rapid draining of agricultural workers for employment in industry, without an adequate supply of farm machines being provided to take their place; (2) peasant resistance to collectivization, including large-scale slaughter of draft animals and other livestock; (3) climatic handicaps (see pp. 237–242); (4) excessively rigid and inefficient management by the Soviet bureaucracy, and (5) devastation of many of the best farming districts in World War II. An extremely significant

[5] Sherman E. Johnson, "Impressions of Agriculture in the Soviet Union." *Foreign Agriculture,* v. 22, no. 10 (October 1958), pp. 3–4.

factor was (6) the government's deliberate policy of draining wealth from agriculture for the support of industry. Farm products were requisitioned from the collectives at low prices and were then sold in state-owned stores at much higher prices to provide funds for industrial investment. Quotas set by the government for forced deliveries tended constantly to rise. By the time a collective had met its financial obligations for seed, fertilizer, other supplies, and services, only a meager surplus of cash and produce was left to be distributed among the members. Under such conditions there was a natural tendency for peasants to shirk their obligations to the collective in favor of work on their small private garden plots. Any surplus from these plots and from privately owned livestock could be sold on the collective-farm market in a nearby town or city, generally at much higher prices than those paid the collectives by the state. Meanwhile, much of the country's farm land suffered from a lack of fertilizer. Chemical fertilizer was given a low priority by government planners and consequently was not available for most crops. Animal manure was also in short supply, due to the slow recovery of livestock from the disastrous slaughter of the early collectivization period and the ravages of World War II.

After World War II, and particularly after the death of Joseph Stalin in 1953, important changes were made in Soviet farming. The government revamped its system of agricultural procurement, pricing, and taxation in the hope of stimulating the peasants to produce more on collectively farmed land. By merging adjoining units, the total number of collective farms was sharply reduced. Some collectives were absorbed by or converted to state farms. By July 1959 the number of collectives had been reduced to about 60,000, as compared with more than 250,000 at the beginning of 1950.

Accompanying the trend to larger units

was a government decision to permit individual collectives to own and operate tractors and farm machines. Heretofore, machines for planting, harvesting, and other farm tasks had been supplied on a custom-work basis by machine–tractor stations (MTS). These stations, employing salaried workers to operate and service the machines, were paid by the collectives partly in cash and partly in farm products. They served as an important channel for collecting farm surpluses to feed urban populations. Furthermore, through their control of tractors and machinery they were able to exercise supervision over the collectives and to acquaint government officials with the true size of the harvest, thus giving the government a basis for demanding that its quotas be delivered. But in 1958 the system of machine–tractor stations was abolished. With limited exceptions in special situations, the stations were directed to sell their tractors and machinery and to transfer their operators and mechanics to the collectives. A new system of repair–technical stations (RTS) was instituted to supply the collectives with fuels, lubricants, spare parts, seeds, fertilizers, insecticides, and so on, to make certain types of repairs to machines owned by collectives, and to make available to the collectives some types of highly specialized machines. Transfer of machinery to the newly enlarged collectives was one facet of a program to give greater powers of day-to-day decision making to the officials of each collective farm. It was contemplated, however, that such decisions would be made within the framework of over-all policies laid down by regional officials and by Moscow.

In 1954 a vast program was instituted to increase the output of grain (mainly spring wheat) by bringing tens of millions of acres of "virgin and idle lands" into production in the steppes of the northern Kazakh SSR in Soviet Middle Asia and adjoining sections of western Siberia and the Volga region (map, right). Hundreds of large new state farms were organized in the area and a network of narrow-gauge railways was constructed to service them. Weather conditions during the first six years were generally favorable, and a serious crop failure occurred in only one year. However, the new lands are distinctly marginal in precipitation; whether they can be cultivated successfully on a long-term basis remains to be seen. It was reported in 1958 that the cultivated area of the USSR had been enlarged by more than 90 million acres between 1954 and 1957 with most of the increase being accounted for by the new wheat lands in Kazakhstan, Siberia, and the Volga region. As a result of the "virgin and idle lands" program and absorption of collectives, state farms increased their share of the Soviet Union's sown acreage from about 12 percent in 1953 to more than a fourth in 1957.

In addition to the reclamation of new lands, a determined effort is being made by the Soviet government to intensify production on the older farm lands of the country through increased fertilization, use of better methods and better seeds, changes in crop emphases, and so on. Major emphasis is being placed on increased production of (1) livestock, (2) forage crops, including a large increase in corn, partly for grain but primarily for silage and green forage, (3) industrial crops such as cotton, sunflowers for vegetable oil, and sugar beets, and (4) vegetables. The announced goal is to surpass the United States in farm output. However, there is a sizable gap to be closed. In 1955–1956 the Soviet Union was estimated to be producing 9.7 percent of the world's total agricultural output (dollar value), while the United States was credited with 16.5 percent.[6] Soviet agriculture lags far behind in degree of mechanization and in output per farm worker. At the beginning of 1957 the Soviet Union was reported to have only

892,000 tractors, compared to 4,975,000 in the United States, despite the fact that the USSR was cultivating a substantially larger acreage. (It should be noted, however, that Soviet tractors are, on the average, somewhat larger than American models.) As compared with the United States, the USSR required over three times as many farm workers in the middle 1950s to produce a much smaller output of crops and livestock.

Irrespective of its status compared to that of the United States, there is no doubt but that the Soviet Union experienced a marked upturn in total output and per capita availa-

The heavy dashed line encloses most of the acreage of new lands brought under cultivation in the period 1954–1957. The lighter dashes show the boundaries of the Kazakh SSR. (After a map in N. N. Baransky, *Economic Geography of the USSR*, Moscow: Foreign Languages Publishing House, 1956, p. 71.)

bility of farm products during the 1950s. Perhaps the most significant increase was in livestock production, long a weak link in Soviet collectivized agriculture. From the end of 1953 to the end of 1959 the total number of cattle in the USSR rose from a reported 56 million to 74 million, while hogs increased in number from 33 million to 53 million and sheep from 100 million to 135 million.

---

[6] *Foreign Agriculture*, v. 22, no. 4 (April 1958), p. 14.

**Industrial Emphases under the Five-Year Plans**

The most important objective of the Five-Year Plans has been a large increase in industrial production, with emphasis on the production of heavy machinery and other capital goods, increased exploitation of minerals, increased development of electric power, and improvement of the existing transportation facilities. On the whole, this phase of Soviet planning has experienced far more success than the planned expansion of agriculture. Since 1928, and especially since 1945, the Soviet Union, which was largely an agricultural country in 1928, has industrialized at a rapid rate. Masses of peasants have been converted into factory workers, great new industrial centers have been created and old ones enlarged, and over-all industrial production has greatly increased. Various estimates credit the Soviet Union with a fivefold to eightfold increase in total industrial output between 1928 and the late 1950s. Nevertheless, in the late fifties production of most lines of goods was still far below that of the United States. The total industrial output of the Soviet Union in 1957 was estimated by one source to be only two fifths as great as total United States output.[7] The gap between the two countries is especially wide in the production of automobiles and many other consumer items, which have been slighted by the USSR in favor of heavy industry.[8] Soviet planners have given the highest priority to iron and steel production, other forms of heavy metallurgy, and the manufacture of machinery, power-generating and transportation equipment, and industrial chemicals. Many of the consumer items that can readily be purchased in any town or city of the United States are in short supply in the Soviet Union, though greater attention has been given to consumer needs in recent years and the output of consumer goods is rising. However, automobiles other than trucks and buses continue to receive a very low priority and the total output is small. In 1959 the Soviet automobile industry produced 124,500 passenger cars, as compared with a production of 5,590,000 in the United States. The Soviet Union is far behind the United States in housing, and has little prospect of closing the gap in the foreseeable future. According to some estimates, the average urban dweller in the USSR has no more than a third of the living space available to the average American urban resident.

The USSR ranks far below the United States as a trading nation, though its foreign trade has been steadily expanding in recent years. About three quarters of the Soviet Union's international trade in 1958 was carried on with other countries in the Communist bloc. More than half of its remaining trade was with countries of western Europe.

## SIZE, BOUNDARIES, AND RESOURCES OF THE SOVIET HOMELAND

We may now proceed to consider some of the pertinent physical and locational characteristics and the territorial evolution of this immense country of 209 million people (1959) which has witnessed such revolutionary developments since 1917, and whose future poses so much uncertainty for mankind.

▶ *Size*

The territorial base from which Soviet ambitions proceed is the largest country in

---

[7] *Fortune* (June 1957), p. 218. Different sources vary appreciably but generally credit the USSR with a total industrial output in the late 1950s amounting to one fourth to one half of total United States output.

[8] See Marshall I. Goldman, "The Soviet Standard of Living and Ours." *Foreign Affairs*, v. 38 (1960), pp. 625–637.

area on the globe. It is, in fact, a country which ranks with the continents in size. With a total area of approximately 8.6 million square miles, Soviet Russia is larger than either the North American mainland or South America. It is more than twice as large as China, Canada, the United States, or Brazil, 40 times as large as France, and 171 times as large as England. One out of every seven square miles of the earth's land surface is Soviet territory (one out of every six if the ice caps of Antarctica and Greenland are excluded).

Even more impressive, perhaps, than its area is the tremendous east-west extent of the Soviet Union. The westernmost point of the country, near Kaliningrad (formerly Königsberg) on the Baltic Sea, is separated from Cape Dezhnev (East Cape) on Bering Strait by approximately 170° of longitude, representing a distance of nearly halfway around the world. In terms of sun time this means a difference of approximately 11 hours between the easternmost and westernmost points of the USSR. When it is 6:00 A.M. by sun time at Kaliningrad, it is already 9:00 A.M. in the Ural Mountains and is approaching 1:30 in the afternoon at Vladivostok. At Cape Dezhnev it is shortly after 5:00 P.M. The time difference between Kaliningrad and Cape Dezhnev is more than twice the difference between New York and London (5 hours) and is nearly four times the difference between New York and San Francisco (3 hours).

[EDITORIAL COMMENT. The concepts of longitude and time are closely related. The meridians of longitude are imaginary straight lines connecting the poles. Every meridian runs due north and south. The meridians converge at the poles and are widest apart at the equator. Longitude, like latitude, is measured in degrees, minutes, and seconds. The meridian which is customarily used as a base, or starting point, runs through the Royal Astronomical Observatory in Greenwich, England. It is known as the meridian of Greenwich, or prime meridian. Every point on a given meridian has the same longitude. The prime meridian has a longitude of 0°. Places east of the prime meridian are in east longitude; places west of it are in west longitude. The meridian of 180°, exactly halfway around the world from the prime meridian, is the dividing line between places east and west of Greenwich. The longitude of Kaliningrad is correctly stated as 20°31′ East of Greenwich, or simply as 20°31′E. The longitude of Cape Dezhnev is 170°W. At the equator, 1° of longitude is equivalent to 69.15 statute miles. Since the circumference of the earth decreases toward the poles, however, a degree of longitude at 60°N., the latitude of Leningrad, is equivalent to only 34.6 miles.

The earth, rotating on its axis, turns completely around once every 24 hours. Thus it turns through 15° of longitude every hour (360° divided by 24) or 1° every four minutes. Since the earth turns toward the east, the day breaks and the sun comes into view on the Pacific side of the USSR while places farther west are still in darkness. It is noon at a place when the earth's turning has brought the meridian of that place directly under the sun, that is, when the sun has climbed highest above the horizon for that day. Noon occurs simultaneously at all points along a given meridian. When it is noon at Vladivostok by sun time, the earth must still turn for approximately 7½ hours before the meridian of Kaliningrad will come under the sun and it will be noon at that place. In other words, the apparent solar time (sun time) at Kaliningrad is about 4:30 A.M. when the time at Vladivostok is 12 noon.

Development of modern means of transportation has made it desirable to establish standard time zones so that the same time prevails over a considerable extent of longitude. Watches of travelers are set forward or back one hour when crossing the boundary of such a zone. The United States, excluding Alaska and Hawaii, has four standard time

THE SOVIET UNION

INDEX MAP

URBAN AREAS
(NATIONAL CAPITAL UNDERLINED)

- ⊙ 5,000,000
- ⊙ 3,000,000
- ● 500,000-1,000,000
- ● 250,000-500,000
- ○ SELECTED SMALLER PLACES

0    200    400    600
MILES

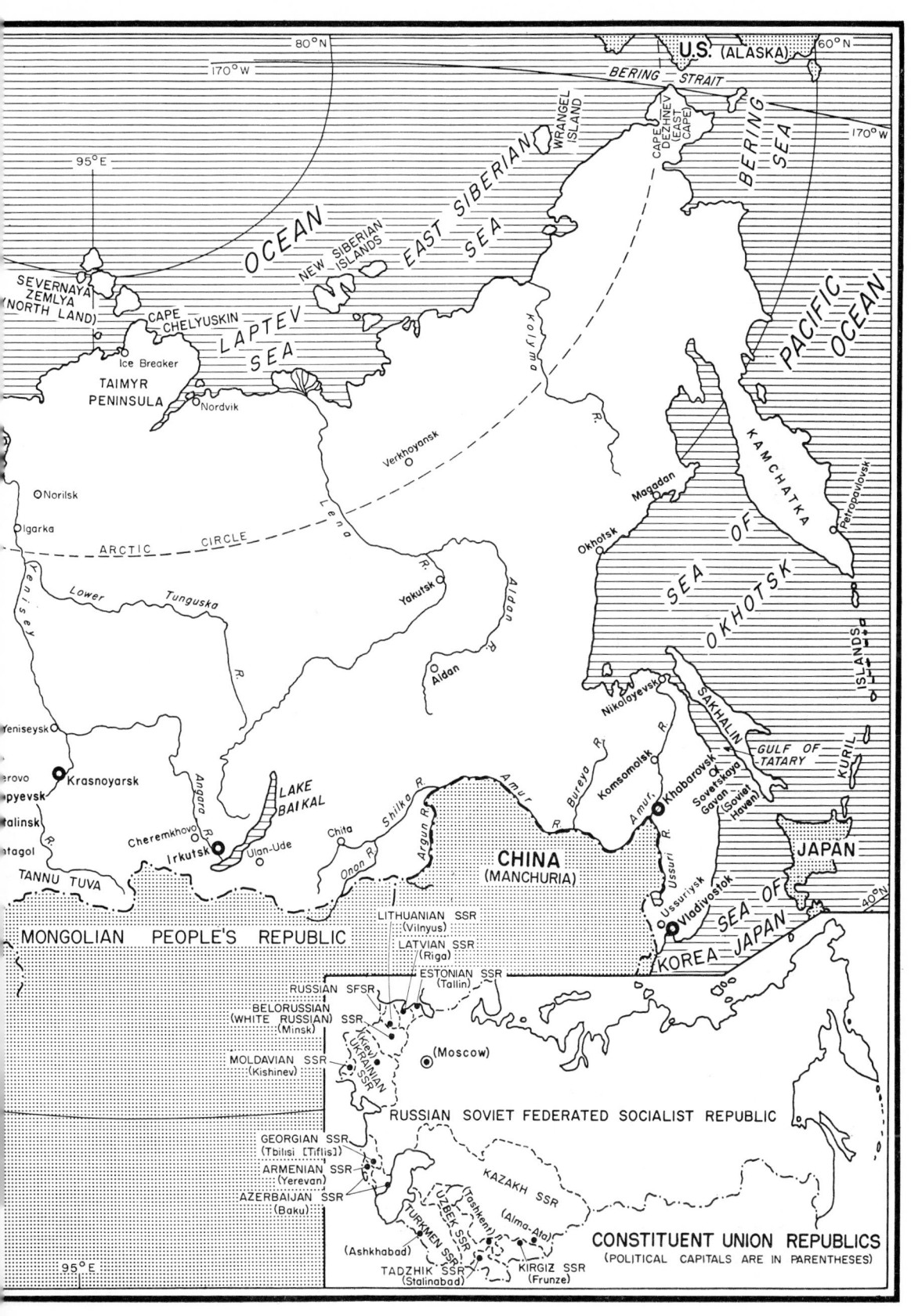

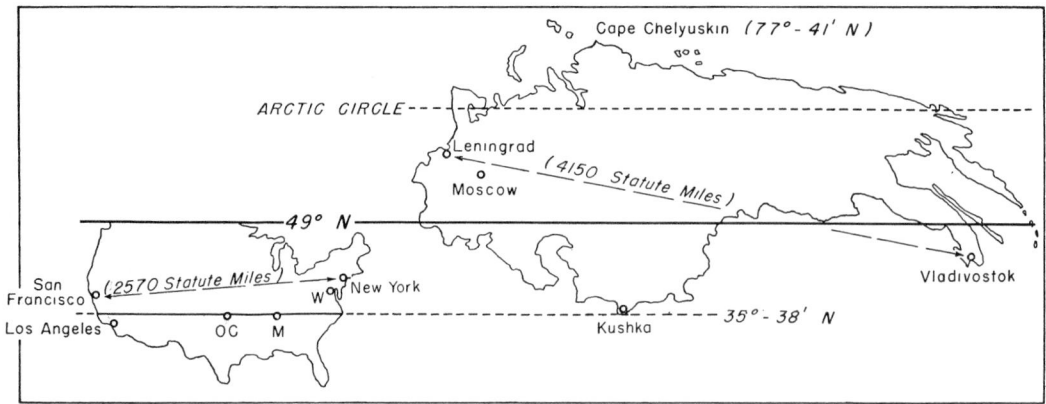

The Soviet Union compared in latitude and area with the continental United States. Key to cities: M, Memphis; OC, Oklahoma City; W, Washington, D. C.

zones (Eastern, Central, Mountain, Pacific). The Soviet Union has eleven such zones.]

The east-west length of the Soviet Union is much greater than its north-south width, but even the latter is impressive. The maximum latitudinal extent, exclusive of islands in the Arctic Ocean, is about 42°, which is short by only 5° of the combined extent of the United States and the Canadian mainland. Cape Chelyuskin (77°41′N.) in the Soviet Arctic is about 6° farther north than any point on the mainland of Canada, while the town of Kushka (35°38′N.) in Soviet Middle Asia is in the general latitude of Memphis, Tennessee, and Oklahoma City, Oklahoma, and is only 1° farther north than Los Angeles, California (map, above).

### ▶ Sea Frontiers

The land and water boundaries of the USSR have a total length of about 37,500 miles.[9] More than two thirds of this distance is coastline, giving the Soviet Union a longer sea frontage than any other country. To only a limited degree, however, does the USSR have unrestricted access to the world ocean. Despite its great length of coast, it is essentially a landlocked country. Most of the main ports are located on seas that have entrances controlled by other countries. The water passages that give access to the Baltic Sea from the Atlantic Ocean (the Danish Straits and the Kiel Canal) pass through Danish, Swedish, or West German territory, while the entrance to the Black Sea is controlled by Turkey. The entrances to the Sea of Japan are controlled or flanked by Japan and South Korea. Acquisition of the Kuril Islands from Japan has given unrestricted access to the Sea of Okhotsk, but that body of water borders remote and sparsely populated regions, is frozen for a considerable period in winter, has no rail connection with the rest of the country, and is used relatively little by shipping.

Most of the Arctic Ocean ports are small, and except in the extreme west are completely icebound for more then half of the year. Nearly all of the major Soviet ports are hampered to some degree by winter freezing, although most ports on the Black Sea, Baltic Sea, and Sea of Japan can be kept open all winter by the use of icebreakers. However, Leningrad, the foremost seaport of the USSR, is frozen in for a few weeks in midwinter. Only in the far northwest does a stretch of coast bordering the Barents Sea give unrestricted access to the open ocean. A tongue of water from the North Atlantic Drift warms this coast in winter and makes

[9] N. T. Mirov, *Geography of Russia*. New York: Wiley; London: Chapman and Hall, 1951, p. 3.

it possible for icebreakers to keep open the harbor of Murmansk. The latter city is connected with Leningrad and Moscow by rail. However, its value as a port is lessened by remoteness from the main centers of population and industry in the USSR.

### ▶ Land Frontiers

The Soviet Union has a common land frontier with no less than twelve other countries in Europe and Asia. Along the 8000-mile boundary between the Black Sea and the Pacific Ocean, it borders Turkey, Iran, Afghanistan, China, the Mongolian People's Republic, and North Korea (map, pp. 232–233). The Soviet frontiers in Asia are mostly found in mountainous or arid regions which form sparsely populated zones of separation between the USSR and the core regions of the bordering countries. In Middle Asia only a narrow corridor of Afghan territory separates the Soviet Union from the northern boundary of the Indian subcontinent. However, the frontier zone lies in extremely rugged and difficult mountain country, so that the narrow political separation as seen on a map does not express the true reality of military and economic separation. In the Far East the Soviet island of Sakhalin is separated by a 25-mile-wide strait from the northernmost main island of Japan, and even narrower straits separate Japan from the Russian-held Kuril Islands. If India, Pakistan, and Japan are included, the Soviet Union in Asia is a neighbor of about half the world's people.

The Soviet frontiers on the west are very different from the frontiers in Asia. This is especially true of the 900-mile-long boundary zone between the Black Sea and the Baltic Sea. Here the USSR abuts on Romania, Hungary, Czechoslovakia, and Poland. The boundary line passes mostly through well-populated lowlands that have long been disputed territory between the Russian state and its western neighbors. The fluctuating boundaries in this area have contrasted with Soviet boundaries in Asia, which have changed relatively little during the twentieth century. Since 1939 the USSR has made important gains of territory along the Black Sea–Baltic frontier. The boundary has been pushed westward 100 to 200 miles in Poland, although not so far west as the boundary of Russian-held territory in Poland prior to World War I. From Czechoslovakia the Soviet Union has acquired a section of the Carpathian Mountains known as Ruthenia or Transcarpathian Ukraine, and thus has gained a common frontier with Hungary. From Romania the USSR has taken Bessarabia and Northern Bukovina, thus pushing the Romanian boundary 50 to 125 miles farther west. Previous mention has been made of the absorption of Lithuania, Latvia, and Estonia in 1940. In addition, the northern half of the former German province of East Prussia has been incorporated by the USSR. (See map, p. 202.)

The Black Sea–Baltic line is seriously lacking in natural defenses. During the course of history it has been crossed many times by invading armies, including the French under Napoleon in 1812 and more recently the German armies in 1941. The recent frontier changes have shortened the boundary and have given the Soviet Union additional defense in depth. Other strategic advantages which have accrued to the USSR are (1) a better frontage on the Gulf of Finland and a new frontage on the Baltic Sea proper, (2) possession of a number of strategic junction points on major rail lines leading westward, including the important rail hub of Lvov (410,000), acquired from Poland, (3) control over important passes leading to the plains of Hungary through former Czechoslovak territory in the low central Carpathians, and (4) a frontage on the northernmost of the three main distributaries of the Danube River.

The USSR has also made important strategic gains along the 900-mile frontier between the Gulf of Finland and the Barents Sea. It has taken from Finland the Karelian Isthmus between Lake Ladoga and the Gulf of Finland (map, p. 164). By this means the defensibility of the important city of Leningrad has been increased. Prior to 1940 the city lay only about 12 or 15 miles from the nearest points on the Finnish border. Conversely, Soviet acquisition of the Karelian Isthmus has lessened the ability of the Finns to defend themselves against a military move by the USSR and has deprived them of the important timber port of Viipuri (now Vyborg; 51,000). A further cession of Finnish territory to the USSR in the far north has given the latter nation a common frontier with Norway and important nickel mines and smelting facilities in the Pechenga (Petsamo) district.[10]

## ▶ Natural Resources

Soviet economic and military strength rests in considerable measure on an outstanding endowment of natural resources. Within the vast confines of the USSR, nature has assembled a rich and varied complement of minerals and water resources, together with enormous areas of forest and grazing land, some of the world's most fertile soils, and sizable resources of fur, fish, and game. Although much of the country is handicapped by excessive cold, low rainfall, poor drainage, acid soils, or rugged terrain, the over-all resource base of the Soviet Union is undoubtedly superior to that possessed by any other nation with the exception of the United States.

### The Superior Mineral Position of the USSR [11]

The resource position of the Soviet Union is particularly strong with regard to minerals. The USSR is well supplied for the foreseeable future with deposits of coal, lignite, petroleum, and natural gas among the mineral fuels; iron, magnesium, titanium, antimony, platinum, and the ferroalloys manganese, vanadium, and chromium among the metals; phosphate, potash, common salt, and sulfur among the major chemical raw materials; and asbestos, bromine, graphite, mica, fluorspar, china clay, fire clay, and mercury among other minerals. Somewhat less adequate are Soviet reserves of the basic nonferrous metals copper and aluminum and the important ferroalloy nickel. Nevertheless, the USSR is known to have sizable reserves and is an important producer of all three. Domestic reserves of aluminum are supplemented by the import of bauxite from Hungary and Greece. Definite deficiencies exist in the case of lead, zinc, and possibly tin among the basic nonferrous metals; cobalt, molybdenum, and tungsten among the ferroalloys; and possibly uranium. However, the USSR has small to medium-sized deposits of even these minerals, and the deficiencies can be at least partly overcome by imports from other nations of the Communist bloc, such as tungsten and tin from China, zinc from Poland, and uranium from East Germany, Czechoslovakia, Bulgaria, and Romania.

The USSR is known to be a major producer of gold, but data on Soviet gold reserves are very meager. Important diamond-bearing formations were discovered in Siberia in 1954–1956 (see p. 271).

The coal and lignite reserves of the Soviet Union are exceedingly widespread, but the known reserves of most other minerals are concentrated in a relatively few areas. The outstanding mineralized areas, together with the minerals for which each area is particularly noteworthy, are as follows (maps, p. 254):

1. The Ukraine (coal, iron, manganese, common salt, natural gas).
2. The Ural Mountains (iron, ferroalloys, copper, aluminum, potash, asbestos).

---

[10] The foregoing discussion of Soviet frontier changes is mainly based on W. Gordon East, "The New Frontiers of the Soviet Union." *Foreign Affairs,* v. 29 (1951), pp. 591–607.

[11] The discussion under this heading is principally based on Demitri B. Shimkin, *Minerals: A Key to Soviet Power.* Cambridge, Mass.: Harvard University Press, 1953, *passim.*

3. The Volga–Urals ("Second Baku") oil field (petroleum, natural gas).
4. The Caucasus-Caspian region (petroleum, natural gas, manganese, lead, zinc).
5. The Kazakh Upland of Soviet Middle Asia (coal, copper).
6. The Altai Mountains (lead, zinc).
7. The Kuznetsk Basin of south central Siberia (coal).

8. The Kola Peninsula, adjoining Finland and Norway (phosphate, nickel, copper, iron).

On the whole, the mineral position of the USSR appears extremely strong, and seems likely to be improved by future discoveries of minerals in the varied geological formations with which the country is endowed.

# THE SEVERE CLIMATE OF THE SOVIET UNION

Despite its immense area and resources, large and growing population, and increasing industrial production, the Soviet Union suffers from a number of important disadvantages which tend to lessen its effectiveness as a political, economic, and military power. Among these might be mentioned (1) the difficulty of providing adequate transportation and communication facilities in a country of such vast distances and containing so much marshy, arid, densely forested, and mountainous terrain, and (2) the additional burden on transportation and the problems of defense caused by the peripheral location of many important centers of population, mining, agriculture, and manufacturing. Not the least among Soviet disadvantages is (3) the severe climate.

## ▶ General Nature of the Climate
Most parts of the Soviet Union have a continental climate characterized by long, cold winters, warm to hot summers, and low to moderate precipitation. The severe winters are the result of a northerly continental location, coupled with mountain barriers on the south and east. Four fifths of the total area is farther north than any point in the continental United States (map, p. 234). The Soviet Union lies principally in the higher middle latitudes of the Northern Hemisphere where the land masses of the world reach their greatest extent relative to the bordering oceans. In these latitudes the climatic influence of the land is paramount over the influence of the sea in continental interiors, and the most extreme continental climates of the world prevail. The effects of continental location are heightened in the Soviet Union by the presence of the Arctic Ocean on the north, which is frozen for most of the year and thus in a sense forms an extension of the land. Continuous chains of mountains and high plateaus occupying the southern and eastern margins of the country act as a screen against moderating influences from the Indian and Pacific oceans. In addition, most of the USSR is a zone of high atmospheric pressure in winter, with resultant outflowing winds. Westerly winds from the Atlantic serve to moderate the winter temperatures somewhat, but their effects become steadily weaker toward the east. Thus Leningrad (60°N., 30°E.) has an average January temperature of 18°F., whereas Yakutsk (62°N., 130°E.) has a January average of −46° and Verkhoyansk (68°N., 133°E.) a January average of −58°.

Aside from the interior of eastern Siberia, most parts of the USSR experience winter temperatures which do not differ greatly from the temperatures of places located at comparable latitudes and altitudes in the interior of North America. Indeed, many places in the west and south of the Soviet Union are actually warmer in midwinter than comparable interior places in North America. Kiev (50°N.) is 24° warmer in January on the average than Winnipeg, Odessa (46°N.) is 12° warmer than Montreal, and Tashkent (41°N.) is 8° warmer than Omaha. Moscow has the same average temperature in January as Minneapolis, although located 11° farther north. Leningrad, located a thousand miles north of Minneapolis, is 4° warmer in January than the latter city.

Nevertheless, the Soviet Union as a whole is definitely handicapped by the winter climate. Huge areas are permanently frozen at a depth of a few feet. The average frost-free season of 150 days or less in most parts of the country except the extreme south and west is too short for a wide range of crops to mature.

Most places are relatively warm during the brief summer, and the southern steppes and deserts are hot. A factor partially offsetting the brevity of the summer is the length of summer days. Leningrad has 19 hours of daylight on June 22, and Moscow has 17½ hours. Throughout the summer long hours of sunlight facilitate the growth of plants and thus compensate somewhat for the shortness of the growing season.

From an agricultural standpoint, lack of moisture is probably an even greater handicap to the Soviet Union than low temperatures. The annual precipitation is less than 20 inches nearly everywhere except in the extreme west, along the eastern coast of the Black Sea and the Pacific littoral north of Vladivostock, and in some of the higher mountain areas. North of the Arctic Circle and in the southern desert zone, the average precipitation is less than 10 inches. Since most of the precipitation is derived from the Atlantic Ocean, the total amount tends to decrease from west to east. Precipitation also decreases toward the south, being 10 to 20 inches in the fertile black-earth belt, but only 5 to 10 inches or even less in the dry steppes and deserts farther south. The country's most important grain-producing region, the black-earth belt (map, p. 252), is subject to severe droughts and to hot, desiccating winds which may greatly damage or destroy a crop. Areas to the north of this belt in European Russia have a somewhat greater and more dependable rainfall, cou-

pled with a lower rate of evaporation resulting from lower temperatures. Thus they are better supplied with moisture than the black-earth belt, but this advantage is offset by their poorer soils, cooler summers, shorter growing season, and larger proportion of poorly drained land.

## ► *Types of Climate*

In the USSR five main east-west climatic belts—tundra, subarctic, humid continental, steppe, and desert—are customarily recognized in classifications of climate. These belts, each with its associated vegetation and soils, succeed each other from north to south in the order named (see front end-paper climatic map).

### Tundra Climate

The zone of *tundra climate* occupies a continuous strip, 50 to several hundred miles in width, along the Arctic coast from the Norwegian frontier to Bering Strait. Tundra is both a climatic and a vegetational term. Climatically, it signifies a region which has at least one month averaging above 32°F. but which has no month averaging higher than 50°. In most areas of tundra two to four months average above freezing. Generally speaking, the climatic conditions of the tundra are too severe for trees to grow, except in a few protected localities and toward the southern margins, where trees are found along the streams. The typical vegetation of this treeless region consists of mosses, lichens, sedges, and scrubby bushes. Some of the islands in the Arctic Ocean, including northern Novaya Zemlya, have temperatures averaging below freezing or only slightly above freezing even during the warmest month of the year. Here much of the land is covered with glaciers and an ice-cap climate similar to that of Antarctica or interior Greenland prevails.

### Subarctic Climate

At the south, the tundra climate gradually merges with the zone of *subarctic climate*. In this climatic zone from one to four months

A lumbering operation in the taiga. The photo was taken in the Karelian Autonomous SSR, adjoining Finland. (Sovfoto.)

average above 50°F. Thus the subarctic climate differs from the tundra climate in having a warmer summer. Winters, however, are extremely long and cold, most places averaging below freezing for five to seven months. This climate type occupies a wedge-shaped area extending from the Finnish border to the Pacific Ocean. It is narrowest at the west and broadens eastward to the neighborhood of Lake Baikal, where it occupies the full width of the country except for a narrow strip of tundra at the north.

The zone of subarctic climate is essentially coextensive with the *taiga,* or northern coniferous forest. The taiga of the Soviet Union is the largest continuous area of forest land on earth. A similar belt of forest covers much of Canada (see back end-paper vegetation map). The prevailing tree species are spruce, fir, larch, and pine. These coniferous softwood trees, while useful for pulpwood and firewood, are frequently too small, twisted, or knotty to make good lumber. Nevertheless, vast reserves of timber suitable for lumber exist in parts of the taiga, and this part of the Soviet Union is one of the major areas of lumbering in the world. Intermixed with the conifers of the taiga are stands of certain broad-leaved species such as birch and aspen. These deciduous trees are of little commercial utility. They are ordinarily second growth, replacing stands of conifers removed by fires or cutting.

Some agricultural settlement occurs in the taiga, especially toward the south. However, the farming is definitely of a marginal character. Agriculture in this forested region is handicapped by (1) the short summers, (2) the severe cold of winter, which makes it difficult for winter grains and fruit trees to survive, (3) the unseasonable frosts that often occur in late spring or early fall, (4) the marshy or swampy character of much of the land, and (5) the prevalence of poor soils. The dominant soils of the taiga are the *podzols* (see back end-paper soils map). This term, derived from Russian words translated as "ashes underneath," refers to a group of soils which characteristically have a grayish, bleached appearance when plowed, are lacking in well-decomposed organic matter, are poorly structured, and are very low in natural fertility. The acidity of these soils is unfavorable for most crops and also for bacteria, earthworms, and other soil-improving organisms.

The boundary between the taiga and the tundra is not a sharp line, although it appears so when generalized on small-scale maps. A transitional area of "wooded tundra" (small forest stands alternating with tundra) marks the contact between the tundra and taiga in most places.

### Humid Continental Climate

South of the subarctic zone a triangular area of *humid continental climate* extends eastward from the western border of the USSR to the vicinity of Novosibirsk. At the west the triangle is more than 600 miles wide, but the Siberian portion averages only 100 to 200 miles in width. Roughly half the total population of the USSR is found within this climate zone. The humid continental climate of the USSR differs from the subarctic climate in having longer summers, milder winters, and more precipitation. However, these are only differences of degree. Even

within the humid continental zone most places have an average frost-free period of 150 days or less, except at the extreme west (Leningrad, 160 days; Kiev, 172 days). Winters are long and cold, with average cold-month temperatures ranging from −3°F. (Novosibirsk) to 24°F. (Riga). The average annual precipitation is relatively low, being only 18 to 25 inches at most places. However, the low rate of evaporation increases the effectiveness of the precipitation, so that the available moisture is generally adequate for the staple crops of this climate zone. The Soviet Union has the short-summer subtype of humid continental climate. A comparable climate is found in the Great Lakes region and the northern Great Plains of the United States and Canada. In this climate zone of the USSR mixed or deciduous forest supplants the evergreen taiga forest. Oak, ash, maple, elm, and other deciduous species alternate with coniferous trees in the vegetation cover. At the south is found the "wooded steppe," a transitional zone between the deciduous forest and the open steppe grassland.

Both climate and soil are more favorable for agriculture in the area of humid continental climate than in the subarctic zone. Soils developed under a cover of deciduous or mixed forest are normally more fertile by nature than the podzols of the taiga, although less fertile than grassland soils. The forest soils in the area of humid continental climate are of major importance in Soviet agriculture, supporting a varied development of crop and livestock farming. Among the climatic regions of the USSR, only the steppe region vies with the humid continental area in total farm production.

### Steppe Climate

The grassy plains of Russia south of the forest zone are known as the *steppe,* or steppes. This term refers both to a type of climate and to the characteristic form of vegetation associated with it. On climatic maps the zone of steppe climate in the USSR is shown as an east-west band of varying width extending from the Romanian border to the Altai Mountains in Soviet Asia. As compared with the humid continental short-summer type of climate, the steppe climate is characterized by warmer summers, a somewhat longer frost-free season, and less precipitation. The average annual precipitation is 10 to 20 inches, an amount barely sufficient for growing crops without irrigation. Recurring periods of drought add to the hazards of farming in the steppe zone. Nevertheless, this part of the Soviet Union is a major area of crop and livestock production. The handicap of low and variable rainfall is partially offset by the fertility of the soils in the famous *black-earth belt*. This expanse of deep, black, exceedingly fertile soils extends for about 3000 miles in an east-west direction and 300 to 600 miles from north to south (map, p. 252). The characteristic soils of the belt are the *chernozems*—a term meaning "black earth." Chernozem soils are exceptionally thick, productive, and durable, being in fact among the best soils to be found anywhere. A similar belt of soils occurs in the eastern Great Plains of North America. The great fertility of the chernozems is largely due to an abundance of well-decomposed organic matter or *humus* in the topsoil and to the presence of sufficient lime to neutralize excessive acidity. Strictly speaking, the term humus refers to organic remains, both plant and animal, which have been decomposed by bacteria and have become part of the soil. Complete decomposition of humus makes available to plants the nutrients it contains, and its presence in the soil is essential to the development of a friable structure that permits easy cultivation and helps the soil to retain moisture. The accumulated remains of annual grasses in mid-latitude prairies and steppes are a better source of humus than the leaves and twigs of a forest. The steppe zone of the USSR includes extensive areas of *chestnut soils* in the areas of lighter rainfall south of the chernozems. The chestnut soils are lighter in color than the chernozems and lack the superb fertility of the latter soils. Nevertheless, they are among the better soils of the world. In North America a belt of chestnut soils occurs to the west of the chernozems in the Great Plains.

Within the zone of steppe climate a considerable range of natural vegetation types is found, varying from tall grass and scattered forest stands in the "wooded steppe," where moisture is more abundant, to a sparse cover of low grasses and shrubs in the drier areas. The most characteristic form of natural vegetation is short grass, forming a carpet which is continuous, or nearly so. The treeless steppe grasslands, stretching monotonously over a vast area between the forest zone and the southern mountains and deserts, were tenanted from an early time by tribes of pastoral nomads with their flocks and herds. Today, however, much of the steppe is cultivated, with wheat as the main crop. In addition to wheat, it is a major producer of sugar beets, of sunflowers grown for vegetable oil, and of various other crops.

Some confusion is occasioned by the fact that the wooded steppe and a portion of the black-earth belt extend into the zone of humid continental climate as customarily defined on climatic maps. However, the treeless part of the steppe is largely outside of the humid continental zone, as is the larger part of the black-earth belt.

### Desert Climate

To the east and immediate north of the Caspian Sea, the steppe zone trends gradually into an extensive area of desert. In the desert zone rainfall is even more scanty and erratic than in the steppe. Widely spaced shrubs and occasional tufts of grass afford only the sparsest pasturage for livestock. Agriculture is largely precluded by lack of moisture, except for oases watered by streams that originate in the high mountains which border this desert region on the south and east. The desert zone of the Soviet

Union includes two extensive areas of sandy desert. Such deserts are a type made familiar by the movies, but are much less common on a world basis than deserts floored by gravel, rock fragments, or the bare bedrock.

### Subtropical, Monsoon, and Highland Climates

A number of relatively small but distinctive climatic areas remain to be mentioned. The south coast of the Crimean Peninsula, sheltered by the Yaila Mountains, has the mild temperatures and summer rainfall minimum associated with the *mediterranean* or *dry-summer subtropical* climate. This picturesque area, with its orchards, vineyards, and resorts, of which Yalta is the most famous, is sometimes referred to as the "Russian Riviera." A subtropical climate also

prevails in the coastal lowlands and valleys south of the high Caucasus Mountains. Mild winters and warm to hot summers are characteristic throughout the lowlands of Transcaucasia. However, the rainfall is very unevenly distributed. The lowlands bordering the Black Sea in western Transcaucasia receive the heaviest rainfall of the USSR (50 to 100 inches annually) and are classed as *humid subtropical* in climate, while the lowlands of eastern Transcaucasia, bordering the Caspian Sea, receive so little precipitation in most places that they are classed as steppe.

The coastal regions of the Soviet Far East, from Vladivostok northward to the mouth of the Amur River, have a humid continental climate characterized by a distinct *monsoon* tendency. As in nearby parts of Korea

## TABLE 11

### CLIMATIC DATA FOR SELECTED SOVIET STATIONS

| STATION | LATITUDE AND LONGITUDE TO NEAREST WHOLE DEGREE | ELEVA- TION ABOVE SEA LEVEL (FEET) | TYPE OF CLIMATE | AVERAGE TEMPERATURE (DEGREES F TO NEAREST WHOLE DEGREE) | | | AVERAGE LENGTH OF FROST-FREE SEASON (DAYS) | AVERAGE ANNUAL PRECIPI- TATION TO NEAREST INCH |
|---|---|---|---|---|---|---|---|---|
| | | | | AN- NUAL | JANU- ARY | JULY | | |
| Arkhangelsk (Archangel) | 65°N., 87°E. | 50 | Subarctic | 32° | 8° | 59° | 120 | 17″ |
| Igarka | 67°N., 87°E. | 115 | Subarctic | 17° | −20° | 59° | no data | 16″ |
| Nordvik | 74°N., 111°E. | 102 | Tundra | 7° | −21° | 41° | no data | 5″ |
| Verkhoyansk | 68°N., 133°E. | 400 | Subarctic | 3° | −58° | 60° | 65 | 5″ |
| Leningrad | 60°N., 30°E. | 30 | Humid continental | 39° | 18° | 63° | 160 | 19″ |
| Moscow | 56°N., 38°E. | 480 | Humid continental | 40° | 14° | 66° | 130 | 21″ |
| Sverdlovsk | 57°N., 61°E. | 925 | Humid continental | 33° | 3° | 63° | no data | 17″ |
| Novosibirsk | 55°N., 83°E. | 436 | Humid continental | 31° | −3° | 66° | 122 | 15″ |
| Irkutsk | 52°N., 104°E. | 1532 | Subarctic | 30° | −6° | 63° | 95 | 15″ |
| Vladivostok | 43°N., 132°E. | 95 | Humid continental | 40° | 7° | 69° (August) | 152 | 24″ |
| Odessa | 46°N., 31°E. | 210 | Steppe | 50° | 26° | 73° | 208 | 16″ |
| Yalta | 45°N., 34°E. | 135 | Mediterranean | 56° | 39° | 75° | 245 | 20″ |
| Batumi | 42°N., 42°E. | 20 | Humid subtropical | 58° | 43° | 73° | 308 | 93″ |
| Baku | 40°N., 50°E. | 0 | Steppe | 57° | 38° | 77° | 296 | 10″ |
| Akmolinsk | 51°N., 71°E. | 1148 | Steppe | 35° | 0° | 70° | no data | 11″ |
| Tashkent | 41°N., 69°E. | 1568 | Steppe | 56° | 30° | 80° | 206 | 15″ |
| Krasnovodsk | 40°N., 53°E. | −56 | Desert | 61° | 37° | 84° | no data | 5″ |

and of China, most of the annual rainfall results from moist onshore winds of the summer monsoon. In contrast, the cold outflowing winds of the winter monsoon produce little precipitation. The average annual precipitation is 20 to 30 inches, of which three fourths or more falls from April through September.

The mountains of the USSR are characterized by climates varying according to altitude. However, the range of climates is smaller than in mountains located closer to he equator.

Climatic data for selected Soviet stations are given in Table 11.

# TERRITORIAL EVOLUTION OF MODERN RUSSIA

Territorial and economic expansion, so much in evidence during recent decades, is not a new theme in Russian history. The gigantic Russian state has reached its present limits through a long process of colonization, conquest, territorial annexation, and associated economic development extending back for more than a thousand years.

The modern phase of this process began toward the end of the European Middle Ages. In the second half of the fifteenth century Ivan III, the ruler of Muscovy, a small feudal state with its capital at Moscow, began to expand his holdings rapidly by military conquest or the threat of conquest. To the north the rival principality of Novgorod was annexed and a domain thus secured which extended to the Arctic Ocean and eastward to the Ural Mountains. Ivan IV, the Terrible or Dread, added large new territories by conquering the Tatar (Tartar) khanates of Kazan and Astrakhan in 1552 and 1554, respectively, thus giving the Russian state control over the entire course of the Volga River. Upon ascending the throne in 1547 Ivan was crowned as tsar (czar or Caesar), being the first Russian ruler to assume this title. Later tsars pushed the frontiers of Russia westward toward Poland and the Baltic Sea and southward toward the Black Sea. Peter the Great (reigned 1689–1725) gained a secure foothold on the Baltic Sea by defeating the Swedes under Charles XII, and Catherine the Great (reigned 1762–1796) secured a frontage on the Black Sea at the expense of Turkey.

Meanwhile the conquest of Siberia had proceeded rapidly. This vast, thinly populated wilderness between the Urals and the Pacific Ocean was already being penetrated by traders and Cossack military pioneers at the end of Ivan the Dread's reign. In 1639 a Cossack expedition reached the Pacific. Russian expansion toward the east did not stop at Bering Strait, but continued down the west coast of North America as far as northern California, where a Russian trading post existed between 1812 and 1841. In 1867, however, Alaska was sold to the United States and Russia withdrew from North America.

## ▶ Role of the Rivers in Russian Expansion

Early Russian expansion in Eurasia followed the river lines. The Moscow region lies in a low upland from which a number of large rivers radiate like spokes of a wheel. The longest rivers lead southward (map, p. 232): the Volga to the landlocked Caspian Sea, the Dnieper (Dnepr) to the Black Sea, and the Don to the Sea of Azov, which is connected with the Black Sea through a narrow strait. Shorter rivers lead north and northwest to the Arctic Ocean and the Baltic Sea. These river systems are accessible to each other by easy portages. In the early history of Russia the rivers formed natural passageways for trade, conquest, and colonization. The technique of expansion followed by the tsars was to dominate the river lines by *ostrogs* (blockhouses) built at portages and other strategic places. From these strong points political control could gradually be extended over the hinterland.

## ▶ Expansion in Siberia

The rivers were especially valuable aids to expansion in the enormous reaches of Siberia. The latter region, half again as large as the United States, is drained by some of the greatest rivers on earth: the Ob, Yenisey, Lena, and Kolyma, flowing to the Arctic Ocean, and the Amur, flowing to the Pacific. By following these rivers and their lateral tributaries the Russians advanced from the Urals to the Pacific in less than a century. The latter movement has been summarized as follows by a specialist on Russian expansion, Robert J. Kerner: [12]

The earliest background of the eastward movement across the Urals is to be found in the fur-trading enterprise of Novgorod. Daring merchants and trappers from Novgorod exploited the lower reaches of the Ob from about the fourteenth century by portaging from the tributaries of the Pechora. They and the Muscovites, who carried out expeditions in 1465, 1483, and 1499, raided the inhabitants beyond the Urals for the purpose of obtaining tributes of furs, of which there was a diminishing supply in European Russia. The Russian raids were often followed by counterraids of Siberian natives, which endangered the security of the Ural frontier. It was the latter which especially concerned Tsar Ivan the Dread. He received news that the Volga pirate Yermak, who was wanted for offenses against the laws of tsardom, had, in the employ of the Novgorodian family of the Stroganovs, raided beyond the Urals. The tsar, in fact, ordered the Stroganovs to bring him back for trial. He feared the Ural frontier would be overrun by the tribesmen of the Tatar khan, Kuchum. Yermak's success in capturing Sibir, the capital of Siberia, caused the tsar to change his intentions in regard to Yermak; instead of beheading him he gave Yermak his blessing and a real coat of armor. Incidentally,

it was this heavy accoutrement that caused Yermak to lose his life by drowning.

Moscow took over in 1538 and ended the practice of raids. It initiated a planned domination of rivers and portages through the building of blockhouses, called *ostrogs* in Russian. This was in line with centuries of Russian tradition in Europe. The original motive for the advance into Siberia was the acquisition of furs. Moscow sought to add to it the search for gold and silver. The conquest of the Tatar khanate gave security to the Ural frontier and created a base for further expansion. Thus from its origins to the present day, Russian rule in Asia was planned and regimented from Moscow.

The first Russians in Siberia were fur merchants and trappers, government officials, Cossacks, and Orthodox priests. The advance was rapid, once the khanate had been subdued. Within a decade and a half after Yermak's death the basin of the Ob had become a Russian possession with the ostrog of Tobolsk on the Irtysh, founded in 1587, as the key, but with ostrogs guarding the route to it from Russia and others built on the lower reaches of the Ob and the upper reaches of its tributaries. The pattern set in the Ob basin was followed, in the years 1607–1625, in that of the Yenisey, directly to the east with its center at Yeniseysk (1618). The basin of the Lena was occupied between 1630 and 1648, with its center at Yakutsk, an ostrog founded in 1632. The Russians reached the Pacific in 1639. Their occupation of the Lake Baikal and Amur region, with its center at Irkutsk (1652) followed in the 'fifties and 'sixties. Forced out of the Amur River region by the Chinese under the Manchu emperor Kang-hsi by the negotiations which resulted in the Treaty of Nerchinsk (1689), the Russians lost the base of an adequate supply of grain and vegetables. This was to make their hold on eastern Siberia precarious for nearly two centuries. Even more than that, they lost easy access to the Pacific, which they did not regain until 1858–1860.

Large areas in the Caucasus region and in Turkestan (the arid or semiarid area east of the Caspian Sea) were not secured by Russia until the nineteenth century. These regions, and Siberia as well, were administered as colonial areas by the tsars.

---

[12] Robert J. Kerner, "The Russian Eastward Movement: Some Observations on Its Historical Significance." *Pacific Historical Review,* v. 17 (1948), pp. 136–137. Spellings of some proper names have been slightly modified. Used by permission of the author and the *Pacific Historical Review.*

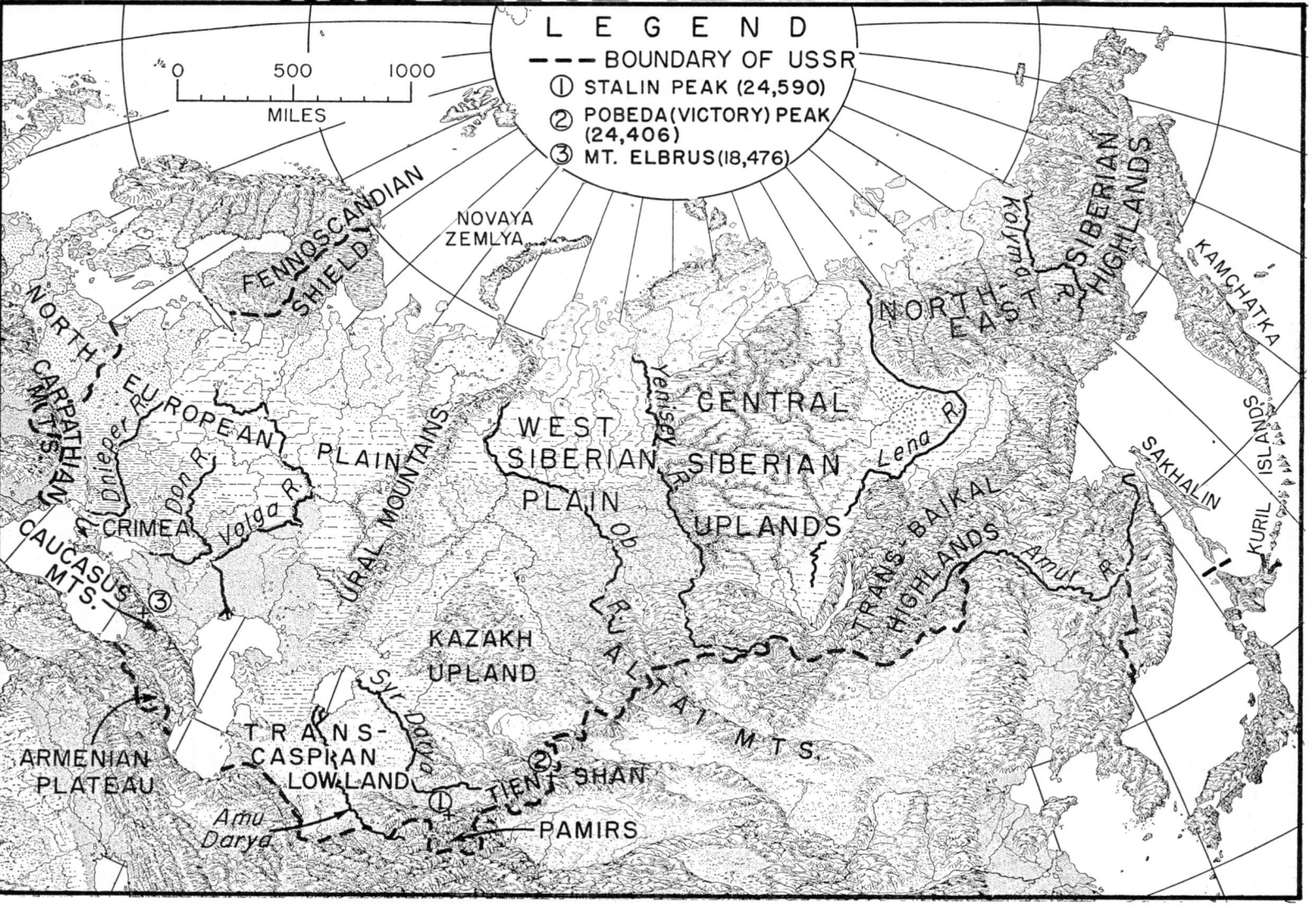

Major landforms of the Soviet Union. (Base map is a portion of A. K. Lobeck's *Physiographic Diagram of Asia,* copyright, The Geographical Press, a division of C. S. Hammond & Company, Maplewood, N. J.)

## ▶ *The Role of Topography*

Most of the important rivers of Russia wind slowly for hundreds or thousands of miles across vast expanses of plain. Early expansion was facilitated not only by the long, continuous highways provided by the rivers themselves, but also by the easy overland connections between river systems. Only in the extreme south and east of Russia are the river basins separated by ranges of high mountains. Elsewhere the divides are ordinarily found in areas of low hills, or even in level plains where the gradients between headstreams are so gentle as to be scarcely perceptible.

Plains and low hills occupy nearly all of Russia from the Yenisey River to the western border of the country (map, p. 245). The only mountains which rise in the midst of this vast lowland are the Urals, a low range located about midway between the western frontier of Russia and the Yenisey. The Urals trend due north and south, but do not occupy the full width of the lowland. A wide gap between the southern end of the mountains and the Caspian Sea permits uninterrupted east-west movement. Actually the Urals themselves do not constitute a serious barrier to transportation, the main range being less than 100 miles wide in most places and cut by river valleys offering easy passageways through the mountains. Today the main rail lines connecting Moscow with Siberia pass directly through the Urals. In general form and elevation these mountains bear many resemblances to the Appalachian Mountains of the United States. Like the Appalachians, they are old, worn-down mountains with rounded contours. The average elevation is less than 2000 feet, and the highest summit, located toward the northern end of the range, is only 6184 feet above sea level. The central Urals are especially low, being little more than high hills. Rail lines connecting Moscow with the important Ural city of Sverdlovsk cross this part of the range over a divide lying at only 1350 feet above sea level. The southern and central Urals are forested, but at the extreme north the mountains extend into the zone of Arctic tundra.

The Russian lowlands west of the Urals are mostly undulating or rolling rather than flat. To the east, however, between the mountains and the Yenisey River, the great lowland of western Siberia is one of the flattest areas on earth. Much of it is covered by immense swamps and marshes through which the Ob River and its tributaries slowly wend their way. This waterlogged country, underlain by a permanently frozen subsoil that blocks drainage, is a major barrier to land transportation and is extremely uninviting to settlement. Large sections are almost devoid of people. In the spring tremendous floods occur when the breakup of ice in the upper basin of the Ob releases great quantities of water while the river channels farther north are still frozen.

The area between the Yenisey and Lena rivers is occupied by hilly uplands lying at a general elevation of 1000 to 1500 feet. Occasional summits reach 3000 feet. East of the Lena River and Lake Baikal the landscape is dominated by mountains. Extreme northeastern Siberia is especially wild and difficult mountain country, with a few peaks reaching elevations of 10,000 feet or more. This bleak region is one of the least inhabited and least known areas on earth.

High mountains border Russia on the south from the Black Sea to Lake Baikal, and lower mountains from Lake Baikal to the Pacific. Elevations of 15,000 feet or higher are reached in the Caucasus Mountains between the Black and Caspian Seas and in the Pamir, Tien Shan, and Altai Mountains east of the Caspian Sea. From the foot of the latter ranges and lower ranges between the Pamirs and Caspian Sea, arid or semiarid plains and low uplands extend northward and gradually merge with the West Siberian Plain and the broad plains and low hills lying west of the Urals.

# Population and Major Territorial Divisions of the USSR

In 1959 the Soviet Union held its first nation-wide census since 1939. The results showed a total population of 208,800,000, as compared with an estimated 1939 population of 190,700,000 and an estimated population total in 1913 of 159,200,000 for the present national territory of the USSR.[1] The increase in population from 1939 to 1959 would, of course, have been much higher had World War II not intervened. It is estimated that this war cost the Soviet Union 30 to 40 million people or more in deaths and unborn children.

[1] Preliminary results from the 1959 census were reported in *Izvestia* for May 10, 1959. Census data cited in Chapters 11 and 12, *including populations of cities,* are from this source. Population figures for cities refer to the city proper and not to the entire metropolitan area as in most chapters of this text. An English translation of the census report was published in the journal *Population Bulletin* for July 1959.

A postwar view of the central thoroughfare in Kiev, the capital of the Ukrainian SSR. The buildings along this street were severely damaged in World War II. (Sovfoto.)

## RECENT POPULATION MOVEMENTS

Two striking movements of population have occurred in recent times. One of these has been a migration, primarily of Russians and Ukrainians, from European Russia to the eastern regions of the country. Between 1939 and 1959 the population of the USSR as a whole (within the present boundaries) increased 9.5 percent, but the Urals region showed an increase of 32 percent, western Siberia an increase of 24 percent, eastern Siberia 34 percent, Soviet Middle Asia 38 percent, and the Soviet Far East 70 percent. (However, the *absolute* shift of population eastward has not been as large as these percentages might suggest. About 70 percent of the Soviet Union's population still lived west of the Urals in 1959, as compared with 76 percent in 1939.) The other population movement has been a migration from rural districts into the cities, resulting in spectacular increases in urbanization. An American geographer, Chauncy D. Harris, has written as follows concerning urbanization in the period 1926–1939.

The rapid growth of cities in the Soviet Union between the 1926 and 1939 censuses is unequaled either in the earlier history of Russia or in the urban development of other countries. The numerical increase in urban population in the Soviet Union in this 12-year period exceeded the total numerical increase in all the previous centuries of Russian history. During this time the urban population more than doubled (112.5 per cent increase), in contrast with the rural population, which decreased slightly. Of the urban increase of 29.6 million, 5.4 million came from the natural increase within the urban areas themselves and 24.2 million from rural areas. The proportion of the total population living in cities increased from 17.9 per cent to 32.8 per cent. A comparable increase in degree of urbanization required about 31 years in the United States (1856–1887) and probably about a century in most European countries, though exact comparisons are difficult because of the incompleteness of early statistics. . . .

In absolute as well as in percentage increases the growth of Soviet cities in the intercensal period from 1926 to 1939 is unparalleled. In this period 38 cities increased in population at the rate of 100,000 per decade. The increase in population in Moscow was 2,108,000 persons, approximately equivalent to 1,740,000 in a decade. This is considerably greater than the American record, held by New York City, which increased 1,329,000 in the period 1900 to 1910. The numerical increase in Leningrad was at about the same rate as that of New York City at its peak of rapid growth, yet in percentage figures Leningrad was below the average of Soviet cities. . . .

Urbanization has been part of the industrialization that has been planned and executed by the government in a series of 5-year plans. The long-delayed impact of the Industrial Revolution has struck in the Soviet Union with a suddenness unknown in Western Europe or the United States.[2]

From 1939 to 1959 the number of urban dwellers continued to climb (from 60 million to 100 million within the present national territory—a much slower *rate* of increase than from 1926 to 1939), while the rural population decreased from 130 million to 109 million. The population of the USSR was listed as 48-percent urban by the 1959 census.

## THE SLAVIC MAJORITY

Slavic peoples represent the dominant population element in the USSR, both in numbers and political and economic power. The major Slavic groups are the Great Russians,

---

[2] Chauncy D. Harris, "The Cities of the Soviet Union." *Geographical Review,* v. 35 (1945), pp. 107–112. Used by permission of the author and the American Geographical Society of New York. Three footnotes are omitted.

often referred to simply as Russians, the Ukrainians, and the Belorussians or White Russians. Great Russians constitute about half, Ukrainians about a fifth, and Belorussians about a twentieth of the total population of the USSR.

### ▶ Early Scandinavian and Byzantine Influences

Slavic peoples have inhabited Russia since the early centuries of the Christian era. During the Middle Ages Slavic tribes living in the forested regions of western Russia came under the influence of Viking adventurers from Scandinavia. These newcomers, known as Rus or Varangians, "fought and traded up and down the waterways between the Baltic and Black seas." [3] In the ninth century they were instrumental in organizing a number of principalities in the upper basin of the Dnieper River and in the region extending northward from the Dnieper headwaters to the Gulf of Finland. One of these units, the principality of Kiev, ruled by a nobility of mixed Scandinavian and Slavic descent, achieved mastery over the others and became a powerful state. The culture which it developed was the foundation on which the Great Russian, Ukrainian, and Belorussian cultures later arose.

Kievan Russia was much affected by its contacts with Constantinople (now Istanbul). This great city, located on the straits connecting the Black Sea with the Mediterranean, was the capital of the Eastern Roman or Byzantine Empire which endured for nearly a thousand years after the collapse of the Western Roman Empire in the fifth century A.D. It became an important magnet for Russian trade and was the fount of much cultural borrowing by the Russians. "At the end of the tenth century, the Kievan Slavs accepted Christianity from Byzantium (A.D. 988), and Byzantine influence in religion, art, and political life became permanently established among the eastern Slavs." [4] After Constantinople fell to the Ottoman Turks, a Moslem people, in the fifteenth century, the Russian tsars carried on the traditions of the Eastern Empire. They came to regard Moscow as a "Third Rome," and the Russian branch of the Orthodox Eastern Church was made the official church of the Russian Empire.

### ▶ The Tatar Invasion

Another cultural influence reached the Russians from the heart of Asia. Since the earliest known times the steppe grasslands of southern Russia had been the haunt of nomadic horsemen of Asiatic origin. During the later days of the Roman Empire and in the Middle Ages these grassy plains, stretching far into Asia, provided a passageway for inroads into Europe by the Huns, Magyars, Bulgars, and other Asiatic peoples. In the thirteenth century the Tatars (Tartars) appeared. Many steppe and desert peoples were represented in their ranks, but they were led by Mongols. In 1240 Batu Khan, grandson of Genghis Khan and leader of the Mongol host called the Golden Horde, launched a devastating invasion which brought all of the Russian principalities except the northern one of Novgorod under his rule. The Khanate of Kipchak, established by Batu, endured for more than two centuries. It was one of the main divisions in a vast Mongol empire stretching eastward to China and southward into the Middle East. Eventually it broke apart into the separate khanates of Kazan, Astrakhan, Crimea, and Sibir. Batu and his successors collected taxes and tributes from the Russian principalities, but generally allowed the rulers of these units considerable latitude in matters of local government. Even the princes of Novgorod, who were not technically under the control of the Golden Horde, paid tribute in order to avoid trouble. The

[3] *Aspects of Contemporary Ukraine.* New Haven, Conn.: Human Relations Area Files, 1955. P. 30.

[4] *Ibid.* P. 31.

Tatars used the southern steppes to pasture their livestock herds, and they established their main camps and political centers there. When their power declined in the fifteenth century, the rulers of the Moscow principality were able to begin the process of territorial expansion previously described, which resulted in the formation of present-day Russia (see pp. 243–244).

## ▶ West European Influences

Thus four different cultures—Slavic, Scandinavian, Byzantine, and Tatar—furnished significant elements in the civilization of Old Russia. Important elements of west European culture were added in early modern times, especially during the reign of Peter the Great. Western manners were introduced into the Russian court, industry was stimulated to develop along Western lines, and the capital was moved in 1713 from Moscow to the new city of St. Petersburg (now Leningrad) on the Gulf of Finland, thus affording a closer contact with western Europe. Further cultural importations from the latter area have continued up to the present. Many of the basic doctrines of the Communist Party were developed by west European thinkers, and the modern industrial techniques which the Soviet leaders have introduced on a large scale in the USSR were originally a west European development.

## ▶ Minority Groups and the Political Structure

About a fourth of the present population of the Soviet Union is composed of non-Slavic peoples. More than 100 ethnic groups can be distinguished, most of which are very small. However, about twenty nationalities, including the three principal Slavic groups, number over a million, and perhaps a dozen additional ones number more than 250,000. Soviet policy has permitted the different minorities to retain their own languages and other elements of their traditional cultures. Alphabets have been created for nationalities that previously had no written language, and newspapers and books are published in most of the existing languages. These procedures have helped to allay discontent and have facilitated mass education, regarded by the Communist Party as a necessity for the success of the Communist system. However, a definite tendency toward Russification of minority areas has been apparent for many years. Instruction in the Russian language is compulsory in all schools, and non-Russians who aspire to rise above an ordinary station must learn to speak it fluently. Immigration of Russians and Ukrainians into non-Slavic areas has been a major theme in Russian history and continues today on a sizable scale.

The multinational composition of the Soviet Union is directly reflected in the political structure. From the standpoint of political control the USSR is, of course, a highly centralized Communist dictatorship. From the standpoint of administrative organization, however, it is a federation of fifteen Union Republics (inset map, p. 233), each organized primarily around a particular national group. The largest and most important is the Russian Soviet Federated Socialist Republic, or RSFSR. It includes more than three fourths of the area and over half of the total population of the Soviet Union. The Great Russian ethnic group constitutes an estimated three fourths to four fifths of its population. The fourteen smaller republics are located around the margins of the RSFSR. They fall into three distinct groups: a Middle Asian group of five republics separating the RSFSR from Iran, Afghanistan, and China; a Transcaucasian group of three republics bordering Turkey and Iran; and a western group of six republics bordering the European satellites. Area and population figures for the fifteen republics are given in Table 12.

Peoples not considered sufficiently numerous or advanced to form Union Republics are organized into Autonomous Soviet Socialist Republics, Autonomous Oblasts

(Regions), or lesser autonomous units. Each autonomous unit is politically subordinated to a Union Republic. The majority are under the jurisdiction of the Russian Soviet Federated Socialist Republic.

## TABLE 12

### UNION REPUBLICS: AREA AND POPULATION DATA

| REPUBLIC | AREA (THOUSAND SQUARE MILES) | POPULATION, 1959 CENSUS (MILLIONS) |
|---|---|---|
| Russian SFSR | 6593.1 | 117.5 |
| Ukrainian SSR | 232.0 | 41.9 |
| Belorussian SSR | 80.3 | 8.1 |
| Moldavian SSR | 13.1 | 2.9 |
| Lithuanian SSR | 25.1 | 2.7 |
| Latvian SSR | 24.7 | 2.1 |
| Estonian SSR | 17.4 | 1.2 |
| Azerbaijan SSR | 33.6 | 3.7 |
| Georgian SSR | 27.0 | 4.0 |
| Armenian SSR | 11.6 | 1.8 |
| Kazakh SSR | 1068.0 | 9.3 |
| Uzbek SSR | 157.9 | 8.1 |
| Kirgiz SSR | 76.4 | 2.1 |
| Tadzhik SSR | 54.8 | 2.0 |
| Turkmen SSR | 188.4 | 1.5 |
| Totals | 8603.9 | 208.8 |

SOURCES OF DATA: Area, *Statesman's Year-Book*, 1959, p. 1446; Population, *Izvestia*, May 10, 1959. Apparent discrepancies in totals are due to rounding of figures.

## THE SLAVIC CORELAND

Most of the Slavic population of the Soviet Union is found within an irregular triangle extending from the Black and Baltic seas to the neighborhood of Novosibirsk and Stalinsk in Siberia. This part of the USSR is customarily referred to as the Slavic Coreland, Fertile Triangle, or Agriculture Triangle (map, p. 252). It is the core region of the country in every sense, containing about three fourths of the total population, all of the principal industrial concentrations, most of the major mining areas, 21 of the 25 cities having populations of 500,000 or more, and by far the greater part of the total sown acreage. The coreland is about two thirds as large as the continental United States in area and has roughly the same population. It is really the "Russia that matters," despite the fact that it occupies only a fourth of the total area of the USSR. Lowlands predominate within the coreland, the only mountains being the Urals, a small segment of the Carpathians, and a minor range in the south of the Crimean Peninsula. The original vegetation was mixed coniferous and deciduous forest in the northern part of the coreland and steppe grassland in the south. Moscow (5,032,000) and Leningrad (2,888,000, or 3,300,000 including suburbs) are by far the largest cities. Moscow, the capital of Russia before 1713 and again since 1918, is today the most important manufacturing city and transportation hub. Leningrad, the capital from 1713 to 1918, is the second indus-

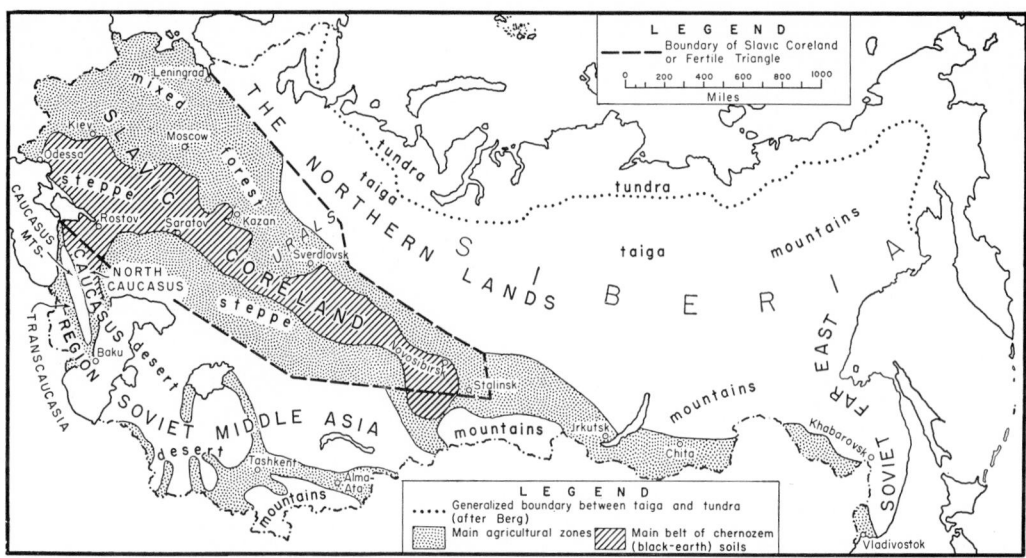

Major regional divisions of the Soviet Union as considered in the present chapter. (Main agricultural zones after Shabad and Baransky.)

trial city and the leading seaport. Most of the other major cities within the coreland are found in the principal industrialized regions, or in other words, in the vicinity of Moscow, in the Ukraine, in the Urals, in the vicinity of the Kuznetsk coal basin in Siberia, or along the Volga River.

## ▶ The Ukraine

Great Russians form the largest ethnic group in the coreland, followed by Ukrainians. Most of the latter are found in the Ukrainian Soviet Socialist Republic. Although closely related to the Great Russians in language and culture, the Ukrainians are a distinct national group. The name Ukraine means "borderland." In this area the Russian tsars fought for centuries against nomadic steppe peoples and also against Poles, Lithuanians, and Turks before the Ukraine was finally brought under control in the eighteenth century.

Today the Ukraine is one of the most densely populated and productive areas in all of Russia. It is a major producer of coal, iron ore, manganese, iron and steel, chemicals, machinery, wheat, livestock, and beet

sugar. Probably no area of equal size contributes more to the total economy of the USSR.

The Ukraine lies partly in the forest zone and partly in the steppe. In the border between these vegetation realms is the historic city of Kiev (1,102,000), the capital of the Ukrainian SSR and a major industrial and transportation center (photo, p. 247).

## ▶ Lesser Republics of the Coreland

The Ukrainian SSR is separately represented in the General Assembly of the United Nations. The same is true of the adjoining Belorussian (White Russian) Republic. By virtue of this arrangement the Soviet Union commands three separate votes in the General Assembly, as compared with one vote for the United States. The Belorussian SSR is much smaller in area and population than the Ukrainian SSR, and is far less productive. The political capital and main industrial center is Minsk (509,000), located on the direct rail line from Moscow to Warsaw and Berlin. This republic suffers from a lack of mineral resources, a retarded industrial development, poor soils, and general economic backwardness. Its cool, damp climate and infertile soils are not favorable for wheat, and most cropland grows rye, hay, potatoes, or flax. Dairy cattle and hogs are the principal livestock. Southern Belorussia incorporates the greater part of the Pripyat (Pripet) Marshes. Much of the marshland has been drained, but extensive reclamation work remains to be done.

The Lithuanian, Latvian, and Estonian SSRs lie between the Belorussian SSR and the Baltic Sea. These small republics were part of the Russian Empire before World War I, but successfully asserted their independence following the Russian Revolution. In 1940, however, they were reabsorbed by the USSR as Union Republics. The Latvians and Lithuanians have some Slavic affinities, but are not considered to be true Slavs. The Estonians, related to the Finns, are distinctly non-Slavic. In the Baltic republics dairy farms alternate with forested areas in a hilly, glaciated landscape. Lumbering is an important activity in all three republics. Mineral resources are generally lacking, although Estonia has extensive deposits of oil-bearing shale. The principal industries are concentrated in a few medium-sized cities, of which the largest is the important seaport of Riga (605,000), the capital of the Latvian SSR. A significant expansion of industry has occurred since World War II. Adjoining the Lithuanian SSR on the southwest is former German East Prussia, the northern half of which is now a part of the Russian Soviet Federated Socialist Republic.

Also included within the coreland at the extreme west is the small Moldavian SSR, largely constituted of territory acquired from Romania in 1940. The Moldavians, a people with many Slavic characteristics, speak a dialect of the Romanian language. Mainly a fertile black-earth steppe upland, the Moldavian SSR is largely agricultural, though industry has shown significant gains since World War II. Agricultural-processing industries predominate. Corn, wheat, and other grains occupy more than two thirds of the republic's crop acreage. Dairy cattle and hogs are the principal livestock in the north, but sheep and goats predominate in the drier south. An important specialty is the growing of vegetables and fruits, especially grapes. This republic is one of the major grape-growing and wine-producing areas of the USSR, its natural environment for vineyards being somewhat similar to that of the famous French district of Champagne.

## ▶ Industrial Development in the Coreland

Although pre-Revolutionary Russia was basically an agricultural country, a slow development of modern industry, partially financed by foreign capital, took place before World War I. At the time of the Revolution industrial development in the country was mainly confined to three areas: the Moscow region, Leningrad (then called Petrograd), and the Ukraine. Under the Soviets, these areas have continued to represent major concentrations of industry. In addition, industry has been greatly expanded in the Urals and in widely spaced cities along the Volga River, and an entirely new industrial concentration has been created in the Kuznetsk Basin. All of these major industrialized areas are within the coreland (see maps, pp. 254–255), along with many smaller industrial centers.

### Industry in the Moscow Region

The industrialized area surrounding Moscow is often referred to as the Central Industrial Region, Old Industrial Region, or Moscow-Tula-Gorkiy Region. These names indicate important characteristics of the region. It has a central location physically within European Russia, and is functionally the major focus for the entire Soviet Union. It lies at the center of the Soviet rail and air nets, and is connected by river and canal transportation with the Baltic, White, Black, and Caspian seas. It is an old region in the sense of being the first major concentration of modern large-scale industry to have been

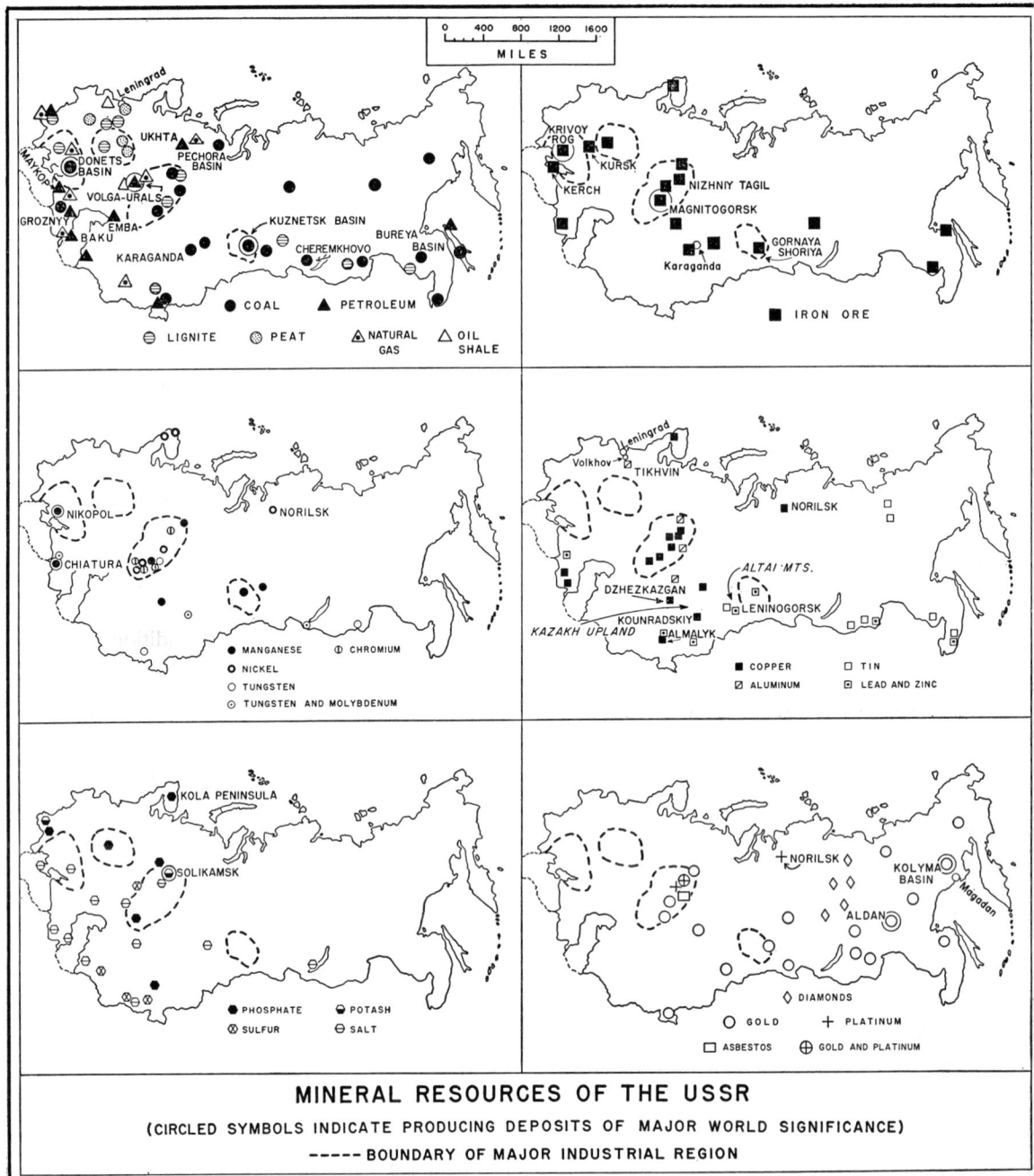

## MINERAL RESOURCES OF THE USSR
(CIRCLED SYMBOLS INDICATE PRODUCING DEPOSITS OF MAJOR WORLD SIGNIFICANCE)
----- BOUNDARY OF MAJOR INDUSTRIAL REGION

These maps are based in considerable part on qualitative data. Most mineral symbols show producing deposits. The basic symbols for industrial centers are arranged in three size groups according to magnitude of manufacturing as estimated by Lonsdale and Thompson (see p. 256). The largest symbols, for Moscow and Leningrad, show cities with an estimated 8.2 percent and 4.9 percent, respectively, of the USSR's manufacturing. Cities in the second size group (Stalino, Rostov, Kiev, etc.) have .65 percent or more of all manufacturing. Cities in the third size group (Ivanovo, Zlatoust, etc.) are selected smaller centers. The subsidiary symbols (oil refining, etc.) have no quantitative significance. On the map of railroads, the line from Chita to Vladivostok via Harbin traverses Chinese territory for most of its length.

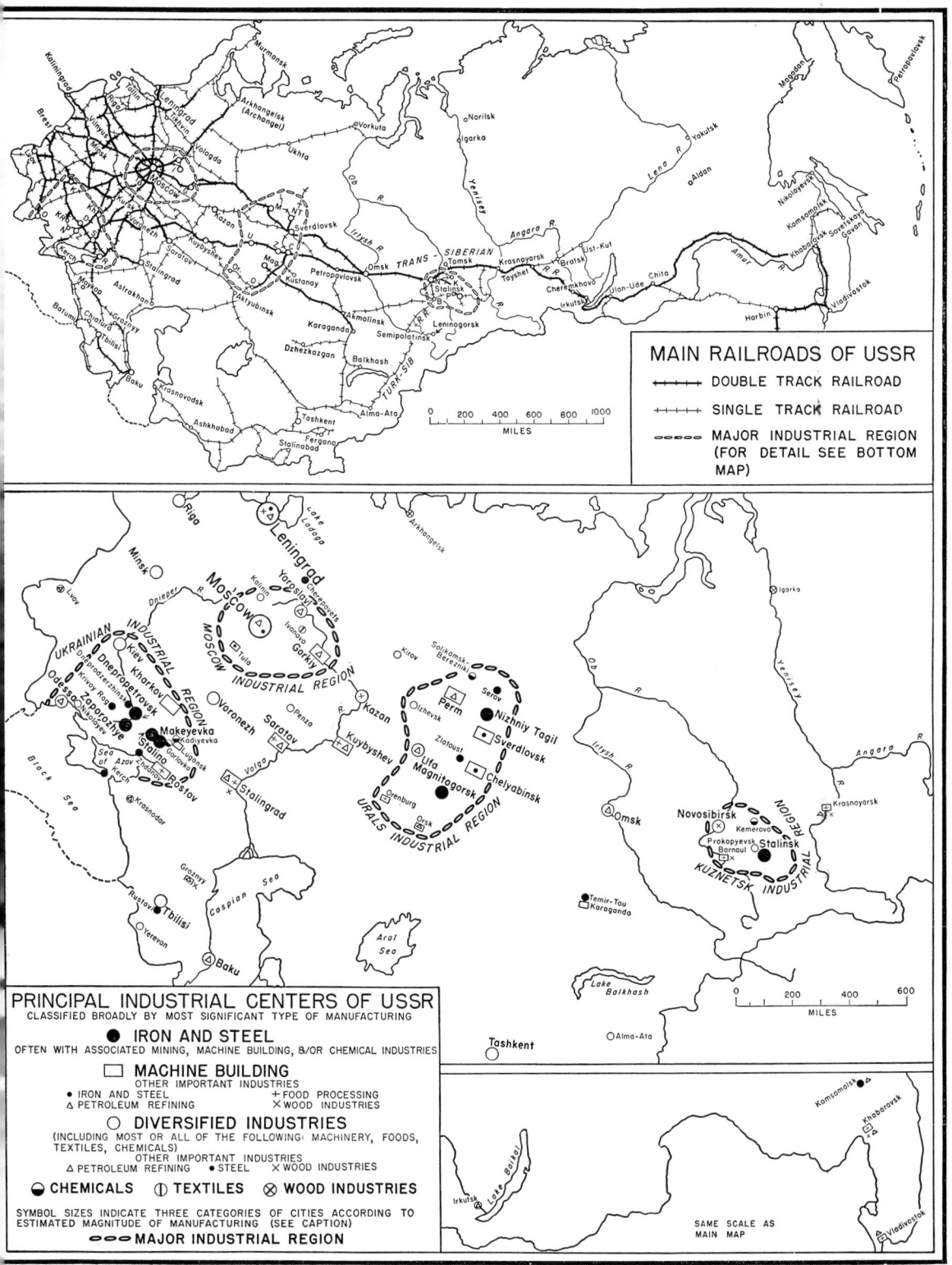

developed in pre-Revolutionary Russia. From Moscow the region extends southward to the mining and metallurgical center of Tula (345,000) and eastward to the automobile center of Gorkiy (942,000)—the "Soviet Detroit." To the north the region includes the major textile center of Ivanovo (332,000)—the "Soviet Manchester"—and Yaroslavl (406,000), important in automobile and synthetic rubber manufacture. Textile milling, largely on the basis of imported American cotton and Russian flax, was the earliest form of large-scale manufacturing to be developed. It gradually replaced the earlier handicraft industries during the nineteenth century. Although the Moscow region is still the largest center of textile production in the USSR, a great variety of other light and heavy manufactures have been developed. Metal-fabricating industries, emphasizing types of construction requiring a relatively high degree of skill and precision, are the most important in value of product. This industrial region accounts for an estimated 18 percent of Soviet manufacturing, as measured by employment and amount of fixed capital in manufacturing. Moscow alone accounts for slightly more than 8 percent of the national total.[5]

The industrial eminence of the Moscow region has been achieved in spite of a notable lack of natural resources. The minerals of greatest consequence are large deposits of lignite south and west of Moscow and peat deposits north and east of the city—both used in steam-generating plants to produce electricity. Iron deposits of only local importance near Tula and phosphate deposits southeast of Moscow complete the list of major industrial minerals present in any quantity. However, the excellent transportation facilities of the capital, partly a product of political centralization, have provided the means for a constant inflow of foods, fibers,

metals, fuels, timber, and other necessary materials, and a return outflow of finished products to all parts of the USSR. A direct trunk rail line brings coal from the rich fields of the Donets Basin in the Ukraine. Natural gas is brought by pipelines from the Volga region, the northern Caucasus, and the western Ukraine, while petroleum products come by various means of transportation from the Volga–Urals and Caucasus oil fields.

The most important trunk route of air transportation in the Soviet Union leads eastward from Moscow to the Urals and Siberia via Kazan, Sverdlovsk, and Novosibirsk. Moscow and the three other cities named handle the greatest number of scheduled flights of any Soviet cities. Other major air routes connect the capital with Kiev and Kharkov in the Ukraine; with Rostov, the principal aerial gateway for the Caucasus region; with Kuybyshev and Stalingrad on the Volga River; with Leningrad in the northwest; and with Tashkent in Soviet Middle Asia.[6]

**Industrial Development in the Leningrad Area**

Leningrad does not form the center of an industrial region comparable in area and population to the Moscow region, the Ukraine, or the Urals. Nevertheless, the city and its immediate environs account for an estimated 5 percent of the USSR's manufacturing. Leningrad is even more handicapped than Moscow from the standpoint of mineral resources. Local deposits of peat and deposits of oil shale and lignite at a somewhat greater distance are supplemented by hydroelectricity from several generating stations to the north, west, and east of the city. High-grade coal and petroleum must be brought from hundreds of miles away, as must all of the metals except aluminum, produced east of Leningrad at Volkhov from bauxite de-

[5] Richard E. Lonsdale and John H. Thompson, "A Map of the USSR's Manufacturing." *Economic Geography*, v. 36 (1960), pp. 36–52. The citation is from p. 41. Percentages cited for other industrial regions in subsequent paragraphs are from this source.

[6] George Kish, "Soviet Air Transport." *Geographical Review*, v. 48 (1958), pp. 309–320.

posits near Tikhvin. Nevertheless, the metal-fabricating industries are by far the most important branch of manufacturing in Leningrad's diversified industrial structure.

Leningrad's highly skilled labor force played an extremely significant role in early Soviet industrialization, pioneering the development of many complex industrial products such as power-generating equipment and synthetic rubber,[7] and supplying groups of experienced workers and technicians to establish new industries in various parts of the USSR.

### The Ukrainian Industrial Region

For more than a quarter-century, Soviet planning has emphasized the heavier types of industry. Today heavy metallurgy, together with associated coal and iron mining and chemical manufacturing, is mainly concentrated in three regions: the Ukraine, the Urals, and the Kuznetsk Basin. In 1950 these regions produced an estimated 86 percent of the total Soviet output of steel (Ukraine 40 percent, Urals 35 percent, Kuznetsk Basin 11 percent).

Heavy industry in the Ukraine is based essentially on major deposits of four indispensable industrial minerals: coal, iron, manganese, and salt. The coal is found in the Donets Basin coal field of the eastern Ukraine, often referred to as the Donbas field. Mining began in this area under the tsars, and as late as 1913 the Donets field accounted for nearly nine tenths of the total tonnage of hard coal (bituminous and anthracite) mined in Russia. Today it accounts for less than half of the national output of hard coal (45 percent in 1955), but it is still the leading field, and its *absolute* production has increased five-fold since 1913. The Donbas produces a variety of bituminous and anthracite coals, including much coal that is suitable for coking. However, its coking coals have a relatively high content of

undesirable impurities (ash and sulfur) as compared with the best American coals. Total coal reserves appear to be sufficient for many decades at present rates of production, though much of the best coking coal has been extracted and costs are rising due to increasing depths of mining.

The Soviet Union's largest iron-mining district is found in the western part of the Ukraine in the vicinity of Krivoy Rog (386,-000). It accounted for 56 percent of the country's output of prepared iron ore in 1956. Ore has been extracted here since tsarist days, and the Krivoy Rog field has been the leading Russian producer for many decades. The best ores are nearing exhaustion, but large reserves of lower-grade ore remain.

Manganese, the most important of the ferroalloys, is mined at Nikopol (81,000), about 60 miles southeast of Krivoy Rog. The Soviet Union is the world's largest producer of manganese and has extremely large reserves. More than nine tenths of these are located in the vicinity either of Nikopol or of Chiatura in Transcaucasia.

The largest concentration of iron and steel plants in the Ukraine is located on the Donets Basin coal field, in the general vicinity of the important coal-mining and heavy industrial centers of Stalino (701,000) and Makeyevka (358,000). Iron ore and manganese are brought by rail from Krivoy Rog and Nikopol. This area is also a major center of chemical manufacturing, based in part on blast-furnace wastes and huge deposits of common salt. Other important iron and steel plants are found along the Dnieper River at Dnepropetrovsk (658,000) and at Zaporozhye (435,000), the site of a large dam and hydroelectric power station. These cities of the Dnieper Bend carry on a variety of electrochemical and electrometallurgical activities, including the manufacture of special steels in electric furnaces at Zaporozhye. An

---

[7] Theodore Shabad, *Geography of the USSR.* New York: Columbia University Press, 1951. P. 150. This book is a comprehensive and authoritative reference.

iron and steel plant at Krivoy Rog that was destroyed during World War II has been rebuilt on an enlarged scale.

South of the Donbas at Kerch (99,000), on the Crimean Peninsula, immense deposits of low-grade, high-phosphorus iron ore are found. The ore is utilized locally for manufacturing iron and steel, and is shipped by water across the Sea of Azov to iron and steel plants at Zhdanov, formerly Mariupol (284,000). Coal and manganese for these operations are brought from the producing fields to the north.

Surrounding the inner core of mining and heavy metallurgical districts in the Ukraine is an outer ring of large industrial cities which carry on metal-fabricating and various other types of manufacturing. These cities include the Ukrainian capital of Kiev (1,102,000) on the Dnieper, the great machine-building and railway center of Kharkov (930,000), about 250 miles east of Kiev, and the seaports and diversified industrial centers of Odessa (667,000) on the Black Sea and Rostov (597,000) on the lower Don River just outside of the Ukrainian SSR. An estimated 19 percent of Soviet manufacturing is found in the Ukraine, or 20 percent including Rostov.

### Industrial Development in the Urals

The Ural Mountains contain an extraordinarily varied collection of economic minerals. Although deficient in coking coal, this highly mineralized area has valuable deposits of iron, copper, nickel, chromium, manganese, tungsten, zinc, lead, bauxite, platinum, gold, asbestos, magnesium, potash, industrial salt, and various other minerals. Much low-grade coal and lignite and some anthracite occur, though relatively little of the coal is suitable for coking. Oil and natural gas are produced in the western foothills of the mountains (see p. 260).

The Soviet regime has placed great emphasis on the development of the Urals as an industrial region well removed from the exposed western frontier of the Union. This emphasis was amply repaid in World War II, when the Ukraine was overrun by German armies and the Urals became the principal arsenal of the USSR. Today the region accounts for an estimated 12 percent of the USSR's manufacturing. The major industrial activities are as follows:

1. Heavy metallurgy, including the manufacture of iron and steel and the smelting of nonferrous ores.

2. The manufacture of heavy chemicals, especially concentrated in the Solikamsk–Berezniki area, where some of the world's largest deposits of potassium and magnesium salts are found.

3. The manufacture of machinery and other metal-fabricating activities, carried on in the important industrial and transportation centers of Sverdlovsk (777,000), Chelyabinsk (688,000), Perm (formerly Molotov; 628,000) Ufa (546,000), and dozens of smaller places.

Old pre-Soviet metallurgical and machine-building plants in the Urals have been modernized and expanded, and a number of immense new plants have been constructed. Probably the most famous and spectacular development has been the creation of an entirely new iron and steel center at Magnitogorsk in the southern Urals. This place, located near a large reserve of exceptionally high-grade iron ore, was not even a village prior to 1931. In that year construction of a huge steel plant was begun and a city was built to house the workers. Today Magnitogorsk is the largest center of iron and steel production in the USSR and has a population of 311,000.

The years that saw the creation of Magnitogorsk also witnessed a large expansion of coal mining in the Kuznetsk Basin (Kuzbas), located in southern Siberia more than a thousand miles to the east of the Urals. A railway shuttle developed, with Kuznetsk coal and coke moving westward to Magnitogorsk and other industrial centers in the Urals, and Urals iron ore (primarily from Magnitogorsk) moving eastward to a new iron and steel plant in the Kuznetsk Basin. Thus was created the famous Urals–Kuznetsk Combine—a spectacular example of the large-scale, integrated industrial development favored by Soviet planners. Each end of the Combine soon became partially independent of the other. A coal field was developed at Karaganda in Soviet Middle Asia to provide fuel for the Urals, while iron mining was developed south of the Kuznetsk Basin at Tashtagol and other places in the foothill area called the Gornaya Shoriya. After 1937 the Combine, as such, was deemphasized following a transportation crisis that led to a search for greater regional self-sufficiency.[8] Nevertheless, the railway shuttle between the Urals and the Kuznetsk Basin has continued, due to qualitative shortcomings of Karaganda coal and Gornaya Shoriya iron ore.[9] Karaganda coal has too high a content of ash and sulfur to make good metallurgical coke, and it is mixed with higher quality Kuznetsk Basin coal in the coke ovens at Magnitogorsk. (Many coke works in the Urals use little or no Karaganda coal, but rely overwhelmingly on Kuznetsk coal.) Similarly, Urals iron ore is mixed with the lower quality local ore in Kuznetsk furnaces. During World War II the best grades of iron ore and coking coal in the major Soviet deposits were heavily exploited, and it is reported that serious shortages of both now exist. The best iron ores of the Krivoy Rog and Magnitogorsk deposits appear to be virtually exhausted; and shortages of high-grade coking coal have been reported from both the Donets and Kuznetsk basins. However, in 1960 the USSR reported a large discovery of high-grade iron ore north of the Donets Basin in a formation called the Kursk magnetic anomaly (from its disturbing effect on compass needles). Only low-grade ores had previously been found in the formation.

Though Magnitogorsk is the primary center of iron and steel production in the Urals, important plants are found at several other places, such as Nizhniy Tagil (338,000) and Chelyabinsk. Zlatoust (161,000) is a metallurgical center that manufactures special alloy steels. The manufacture of high-quality charcoal steel, instituted in the Urals as early as the reign of Peter the Great, is still carried on at many small works. It is facilitated by the abundant forests and numerous small deposits of high-grade iron ore in the region.

Sverdlovsk, located on the eastern flank of the mountains, is the largest city of the Urals and the pre-eminent economic, cultural, and transportation center. Direct trunk rail lines connect the city with Moscow and Leningrad. The second most important rail center is Chelyabinsk, about 120 miles south of Sverdlovsk. Chelyabinsk also has direct rail connections with Moscow. In western Siberia between the Urals and the large industrial and trading center of Omsk (579,000), rail lines from Sverdlovsk and Chelyabinsk join to form the Trans-Siberian Railroad, the main artery linking the Soviet Far East with the coreland (railroad map, p. 255).

**The Kuznetsk Industrial Region**

From Omsk the Trans-Siberian leads eastward to the Kuznetsk industrial region, which accounts for about 4 percent of the Soviet Union's manufacturing. The principal localizing factor for industry in this region is an enormous deposit of coal, much of it suitable for coking. The total reserves are estimated to be about four or five times the size of the reserves in the Donbas field.

The manufacture of iron and steel is the pre-eminent industrial activity of the Kuznetsk region. Iron ore is secured partly from deposits to the south of the coal field and partly from Urals deposits. The major

---

[8] Franklyn D. Holzman, "The Soviet Ural-Kuznetsk Combine: A Study in Investment Criteria and Industrialization Policies." *Quarterly Journal of Economics*, v. 71 (1957), pp. 368–405.

[9] M. Gardner Clark, *The Economics of Soviet Steel*. Cambridge, Mass.: Harvard University Press, 1956. *Passim.*

steel center is Stalinsk (377,000). Its iron and steel industry began to be developed in 1932, concurrent with the development of Magnitogorsk. North of Stalinsk coke is made and chemical manufacturing is carried on at Kemerovo (277,000). The largest urban center of the Kuznetsk region, however, is Novosibirsk, a diversified industrial, trading, and transportation center located on the Ob River at the junction of the Trans-Siberian and Turkestan-Siberian (Turksib) railroads. Sometimes called the "Chicago of Siberia," Novosibirsk has developed from a town of a few thousand at the turn of the century to 887,000 in 1959.

### The Volga Cities

Various industrial cities outside of the five industrial concentrations discussed above are scattered through the coreland. The most notable of these are a group of cities spaced at fairly regular intervals along the Volga River between Gorkiy and the Caspian Sea. They include Kazan (643,000), the major center of the Soviet fur-processing industry, and the diversified metal-fabricating, food-processing, and oil-refining centers of Kuybyshev (806,000), Saratov (581,000), and Stalingrad (591,000). The smaller city of Astrakhan (294,000) in the Volga delta is a food-processing center and the main headquarters for the fishing industry of the Caspian Sea.

In recent years the cities and towns along the Volga have experienced a marked upsurge of industrial activity. One of the most publicized aspects has been the construction of immense dams and hydroelectric power stations on the river in the vicinity of Kuybyshev and Stalingrad. The Volga, the most important internal waterway of the USSR, is connected with Moscow by the Moscow Canal, with the Baltic Sea by the Mariinsk Canals, and with the Don River and Black Sea by the Volga–Don Canal, opened in 1952 (map, p. 232). It is estimated that the main river, its tributaries, and connecting canals carry more than two thirds of the USSR's river and canal traffic. Petroleum and its products from the Volga–Urals and Caucasus fields and timber from the taiga constitute the largest tonnages. Much of the timber is processed at Stalingrad, which has become one of the largest sawmilling centers in the Soviet Union.

### The Volga–Urals Oil Field

The Soviet Union's main area of oil production is found in the Volga–Urals field, sometimes referred to as "the Second Baku." This field, stretching from the Volga River to the western foothills of the Ural Mountains and containing many separate deposits of oil, has four fifths of the USSR's proved reserves [10] and now accounts for more than three fourths of the country's production. It also has very large deposits and is a sizable producer of natural gas. The USSR tripled its output of oil between 1950 and 1958, with most of the expansion taking place in the Volga–Urals field. In the past the Soviet economy has been oriented to coal as its major source of power. But it is anticipated that oil and gas, which supplied less than a third of the country's power requirements in 1958, will provide more than 60 percent by 1972. Soviet railroads, which carried about nine tenths of all intercity freight traffic in the 1950's, are converting more and more from steam to diesel or electric traction. Targets for 1965 call for a decrease in steam traction to 13 percent of all freight ton-miles.[11]

### ▶ Agriculture in the Coreland

Nearly all of the important crops of the middle latitudes are grown in the Soviet Union. Grain crops lead in acreage and production,

[10] David J. M. Hooson, "The New Pattern of Soviet Oil." *Geographical Review*, v. 49 (1959), pp. 422–424. And P. E. Lydolph and T. Shabad, "The Oil and Gas Industries in the U.S.S.R." *Annals AAG*, v. 50 (1960), pp. 461–486.

[11] Holland Hunter, "Soviet Transportation Policies—A Current View," in Joint Economic Committee, 86th Congress, 1st Session, *Comparisons of the United States and Soviet Economies* (Washington, D. C., 1959), p. 194.

Dairy farming in the nonblack-soil zone of the coreland. This view was taken on a collective farm in the Minsk region. (Sovfoto.)

wheat and rye being the principal bread grains and oats, barley, and corn the major feed grains. Millet, buckwheat, and rice occupy smaller though substantial acreages. Potatoes and sugar beets are the most important root crops; flax, cotton, and hemp the main fiber crops; and sunflowers the major source of vegetable oil.[12] Substantial quantities of tobacco, citrus fruits, hardy fruits, and various other crops are grown. Cattle, sheep, hogs, and horses are the major types of livestock.

The Fertile Triangle is the agricultural core of the Union. It is by far the leading area of production for all of the major crops except cotton and subtropical fruits and for all the major types of livestock. Within the Fertile Triangle two major crop zones have long been recognized: a black-soil zone in the southern steppes and a nonblack-soil

zone roughly corresponding to the region of mixed forest. Although some of the same crops and types of livestock are raised in each, the differences tend to outweigh the similarities, and these zones are essentially complementary rather than competitive.

### The Black-soil Zone

The black-soil zone includes not only the chernozem soils proper, but also associated areas of chestnut and other grassland soils. These are excellent wheat soils, and this crop zone is one of the major wheat-growing areas of the world. Wheat is ideally suited to the large-scale, mechanized agriculture stressed in Soviet planning. Winter wheat is grown west of the Dnieper and spring wheat east of the Volga; areas between the two rivers grow both winter and spring wheat. The black-soil zone is also the

[12] Oil pressed from sunflower seeds is used as a cooking oil and for the manufacture of increasing quantities of oleomargarine. The oil-cake residue is fed to livestock and poultry. Since 1954, sunflower-seed oil has accounted for more than half of the total output of vegetable oils in the USSR, with cottonseed oil contributing an additional fourth of the total.

principal producing area for sugar beets, sunflowers, hemp, barley, and corn.

### The Nonblack-soil Zone

In the nonblack-soil zone, with its cooler and more humid climate and poorer soils, rye replaces wheat as the major grain crop and well over half of the country's rye is grown in this zone. This is also the major producing region for potatoes, oats, and flax. Dairy farming is a major branch of agriculture in this zone (photo, p. 261).

## THE OUTLYING REGIONS

The majority of the non-Slavic population of the USSR is found outside the coreland. Four major outlying regions can be distinguished: the Caucasus region, Soviet Middle Asia, the Soviet Far East, and the Northern Lands (map, p. 252).

### ▶ *The Caucasus Region*

The Caucasus region occupies the mountainous southern borderland of the USSR between the Black and Caspian seas. It includes the rugged Caucasus Mountains, a fringe of foothills and level steppes north of the mountains, and the area to the south known as Transcaucasia.

The Greater Caucasus Range (photo, right) forms practically a solid wall from the Black Sea to the Caspian. It is similar in age and general character to the Alps, but is considerably higher: Mt. Elbrus, the highest summit, stands at 18,476 feet, as compared with 15,771 feet for Mt. Blanc, the highest peak of the Alps. Railroads to Transcaucasia follow narrow coastal lowlands at either end of the range. In the south of Transcaucasia is the Armenian Plateau, a mountainous highland reaching 13,435 feet. Between the Greater Caucasus Range and the Armenian Plateau are subtropical valleys and coastal plains where the majority of the people in Transcaucasia are found. Russians and Ukrainians predominate in the North Caucasus, but non-Slavic groups form a large majority in Transcaucasia. The Caucasian isthmus between the Black and Caspian seas has been an important north-south passageway for thousands of years, and the present population is composed of many different peoples who have migrated into this region at various times. At least 25 or 30 nationalities can be distinguished, most of which are small in numbers and largely confined to mountain areas that have served as places of refuge in past times. Besides Russians and Ukrainians, mostly found north of the Greater Caucasus, the nationalities of greatest importance are the Georgians, Armenians, and Azerbaijanians, each represented by a separate Union Republic.[13]

Subtropical crops and minerals are the main contributions of the Caucasus region to the economy of the USSR. The lowlands bordering the Black Sea, with the heaviest rainfall and warmest winters of the USSR, produce such specialty crops as tea, tangerines, lemons, grapefruit, oranges, tobacco, tung oil, almonds, camphor, silk, and wine. This area, the most densely populated part of Transcaucasia, is located in the Georgian SSR. The Caspian lowlands of eastern Transcaucasia, located in the Azerbaijan SSR, have colder winters and less rain; here irrigated cotton, grown in rotation with alfalfa, is the main crop except in the narrow coastal lowlands at the extreme south where warmer temperatures and greater precipita-

---

[13] These nationalities have racial characteristics and cultural traditions that are primarily Asian or Mediterranean in origin. They differ in religion, with the Azerbaijanians (also known as Azeri Turks) being Moslems, while the Georgians and Armenians belong to separate branches of the Orthodox Eastern Church. There has been a considerable history of animosity between the Armenians and Azeri Turks, growing out of the persecution of Armenians in the Ottoman Empire prior to and during World War I.

Rugged, snow-capped heights in the Georgian Caucasus. (Sovfoto.)

tion permit the culture of rice, tea, citrus, and other subtropical specialty crops. Temperate fruits and nuts, including apples, pears, apricots, peaches, plums, chestnuts, and walnuts, are grown in many parts of Transcaucasia, and viticulture and sericulture are widely practiced, not only in the lowlands but also on the warmer slopes of the mountains. Livestock, principally sheep and cattle, are grazed on mountain pastures during the summer months and wintered in the lowlands. The dry steppes of eastern Transcaucasia are especially prominent as a winter grazing ground.

Petroleum is the most important mineral of the Caucasus region. The main field is on the Caspian Sea at Baku (636,000, or 968,-000 incl. suburbs), and lesser fields occur north of the mountains in the vicinity of Groznyy (240,000) and Maykop (82,000). Baku, the largest city of Transcaucasia and capital of the Azerbaijan SSR, was the leading center of petroleum production in Old Russia (in fact, it was for a time at the turn

of the century the leading center in the world), and under the Soviets it maintained its position as the oil capital of the country for several decades. But during World War II its production declined, and since the war it has been decisively surpassed by the large new Volga–Urals field (see p. 260).

In addition to petroleum, this region has deposits of natural gas and coal and is an important producer of metals. At Chiatura in the Georgian SSR is one of the largest known deposits of manganese. Other metals include zinc and lead, mined on the northern slopes of the Greater Caucasus, copper in Armenia, and iron in Azerbaijan. The Caucasus region is estimated to have reserves of hydroelectric power equal to the reserves of the remainder of the Soviet Union west of the Ural Mountains. Hydroelectric installations are found in many different parts of the region.

Besides Baku, only two cities of the Caucasus region exceed half a million in population: Tbilisi or Tiflis (694,000), the capital of the Georgian SSR, and Yerevan (509,-000), the capital of the Armenian SSR. Both are diversified industrial centers.

The Caucasus region vies with the Crimea as a center of resort development. The principal resorts are found along the Black Sea coast and in the mountains of the Georgian SSR.

## ▶ Soviet Middle Asia

Across the Caspian Sea from the Caucasus region lies a vast expanse of deserts and dry grasslands, bounded on the south and east by high mountains. Like Transcaucasia this region, Soviet Middle Asia, is mainly peopled by non-Slavic nationalities. The most numerous are four peoples speaking closely related Turkic languages—the Uzbeks, Kazakhs, Kirgiz, and Turkmen—and a people of Iranian origins, the Tadzhiks. Each has its own Union Republic. By far the largest in area is the Kazakh Republic (Kazakhstan), which covers a million square miles and is more than twice as large as the remaining four republics combined (Table 12).[14]

Soviet Middle Asia is predominantly composed of plains and low uplands except for the Tadzhik and Kirgiz SSRs, which are extremely mountainous. In these republics are found the highest summits of the USSR: Stalin Peak, 24,590 feet, in the Pamirs (Tadzhik SSR), and Pobeda (Victory) Peak, 24,400 feet, in the Tien Shan (Kirgiz SSR) (map, p. 245). The Kazakh Upland in east central Kazakhstan is a hilly area with occasional ranges of low mountains. Soviet Middle Asia is remote from the world ocean, and is almost entirely a region of interior drainage. Only the waters of the Irtysh, a tributary of the Ob, reach the open sea; all the other streams either drain to enclosed lakes and seas or gradually dry up and disappear in the arid wastes of the Middle Asian deserts.

The native peoples of Soviet Central Asia and Kazakhstan are Moslems (Muslims). But the twentieth century has seen a large incursion of Russians and Ukrainians, who now comprise more than a third of the population in the five republics combined. Most of these newcomers live apart from the Moslems, either in separate quarters of the cities or in separate agricultural villages. A specialist on Russian-Moslem relationships, Richard Pipes, has described the situation in the cities of Soviet Central Asia as follows:

In pre-Revolutionary times the Russians moving into the cities of Turkestan followed the custom of Europeans in other colonial areas of the world, and rather than make their homes in the Oriental quarters, insanitary and overcrowded by Western standards, or build new cities from scratch, they constructed separate European sections adjoining the native towns. . . . After the advent of the Communists this basic pattern remained, with one important change: leaving the Old and the New sections of the towns intact, the Soviet authorities constructed in most towns new quarters to house the officials, employees, and other privileged elements of Soviet society, who are predominantly, but not exclusively, European. Thus most Central Asian towns today are divided into three parts, one predominantly native, another predominantly European, and a third one mixed, with Europeans dominant. The new quarters house alike native and Russian employees of the state; the natives living there, however, belong exclusively to the so-called "intelligentsia," which is Westernized and bilingual and constitutes a relatively small segment of the total native urban population.[15]

### Irrigated Agriculture

The majority of the people in Soviet Middle Asia live in irrigated valleys at the base

---

[14] The four smaller republics are often referred to as Soviet Central Asia or Turkestan. But some writers apply these names to the region as a whole, including Kazakhstan. In the present chapter the name Soviet Middle Asia will be employed when the five republics are referred to as a group.

[15] Richard Pipes, "Muslims of Soviet Central Asia: Trends and Prospects (Part II)." *Middle East Journal,* v. 9 (1955), p. 299. Reprinted by permission of the author and the *Middle East Journal.* Students are urged to read the entire article, pp. 147–162 and 295–308. It contains material of the highest interest and value.

of the southern mountains. Here the soils are generally fertile, the growing season is long, and rivers issuing from the mountains provide large supplies of water for irrigation. The irrigated area has been substantially increased in size and productivity under the Soviets, and further increases are planned. The principal rivers of the region are the Amu Darya (Oxus) and Syr Darya, both of which empty into the enclosed Aral Sea. But a large share of the irrigation water is not obtained from these streams directly, but from their tributaries or from other rivers. The most important future source of water is the Amu Darya. It has two to three times the volume of the Syr Darya but is used less for irrigation. Elaborate and expensive control works will be needed before it can be fully utilized. Two ambitious projects to divert water from the river through giant canals were begun following World War II but no work on either of them has been reported in recent years.

Most of the larger irrigated districts are found in the Uzbek SSR. Especially important are the fertile Fergana Valley and the oases surrounding the cities of Tashkent (911,000), Samarkand (195,000), and Bukhara (69,000). The latter cities are historic trading centers on ancient caravan routes connecting southwestern Asia and the Mediterranean basin with the Far East. Today Tashkent, the capital of the Uzbek SSR, is the largest city and principal center of diversified industry in Soviet Middle Asia. Among the prominent factories in the Tashkent area are an agricultural machinery plant, several large cotton mills, and a plant utilizing hydroelectric power to manufacture nitrate fertilizers from atmospheric nitrogen.

The major crop of the Middle Asian oases is cotton (photo, below). This area grows more than nine tenths of the USSR's cotton. Early-maturing American-upland varieties account for the bulk of the crop, though

Soviet-made mechanical cotton-pickers in operation on irrigated land in the Uzbek SSR near Tashkent. (Sovfoto.)

some long-staple Egyptian-type cotton is grown in the Turkmen and Tadzhik SSRs. A recent visitor described as follows the importance of cotton in the most concentrated areas of production:

The concentration on cotton growing is so heavy . . . that it resembles the one-crop system existent in the U. S. Cotton Belt 30 years ago. Alfalfa needed for winter feed is the only commercial crop used for partial rotation with cotton except for small fields of melons and rice. Cultivable areas are seldom used as pasture even for rotation. Livestock consist mainly of sheep, goats, burros, and cattle (small numbers), tethered individually along the banks of irrigation ditches or tended by shepherds in rocky areas not suitable for cultivation. There are no fences along cotton fields or pasture areas.

The areas nearest the sources of water were developed first, resulting in a heavy concentration of cotton cultivation in the eastern portion of Uzbekistan. This republic accounts for two thirds of the Soviet crop.[16]

Mulberry trees to feed silkworms are grown around the margins of irrigated fields in some areas. Sugar beets are increasingly important as an irrigated crop, while irrigated rice is grown in sufficient quantities in the Uzbek SSR to make that republic the Soviet Union's leading producer. Vineyards and fruit orchards (apples, pears, peaches, apricots) are found in many oases; commercial orchard farming is most prominent around Alma-Ata ("father of apples"; 455,000), the capital of the Kazakh SSR.

### Nonirrigated Grain Farming and Livestock Herding

Most of the area outside of the oases is too dry for cultivation, although a considerable amount of nonirrigated grain farming is carried on by Russians and Ukrainians in the north of Kazakhstan, which extends into the black-earth belt. Huge acreages, primarily on chestnut soils, were planted in wheat under the "virgin and idle lands" program of 1954–1957 (see p. 228). Nonirrigated grain culture is also found on the rainier slopes in mountain foothills of the south. In former times nomadic herding provided the livelihood of many Middle Asian tribes. It was based primarily on the natural forage of the steppes and on mountain pastures in the Altai and Tien Shan ranges. But over the centuries there was a slow drift away from nomadism, and this process was accelerated by the Soviet government, which collectivized the remaining nomads and settled them in permanent villages. Often such villages were made possible by the drilling of deep wells to provide a dependable year-round supply of water and by the planting of forage crops for supplemental feed. Livestock raising in Soviet Middle Asia has now become a form of ranching, although herdsmen must often accompany the grazing animals for considerable distances as the latter are moved from one area of range to another. Sheep and cattle are the principal types of livestock.

### Mining and Manufacturing

During recent decades Soviet Middle Asia has become increasingly important as a producer of minerals, particularly coal, nonferrous and ferrous metals, petroleum, and chemical materials (maps, p. 254). Large reserves of bituminous coal are found in the vicinity of Karaganda in central Kazakhstan. The Karaganda coal basin has become the third largest producer of bituminous coal in the USSR (after the Donets and Kuznetsk basins), and Karaganda itself has experienced spectacular growth from a tiny village in 1926 to a city of 398,000 in 1959. Much of the coal mined here is shipped to metallurgical works in the Urals. However, Karaganda coal has an excessively high content of ash and sulfur, which limits its utility for coking (see p.

[16] Foreign Agricultural Service, U. S. Department of Agriculture, *Cotton in the Soviet Union* (Washington, D. C.: Government Printing Office, 1959), pp. 1–2.

259). Karaganda and Kuznetsk coals as well as coal from smaller deposits in the Kirgiz SSR provide fuel for large-scale metallurgy in Soviet Middle Asia itself. Of primary importance is the smelting of nonferrous metals, especially copper, lead, and zinc. The largest copper reserves of the USSR are mined in central Kazakhstan at Dzhezkazgan, about midway between Karaganda and the Aral Sea. Other important copper mines are found at Kounradskiy, just north of Lake Balkhash, and at Almalyk in Uzbekistan. Complex ores yielding zinc and lead, plus silver, gold, and copper are mined in the Altai Mountain foothills of eastern Kazakhstan near Leninogorsk (67,000). The Leninogorsk area is the Soviet Union's chief source of zinc and lead. Smelting works are found in close proximity to all of the nonferrous deposits named. Impressive reserves of chrome and nickel in the Urals foothills of northern Kazakhstan, petroleum in the Emba field bordering the Caspian Sea, large iron-ore deposits in the vicinity of Kustanay (86,000) in northern Kazakhstan, and smaller deposits of these and many other minerals scattered throughout the region add further to the picture of Soviet Middle Asia as a rich and diversified mineralized area. Uranium is thought to be mined at a number of places in the Kirgiz, Tadzhik, and Uzbek SSRs, though specific data are not available.

Manufacturing in Soviet Middle Asia is steadily increasing in importance. Except for handicrafts, manufacturing scarcely existed at the time of the 1917 revolution. But under the Soviets textile-milling and agricultural-processing industries have been developed on a sizable scale and these have been supplemented, especially since 1940, by important machine-building and chemical industries and by steel mills at Temir-Tau (54,000) near Karaganda and at Begovat in the Uzbek SSR. A considerable number of electric power stations have been built, both thermal stations and hydroelectric stations.

## ▶ The Soviet Far East

The Soviet Far East is the mountainous Pacific margin of the USSR. Most of it is a thinly populated, undeveloped wilderness in which the only settlements are fishing ports, mining or lumber camps, or the villages or encampments of aboriginal tribes. It is remote from the main centers of Soviet life, and its contribution to the national economy is relatively meager. Most of the Russians and Ukrainians who compose the overwhelming majority of its population are found in a narrow strip of lowland behind the coastal mountains in the southern part of the region. This lowland, drained by the Amur River and its tributary, the Ussuri, is the main axis of industry, agriculture, transportation, and urban development in the region. Five main cities form a north-south line along two important arteries of transportation: the Trans-Siberian Railroad and the lower Amur River. At the south on the Sea of Japan is the important port of Vladivostok (283,000). It is the main terminus of rail, sea, and air routes connecting the Far East with the rest of the Union. Vladivostok has modern port facilities and its harbor is kept open throughout the winter by icebreakers. About 50 miles to the north is Ussuriysk (formerly Voroshilov; 104,-000), a food-processing center located in the most important agricultural district of the Soviet Far East. Mills in the city prepare cereals (including rice), soybeans, sugar beets, and milk from the surrounding farms for Far Eastern consumption. The diversified industrial and transportation center of Khabarovsk (322,000) is located at the confluence of the Amur and Ussuri rivers about 400 miles northeast of Ussuriysk. Here the main line of the Trans-Siberian Railroad turns south to Vladivostok and the Amur River turns north to the Sea of Okhotsk. To the northeast in the Amur Valley is Komsomolsk (177,000), the only center of steel milling in the region. A branch line of the Trans-Siberian reaches Komsomolsk and Sovetskaya Gavan on the Gulf of Tatary (map, p. 255). Farther downstream on the Amur near its mouth is the fishing port of Nikolayevsk.

The Pacific littoral north of Nikolayevsk is very mountainous and sparsely populated. The largest settlement is Magadan (62,-000), the supply port for an important gold-mining district in the basin of the Kolyma River.

Prior to World War II the Soviet Union and Japan held the northern and southern halves, respectively, of the large island of Sakhalin. But since the war the USSR has annexed southern Sakhalin and the Kuril Islands, and has repatriated the Japanese population of these areas. Sakhalin has considerable mineral wealth, including coal and petroleum, and important forest and fishing industries. The Kurils are a sparsely populated chain of small volcanic islands that screen the Sea of Okhotsk from the Pacific. Fishing is the main economic activity. At the north the islands approach the large peninsula of Kamchatka. Like the Kurils, Kamchatka is a region of active vulcanism, having many hot springs in addition to 19 active volcanoes, one of which reaches a height of 15,912 feet. Petropavlovsk (86,-000) is a fishing port in southern Kamchatka.

### Fisheries and Forest Industries

The Soviet Far East is of minor economic significance to the Soviet Union. This region is generally poorer in known mineral resources than the Urals, the Ukraine, or Kazakhstan, although the gold of the Kolyma Basin and the petroleum of Sakhalin (refined at Komsomolsk, Khabarovsk, and Vladivostok) have considerable economic importance, and deposits of coal, iron ore, lead and zinc, and other minerals are worked to some extent (maps, p. 254). Fish, lumber, gold, and furs are the major commodities produced for sale outside the region. Salmon, herring, sardines, and crabs are abundant in the waters bordering the re-

gion and provide the basis for a fishing industry of major importance. Herring and sardines caught in coastal waters of the Sea of Japan are processed by canneries at Vladivostok. The Sea of Okhotsk is also a source of herring but is more important for coastal salmon and crab fisheries. In recent times Kamchatka, particularly the west coast, has come to the fore as a leading center of fishing. The crab fisheries of Kamchatka are reputed to be the world's largest, and salmon are caught in large numbers as they ascend the streams of the peninsula to spawn. The estuary of the Amur River is also an important center of salmon fishing.

Lumber exports from the region consist primarily of softwoods, but include some oak and other hardwoods from the basin of the Ussuri River. Sawmilling is centered at Khabarovsk, at Vladivostok, at points between these cities where the Trans-Siberian Railroad crosses tributaries of the Ussuri River, and at Sovetskaya Gavan. Southern Sakhalin is the main area of pulp and paper milling. Several mills developed by Japan were taken over by the USSR when it annexed the area in 1945.

### ▶ The Northern Lands

To the north and east of the Agricultural Triangle and west of, and partially including, the Pacific littoral are enormous stretches of coniferous forest (taiga) and tundra extending completely across the USSR from the Finnish and Norwegian borders to the Pacific. These outlying areas of wilderness may be designated for convenience as the Northern Lands, although parts of the Siberian taiga extend to the southern border of the USSR. The Northern Lands include more than half of the Soviet mainland and also a number of island groups in the Arctic Ocean, among which the two mountainous, fiorded islands of Novaya Zemlya are especially well known.

These difficult lands comprise one of the most sparsely populated large regions of the world. Ordinary types of agriculture are

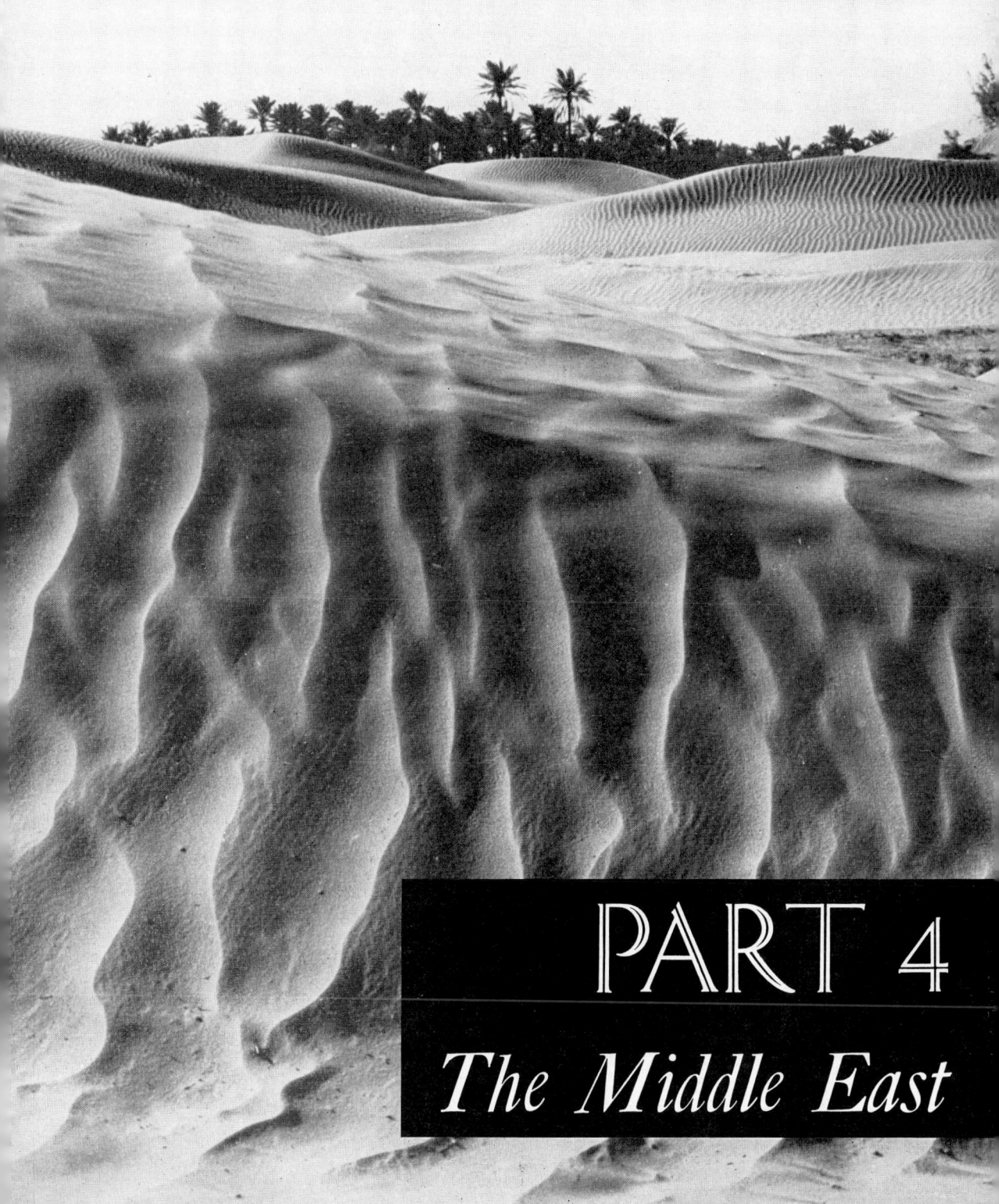

# PART 4

## *The Middle East*

# Introduction to the Middle East

The term Middle East, as used in this book, refers to an elongated region stretching for 6000 miles across northern Africa and southwestern Asia from the Atlantic Ocean to the borders of India, China, and Soviet Asia. This region includes numerous countries (map, p. 279), but many of these are small. Only nine countries have populations of 10 million or more: West Pakistan (37 million), Turkey, the United Arab Republic, Iran, and Ethiopia (15–30 million); and Afghanistan, the Sudan, Morocco, and Algeria (10–15 million) (Table 13). But in the Middle East, as in other world regions, the importance of countries is not necessarily a function of size. The small state of Israel, for example, has carved out a niche for itself despite the opposition of larger neighbors, and the rich petroleum deposits of Kuwait and Qatar have magnified the importance of these small units.

The margins of the Middle East are mainly occupied by oceans, seas, high mountains, and deserts: to the west the Atlantic Ocean; to the south the Sahara Desert, the highlands of East Africa, and the Indian Ocean; to the north the Mediterranean, Black, and Caspian seas, together

Many ingenious devices are employed to secure water in the deserts and steppes of the Middle East. The donkeys in this photo, taken in Saudi Arabia, walk back and forth on the runway to pull up to the surface camel skins filled with water, which are automatically dumped into an irrigation ditch. (Standard Oil Company, N. J.)

275

## TABLE 13

### MIDDLE EAST: AREA AND POPULATION DATA

| POLITICAL UNIT | POLITICAL STATUS (EARLY 1961) | AREA (THOUSAND SQUARE MILES) | POPULATION (MILLIONS: 1959 ESTIMATES) | DENSITY (PER SQUARE MILE: TO NEAREST WHOLE NUMBER) |
|---|---|---|---|---|
| Arab League states [a] | | 3229.8 | 76.98 | 24 |
| United Arab Republic [b] | Independent republic | 457.3 | 29.63 | 65 |
| Lebanon | Independent republic | 4.0 | 1.55 (1958) | 386 |
| Iraq | Independent republic | 171.6 | 6.59 (1958) | 38 |
| Jordan | Independent kingdom | 37.3 | 1.64 | 44 |
| Saudi Arabia | Independent kingdom | 617.8 [c] | 6.04 (1956) | 10 |
| Yemen | Independent kingdom | 75.3 | 4.50 (1949) | 60 |
| Sudan | Independent republic | 967.5 | 11.39 | 12 |
| Libya | Independent kingdom | 679.4 | 1.17 | 1.7 |
| Tunisia | Independent republic | 48.3 | 3.93 | 81 |
| Morocco | Independent kingdom | 171.3 | 10.55 | 62 |
| Other independent states | | | | |
| Turkey | Independent republic | 301.4 | 26.88 | 89 |
| Iran | Independent kingdom | 636.3 | 20.15 | 32 |
| Afghanistan | Independent kingdom | 251.0 | 13.15 | 52 |
| West Pakistan [d] | Province of independent Republic of Pakistan | 310.2 | 37.40 (1958) | 121 |
| Kashmir [d] | Area disputed between Pakistan and India | 85.9 | 4.41 (1951) | 51 |
| Israel | Independent republic | 8.0 | 2.06 | 258 |
| Cyprus | Independent republic | 3.6 | 0.56 | 156 |
| Ethiopia [e] | Independent empire | 457.3 | 21.80 [f] | 48 |
| Somali Republic [g] | Independent republic | 246.2 | 2.00 | 8 |
| Muscat and Oman | Independent sultanate in close treaty relationship with Great Britain | 82.0 | 0.55 | 7 |
| Totals: All independent states | | 5611.6 | 205.94 | 37 |
| British dependencies and protected states | | 159.4 | 1.29 | 8 |
| Aden [h] | Colony and protectorate | 112.4 | 0.80 | 7 |
| Kuwait | Protected sheikdom | 6.0 | 0.22 | 37 |
| Bahrein | Protected sheikdom | 0.23 | 0.14 | 619 |
| Qatar | Protected sheikdom | 8.5 | 0.040 | 5 |
| Trucial Oman | Group of seven protected sheikdoms | 32.3 | 0.087 | 3 |

[a] Apparent discrepancies in totals and averages in this table are due to rounding of figures.

[b] Comprised of Southern or Egyptian Region (386,100 sq. mi.; est. pop. 25,365,000; density 66/sq. mi.) and Northern or Syrian Region (71,227 sq. mi.; est. pop. 4,267,000; density 60/sq. mi.).

[c] This figure omits the large southern desert called the Empty Quarter, where political boundaries are undefined. Other sources estimate Saudi Arabia's area at 850,000 to 900,000 sq. mi. There is also much variation in estimates for other political units of the Arabian Peninsula.

[d] Pakistan is divided into two provinces, West Pakistan and East Pakistan, separated by the Republic of India. West Pakistan and the disputed area of Kashmir are considered in this text to be transitional between the Middle East and the Orient. East Pakistan has a very different type of natural environment and economy. For the purposes of this text it is not considered a part of the Middle East.

[e] Figures include the autonomous state of Eritrea (48,000 sq. mi.; est. pop. 1,040,000 in 1957; density 22/sq. mi.), which is federated with Ethiopia.

[f] This figure, an official estimate by the Ethiopian government, is probably several million too high (see p. 327).

[g] Comprised of former Italian Somaliland and former British Somaliland.

[h] Comprised of Aden Colony and Aden Protectorate. Aden Colony, excluding a number of minor islands, has an area of about 75 sq. mi. and had a population of around 150,000 in 1959. The Aden Protectorate includes some 25 separate units (sultanates, amirates, or sheikdoms).

**TABLE 13 (Continued)**

**MIDDLE EAST: AREA AND POPULATION DATA**

| | | | | |
|---|---|---|---|---|
| Affiliated with France | | 928.1 | 11.00 | 12 |
| Algeria [i] | 17 overseas departments | 919.6 | 10.93 | 12 |
| French Somaliland | Overseas territory | 8.5 | 0.070 | 8 |
| Affiliated with Spain | | 103.4 | 0.217 | 2 |
| Ifni | Overseas province | 0.58 | 0.053 | 92 |
| Spanish Sahara | Overseas province | 102.7 | 0.019 | 0.2 |
| Places of Spanish sovereignty in Morocco [j] | Administered with Spain | 0.082 | 0.15 (1958) | 1768 |
| Totals: European dependencies and affiliates | | 1190.8 | 12.51 | 10.5 |
| Grand totals | | 6802.4 | 218.44 | 32 |

[i] Includes 15 departments in Algeria proper and two Saharan departments. The departments in Algeria proper occupy only about one tenth of the total area but had about 95 percent of the estimated population in 1959.
[j] Comprised of five small enclaves along the Mediterranean coast of Morocco; the most important are the cities of Melilla (85,000) and Ceuta (61,000).

with mountains and deserts lining the southern land frontiers of the Soviet Union; to the east the Thar Desert of India and the great mountain knot of Inner Asia. The Middle East itself is mainly composed of arid or semiarid plains and plateaus, together with considerable areas of rugged mountains.

Although this region exhibits much variety from place to place, two important factors help to give it unity: (1) the dominance of dry climates and (2) the Moslem (Muslim) religion. The latter is the principal religion in all of the Middle Eastern countries except four: Israel, where Judaism prevails; Lebanon and Ethiopia, where ancient forms of Christianity are of major importance; and Cyprus, where the population mainly adheres to the Greek Orthodox Church. Even these countries have Moslem minorities; indeed in Lebanon Moslems comprise around two fifths of the population according to one estimate, and may possibly constitute a majority.

# WORLD IMPORTANCE OF THE MIDDLE EAST

Throughout history the sparsely populated deserts and mountains of the Middle East, separating the humid lands of Europe, Africa, and Asia, have been a barrier to overland travel between those regions. Yet circulation of people, goods, and ideas has been possible along certain favorable routes, and the scattered population centers of the region have had a history of vigorous interaction with the outside world and with each other. No areas of the world have been invaded so often, have seen so many empires rise and fall, or have been subjected to such a variety of cultural influences and political pressures. None have made greater contributions to mankind. The earliest foundations of Western Civilization were laid in the river valleys of ancient Egypt and Mesopotamia. From the Middle East came the great monotheistic religions of Judaism, Christianity, and Islam (the Moslem faith). Many of the plants and animals upon which the world's agriculture is based were first domesticated in this region.

Most of the vegetable foods we eat originated in this area. Wheat, barley, and rye, of the small grains, and possibly millet. Broad beans, chickpeas, lentils, and vetches, of the legumes. On-

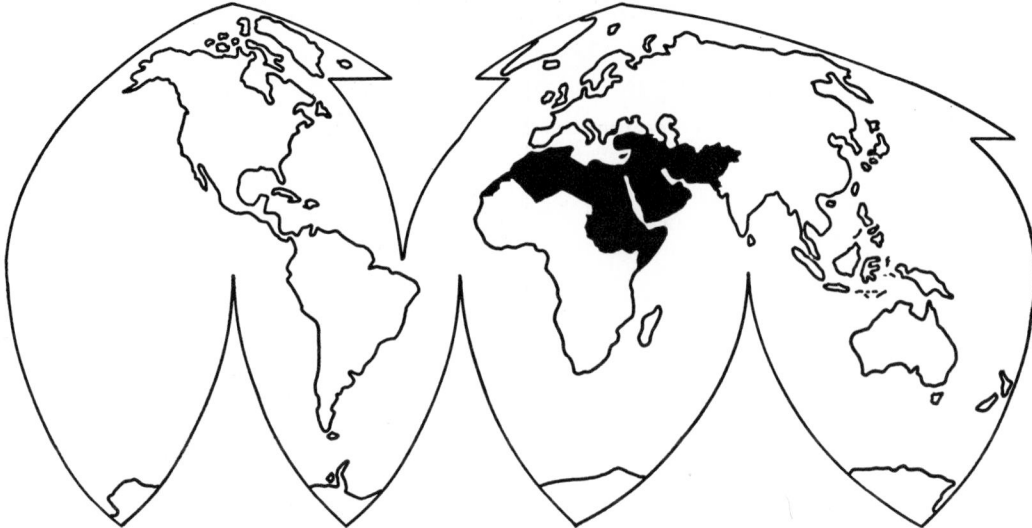

Location of the Middle East. (Boggs Equal Area Projection, copyright A. J. Nystrom and Co.)

ions, leeks, garlic, of the lilies. Figs and the vine, and all the delicious varieties of muskmelon that cool and slake the thirsty traveler in the heat of summer. Pomegranates . . . ; olives and sesame for oil; apples, quinces, and pears, of the roses . . . ; peaches, plums, apricots, and almonds; walnuts, saffron. Dates in the desert oases and along the exotic rivers.[1]

The list of common animals domesticated in this region includes horses, oxen, sheep, goats, pigs, and dogs.

We who eat roast beef on Sundays and pork with our beans seldom wonder whom to thank for these gifts, other than the ultimate and divine Source of all bounty. It was the ancient hunters and earliest farmers of the Middle East who first rounded up these animals and tamed them for their use. Try to imagine yourself on foot, armed with a bow and arrow, a length of cordage, and a stone ax, either alone or accompanied by a dozen of your fellows, setting out to catch a wild bull in the forest or a wild sheep on the mountain crags.[2]

Most of the world's great empires have included portions of the Middle East. Some of these empires were indigenous, while others, such as the Roman Empire, were imposed from outside. In the early Middle Ages a powerful Islamic empire, organized by Arabs, arose in the Middle East and evolved the most brilliant civilization of its day (see p. 292). Later it decayed. In the sixteenth century most of the territories it had controlled were conquered by the Ottoman Turks. Still later, when the Ottoman Empire was declining, Great Britain, France, and Italy extended their control over sizable areas. For centuries, while the Great Powers of the Western world were industrializing and achieving high levels of living, most of the Middle East remained a poor and backward area dominated by foreigners. Today, however, the peoples of the region are reasserting their independence and importance. The Ottoman Empire was liquidated at the end of World War I and the Italian Empire following World War II. Since World War I most of the Middle Eastern possessions of Great Britain and France have gained independence, though in 1960 France still held Algeria and French Somali-

---

[1] Carleton S. Coon, *Caravan: The Story of the Middle East*. New York: Holt, Rinehart and Winston, 1951. P. 23. Used by permission of the author

and the publisher.

[2] *Ibid*. P. 24. Used by permission of the author and the publisher.

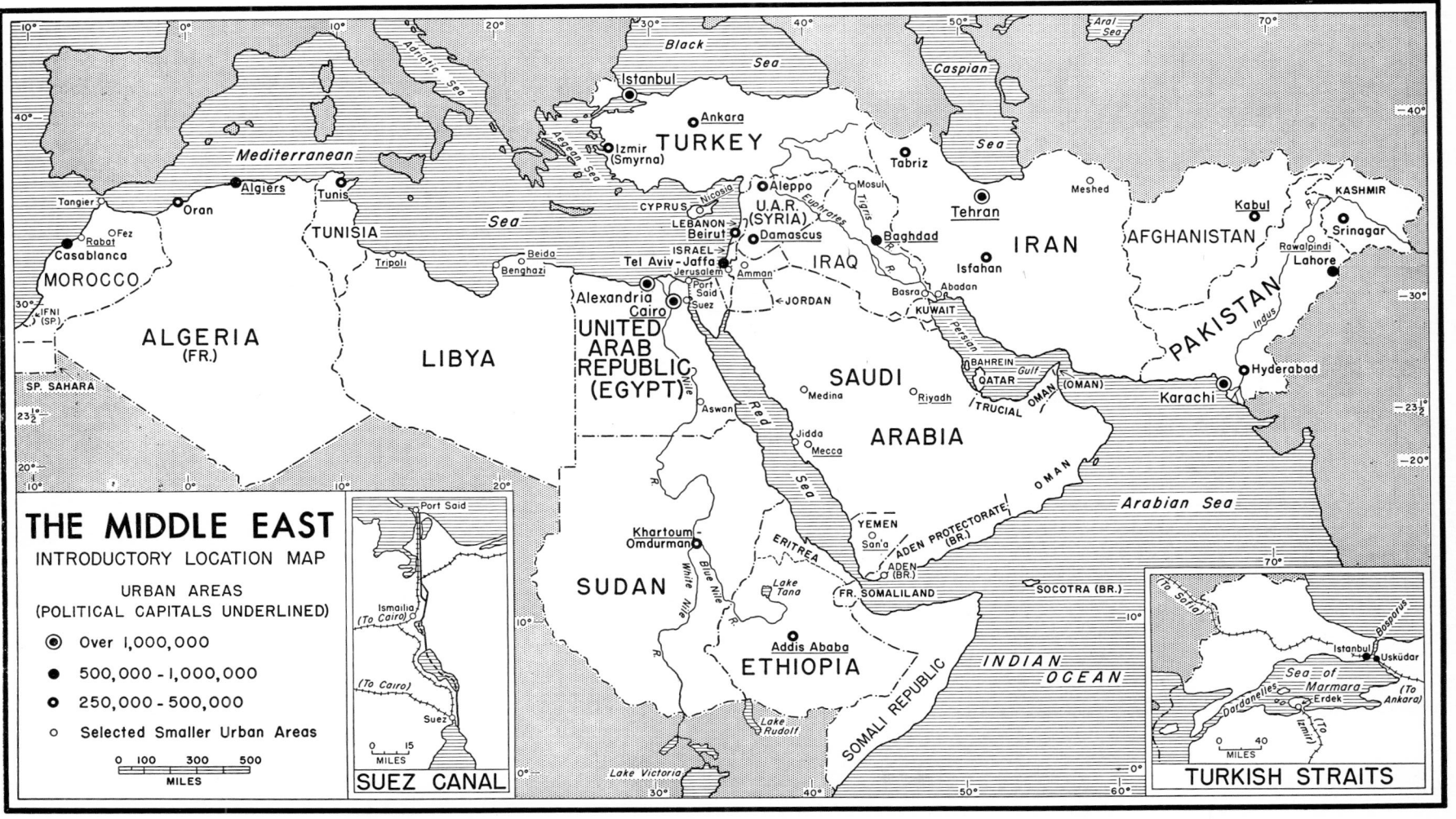

## THE MIDDLE EAST

INTRODUCTORY LOCATION MAP

URBAN AREAS
(POLITICAL CAPITALS UNDERLINED)

◉ Over 1,000,000
● 500,000 - 1,000,000
◒ 250,000 - 500,000
○ Selected Smaller Urban Areas

0  100  300  500
MILES

SUEZ CANAL

TURKISH STRAITS

Introductory location map of the Middle East, showing political units as of January 1, 1961. The island of Socotra is a part of the Aden Protectorate. The Somali Republic is comprised of former Italian Somaliland (later the Trust Territory of Somalia) and former British Somaliland.

A scene in the Middle Eastern deserts. Camels wait patiently as their Arab masters face meditatively toward Mecca and pray during one of the five prayer periods of the day which Moslems observe. (Arabian American Oil Company.)

land, and Great Britain retained a foothold in the southern and eastern margins of the oil-rich Arabian Peninsula.

As European colonialism has declined in the Middle East, many political trouble spots have developed. Palestine and Algeria are familiar examples. The region lacks political stability, a fact partly associated with the illiteracy and povery of its people. Several international crises have been precipitated by Middle Eastern questions since World War II. These reflect the growing importance of the region in world affairs. One of the main factors is the rich oil deposits of the Persian Gulf area and the Sahara Desert. Great Britain, France, and several other European countries are dependent upon oil imports from the Middle East, and European companies, especially British, French, and Dutch, play a prominent role in the region's oil industry. American companies are prominent also, though the United States is less dependent than Europe upon oil imports.

One of the world's major routes of sea transportation, the Mediterranean-Asiatic route, crosses the heart of the Middle East by way of the Suez Canal and Red Sea. It

Areas of *steppe climate,* while dry, are better supplied with moisture than the deserts because of greater rainfall, less evaporation, or a combination of these. Such areas are classed as semiarid rather than arid. An annual average of 10 to 20 inches of precipitation is typical, though deviations occur at both the upper and lower ends of this scale. The natural vegetation is more closely spaced than in the deserts and includes a larger proportion of grasses. Thus better forage is available for livestock, and the steppes are far superior to the deserts as grazing lands. However, the undependable nature of the rainfall renders crop

growing precarious except where irrigation water is available.

The Middle Eastern areas of *mediterranean* or *dry-summer subtropical climate* are principally confined to the borderlands of the Mediterranean Sea in northwestern Africa and southwestern Asia. This climate zone encloses Lebanon and Cyprus, and the most productive farming areas of Morocco, Algeria, Tunisia, Turkey, Syria, Israel, Jordan, and Libya are found within it. Rainfall averaging 15 to 40 inches annually provides more moisture for crop growth than is available in the steppe climate, but the characteristic regime of rainy winters and dry sum-

TABLE 14

CLIMATIC DATA FOR SELECTED MIDDLE EASTERN STATIONS

| STATION | LATITUDE TO NEAREST WHOLE DEGREE | ELEVATION ABOVE SEA LEVEL (FEET) | TYPE OF CLIMATE | AVERAGE TEMPERATURE (DEGREES F TO NEAREST WHOLE DEGREE) | | | PRECIPITATION | |
|---|---|---|---|---|---|---|---|---|
| | | | | ANNUAL | JANUARY (OR COOLEST MONTH) | JULY (OR WARMEST MONTH) | ANNUAL AVERAGE (TO NEAREST INCH) | PERCENT OCTOBER–MARCH |
| Tehran (Iran) | 36°N. | 4002 | Steppe | 62° | 34° | 85° | 9″ | 76% |
| Baghdad (Iraq) | 33°N. | 110 | Desert | 73° | 49° | 95° | 7″ | 84% |
| Karachi (Pakistan) | 25°N. | 13 | Desert | 78° | 65° | 87° (June) | 8″ | 21% |
| Cairo (Egypt) | 30°N. | 67 | Desert | 70° | 55° | 82° | 1″ | 85% |
| Khartoum (Sudan) | 16°N. | 1247 | Desert | 84° | 73° | 93° (May, June) | 6″ | 4% |
| Istanbul (Turkey) | 41°N. | 164 | Mediterranean | 57° | 41° | 74° | 29″ | 68% |
| Algiers (Algeria) | 37°N. | 194 | Mediterranean | 65° | 53° | 78° (Aug.) | 30″ | 81% |
| Jerusalem (Israel-Jordan) | 32°N. | 2485 | Mediterranean | 61° | 44° | 73° (July, Aug.) | 25″ | 93% |
| Mongalla (Sudan) | 6°N. | 1440 | Tropical savanna | 79° | 83° (Mar.) | 76° (July, Aug.) | 39″ | 23% |
| Addis Ababa (Ethiopia) | 9°N. | 8038 | Tropical highland | 62° | 59° (Nov., Dec.) | 66° (May) | 50″ | 14% |

mers is a handicap to agriculture. Both the climate and associated agricultural activities conform generally to the pattern described for Southern Europe in Chapter 9.

Areas of *tropical savanna climate* are found near the equator in parts of the Sudan, Ethiopia, and Somaliland. This humid climate type, occupying the outer margins of the rainy tropics, is not typical of the Middle East. It is characterized by high temperatures the year round, a complete absence of frost, an annual rainfall averaging 20 to 60 inches or more, and a dry season lasting most or all of the winter half-year. The tropical savanna climate is described more fully in Chapters 15 and 22.

*Highland climates,* varying in character according to altitude and distance from the equator, are found in the higher mountain areas of the Middle East. Table 14 gives climatic data for some representative Middle Eastern stations. Note the unbalanced rainfall regime at all stations listed.

### ▶ Role of the Mountains in Water Supply

Mountains play a vital role in the economy of the Middle East. Indeed, by furnishing the principal supplies of water for irrigation and household use, they make life possible for most of the inhabitants of this dry region.

The mountains of the Middle East are found in three principal areas (map, p. 282). (1) In northwestern Africa the Atlas Mountains of Morocco, Algeria, and Tunisia lie between the Mediterranean Sea and Atlantic Ocean and the Sahara Desert. The High Atlas of Morocco reaches 13,665 feet. (2) A larger area of mountains occupies the northeastern quarter of the Middle East. It stretches across Turkey, Iran, Afghanistan, and West Pakistan, and includes the highest

A cedar forest in the Atlas Mountains of Morocco. Forests of this quality are found in only a few parts of the Middle East. (French Embassy Press and Information Division.)

peaks in the region. The loftiest and best-known mountains in Turkey and Iran are the Taurus, Anti-Taurus, Elburz, and Zagros mountains, which radiate outward from the rugged Armenian Knot in the tangled border country where Turkey, Iran, and the Soviet Union meet. The higher summits attain elevations of 10,000 to nearly 19,000 feet. The mountains in this quarter of the Middle East culminate in the great Hindu Kush mountain system of Afghanistan and West Pakistan, which reaches 25,426 feet, and the Karakoram Range, in Kashmir, where Mount Godwin Austen ($K^2$), second highest in the world, rises to 28,250 feet. (3) The third principal area of mountains is found in Ethiopia and Yemen, bordering the southern end of the Red Sea. The extensive highland of Ethiopia has a number of scattered summits higher than 13,000 feet, and one of 15,158 feet. The smaller highland of Yemen reaches 12,336 feet. Lower, discontinuous mountain ranges extend northward from Ethiopia and Yemen along either side of the Red Sea.

Scattered mountain areas occur elsewhere in the Middle East, for example, the Tibesti Mountains in the central Sahara, which rise to 11,204 feet.

Water originating in mountain rainfall or snowfall often percolates for long distances underground and reaches the surface in springs or is drawn upon by wells in populated areas at the base of the mountains or beyond. Water supplies of this kind are ordinarily sufficient for only a limited local development of irrigation farming. Most of the larger irrigated districts depend on water carried from the mountains by surface streams, a few of which are among the great rivers of the world. The Nile, Tigris-Euphrates, and Indus rivers provide water for many millions of farmers, and urban dwellers as well, in Egypt and the Sudan, Iraq, and West Pakistan. The earliest known civilizations arose in the valleys of these rivers, each of which has supported agriculture for at least forty or fifty centuries.

## ▶ *The Scarcity of Wood*

Extensive forests existed in early times in the Middle East, but overcutting and overgrazing have almost wiped them out. Timber has been cut faster than nature could grow it, and the young seedlings have been grazed off by sheep, goats, and camels, with the result that the forests have been unable to reproduce themselves. Lumber in commercial quantities can still be obtained from a few mountain areas, such as the Atlas region of Morocco and Algeria, but the total supply falls far short of the need.

Carleton S. Coon, a leading authority on the Middle East, has written as follows concerning the scarcity of wood:

The fact is that except for China no part of the earth's surface seems to have been so denuded as the Middle East. We read of the orchard that was Morocco in Roman times and see barren hillsides. The Egyptians imported thousands and thousands of trunks of the cedars of Lebanon; and in every museum in the world which contains Egyptological specimens, pieces of that wood appear in the form of coffins or other types of furniture. Solomon used the cedar of Lebanon in building his temple. If you go to Lebanon today, you will see the cedar depicted on the flag of the republic and on the hats of its customs inspectors. But on Mount Lebanon itself, despite recent attempts at conservation and reforestation, not enough remains to furnish the timber for one Gloucester schooner.

. . . In Iran one is struck by the difference between the complete barrenness of the landscape which is either under cultivation or within walking distance of a village, and that of the uninhabited deserts. In the inhabited land children go out every morning with long-handled hoes and sacks to remove every spear of inflammable vegetation, including camel thorn, that the sheep and goats have left behind them; their work is thorough. In the desert, in places too distant from villages to warrant this attention, the traveler is impressed by the abundance of natural flora, in the form of sagebrush and dry stalks of aromatic annuals. Up on the eastern flank of the Elburz . . . I once saw some juniper trees which had been lopped for firewood. "Aren't these protected by law?" I asked a soldier who was with me. "Yes," he replied, "but the government cannot afford to station one of us beside each tree.". . .

In Iran one of the most striking sights is the half-acre patch of dense poplar forest that grows up-ditch beside each village. These trees grow quickly, and their limbs cling close to the trunks; trees with 4-inch stems grow no more than 18 inches apart. No more efficient way of producing 20-foot poles quickly and on a minimum space could be found. These poplar poles are the standard units of material for rafters, door jambs, window frames, and the like. The forest has moved from the mountain to the valley.

It is easy for us, newly aroused to an interest in conservation, to decry the deforestation of the Middle East. We have lived in a rich land for periods ranging from one to three hundred years, depending on the part of the country, and we have wasted probably no more than half our natural resources in forest and topsoil during that time. In a far poorer environment, over a period of 5000 years and more, the peoples of the Middle East have destroyed only 90 percent of it. What if they had proceeded at our pace! [3]

## ▶ *Shortage of Minerals*

The Middle East is further handicapped, especially as regards industrialization, by a serious lack of mineral resources. Good deposits of coal are rare. The region is rich in petroleum and natural gas, but the largest deposits are confined to a few countries bordering the Persian Gulf, plus Algeria and probably Libya. Although scattered deposits of metals occur, few offer much prospect for large-scale exploitation. Good-sized deposits of salt are fairly common, and important reserves of phosphate rock, useful as a chemical and fertilizer material, exist in Morocco, Algeria, Tunisia, Egypt, Jordan, and Israel. However, the general outlook for extraction of minerals is rather poor. Among the Middle Eastern countries, Turkey and Morocco have the most varied endowment of minerals, including metals, fuels, and chemical materials, but their over-all output and reserves are not outstanding in world terms. The total value of their output is much less than that of the main Middle Eastern oil producers.

---

[3] *Ibid.* Pp. 20–23. Used by permission of the author and the publisher.

This pipeline across the desert (Trans-Arabian Pipe Line) carries oil for more than a thousand miles from fields in Saudi Arabia to a shipping point on the Mediterranean Sea in Lebanon (map, p. 313). (Trans-Arabian Pipe Line Co.)

These shafts (below) in Saudi Arabia mark the course of a tunnel used to carry irrigation and drinking water from an underground source by gravity flow. Such devices, called "qanats" (kanats), "karez," or "foggaras," are very common in some Middle Eastern countries, notably Iran, Afghanistan, Algeria, and Morocco. "The essential idea is that of a gently sloping tunnel, often along the radius of an alluvial fan, which extends upslope until the water table is tapped and emerges at the downslope end to supply an oasis. To give access to the tunnel, vertical shafts are dug at closely spaced intervals. The length of a qanat ranges from a few hundred yards to tens of miles, and the upper end may be several hundred feet below the surface. . . . By this means thousands of acres are irrigated and hundreds of villages receive their sole water supply." (George B. Cressey, "Qanats, Karez, and Foggaras." *Geographical Review*, v. 48, 1958, p. 27. Used by permission of the author and the American Geographical Society of New York. Students are urged to read the entire article, pp. 27–44.) (Photo: Standard Oil Company, N. J.)

## THE MIDDLE EASTERN LANDSCAPE

The landscape of this dry region alternates between green and brown, according to the presence or absence of water. George B. Cressey has described the land surface as one might view it from a plane flying by either of two alternate routes across the heart of the Middle East:

What does one see on a flight between Cairo and the Persian Gulf? For 5 hours, at 300 miles an hour, there is an almost total absence of life. As soon as one leaves the last irrigation ditch outside Cairo, the green of the Nile oasis instantly changes to the brown of the desert. One hour eastward there is a glimpse of the Red Sea. Then for 4 hours or more there is the desolation of Arabia. One looks down from the plane at sand dunes and bare rock. If there is an occasional stunted tree or water hole, it is not visible from the air. Not a trace of green is to be seen. Once or twice a keen eye will catch a group of a dozen mud houses, nothing more. This may be a place to study geomorphology, but it is not an attractive spot to make a living.

Then comes the green blue of the Persian Gulf, and one flies over the fabulous oil fields of Dhahran and Bahrein Island, with oil wells, refineries, docks, and air-conditioned comfort, American style.

Or fly from Cairo northeast to Tehran, 7 hours away. Here there is plenty of desert, but more of interest. Such a route provides a better glimpse of the Suez Canal, and, in peace time, of Jerusalem and the Dead Sea. It is a commentary on the size of Palestine that while one is over the Dead Sea, the Mediterranean is still in sight. . . . Near Baghdad one crosses the thin green strips of cultivation along the Tigris and Euphrates. In places old irrigation works, long abandoned, stand out in the desert, and ruined cities recall the dramatic history of these valleys. Eastward across the mountains, snow-capped in winter, lies the barren plateau of Iran and the capital city of Tehran. Radiating down the broad alluvial fans one may notice heaps of earth at intervals of a hundred yards. These locate the shafts spaced along the underground tunnels called qanats or karez which bring irrigation water from water-bearing gravels at the base of the mountain [photo, p. 287]. This route from Cairo crosses the Dead Sea depression, with a minus elevation of 1297 feet, and comes within sight of Mount Demavend at [18,934] feet. This is an area of contrasts.[4]

## PEOPLES AND WAYS OF LIFE

The Middle East is principally inhabited by dark-haired peoples of the Caucasoid racial group. Especially important among the many languages spoken in the region are Arabic and other Semitic languages, Berber and other Hamitic languages, Turkish, Persian, and Urdu (spoken in West Pakistan). Most of the inhabitants of the Middle East are farmers or nomadic herdsmen. The principal areas of dense population are the irrigated valleys of the major rivers and the coast lands of the Mediterranean Sea. The few large cities are mostly political capitals or seaports. Only twelve metropolitan cities have estimated populations of 450,000 or more—Cairo, Tehran, Istanbul, Karachi, Alexandria, Lahore, Casablanca, Algiers, Baghdad, Tel Aviv-Jaffa, Tunis, and Addis Ababa. Manufacturing is still mainly confined to handicrafts or small scale factory industries, although large modern factories are gradually appearing in the larger cities.

The Middle East, like other world regions, is sufficiently varied in its ways of living that generalizations concerning the culture of the region as a whole nearly always contain a certain amount of distortion. Nevertheless, a surprising amount of similarity, at least on a superficial level, can often be discerned in the modes of life pursued

[4] George B. Cressey, "The Land of the Five Seas." *Journal of Geography*, v. 51 (1952), pp. 222– 223. Used by permission of the author and the *Journal of Geography*.

in places as far apart as Morocco and Afghanistan. In a broad way, it is possible to distinguish a "Middle Eastern culture" which is characteristic of the entire region in greater or less degree. This culture in its original form has been much affected by influences from Europe and America, particularly in the cities. However, much of the old culture still remains in rural areas and in the older sections of urban places. Some of its characteristic features have been described as follows by Carleton S. Coon: [5]

Although late to take over the fruits of the industrial revolution, these countries originated two earlier and equally important crises without which the third could not have arisen: the neolithic revolution which brought in agriculture and animal husbandry, and the urban revolution which introduced city life, metalworking, and writing. For over 5000 years the peoples of these countries . . . have been experimenting in the arts of getting a living out of the landscape and getting along with each other. . . .

## ▶ City Life

Three major ways of life have arisen in concert with one another. One is city life, with thousands of skilled workers, specialists in all kinds of hand industries; with merchants prepared to handle both local and international trade; with palaces and courts in which the political institution functions; with mosques, churches, and temples housing the religious hierarchies, whose prime duty is to maintain the equilibrium of the whole society; and with universities and other educational institutions preparing students for both religious and secular leadership. . . .

Some of the cities, notably Mecca, Kerbela [Karbala], and Meshed, are centers of pilgrimage, and in them the mechanism of caring for religious visitors is well worked out. Pilgrims, coming from all parts of the Islamic world to the holy places, from the Philippines and Morocco, India and Bukhara and China, do much to fortify the unity of the countries with which we are concerned. On the pilgrimage, fellow devotees from different countries meet and converse and exchange ideas. Every year a number of pilgrims decide to stay in

one of the countries en route, rather than going home. The uniformity of skills, of architecture, of music, and of literature in these countries reflects this annual intercourse. . . .

## ▶ Village Life

From the life of cities one can move without pain to that of villages, for the city is a big village as well as a center of industry. The land on the outskirts of the city is tilled by farmers who commute in reverse, and they have done this since the days of Hammurabi. A village is a group of houses located near water and surrounded by agricultural land. It contains a dozen to several hundred families, usually closely related. If the village is on the flatlands, it is usually owned by a sheik or a landlord. While the sheik may be in residence, the landlord usually lives in the city, governing through a local, appointed agent who is in effect the mayor or headman. Rarely, such a village is free, in that the farmers own their land and select their own leader.

If the village is in the mountains, its inhabitants usually form part of a tribal system, and their allegiance is to their tribal chiefs. Since the plains are accessible and defenseless, lowland villagers are seldom noted as fighters, and are usually docile subjects of the central government, whatever it may be. The mountain villagers are relatively healthy, and more warlike, since they have some chance of defending their rocky hideouts, and are used to intervillage and intertribal raids and feuds arising from population pressure. The mountaineers often preserve some archaic form of speech, foreign to that of the dwellers on the plain, wear distinctive clothing, sing distinctive songs, nurse their children on distinctive tribal lore, and have long been a problem to shahs and sultans.

Some of these tribes are seasonally migratory. They pasture their animals in the mountain meadows in summer, and in the fall pack all their belongings onto horses, donkeys, and cattle, and move in a wild rush of dust and sheep dung down to the warmer plain, where they spend the winter pasturing their animals in the new grass which grows with the rain. In the spring they climb back to the mountains. This annual migration may involve the movement of several thousands of human beings and hundreds of thousands of animals over a dis-

---

[5] Carleton S. Coon, "Point Four and the Middle East." *Annals of the American Academy of Political and Social Science,* v. 270 (1950), pp. 88–92.

One heading has been changed. Used by permission of the author and the *Annals.*

tance of several hundreds of miles. The country through which they move is inhabited by sedentary people, with whom all kinds of conflicts could easily arise. Hence the tribe needs leadership and a competent private police force to keep all hands in line. This policing of the migration is the practical basis of the tribal organization, which follows patriarchal family lines. Since international boundaries often follow watersheds, and since mountain watersheds make prime summer pasture, many of these tribes are international; hence the worries of shahs and sultans.

### ▶ Desert Life

Another kind of nomadism exists in the deserts. The Baluchi, the Bedouin, the Tuareg, and other camel people of the South Iranian, Arabian, and Sahara deserts are probably the best known of all Middle Easterners to the American public, but the American public little realizes what complex lives the nomads lead. It is as true as it is trite to liken the desert to a sea and the camel to a ship. The agricultural communities along the shore serve as ports and havens to which the fleets of Bedouin come for victualing and re-equipping. But the ships carry their carpenters and machinists, and supply ships come out to service them when they are too busy to leave the banks.

Speaking less metaphorically, the camel nomads are not simple strangers at all, but Arabs or Berbers like their sedentary kinsmen, just as cowboys are Americans or Canadians, and not some special breed or nation. In years of good rainfall the desert provides bountiful pasture during the cool weather; in dry years there must be a scramble for greenery and for water, and in their scramble the strong may well push out the weak. We have had similar troubles over water holes and range in the West. In the good season, traders come out to live with the Bedouin and sell them the goods they need against livestock. At all seasons, a blacksmith will accompany each camp. He is no kin to the men he serves, and hence if they are raided, he, like the merchants, will not be harmed. Thus automatically the supply of metal tools and implements is assured.

If one walks down the streets and through the markets of any large [Middle Eastern] city, one is likely to see not only city men, but also villagers, mountain men, and camel men off the desert. . . . These people have come to town to see the sights and to trade. . . .

### ▶ Some Details of Middle Eastern Material Culture

Many of the picturesque details of Middle Eastern material culture are based on excellent common sense and a maximum utilization of scarce raw materials. Old-fashioned Moslems have little furniture in their houses. They take off their shoes when they enter a room, and sit on clean carpets. They have enough wool to weave carpets, but not enough wood to build bulky tables and chairs. Their food includes much butter, cheese, curds, and other milk products, but little meat. Milking animals in a land of little abundance is less extravagant than butchering them. Pigs have long been forbidden, and one must remember that in a barren land where all vegetable foods grown are needed to feed men, it would be antisocial to fatten a pig.

Old-fashioned Middle Eastern clothing is designed to give the wearer the maximum of comfort, privacy, and dignity. The jellaba of the North African keeps him warm in winter and cool in the hot sun; he can sleep in it, and shield himself from the public gaze when performing natural acts on a barren landscape. The chuddar of the Persian lady covers her decently, and conceals the state of her clothes underneath. On the street, the widow and the judge's wife look alike. Middle Eastern street clothing, by its uniformity and voluminousness, is an instrument of democracy. The shift to Western garb can hardly be in every sense an improvement.

Middle Eastern architecture, with its adobe walls and clever domes, creates out of local mud and a few sticks what we cannot erect here, from exotic materials, for a dollar a cubic foot—a comfortable home. Fuel is a huge bottleneck in the Middle East, and hence the scarcity of burnt brick. . . . We can teach the Middle Easterners little about noninstitutional building.

# Individual Middle Eastern Countries and Their Characteristics

In this chapter the individual countries of the Middle East are surveyed under the following headings: (1) The Arab World and Israel, (2) Persian Gulf Oil and the States That Produce It, (3) Turkey and Afghanistan, (4) Ethiopia and Somaliland. West Pakistan and Kashmir are discussed with the Indian Subcontinent in Chapter 16.

## THE ARAB WORLD AND ISRAEL

The Arab world, stretching from the Persian Gulf to Morocco and southward to the fringes of Negro Africa, is a major component of the Middle East. The peoples who inhabit it are racially and culturally diverse, but the majority speak some form of Arabic

---

An Egyptian fellah breaks the rich alluvial earth of the Nile Delta in preparation for a fall-sown crop. Note the date palms and field of ripening corn in the background. Corn bread is a staple in the Egyptian diet. (Peter Schmid—Pix, Inc.)

and are thought of broadly as Arabs. Originally the Arabs were inhabitants of the Arabian Peninsula. Here arose, in the seventh century A.D., the Moslem (Muslim) religion which most Arabs profess. It was founded on the teachings of the Prophet Mohammed.

The Prophet was born in A.D. 570 at Mecca and died at Medina some sixty-two years later. His contribution was not so much a new religious concept as a new pattern of life. At the time of his birth, Arab society was virtually without moral precept or guidance. Mohammed conscientiously set out to correct what he thought were the worst features of that society. For example, he ended the practice of female infanticide, which before that time had been left to the judgment of the father. Through his teachings, the position of women greatly improved, as the number of wives was limited to four at a time and divorce was regularized. Mohammed laid down laws for what he considered the proper treatment of orphans, slaves, prisoners, and animals. He forbade bearing false witness, worshiping idols, or speaking ill of chaste women. Because the main drink of the Arabs then was a potent beverage made from the heart of palms, which quickly reduced the user to a state of belligerent stupidity and led to many quarrels and sometimes to bloodshed, Mohammed forbade the use of intoxicating liquors. He also felt that the practice of gambling had weakened Arab society in his day and prohibited it too.

In the eyes of true Moslems, the Koran is the word of God, or Allah, which was transmitted through the Angel Gabriel to Mohammed and then recited by him to the faithful. . . . The Koran is not only the Holy Book of Islam, . . . but it is the textbook used by most Moslems in learning to read; thus it standardizes written Arabic throughout the entire world. . . .

The duties of a Moslem are built around the five Pillars of Islam. The first of these is the profession of faith: "There is but one God, and Mohammed is his apostle." The second is frequent daily prayer, which is largely supplica-

tion. . . . The most important prayer of the week occurs at noon on Friday, a public ceremony which must be observed by all Moslems. Mohammed emphasized the necessity for this gathering, and the need for the pilgrimage to Mecca, in order to bring Moslems together and weld them into a single community.

The third Pillar of the Moslem faith is the giving of alms. This started as a voluntary act, became obligatory for a while, and in most parts of the Arab world today has again become voluntary. The fourth Pillar is fasting in the month of Ramadan, the month during which the Koran was first revealed to Mohammed. . . . During this month the true believer can eat no food and swallow no drink from dawn until sunset, unless he is ill or on a journey. . . .

Making the pilgrimage to Mecca is the fifth Pillar of Islam. Every true Moslem tried to do this once during his lifetime. . . . Special ceremonies peculiar to the pilgrimage include striking down the devil with stones in the Valley of Mina, sacrificing a sheep or camel there, entering into the prescribed holy places wearing a seamless garment, walking seven times around the Kaaba, and devoting oneself to prayer.[1]

After the death of the Prophet in 632, his Arab followers spread the Moslem faith through a vast area in Asia, Africa, and Europe. Before a century had passed, Arab armies had subjugated an empire reaching to Morocco and Spain on the west, to present-day West Pakistan on the east and Soviet Middle Asia and Transcaucasia on the north, and southward into the Sahara Desert. Within the new empire a high civilization developed. Great architectural works were created, significant advances were made in agriculture, medicine, mathematics, and science; and a vigorous intellectual life flourished in such university centers as Cairo, Fez, Baghdad, Damascus, Cordova, Toledo, Seville, and Granada. At a time when western Europe was relatively stagnant, the Arab lands contained many of the

---

[1] Richard H. Sanger, *The Arabian Peninsula.* Ithaca, N. Y.: Cornell University Press, 1954. Pp. 95–97. Used by permission of the publisher. The word Islam means "submission" (to the will of God or Allah; a Moslem is "one who submits"). The

Kaaba, a building at Mecca housing the venerated Black Stone, is the chief shrine of the Islamic world. It was a holy place long before Mohammed's time.

foremost centers of culture and learning in the world.

But these lands did not enjoy an over-all political unity for very long. The original empire, ruled from Medina, then from Damascus, and finally from Baghdad, commenced to disintegrate soon after it was established. Separate Moslem states arose in Spain, northwestern Africa, Egypt, and elsewhere. Beginning in the eleventh century there were conquests of portions of the empire by Christian Crusaders and somewhat later by Turkic and Mongolian peoples. In the fifteenth century Christian armies of the Spanish kingdom, after centuries of intermittent warfare by Spaniards and Portuguese against the Moslems, completed the reconquest of the Iberian Peninsula. By the middle of the sixteenth century most parts of the original Arab empire, weakened and disunited, had been conquered by the Ottoman Turks.

Today most Arabs are found in countries that belong to the League of Arab States. This organization, formed in 1945, is comprised of the United Arab Republic (Egypt-Syria), Iraq, Jordan, Lebanon, Saudi Arabia, Yemen, the Sudan, Libya, Tunisia, and Morocco. Quarrels and jealousies among the Arab states have often hindered their functioning as a group. But these divisive tendencies are being counteracted in some measure by a consciousness of an over-all Arab unity or solidarity that is developing among the peoples and governments of these lands. This feeling has several important roots. Partly it is the product of a common language, religion, and cultural heritage, coupled with pride in past achievements and a desire to regain past glories. Partly it is due to the realization of a need for united effort to improve social and economic conditions throughout the Arab lands. And partly it grows out of opposition to foreign economic and political domination and opposition to the state of Israel, which was founded under foreign auspices and is looked upon as usurping territory that is rightfully Arab.

## ▶ Israel and Its Neighbors of the Fertile Crescent

Since 1948, when Israel was formed from the British mandated territory of Palestine, antipathy to the new state has been a major rallying point for the League of Arab States, particularly the members that are Israel's immediate neighbors. To the north and east these neighbors include Lebanon, Syria, and Jordan (formerly Transjordan) (map, p. 294). All three, and Israel, were held by Turkey prior to World War I. When the Ottoman Empire was liquidated following the war, Syria and Lebanon were mandated to France by the League of Nations, while Great Britain received a mandate for Palestine and Transjordan. Syria and Lebanon secured independence by stages in the period 1943–1946, and Transjordan was granted independence in 1946. In 1958 Syria formed a political union with Egypt called the United Arab Republic.

Palestine was partitioned among Israel, Jordan, and Egypt when Israel was constituted in 1948 as an independent homeland for the Jewish population of the world. This action, the result of warfare after British and United Nations' efforts at peaceful partitioning had failed, gave Israel approximately 77 percent of the territory of the Palestine mandate, including the coastal areas (except the Gaza Strip, which was occupied by Egypt), the northern hill country of Galilee, the dry, thinly populated southern triangle called the Negev, and a portion of the city of Jerusalem in the Judean hills, plus a corridor leading to the city from the coastal plain. A total of 708,000 Jewish immigrants, mostly from Eastern Europe or the Middle East, entered Israel between May 14, 1948, when the new state was officially proclaimed, and the end of 1952. By 1958 Israel's population was about 2 million, including 904,000 Jews resident before 1948

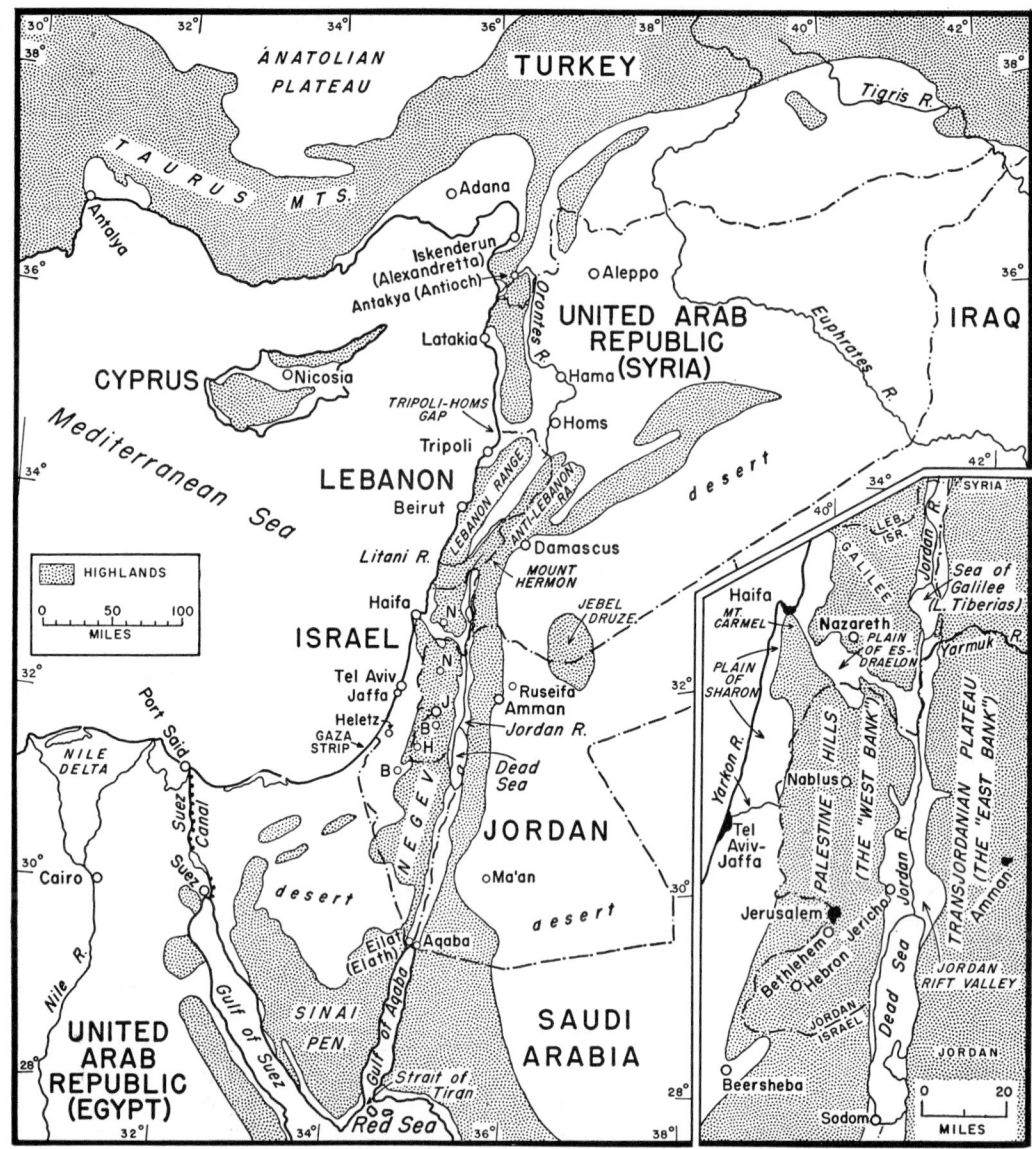

Israel and its neighbors. Most of the stippled highland areas consist predominantly of mountains except in Israel and Jordan, where hill lands predominate.

or born in Israel, 870,000 new immigrants, and 218,000 non-Jews (mostly Moslem or Christian Arabs). (It should be noted that prior to the independence of the State of Israel, the Zionist movement had brought Jews back to Palestine since about 1880.)

Aided by large amounts of outside capital, primarily from the United States, the Israelis are developing their small republic as a modern Westernized state. The number of agricultural settlements and the total cultivated acreage have more than doubled since 1948, and the area under irrigation has quadrupled. Citrus fruits (mainly oranges) grown in irrigated groves are the country's leading export, accounting for one third to two fifths of all exports by value in recent years. Production for the domestic market concentrates on dairying, beef production, poultry raising for eggs and meat, and vegetable growing. Pond fisheries play a significant role in the agricultural economy. Grain production is inadequate, and large wheat imports are required. The intensive, mechanized agriculture of Israel, oriented to nearby urban markets, resembles in many ways the agriculture of densely populated areas in western Europe. But in Israel a distinctive touch is added by the collectivized settlements called *kibbutzim* (sing., *kibbutz*), in which the land is held and worked by all families in common and meals are served in a central dining hall. Such settlements exist side by side with villages of private farmers and with cooperative villages called *moshavim*.

Existing agricultural development in Israel is concentrated in the northern half of the country, with its heavier rainfall (largely confined to the winter half year) and ampler supplies of surface and underground water for irrigation. Annual rainfall averages 20 inches or more in most sections north of Tel Aviv and in the interior hills where Jerusalem lies, though it drops below that figure in the deep rift valley of the Jordan River. But from Tel Aviv southward to Beersheba, in the northern Negev, the rainfall decreases to 8 inches, and in the central and southern Negev it drops to 4 inches or less. Long-range water planning in Israel contemplates the transfer of water from the north through conduits and canals to irrigate lands in the semiarid or arid south. Water is already being supplied to agricultural settlements in the northern Negev by pipelines from the Yarkon River, though utilization of the country's largest source of surface water, the River Jordan, is blocked by disagreements between Israel and its Arab neighbors (see p. 296). Existing irrigation development in the Negev is concentrated on fertile loess soils in the region around Beersheba.

But Israel's main hope for future support of its growing population, three fifths of which is concentrated in towns or cities of over 10,000, lies in expanded industry and trade. The country has been steadily industrializing, though it is hampered somewhat by a lack of mineral resources. Especially critical is the deficit in mineral fuels. Israel has no coal production, and its oil deposits supply only a tiny part of the country's requirements. Oil imports are the main source of mechanical energy. Much emphasis is being placed on expansion of chemical manufacturing, based in part on potash and other chemical salts extracted from the brines of the Dead Sea and on rock phosphate mined in the Negev. Many skilled craftsman have immigrated to Israel, and industries have been developed to capitalize on their skills, for example the cutting and polishing of industrial diamonds. Diamonds accounted for one fifth or more of all exports in the period 1955–1958.

Tel Aviv–Jaffa (572,000) on the Mediterranean coast is Israel's largest city and industrial center. (Unless otherwise noted, city populations cited in this chapter are metropolitan area estimates—see p. 62.) Its industries produce textiles and a variety of other consumer goods. A factory in one of its suburbs is the Middle East's largest producer of heavy electrical equipment. The leading seaport and center of heavy industry is Haifa (230,000) in northern Israel. Among the factories in its metropolitan area are an oil refinery, a large chemical plant manufacturing superphosphate fertilizers, a plant for smelting nonferrous metals, and a steel mill. Approximately three quarters of Israel's population is concentrated in Tel Aviv, Haifa, or the narrow coastal strip between them. The ancient town of Beersheba (city proper, 40,000 in 1958) is being developed as the northern gateway, administrative center, and main industrial center of the Negev frontier region. A rail line from Tel Aviv reaches Beersheba, and highways connect the city with potash works on the Dead Sea and with Israel's small Red Sea port of Eilat

(Elath) on the Gulf of Aqaba. Eilat, useless from 1950 to 1956 because of an Egyptian–Saudi Arabian blockade of the entrance to the gulf, is the southern terminus of a 16-inch pipeline carrying Persian Gulf oil to the refinery at Haifa. Small amounts of oil from Israel's own field at Heletz also move through the pipeline.

Meanwhile, Israel's relations with her Arab neighbors continue to cloud the country's future. Immediately after the proclamation of independence in 1948, armed forces of Jordan, Egypt, Iraq, Syria, and Lebanon invaded Israel, but they were defeated or stalemated by the Israeli army. Armistice agreements were signed in 1949, though sporadic border fighting continued. Prior to and during the fighting of 1948, over 500,000 Palestinian Arabs fled to the neighboring Arab countries. These displaced persons, many of whom still live in refugee camps maintained by the United Nations in Jordan, Egypt, Lebanon, and Syria, have been a major source of bad feeling between Israel and the Arab states. By 1960 the total number of Arab refugees on United Nations relief rolls had swelled through natural increase and illegal registration to over 1,000,000, of whom more than half were in Jordan and another quarter in the Gaza Strip administered by Egypt.

Other difficulties have arisen over the city of Jerusalem, partitioned between Israel and Jordan (population of Israeli side, 156,000; Jordan side, 75,000). The problem of Jerusalem originates in the fact that the city is a holy place of Islam as well as Judaism and Christianity, being regarded as the third holiest city in the Islamic world (after Mecca and Medina). Despite its perilous situation on the boundary with a hostile country, the Israeli-held part of Jerusalem, incorporating most of the "New City," was made the capital of Israel. Most of the sacred shrines, however, are in the "Old City" in the Jordanian sector.

One of the most publicized disputes between Israel and her Arab neighbors concerns the use of water from the Jordan River. This famous stream rises in Lebanon and Syria, flows southward along the northeastern edge of Israel (where one segment forms part of the boundary between Israel and Jordan), and empties into the Dead Sea in Jordan. Israel desires to use the water of the river for irrigation and hydroelectric development, and has expressed willingness to share the water with Jordan, but Jordan, Syria, and Lebanon have objected strenuously to schemes for developing the river which Israel, the United States, and the United Nations have proposed.

*Jordan,* bordering Israel on the east, is mostly desert or semidesert. The main agricultural areas and centers of settlement, including the principal city and capital, Amman (120,000), are in the northwest. This section, extending west and north from Amman to the Israeli and Syrian frontiers and south to the general latitude of the Dead Sea, is composed of two highland areas, the Palestine Hills on the west and the Transjordanian Plateau on the east, separated from each other by the deep rift valley occupied by the Jordan River, the Sea of Galilee (Lake Tiberias), and the Dead Sea (map, p. 294). The valley is the deepest depression on the earth's land surface, being about 600 feet below sea level at Lake Tiberias and nearly 1300 feet below sea level at the Dead Sea (the bottom of the Dead Sea reaches −2600 feet). Though the rainfall gradually increases northward to an average of more than 12 inches in the vicinity of Lake Tiberias, nearly all of the valley bottom from the Dead Sea to the frontier of Israel lies in deep rain shadow and receives less than 4 inches of precipitation a year. But the highlands that border it, rising to heights of 2000–3500 feet or more above sea level and lying in the path of moisture-bearing winds from the Mediterranean, receive precipitation during the cool season that averages 20 inches or more annually within

An age-old scene in the hills of Jordanian Palestine: olive trees and a well along the road from Jerusalem to Bethlehem. (Trans World Airlines, Inc.)

two north-south strips about 80 miles long by 15–20 miles wide. It is within or near these belts of maximum precipitation, one in the Palestine Hills (the "West Bank") and the other in the hilly Transjordanian Plateau (the "East Bank"), that most of Jordan's people are found. The largest percentage are villagers who support themselves primarily by the cultivation of winter grains (wheat and barley), vegetables (grown both winter and summer on irrigated and nonirrigated land), and fruits, especially olives and grapes. The Transjordanian Plateau is the major area of grain production, while olives are heavily localized in the Palestine Hills (photo, above). Measured by value, wheat is Jordan's leading grain crop, olives are its lead-

ing tree crop, and tomatoes its leading vegetable.

Less than 5 percent of Jordan is cultivated, and less than 10 percent of the cultivated land is irrigated. But irrigated land accounts for an estimated sixth of the country's crop production by value and an even higher percentage of its crop exports. Jordan badly needs a large extension of its present irrigated acreage. Neither of the country's two largest rivers, the Jordan and its tributary the Yarmuk, is used much for irrigation, and they could supply considerable amounts of water to expand irrigation in the Jordan rift valley. But these rivers touch other countries besides Jordan (Israel and Lebanon in the case of the Jordan; Israel and Syria in the case of the Yarmuk), and up to the present their full utilization has been delayed by the failure of the nations concerned to reach agreement regarding control works to be established and apportionment of the water. However, Jordan has a project under way to irrigate lands on the east side of the rift valley with water diverted from the Yarmuk.

Jordan's manufacturing establishment is extremely modest, consisting chiefly of flour mills, olive presses, vegetable canneries, soap factories, cement mills, and other uncomplicated enterprises, mostly small. Amman is the leading industrial center, with Nablus (city proper, 45,000), the center of the olive industry, ranking second. The country is poorly endowed with minerals. But phosphate rock, quarried at Ruseifa, northeast of Amman, and potash, secured from the Dead Sea, are produced on an export basis.

Prior to the establishment of Israel, Jordan's trading relationships were primarily with coastal Palestine, and most of the country's seaborne trade moved through Haifa. But these relationships have been severed. Today Jordan's overseas trade moves through Beirut, Lebanon, or the small Jordanian port of Aqaba, located on the Gulf of Aqaba a few miles east of the Israeli port of Eilat (map, p. 294). Jordan is striving to improve the facilities at Aqaba, as well as the road and rail transportation which links it to the country's core area.

Jordan's economic and political situation has been precarious. The country's creation under British auspices following World War I was largely a matter of political expediency. From the outset its trade balance was heavily adverse, and sizable grants and loans by foreign nations (primarily Great Britain and the United States) have been required to keep its economy operative. In 1946 its population was approximately 400,000, of whom about one quarter were desert nomads or seminomads and the remainder villagers or urban dwellers. But by 1950 the population had more than

tripled, due to the annexation of 400,000 "West Bank" Palestinians and the entry of 572,000 refugees or exiles from areas incorporated by Israel. On the whole the Palestinian newcomers were more literate, skilled, and Westernized than the native "East Bank" Jordanians, and their presence has created internal stresses that have added to the country's political instability. It is among the Palestinians that the main anti-Israel and anti-Western elements are found.

Israel's neighbors to the north, Syria (now the Syrian or Northern Region of the United Arab Republic) and Lebanon, exhibit a pattern of physical and climatic features broadly similar to that of Israel and Jordan. As in Israel, narrow coastal plains backed by highlands front the sea. But the highlands of Lebanon and Syria are loftier than those of Israel and Jordan; indeed, the Lebanon and Anti-Lebanon ranges and Mount Hermon are high mountains, rising to slightly more than 10,000, 7000, and 9200 feet, respectively. The coastal mountains of Syria rise to about 4000 feet. Thus to cyclonic precipitation brought by air masses off the Mediterranean is added a considerable fall of orographic rain and snow created by the mountain chains that parallel the coast and block the path of the prevailing winds. Precipitation averages 20 to 40 inches annually in most areas that lie within 50 miles of the sea. West-facing slopes of the mountains often receive 40 to 50 inches.

Lebanon and Syria conform to the customary mediterranean pattern of winter rain and summer drought. In both countries the coastal plains and seaward-facing mountain slopes that border them are settled by a rather dense population of villagers. These people depend for a livelihood primarily on subsistence or semisubsistence cultivation of characteristic mediterranean crops: wheat, barley, vegetables, legumes, grapes, melons, olives, figs, citrus (in Lebanon) and nuts. Tobacco is a prominent cash crop in coastal Syria. Livestock play a relatively minor role in the farming system; in most areas cattle tend to be less prominent than goats or sheep.

In Syria and Lebanon, as in Jordan, precipitation decreases toward the east and the importance of pastoral activities becomes greater. The Anti-Lebanon range and Mount Hermon are drier than the Lebanon range, which screens out moisture that they would otherwise receive. These mountains, and the eastern slopes of the Lebanon range as well, are used primarily for grazing.

East of the mountains a zone of semiarid climate with an annual precipitation of 8 to 20 inches covers central and northern Syria. In southeastern Syria it trends gradually into the Syrian Desert, most of which lies in Iraq and Jordan. The semiarid region, more sparsely populated than the coastal areas, is Syria's main producer of cotton, wheat, and barley. These crops and wool are the country's largest exports. Cotton is grown as an irrigated summer crop, while wheat and barley, primarily non-irrigated, are winter crops. The cultivated areas of interior Syria are not continuous, but are separated by much land that is vacant or used for grazing. The principal cotton and barley district lies between Homs (133,000) and Aleppo. The Orontes River is its main source of irrigation water. Wheat is also prominent in this district, although Syria's main wheat region stretches eastward from Aleppo across the northern edge of the country. Most surplus wheat for export comes from the north, much of it being produced on farms that are larger, more mechanized, and more purely commercial than most farms in Syria and Lebanon. Small irrigated districts growing cotton and grain are found along the valley of Syria's largest river, the Euphrates.

An estimated 22 percent of Syria is cultivated, of which perhaps 14 or 15 percent is irrigated. A much larger percentage could profitably be irrigated and much uncultivated land could be reclaimed if the necessary water were made available. The government of the United Arab Republic is constructing dams on the Euphrates, Orontes, and other rivers to provide a larger supply of irrigation water and hydroelectric power. In both Syria and Lebanon probably two thirds of the people are supported directly by agricultural or pastoral pursuits, and many others derive support from agricultural processing and trade. Possibly half a million camel-herding nomads inhabit the steppes and deserts of eastern Syria. Lebanon's peasantry is more literate, includes a larger proportion of landowners, and has a somewhat higher standard of living than Syria's (though Syria's peasants are better off than those of Egypt or Iraq). In these respects Lebanon stands at or near the top among the countries of the Arab world. It should be noted that Lebanon's population includes a large and highly influential Christian element—a major point of difference between Lebanon and the other Arab states. Syria is somewhat more industrialized than Lebanon, but in neither country are modern factories very numerous. As in most underdeveloped countries, textile milling and agricultural processing industries predominate. Both countries are seriously deficient in mineral resources.

Western and northern Syria, Lebanon, northern Israel, and northwestern Jordan form the western half of the Fertile Crescent, a famous strip of cultivable land between the Syrian Desert and the high mountains of southeastern Turkey and southwestern Iran. The eastern half of the crescent lies mostly in the plain of the Tigris and Euphrates rivers (plain of Mesopotamia) in Iraq. Through the centuries, from the beginning of recorded history, this semicircle of land, leading from the Persian Gulf and the Iranian plateaus to the Mediterranean coast and southward toward the Nile Delta, has been followed by the main caravan tracks from interior Asia to the Mediterranean and northern Africa. It has also served as a pathway for marching armies—Assyrians, Hittites, Persians, Egyptians,

Macedonians, Romans, Crusaders, Arabs, Mongols, Turks, and others have come this way at various times. The countries of the Fertile Crescent have probably been overrun by foreign armies more times than any other group of countries in the world. These are historic lands, with a record of civilized human settlement dating back for thousands of years.

Three of the five largest cities in the Fertile Crescent are located in Syria or Lebanon. All of them have been important cities for many centuries. Damascus (409,-000), the capital of Syria, is situated in a large irrigated district in the southwestern part of the country. The main city of northern Syria is Aleppo (408,000), an ancient caravan center located in the "Syrian Saddle" between the Euphrates Valley and the Mediterranean. Aleppo and Damascus are the leading industrial and commercial centers of present-day Syria. Aleppo is the country's principal grain and cotton market.

The old Phoenician city of Beirut (296,-000), on the Mediterranean, is the capital, largest city, and main seaport of Lebanon. Equipped with modern harbor facilities and an important international airport, Beirut is one of the busiest centers of transportation and commerce in the Middle East. This thriving port symbolizes the importance of Lebanon as a trading nation. Income from transit and entrepôt trade and financial transactions helps redress the country's unfavorable balance of trade, as do tourist revenues and remittances from the many Lebanese who have emigrated to the Americas and other overseas areas. In recent years Beirut has become an important banking and investment center for oil revenues accruing to the Arab states. Lebanon handles an important share of the overseas

trade of Syria and Jordan. But Syria has been expanding its port of Latakia (city proper, 105,000), which now handles most of the country's cotton and grain exports, and Jordan is attempting to orient its trade to its small Red Sea port of Aqaba as much as possible.

A complex pattern of minorities exists in both Syria and Lebanon and in Iraq and Jordan as well. Religious minorities are the most prominent. However, in Syria Moslems of the Sunni (Orthodox) persuasion constitute an estimated 70 percent of the population, though seventeen significant religious minorities are present.[2] In Lebanon, the composition of the population has been estimated as follows: Maronite Christians 30.0 percent, other Christians 24.7 percent; Sunni Moslems 20.3 percent, Shia Moslems 17.7 percent, Druzes 6.2 percent, others 1.0 percent. But no census has been taken in several decades, and some authorities believe that Moslems now outnumber Christians. For many years the Maronites have been the most influential element in Lebanon politically and economically.

▶ *Egypt—The "Gift of the Nile"*

At the southwest, Israel borders Egypt, the largest in population and the most influential of the Arab countries. In 1958, as a result of a political merger with Syria it became the Egyptian or Southern Region of the United Arab Republic. This ancient land, the home of one of the oldest known civilizations, is described in the following selections:

As long ago as 430 B.C., Herodotus observed in his *History* that "Egypt is an acquired country, the gift of the river." This characterization is just as valid today; for, with the excep-

---

[2] Sir Reader Bullard, ed., *The Middle East* (London, New York, Toronto: Oxford University Press, 3d ed., 1958). P. 453. The Islamic community of believers is divided into two main branches, the Sunni (Sunnite) Moslems and the Shia (Shii or Shiite) Moslems. Sunni Moslems are in the majority in most Moslem countries, though Shia Moslems predominate in Iran and are very influential in Iraq and in Yemen.

tion of the Faiyum depression and some smaller oases in the Western Desert, the only part of Egypt that is regularly in cultivation is the 3½ percent of the land that can be irrigated from the Nile. . . . In this small area, made up of the triangular delta north of Cairo and the narrow, ribbon-like valley to the south, live more than 95 percent of Egypt's [25] million people. The rest live either in the oases or on the surrounding deserts in the wake of their wandering flocks.

Nowhere else in the world is the contrast between the desert and the sown so dramatic, or the transition from solitary waste to teeming valley so sharp. And nowhere else does the well-being of man hang by so tenuous a thread. Fortunately the "thread" never breaks. Formerly, it is true, the annual fluctuations of the Nile gave rise to constant anxiety, but the construction of the dam at Aswan in 1902, and the six supplementary barrages downstream, as well as the two upstream, have removed the grim specter of famine. Even so, the rises and falls of the water level are still the subject of as much comment among the *fellahin* [peasants] as the oscillations of the barometer are among the farmers of the prairies. Indeed, the Nile is to the Egyptian's conversation what the weather is to the American's.

The ancient Egyptians, who believed that the swelling of the Nile represented the tears of the goddess Isis shed in compassion for her rain-starved people, early learned to raise crops on the flooded margins of their river and to supplement the floods by means of simple water-lifting devices. In most parts of the Nile Valley the ancient *shaduf* (consisting of little more than a pole and bucket), the *saqia* (in which the water is raised by a rotary wheel furnished with buckets, powered by a beast of burden), and the Archimedean screw are still employed to fill the irrigation ditches. Thanks to these and more modern machinery, including the motor-driven pumps now coming into vogue, especially in the Delta, [about 65–70 percent] of the total population of Egypt contrive to live off the soil. In few other places on earth is land cropped so intensively or so continuously. Two, and even three, crops are often raised off the same piece of soil in the course of a twelve-month, and yields are generally high; for this the well-regulated water supply, the long-lasting fertility of the valley silts, and the growing employment of artificial manures are primarily responsible. Given a more lavish use of such manures, the demand for which at present out-

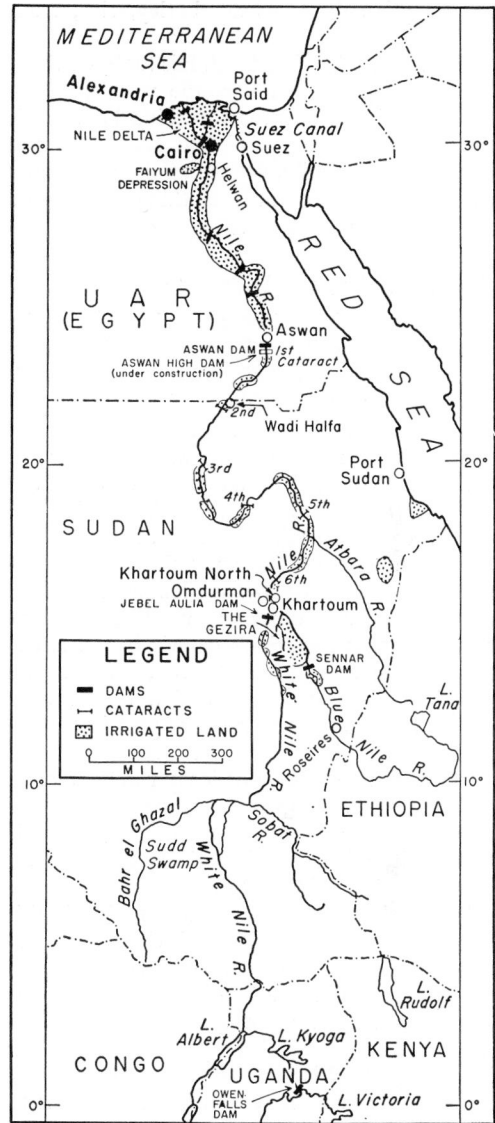

The Nile Basin. The width of the irrigated strips along the Nile is somewhat exaggerated. (Based partly on a map in *Focus*, published by the American Geographical Society.)

strips the supply, even greater yields could be obtained.

Cotton, the long-staple Egyptian variety, is the leading commercial crop; although occupying only 20 percent of the total cultivated area, it accounts for [70 percent or more] of the country's exports. . . .

The usual food crops are corn (a staple in

the Egyptian diet), wheat, barley, rice, fruit, grain sorghum, and sugar cane.[3]

For the fellah, life is hard. His tools are those of his ancestors—the hoe, the wooden plow, the hand sickle, and the threshing board. His dwelling is a crude, fly-infested, two-room mud hut sheltering family, water buffalo, and chickens alike. He owns little clothing and knows few comforts.[4]

### Diet, Sanitation, and Disease [5]

Lacking both variety and abundance, the diet of the majority of Egyptians is dominated by a single staple, *bettai* (maize bread), which provides 80 percent of their caloric intake and 50 percent of their protein intake. In the south, millet and wheat are more widely used as a maize substitute. Vegetables and fruits are available in limited quantities. These include onions, eggplants (the potatoes of the Middle East), tomatoes, turnips, cucumbers, green peppers, lettuce, green beans, lentils, marrows, citrus fruits, and dates. At most, 10 percent of the average Egyptian's caloric intake is obtained from these products; to them may be added an occasional egg and a coarse sour variety of cream cheese made of goat or buffalo milk preserved in salt water. . . .

Meat is an expensive delicacy rarely enjoyed by the fellah. A prosperous peasant family might have meat once a week; the poorer families see it only at festival times or when an animal has been killed by accident. . . .

The lack of pure water is a major health problem in Egypt. Cities and villages all depend on the Nile for their water supply; cities have filtration and chlorination plants, but relatively few villages know this protection. Even where pure water has been provided, the fellah is apt to go on drinking the untreated waters of the Nile—his wife may find it inconvenient to go to the pump, the smallest fee for the pure water will seem too much, or, if he is not one of the many who believe that raw Nile water will enhance his fertility, he is convinced that it is pure by reason of the river's flow. Even more polluted than the Nile are the irrigation

canals, which are laden with human and animal waste—and continue to be a major source of water supply.

The general sanitation of all but a few "model" villages is extremely poor. Dust beclouds the air of narrow alleys strewn with offal and rubbish. The village *birka* (reservoir) is usually a greenish pool of stagnant water which provides drinking water, a bathing place for the children, and a laundry for the women. There is also the inevitable village dump where dirt, dung, and carrion are constantly being heaped and left for the village dogs or birds to dispose of. Sewage disposal facilities in the village are few and primitive. Pits dug near the houses serve as latrines, as do the irrigation ditches in the field.

Weakened by malnutrition and living in unsanitary and crowded surroundings, the Egyptian is prey to an impressive array of debilitating or fatal diseases. Prominent among these are bilharzia, hookworm, trachoma, tuberculosis, venereal diseases, typhoid, paratyphoid, typhus, diarrhea, enteritis, and malaria.

### Land Reform and Industrialization

In 1952 the corrupt and inefficient government of King Farouk was overthrown by a revolution sponsored by certain elements of the Egyptian army. An army lieutenant colonel, Gamal Abdel Nasser, soon rose to leadership in the new regime. In June 1953 the revolutionary government proclaimed Egypt a republic. One of its earliest important acts was to institute a nation-wide program of land reform. Much of the Egyptian countryside had been dominated by large estates worked by tenants (generally sharecroppers) or wage laborers. Often such estates were absentee-owned, generally by urban merchants, professional men, bankers, or industrialists, and their actual operation was delegated to hired managers and overseers. Rents were often

---

[3] *Editorial Note.* Four Egyptian crops—cotton, corn, wheat, and berseem (clover)—stand out from the others in total acreage. Each occupies about 1½ to 2 million acres annually. Wheat, barley, and berseem are winter crops, whereas cotton and corn are grown in summer, as are sugar cane, grain sorghums, and rice. Berseem, a legume, is grown for livestock feed and to enrich the soil with nitrogen. An important development in recent years has been the rapid rise of rice production on an export

basis. However, sizable wheat imports made Egypt a net importer of grain in 1957–1958.

[4] George H. T. Kimble and Dorothy L. Weitz, "Egypt." *Focus,* v. 2, no. 4 (1951), pp. 1–2. Used by permission of *Focus,* published by the American Geographical Society of New York.

[5] Quoted material under this heading by George L. Harris and others, *Egypt.* New Haven, Conn.: Human Relations Area Files Press, 1957. Pp. 274–276. Reprinted by permission.

excessively high. Rising land values and the dire poverty of most peasants made it exceedingly difficult for landless peasants to acquire land or for small owners to increase their holdings. Under a land-reform decree of September 1952, the revolutionary government expropriated several hundred thousand acres from large landholders over a five-year period (with compensation in government bonds except for 190,000 acres expropriated without compensation from the royal family), and redistributed this land among the peasants. To enable the latter to pay for it, long-term government loans at a low rate of interest were extended. A program of land reform broadly similar to Egypt's was enacted for Syria in 1958.[6]

Land reform alone cannot solve the problem of rural poverty in Egypt, though the decree of 1952 was a desirable measure and has had beneficial results. The basic difficulty is one of rapid population increase in rural areas that are already overcrowded. Improved living standards resulting from land reform, reclamation of new land, or greater output from the existing land will eventually be nullified unless the increasing pressure of population on the land can be checked. An increase in manufacturing offers one means for drawing surplus population off the farms, and the regime has thrown its weight behind a program to industrialize. Many additional considerations have motivated this program, among them the desire to overcome the economic and military weakness that made Egypt a pawn of foreign powers for many centuries and that recently led to humiliating defeats by Israel in the Palestine war of 1948–1949 and the Sinai invasion of 1956.

Actually Egypt has been industrializing in a modest way for a long period and already has undisputed industrial leadership among the Arab countries. But in the late 1950s less than one tenth of the country's working population was employed in manufacturing. Although Egypt has more than 27,000 establishments classified as factories, many of them are small workshops. A small number of large industrial plants owned by a handful of companies dominate the industrial scene. Though the types of industry are fairly diverse, two branches, textile milling and food processing (sugar refining, grain milling, vegetable canning, and so forth), are by far the largest employers of industrial labor. Other prominent industries include cotton ginning, chemical manufacture, petroleum refining, cement manufacture, and the manufacture of cigarettes.

The principal industrial centers are Cairo (2,770,000), the capital, and Alexandria (1,170,000), the principal seaport, located, respectively, at the head and western seaward edge of the Nile Delta (map, p. 301). "The new, Western side of Egypt is most in evidence in Cairo, Alexandria [photo, p. 304], and other urban centers; here air-conditioned apartment buildings (many of them built on erstwhile productive farmland), Parisian fashions, chromium-plated automobiles, American movies, and European sports command a wide and ever-growing acceptance." [7]

Egypt shares the customary handicaps of underdeveloped countries that attempt to industrialize: an impoverished home market, a shortage of investment capital and skilled managerial and technical personnel, and a dearth of skilled and semiskilled industrial labor. But unlike many underdeveloped countries, Egypt is also notably lacking in natural resources. The country has no forests or coal mines; oil deposits are present along both sides of the Gulf of Suez (the largest fields are on the Sinai side),

[6] See Earl B. Shaw, "Land Reform in Egypt." *Journal of Geography,* v. 53 (1954), p. 230. And Kenneth H. Parsons, "Land Reform in the United Arab Republic." *Land Economics,* v. 34 (1959),

pp. 319–326.
[7] Kimble and Weitz, *op. cit.,* p. 3. Used by permission.

A view of downtown Alexandria, UAR. Note the tall minaret of the Moslem mosque in the background. (Arab Information Center.)

but the production, though it more than supplies Egypt's needs for heavy crude oil, does not include lighter grades of petroleum that yield gasoline.[8] The country does have a fairly sizable reserve of iron ore in Upper Egypt,[9] a short distance east of Aswan. This ore and imported coke are utilized in an iron and steel plant opened in 1958 at Helwan on the Nile River about 20 miles south of Cairo (map, p. 301).

Egypt's deficiency in mineral fuels can be partially compensated for by the development of hydroelectricity at sites along the Nile River. A large generating station at

the Aswan Dam was opened in 1960. A new fertilizer plant near by is utilizing part of the power to produce nitrate fertilizers. The most celebrated of Egypt's development projects, however, is the High Dam. This enormous undertaking envisions a rock-filled dam over 2½ miles long and over 400 feet high, to be constructed about five miles upstream from the present Aswan Dam. Its reservoir, when filled, will be more than 350 miles long. By storing water in years of high flood for use in years of low, the High Dam will regularize the flow of the river to a much greater extent than is possible with

---

[8] Alexander Melamid, "The Oil Fields of the Sinai Peninsula." *Middle Eastern Affairs,* v. 10 (1959), pp. 191–195.

[9] Since ancient times the triangular Nile Delta

has been referred to as Lower Egypt; the narrow Nile Valley between Cairo and the Sudan is Upper Egypt.

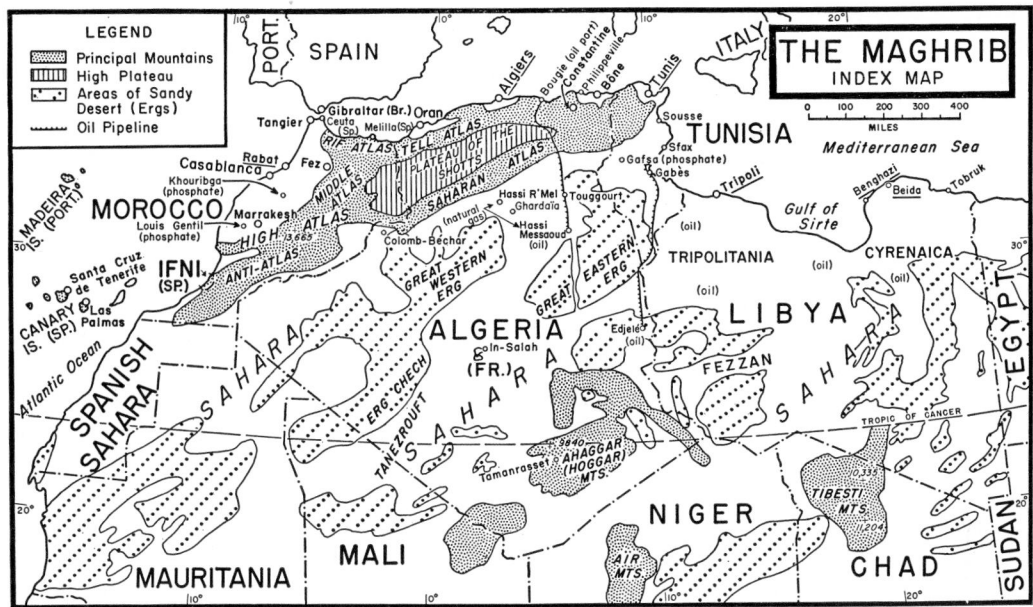

Index map of northwestern Africa and Libya. Political capitals are underlined. Notations of oil in Libya mark the general areas where the principal strikes have been made.

class of business and professional people, administrators, office workers, and skilled artisans. In Algeria possibly 25,000 Europeans are supported directly by agriculture. Their farms, worked by Moslem laborers or tenants, are generally much larger and more mechanized than farms owned by Moslems, and they include a large share of Algeria's best agricultural land. European farmers are also found in Morocco and Tunisia, but their numbers are much smaller than in Algeria. Many thousands of Europeans, both urban and rural dwellers, have left Tunisia and Morocco since 1956.

Most of the people in the Maghrib live in the coastal belt of mediterranean climate (called in Algeria "The Tell"), with its cool-season rains and hot, rainless summers. Here in a landscape of hills, low mountains, small plains, and scrubby mediterranean vegetation, are grown the familiar products of mediterranean agriculture—wheat, barley, legumes, olives, grapes, citrus fruits, and vegetables. Wine from the vineyards of French *colons* (colonists) has made Algeria

the fourth largest producer and the largest exporter of wine in the world. Other important agricultural exports from Algeria include citrus fruits (primarily oranges), vegetables, and dates from Saharan oases. Most of Algeria's agricultural exports come from farms operated by Europeans, though such farms account for only a third of the country's cultivated land. Mainland France is the principal market for these products and is the principal supplier of Algerian imports. In Tunisia the main agricultural exports are olive oil (Tunisia has 27 million olive trees and is the world's largest exporter of olive oil) and wine; in Morocco, citrus fruits. Most livestock (primarily sheep and goats) are owned by Moslems. Farming by the Moslem population in all three countries is mainly on a subsistence or semi-subsistence basis; the majority eke out a living from small farms or drift off to *bidonvilles* (shantytowns) in the cities. About two thirds of the total population of the Maghrib is classed as rural. Dissatisfaction with French rule has stemmed partly from low standards of living among the Moslems, aggravated by rapid increases in population.

Inland from the coastal belt, the Atlas Mountains extend in relatively continuous chains from southern Morocco to northwestern Tunisia. These mountains block the path of moisture-bearing winds from the Atlantic and the Mediterranean, and some mountain areas receive 40 to 50 inches or more of precipitation annually. In places the precipitation nourishes good forests of cork oak or cedar (photo, p. 284). The highest peaks are found in the High Atlas of Morocco, where one summit reaches 13,665 feet. In Algeria the mountains form two east-west chains, the Tell Atlas nearer the coast and the Saharan Atlas (map, p. 309); between them lies the semiarid Shotts Plateau (average elevation about 2700 feet), with its basins of interior drainage ("shotts"), subsistence grain fields, patches of esparto grass (gathered for export to the world's paper industry), and herds of sheep and goats. In Tunisia the mountains are lower than in Morocco or Algeria, but they contain many deep valleys.

At the south all three countries reach the Sahara; indeed the greater part of Algeria is Saharan. A prominent line of oases fed by springs, wells, mountain streams, and foggaras (photo, p. 287) is found along or near the southern base of the Atlas Mountains. A sparse population of nomads roams the Sahara, and clusters of oases exist in a few places where mountains rise high enough to catch moisture from the passing winds. Several large areas of sandy desert (*ergs*) and a barren, lifeless gravel plain, the *Tanezrouft*, occupy portions of the Algerian Sahara (map, p. 309).

The economic future of the Maghrib is tied in considerable measure to the most diversified endowment of minerals in the Arab world (map, p. 467). Morocco, Tunisia, and Algeria rank third, fourth, and

A flat-roofed village at the base of barren mountains in the Atlas region of Morocco. (French Embassy Press and Information Division.)

fifth, respectively, among world producers of phosphate rock (after the United States and USSR), and all three countries have substantial reserves and production of high-grade iron ore. Large, unexploited reserves of iron ore and manganese exist in western Algeria near the Moroccan border. Both Algeria and Morocco have a modest production of coal, and all three countries of the Maghrib produce lead, with Morocco the leader. The most varied collection of ferro-alloys and nonferrous metals is found in Morocco, which produces manganese, co-balt, lead, zinc, and small quantities of several other metals. But the great minerals of the future are the oil and natural gas of the Algerian Sahara: in 1956 large oil fields—the Hassi Messaoud and Edjelé fields (map, p. 309)—and large gas deposits were discovered in eastern Algeria.

A 24-inch pipeline over 400 miles long was completed in 1959 from the Hassi Messaoud field to the oil port of Bougie on the Mediterranean coast, while a similar pipeline was under construction in 1960 from the Edjelé field to a shipping point on the coast of Tunisia near Gabès. One of the world's largest deposits of natural gas was discovered in 1957 at Hassi R'Mel, located in the northern edge of the Sahara near the oasis city of Ghardaïa (map, p. 309). Natural gas deposits of major size also exist at Hassi Messaoud. Gas pipelines from Hassi R'Mel to Algiers and the port of Arzew near Oran were under construction in 1960.

In the Maghrib modern factories are not very numerous, though this area is more industrialized than the Sudan, Saudi Arabia, or Jordan. Cheap textiles, processed foods, and miscellaneous other types of simple, consumer goods are the main products.

## PERSIAN GULF OIL AND THE STATES THAT PRODUCE IT

No mineral resource is more vital to present-day civilization than petroleum. Modern transportation is mainly powered by it, and it provides the essential lubricants that enable power-driven vehicles and machines to function. The world demand for petroleum is constantly rising. In 1947 world production amounted to about 8 million barrels per day; by 1957 this had risen to 16 million; and by 1966 it was expected to reach 28 million barrels per day.[12]

Although the United States produces more petroleum than any other country or region (an estimated 37 percent of the world total in 1959), the Middle East has become the leading area of *surplus* production. It produces two thirds as much oil as the United States and sells most of its output in overseas markets. The United States, by contrast, uses most of its own production for domestic needs and imports additional quantities of oil, partly from the Middle East.

Most of the known reserves of oil in the Middle East are found in a group of states that ring the Persian Gulf. All but one of these states belong to the Arab world; the remaining state, Iran, has had close historical and cultural relations with the Arab countries and shares their Islamic religion, but most of its people are not Arabs. The oil deposits of the Persian Gulf states are by far the largest in the world. In 1958 their proved reserves were reported to be approximately 174 billion barrels, or more than three fifths of the estimated world total of 276 billion barrels.[13] Most of the deposits lie along, under, or relatively near

---

[12] *Fortune* (May 1958), p. 127. A barrel of oil is equivalent to 42 gallons.

[13] "Facts and Figures: Middle East Oil 1958." *Middle Eastern Affairs,* v. 10 (1959), p. 196. Most of the statistical data on Middle Eastern oil in the present chapter are from this source, or from Benjamin Shwadran, "Middle East Oil in 1959," *Middle Eastern Affairs,* v. 11 (1960), pp. 218–238.

the Persian Gulf. This shallow, desert-rimmed arm of the Indian Ocean, three times the size of Lake Superior, ranks with the Gulf of Mexico and Caribbean Sea among the world's great centers of oil production and transportation. In 1947, production of oil in the Persian Gulf states averaged 839,000 barrels a day; by 1959 this had risen to an estimated 4.6 million barrels a day, or 24 percent of the world total.

Western Europe is the principal market for Middle Eastern oil, though substantial amounts are shipped to the Western Hemisphere, the Orient, and Africa. In recent years, Middle Eastern oil has normally supplied more than three fourths of western Europe's requirements. Most of the oil is shipped to market in crude form, though some of it is processed at refineries located along the Persian Gulf, at pipeline termini on the Mediterranean coast, or at the northern and southern entrances to the Red Sea (map, right).

Large corporations, principally British or American in ownership, dominate the oil business. Foremost among them are the British Petroleum Company (formerly the Anglo-Iranian Oil Company); the Arabian American Oil Company (Aramco), owned by four United States concerns; the Kuwait Oil Company, part British and part American in ownership; and the Iraq Petroleum Corporation, owned by British, American, French, and Dutch interests, with a 5-percent interest being held by the C. S. Gulbenkian estate. The British government is the majority stockholder in the British Petroleum Company, which holds a half interest in the Kuwait Oil Company, slightly less than a quarter interest in the Iraq Petroleum Corporation, and substantial interests in Iran and Qatar. Middle Eastern oil is extremely important to Great Britain, not only because it supplies four fifths of the country's annual requirements, but also because sales of oil and refined products in world markets are a much-needed source of foreign exchange.

Royalty and tax payments by the companies that produce and market the oil supply the bulk of the governmental revenues of the Persian Gulf states and are making possible a variety of projects to raise the level of living in these lands. Several Arab countries that contain only modest oil deposits or none at all derive profit from oil operations through their control of transportation routes; they include the United Arab Republic, which controls the Suez Canal plus pipeline routes in Syria; and Lebanon and Jordan, whose territories are crossed by pipelines (map, right). These countries are paid transit fees and taxes by the oil interests.

▶ *Oil Wealth and Rural Poverty in Iran*

Iran (Persia) was the earliest of the Middle Eastern countries to produce oil in large quantities. The initial discovery at Masjid-i-Sulaiman dates from 1908, and commercial production commenced in 1912. Iran's six main oil fields form a line, oriented northwest-southeast, along the foothills of the Zagros Mountains in the southwestern part of the country (map, right). The oil facilities were originally developed by the Anglo-Iranian Oil Company, now the British Petroleum Company. This concern built a huge refinery on tidewater at Abadan (226,000; population figures cited for Iranian cities are estimates for the city proper) and a series of pipelines to the inland oil fields. Abadan lies on the Shatt al Arab (the "River of the Arabs," formed by the junction of the Tigris and Euphrates rivers) about 50 miles from the Persian Gulf. It is accessible to tankers up to 20,000 tons in size. Such vessels haul refined products economically, but they are not large enough for economical long-distance transportation of crude oil. A loading terminal for tankers up to 40,000 tons has been developed at Bandar Mashur (map, right), while a new terminal at Kharg Island will allow the largest tankers afloat (100,000 tons) to load in deep water in the Persian

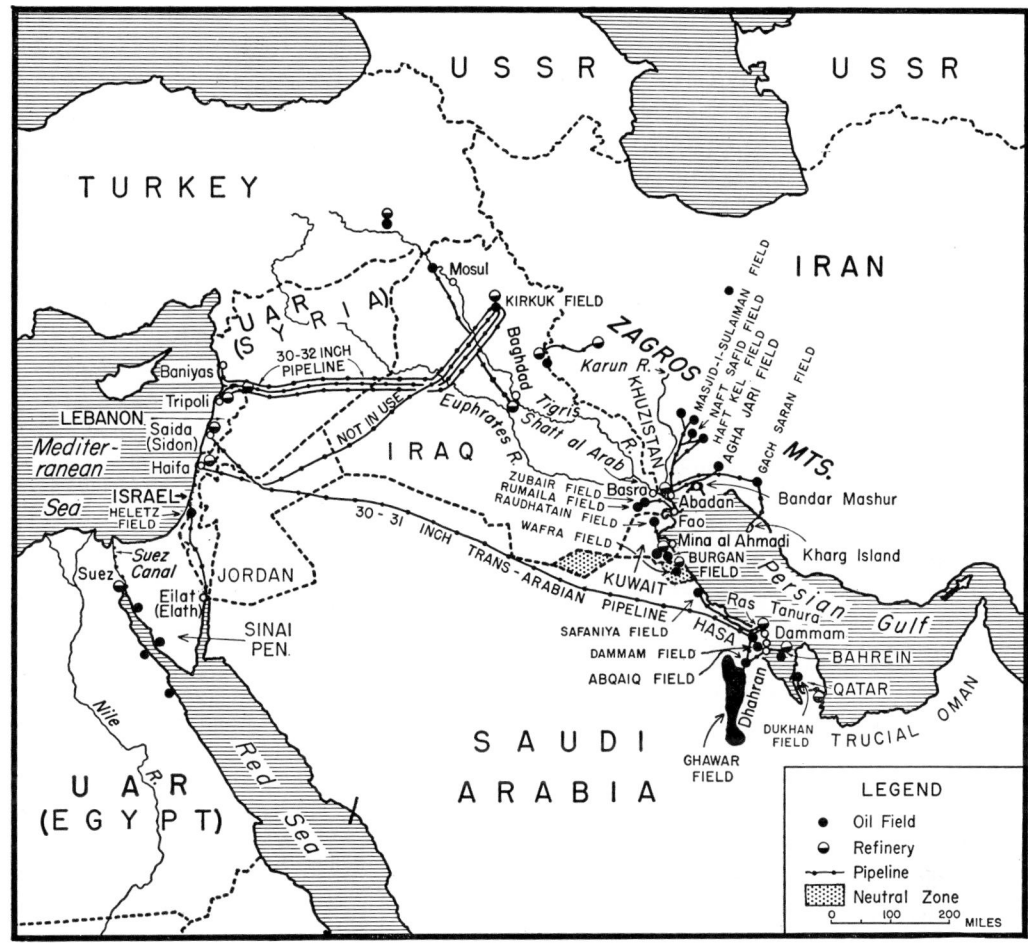

Principal oil fields, pipelines, and refineries of the Middle East. The four pipelines connecting the Kirkuk Field with the Mediterranean coast include (1) a 30–32-inch line to Baniyas in Syria, (2) a 16–inch and a 12-inch line to Tripoli in Lebanon, and (3) a 12-inch line to Haifa in Israel (not operating in 1961 due to hostile Arab attitudes toward Israel).

Gulf. Prior to 1951, Iran's oil production was the greatest in the Middle East. However, in 1951 as a result of anti-British agitation and a strong tide of nationalist feeling, the oil facilities were nationalized, despite strong British protests. Most of the British managers and technicians left the country, and Iranian oil was boycotted by the major oil interests, which refused to buy it. Production soon declined to a very low figure. Not until the summer of 1954 was a compromise settlement of the dispute finally reached. Since then, production has been carried on by the National Iranian Oil Company in cooperation with a consortium of seventeen foreign companies. The British Petroleum Company holds a 40-percent interest in the consortium. Iran's total oil production in 1959 was an estimated 338 million barrels, the third highest in the Middle East (after Kuwait, 497 million, and Saudi Arabia, 400 million; Iraq, the fourth-ranking country, produced 306 million). New discoveries of oil in northern Iran have recently been reported.

Aside from its oil wealth, Iran is a country with scanty resources and much poverty. The bulk of the land is comprised of arid plateaus and basins, bordered by high, rugged mountains. Only an estimated 10 to 15 percent of Iran is cultivated; the land actually in crops at any one time may amount to as little as 3 percent. Enough rain falls during the winter half year in the northwestern part of the country to permit unirrigated cropping. Rainfall sufficient for intensive agriculture, however, is largely confined to a densely populated strip of lowland between the Elburz Mountains and the Caspian Sea. The western half of this lowland receives more than 40 inches of precipitation annually, including both summer and winter rainfall, and produces a variety of subtropical crops, such as rice, cotton, oranges, tobacco, silk, and tea. In the other regions of Iran, agriculture depends mainly or exclusively on irrigation. Many of the irrigated districts are located on alluvial fans at the foot of the Elburz and Zagros mountains; the capital, Tehran (Teheran; 1,513,000) is found in one of these areas south of the Elburz. Qanats (tunnels) furnish the water supply for an estimated three fifths of the country's irrigated acreage (see photo and caption, p. 287). Approximately two thirds of the crop acreage in Iran is devoted to either wheat or barley, while an estimated 3.5 million cattle, 18 million sheep, and 10 million goats comprise the bulk of the livestock. A considerable share of the livestock are raised by seminomadic mountain peoples—the Kashgai, Baktiari, Lurs, Kurds, and others—whose independent ways have long been a source of friction between these tribesmen and the central government. The area inhabited by the Kurds extends into Iraq, Turkey, Syria, and the Soviet Union. Agitation for an independent Kurdistan has been prominent in past times, but seems quiescent today.

The Iranian people, an estimated four fifths of whom are peasant farmers or seminomadic tribesmen, are beset by the customary Middle Eastern ills of drought, dusty winds, hunger, illiteracy, disease, poverty, and landlordism. In the villages modern conveniences and sanitation are largely lacking. Farming is mostly on a subsistence or near-subsistence basis, by traditional methods with crude tools. Justice William O. Douglas, a frequent and perceptive visitor to Iran, has given an effective picture of the customary methods of threshing grain:

There is not much farm machinery in Iran. Most of the wheat is cut by hand sickles, and the wheat is tied in sheaves or bundles and stacked in the field. These are loaded on donkeys and taken to a central thrashing floor. The floor is usually a flat place in the field with no covering. The sheaves are untied here and the wheat stalks scattered on the floor. Some farmers hitch cattle or donkeys, or cattle and donkeys together shoulder to shoulder and drive them around and around the floor, depending on the beat of the hoofs to dislodge the wheat from the head. More often, they use a heavy sled to help thrash the wheat. Frequently the animals draw a crude drag that has one or more large drumlike wheels that pound the heads of the wheat. Women and children usually drive the animals. Round and round they go for days until the wheat is separated. Then men use a fork (usually a wooden one) to toss the residue into the air. The wind catches the chaff and blows it to one side. Sometimes a large round wooden traylike vessel is used to pick up the residue. A man shakes it until the kernels are at the bottom. Then, tipping the tray, he blows the chaff away. After many backbreaking days, the golden kernels lie in piles and are transferred by hand into burlap sacks. The landlord comes to the thrashing floor and takes his half or three fifths or four fifths—whatever the rental arrangements may be.[14]

Iran exhibits the common Middle Eastern picture of an illiterate peasantry living un-

---

[14] William O. Douglas, *West of the Indus*. New York: Doubleday, 1958. P. 295. Copyright, 1958, by William O. Douglas. Copyright, 1958, by the National Geographic Society. Reprinted by permission of William O. Douglas. Under customary sharing arrangements, the landlord receives 20 percent of the crop as land rental, another 20 percent if he supplies irrigation water, a third 20 percent if he furnishes draft animals, and a fourth 20 percent if he furnishes seed.

der conditions of grinding and almost intolerable poverty and contrasting sharply with a relatively small well-to-do upper class which owns most of the land, holds most of the money, and exercises considerable control over political affairs. The Iranian government, aided by the United States, has inaugurated programs designed to improve the condition of the rural people. Considerably larger areas could be irrigated if the necessary facilities were installed, particularly in the alluvial plain of the Karun River in Khuzistan Province adjoining Iraq (map, p. 313). Much could be accomplished through education, introduction of better sanitation, the use of insecticides, provision of better seeds, increased use of artificial fertilizers, improved systems of farm credit and land tenure, and the like. However, efforts to introduce these advances have not met with conspicuous success thus far, due to the lack of capital, the inertia and suspicion of the conservative Moslem peasantry, and the active or passive opposition of intrenched interests, including many of the larger landowners. But efforts to improve the situation are continuing and will be facilitated by the country's increasing revenues from oil.

Iran's small but growing industrial establishment is dominated by the petroleum, textile, and food-processing industries. A few traditional handicrafts survive, including the manufacture of the famous Persian rugs. Modern factories are confined almost exclusively to Tehran, Abadan, Tabriz (290,000), Isfahan (255,000), Meshed (242,000), and a few other cities. The national government has stimulated, closely controlled, and partially financed the development of modern industries.

## ▶ *Iraq*

Prior to 1958, all of the Persian Gulf states were monarchies. But in July of that year a short revolution precipitated by army officers made Iraq a republic. The revolution stemmed partly from resentment against Great Britain, though other factors were involved. Britain had governed Iraq for a decade under a League of Nations mandate when the country was brought into existence following World War I (previously it had been a part of the Ottoman Empire), and British influence continued to be strong after independence was granted in 1932. In 1955 the government of the monarchy had aligned itself militarily with Great Britain, Turkey, Iran, and Pakistan in the Baghdad Pact.[15] But despite their anti-British leanings, the revolutionists did not interfere with the operations of the Iraq Petroleum Corporation, which is partly British in ownership. Revenues from oil are a major source of income for the government, which sets aside an important share for a Development Board that is engaged in a long-term program of public works to raise the country's miserably low standard of living.

Iraq's principal oil field, first opened in 1927, is located in the vicinity of Kirkuk (city proper, 90,000) in northern Iraq (map, p. 313). The Kirkuk field, approximately 60 miles long by 2 miles wide, is one of the largest oil-bearing formations in the world. It is connected by pipelines with shipping points on the Mediterranean coast at Tripoli, Lebanon, and Baniyas, Syria. The pipelines also carry oil from wells near Mosul (155,000). The new Zubair and Rumaila fields, located in southern Iraq near the country's main seaport, Basra (205,000), are connected by pipeline with the oil port of Fao on the Persian Gulf.

Iraq, formerly known as Mesopotamia, occupies a broad plain drained by the Tigris and Euphrates rivers, together with fringing highlands (in the north) and deserts (in the west). In ancient times the country had an elaborate system of irrigation works on the

---

[15] Iraq withdrew from the pact in 1959. The remaining members then changed the name of their alliance to Central Treaty Organization.

Tigris-Euphrates plain, and its population at certain periods is thought to have been four or five times as great as it is today. But in the Middle Ages much of the irrigation system was destroyed or fell into disrepair during periods of political disorder and foreign invasion, and it has never been reconstructed. Today Iraq is underpopulated in relation to the amount of land that is irrigable. The Iraq Development Board is attempting to expand irrigation, partly through the construction of multipurpose dams (for flood control and hydroelectric development as well as irrigation storage) on the Euphrates and on the Tigris and two of its tributaries. The board is also attempting to reclaim land by draining portions of large swamps in southern Iraq and by flushing salt from fields that were formerly irrigated but had to be abandoned because of salification due to improper drainage.

Possibly two thirds of Iraq's people are villagers depending directly on agriculture for a living. Small groups of Bedouin raise camels, sheep, and goats in the western deserts. Some of the Kurdish tribesmen in the mountain foothills of the north are seminomadic livestock graziers, though most Iraqi Kurds are sedentary agriculturalists. The Kurds are the country's largest minority, accounting for a sixth of the total population. They have revolted against the central authority on various occasions, but relations with the central government have generally been good in recent times.

Agriculture is dependent on irrigation in most parts of Iraq, though the northern highlands receive 10 to 20 inches or more of precipitation in the winter half year and thus are able to support nonirrigated fall-sown crops. Three food grains—wheat, barley, and rice—occupy most of Iraq's cultivated acreage. Barley is the leading export crop in most years, but accounted for only 3 percent of the country's total exports by value in the period 1954–1958 (petroleum accounted for 91 percent). Dates comprise the second export crop, contributing 2 percent of total exports in 1954–1958. Iraq normally supplies more than three fourths of the dates that enter international trade. Most of them are produced in irrigated gardens that stretch for a hundred miles along the Shatt al Arab in lower Iraq. Irrigation is facilitated by the changing water level of the Shatt al Arab, which fluctuates with the tides in the Persian Gulf. At high tide, water from the river is led through gates to the plantations. The water is brackish but can be utilized by the date palms, which are tolerant of salt.

The limited manufacturing of Iraq is centered in the historic capital city of Baghdad (580,000) on the Tigris River.

### ▶ The Desert Kingdom of Saudi Arabia

Oil production in Saudi Arabia has been developed by the Arabian American Oil Company (Aramco). The company is officially a Saudi corporation but is owned by four United States companies. The first discovery of oil in commercial quantities was made at the Dammam Dome in 1938, but large-scale production was delayed until after World War II. The oil fields, the largest of which are the 150-mile-long Ghawar field and the Abqaiq field, are located in the province of Hasa in the eastern part of the country (map, p. 313). The company has its headquarters and homes for its employees and their families at the town of Dhahran, where the United States maintains a large air base. Though some oil is refined at Ras Tanura or on nearby Bahrein Island, more than two thirds of the production leaves Saudi Arabia in crude form via the Trans-Arabian Pipeline (photo, p. 287) to Saida (Sidon), Lebanon, or via tanker from Ras Tanura.

Saudi Arabia occupies the greater part of the Arabian Peninsula, the original homeland of Arab civilization and the Moslem religion. The Saudi state, a feudalistic, almost medieval monarchy, was gradually consolidated by the late King Ibn Saud be-

and concentrated in the winter half year, is barely sufficient for grain. The plateau lies at an elevation of 2000 to 6000 feet; it is highest in the east where it adjoins the high mountains of the Armenian Knot. Its surface is rolling, treeless, windswept country, hot and dry in summer and cold and snowy in winter, with a natural vegetation of short steppe grasses and shrubs. The farming system on the plateau combines cereals and livestock raising; a representative family may own a cow, a yoke of oxen for draft power, a dozen sheep, six or eight goats, and a donkey.[16] There has been a substantial increase in farm mechanization since World War II, but the bulk of the farming is still done by traditional methods.

Along its northern side, the Anatolian Plateau is bordered by the Pontic Mountains. These ranges, lying generally at 3000 to 6000 feet in the west but rising to a maximum of over 12,000 feet in the east, are clothed with Turkey's best forests. The trees, mainly hardwoods, are nourished by the heavy precipitation that these mountains receive the year round. The Taurus Mountains, bordering the plateau on the south, are in general somewhat higher than the Pontic Mountains, lying mostly at 6000 feet or higher. But their annual precipitation is smaller and their summers are dry; mediterranean woodland of little commercial value is the predominant vegetation. Turkey's forests have long been subjected to overcutting and destructive grazing practices. It is estimated that more than half of the country's timber needs are met by imports.

### Aegean, Black Sea, and Mediterranean Coastlands

The coastal plains and valleys along or near the Aegean Sea, Sea of Marmara, and Black Sea are, in general, the most densely populated and productive parts of Turkey. Here are grown several of the country's principal export crops, including tobacco, hazelnuts (filberts), grown primarily in the Black Sea section, and grapes for sultana raisins, and figs, raised in the central Aegean section around Izmir (Smyrna). Izmir (336,000), located on an excellent natural harbor, is Turkey's second-ranking seaport (after Istanbul). It exports a varied list of characteristic mediterranean products: tobacco, raisins, figs, olive oil, wheat, and others. The Black Sea coastlands differ from the rest of Turkey in having summer as well as winter rain (though even here the maximum rainfall comes in the winter half year) and in having a much greater total precipitation, 35 to 100 inches annually in most sections, than other parts of the country. The easternmost section has the heaviest rainfall and, like the adjoining Georgian SSR in the Soviet Union, grows tea and citrus fruit. Most of Turkey's corn crop is grown in the Black Sea coastlands. Corn is the country's third-ranking grain in total production, after wheat and barley. In the interior of Thrace (European Turkey), sugar beets have become the leading commercial crop. Turkey was formerly a large importer of sugar, but in recent decades has achieved self-sufficiency through the widespread introduction of sugar beets.

The southern (Mediterranean) coast of Turkey is more sparsely populated than the Aegean or Black Sea coasts. Most of this coast is mountainous, and only a few sizable lowlands or valleys occur. The most important is the plain that centers on the city of Adana (172,000) in southeastern Turkey. Irrigated cotton grown on the Adana Plain has in recent years become Turkey's largest export.

### Industry, Mining, and Transportation

Except for handicrafts there was almost no industrial development in Turkey under the Ottoman Empire. During the latter part

---

[16] Nicholas Helburn, "A Stereotype of Agriculture in Semiarid Turkey." *Geographical Review,* v. 45 (1955), p. 377.

of the Ottoman period various European powers secured an increasing hold over Turkish finances by virtue of loans made to the Ottoman sultans. When the Turkish Republic was formed in 1923, its leaders were anxious to avoid further financial involvement with foreign nations, and they imposed severe restrictions on foreign investment in Turkey. This policy handicapped Turkish industry, because Turkey itself had insufficient capital to finance industrial development. Private capital was so lacking that the state, which was anxious to stimulate industry, was forced to play a large role in financing it. Many of the present industries are state-owned, and the state exerts a close control over many private industries.

Turkey's predominant industries are those customarily found in underdeveloped nations: textiles, agricultural processing, cement manufacture, simple metal industries, and so on. The country is very dependent on imports for much of its machinery as well as many other types of manufactured goods. An integrated iron and steel mill at Karabuk, located in the northern interior about 100 miles from Ankara (map, right), is the principal heavy industrial establishment. The plant has two blast furnaces, several open-hearth steel furnaces, three rolling mills, a plate mill, and a pipe factory. Coke is manufactured from coal supplied by the Zonguldak coal basin (map, right). The coal is brought by rail a distance of about fifty miles through mountainous terrain. High-grade iron ore comes by rail from Divrigi, about 500 miles away. Turkey's steel mill, the largest in the Middle East, was located with strategic rather than purely economic considerations in mind, and its operations have never been particularly efficient or economical.

In addition to having the largest coal field in the Middle East (the Zonguldak field) and substantial deposits of iron ore, Turkey has important deposits of chrome and is one of the world's principal exporters of that ferroalloy. Other mineral production includes salt and sulfur for chemical manufacturing,

copper, and a variety of other metallic and nonmetallic minerals produced in small quantities. Production of oil from a small field in southeastern Turkey has been increasing. Turkey is not outstanding as a mineral producer in world terms. But it is one of the largest Middle Eastern producers of minerals other than oil, and its resources offer scope for much future expansion.

Turkey's transportation system is more adequate than that of most Middle Eastern countries, though it falls far short of western European standards. A coarse mesh of rail lines extends into all major sections of the country (map, right), and a network of all-weather automobile roads is slowly developing. Financial and technical assistance by the United States has been a major factor in the improvement of the road system.

### Istanbul and the Straits

Istanbul (1,365,000), formerly Constantinople or Byzantium, is Turkey's main metropolis, industrial center, and port. It handles more than two thirds of the country's foreign trade by value. One of the world's most historic and cosmopolitan cities, Istanbul was for many centuries the capital of the Eastern Roman (Byzantine) Empire. It became the capital of the Ottoman Empire when it fell to the Turks, after withstanding many sieges, in 1453. However, the capital of the Turkish Republic was established in 1923 at the more centrally located and more purely Turkish city of Ankara (408,000) on the Anatolian Plateau.

Istanbul is located at the southern entrance to the Bosporus, the northernmost of the three water passages (Dardanelles, Sea of Marmara, Bosporus) that connect the Mediterranean and Black seas and are known as the Turkish Straits (inset map, p. 279). The Straits have long been a focus of contention between Turkey and its powerful northern neighbor, Russia. Several of the main Russian seaports are located on the Black Sea or Sea of Azov, and Russia has often demanded a voice in the control of the straits outlet to the Mediterranean. But her

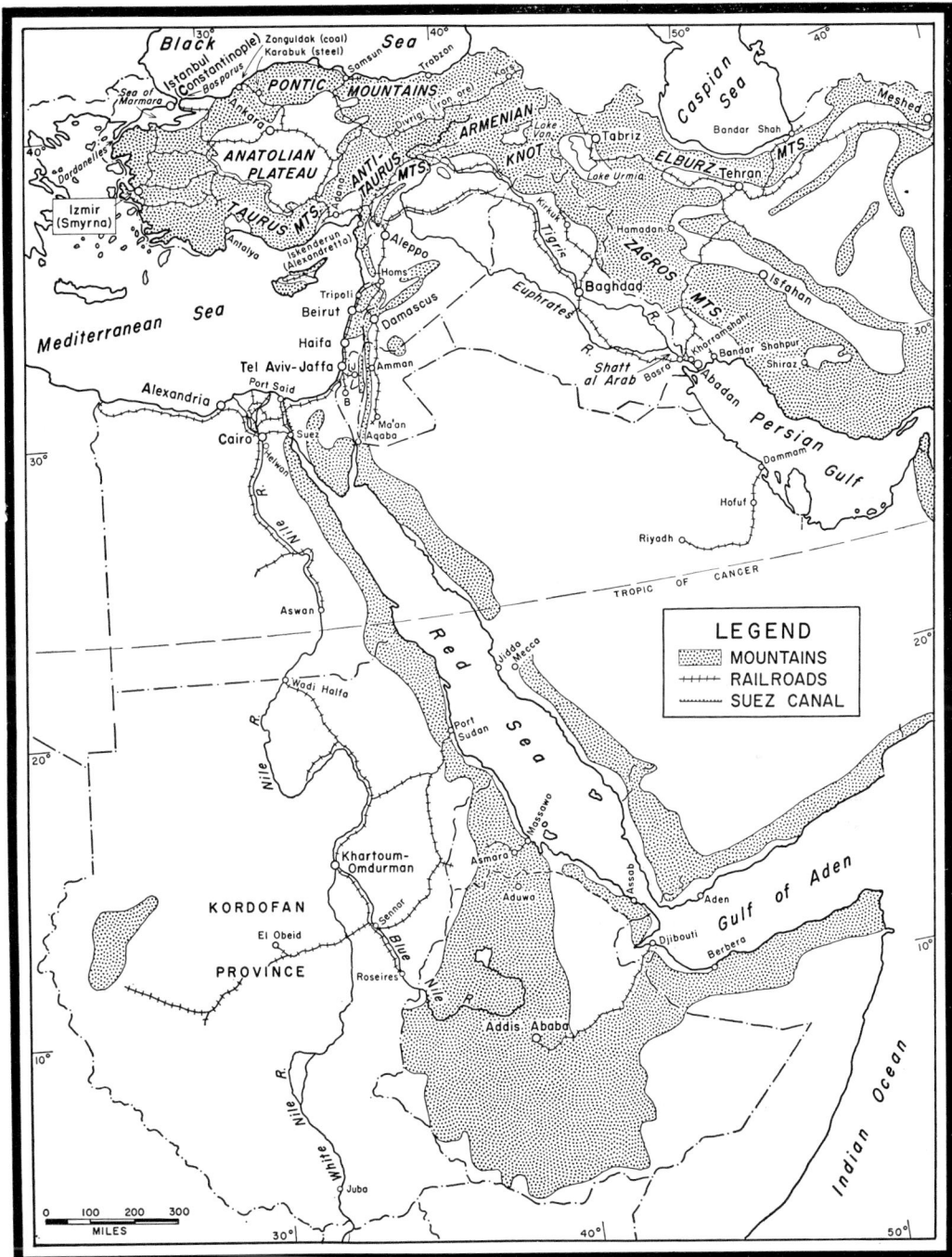

Mountains, railroads, and selected rivers and cities in the central part of the Middle East. The areas of mountains shown in a stipple have been broadly generalized and often incorporate important agricultural valleys (as in western Turkey) or agricultural uplands (as in Ethiopia).

chances of achieving this goal by any means except force have seemed increasingly poor since World War II, as Turkey has gravitated toward the side of the Western nations and has become one of the strongest and most active members of the North Atlantic Treaty Organization. Turkey's position vis-à-vis the Soviet Union has been bolstered by extensive economic and military aid from the United States.

### The Problem of Cyprus

Most of the islands that border the Aegean and Mediterranean coasts of Turkey are predominantly Greek in population and

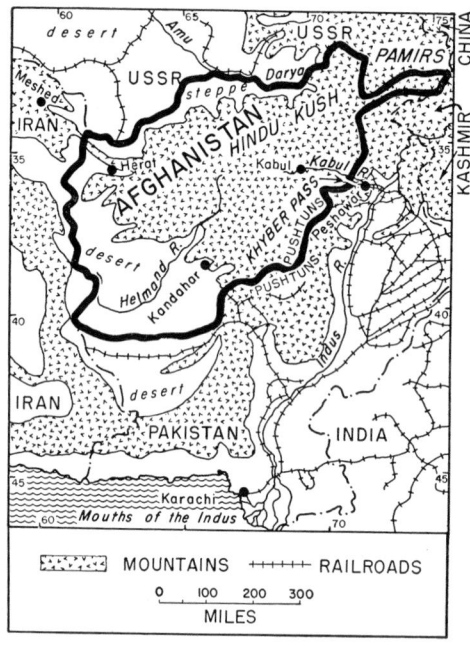

Afghanistan in its regional setting. The wave pattern at the lower left marks the Arabian Sea.

are controlled by Greece. But the large Mediterranean island of Cyprus, located about 40 miles off the coast of southwestern Turkey, came under British control in 1878 after centuries of Ottoman rule. About four fifths of the island's population of half a million is Greek, the remaining fifth, mainly Turkish. Agitation by the Greek majority for union with Greece (*enosis*) was promi-

nent after World War II and led in 1954 to serious rioting and disorder. Both Great Britain and Turkey opposed *enosis* on the ground that the island's Turkish minority could not be safely entrusted to political control by Greece. In addition, Great Britain was anxious to retain control of military bases in Cyprus. An agreement to make Cyprus an independent republic was signed in 1959 by the United Kingdom, Greece, and Turkey. Approved by the leaders of both the Greek and the Turkish Cypriotes after lengthy negotiations, it guaranteed the United Kingdom's right to the continued use and control of its bases on the island. The Republic of Cyprus was proclaimed on August 16, 1960. It has remained within the Commonwealth of Nations.

### ▶ The Highland Kingdom of Afghanistan

In the twentieth century the kingdom of Afghanistan has been remote from the main currents of world affairs. A landlocked and mountainous country with limited resources, poor internal transportation, and relatively little foreign trade, it is today one of the least developed and least known of the world's nations. But the territory it occupies played a strategic role in empire building of the past by virtue of important routeways and passes leading across it from the steppes and oases of Central Asia and the plateaus of Iran to the plains of northern India that have been a goal of Asian conquerors for thousands of years.

The present Afghan state arose in the eighteenth century. Throughout much of the nineteenth century its independence was jeopardized by its position between the expanding British and Russian empires. In the latter part of the century it became, in effect, a British protectorate. But in 1907 Great Britain and Russia agreed to maintain it as an independent buffer state between their respective empires. British influence continued to be strong, however, until after World War I.

Even today no rail line across Afghanistan connects Soviet Russia with the Indian subcontinent, though the Soviet and Pakistani rail systems extend to its borders (map, left). The limited overseas commerce of the country has customarily been routed through the port of Karachi, now in West Pakistan. But strained relations between Afghanistan and Pakistan caused the latter nation to halt Afghan traffic for several months in 1955. Recently Afghanistan has gravitated toward the economic orbit of the Soviet Union. The Soviet government has extended loans, gifts, and technical assistance to help the country build up its economy, road system, and social services, and it has made energetic and successful efforts to attract Afghan trade. The United States also has extended a sizable amount of economic and technical aid, particularly for road improvement and for irrigation and power development in the Helmand Valley (see discussion in the next column).

### Afghanistan's Population and Economy

No nation-wide census has ever been taken in Afghanistan, and estimates of the country's population range from 8 million to 15 million. An estimated 90 percent or more of its people are illiterate. Most of the population is found in irrigated valleys around the fringes of a mass of high mountains occupying a large part of the country. The most heavily populated section is the southeast, particularly the fertile valley of the Kabul River in which the capital and largest city, Kabul (estimated population of city proper, 310,000; elevation, 6200 feet), is located. Most of the inhabitants of the southeast are Pushtuns, also known as Pashtuns, Pakhtuns, or Pathans. The Pushtuns are the largest and most influential of the numerous ethnic groups that comprise the Afghan state. Sometimes they are referred to as Afghans, although this name is being applied more and more to all inhabitants of Afghanistan regardless of ethnic affiliation. Their language, Pushtu, is related to Persian. It is the principal language of Afghanistan in number of speakers, though Persian

is a strong second and is the main language of administration and commerce.

Afghanistan's second most populous area occupies a belt of foothills and steppes on the northern side of the central mountains. Most of its inhabitants are found in a series of oases that form an east-west chain along the base of the mountains. But the area's most valuable commercial product, karakul lambskins, is provided by the millions of sheep that graze on the adjoining steppes. The skins, taken from lambs soon after birth, are Afghanistan's largest export. They are marketed primarily in the United States. Northern Afghanistan faces the Soviet Union, and millions of people on the Afghan side of the boundary are ethnically related to peoples of Soviet Central Asia. Tadzhiks are the most numerous, followed by Uzbeks, Turkmen, and Kirgiz.

Southwestern Afghanistan is comprised of a large desert basin, part of which extends into Iran. An area of interior drainage, it receives the waters of the Helmand River (map, left) and several others originating in Afghanistan's central mountain region. Extensive irrigation works supported a large population in this region in ancient times, but the water system was largely destroyed by Mongolian invaders in the thirteenth and fourteenth centuries and the damage has never been repaired. Today the government of Afghanistan, through its Helmand Valley irrigation and power project, is attempting to reclaim and resettle large acreages of land by providing irrigation water from storage and flood-control reservoirs on the Helmand and other rivers. Most of the present inhabitants of southwestern and western Afghanistan are found in oases that lie in the zone of contact between the central mountains and the desert. The largest oases surround Afghanistan's second and third cities, Kandahar (80,000–100,000) and Herat (75,000–100,000) (populations of both cities are rough estimates for city proper). Persians form the largest population element in this part of the country.

Afghanistan is overwhelmingly a rural

and agricultural or pastoral country. There are only a handful of modern factories, though craft and household industries are fairly numerous. The country is so mountainous and arid that only an estimated 2 percent is cultivated. Enough rain falls in the main populated areas during the winter half year to permit nonirrigated growing of winter grains. Fall-sown wheat is the country's staple food grain. In most parts of Afghanistan irrigation is necessary for summer cropping. Livestock raising on a seminomadic or nomadic basis is a widespread and important part of the country's economy. Most livestock graziers raise some crops. Afghanistan's agriculture bears many of the customary Middle Eastern earmarks: excessive reliance on traditional methods, crude tools, inadequate fertilization of the soil, poor varieties of crops and animals, low yields. But landlordism is less prominent and less rapacious than in some Middle Eastern countries (though large acreages are held by a comparatively small number of big landowners), and the country's total food supply is probably as adequate as that of most Middle Eastern areas. Afghanistan exhibits a wide range of temperature conditions, corresponding in general to differences in altitude. A great variety of cultivated crops, fruits, and nuts are locally important.

### The Pushtunistan Issue

Present-day Afghanistan is an amalgam of many ethnic and tribal groups. Traditional modes of thought and behavior based on family, tribal, or religious custom and allegiance are dominant influences in Afghan life. The conservative Moslem clerics (*mullahs*) are more powerful than in most Middle Eastern countries. But a leaven of modernity is stirring, and a united, detribalized Afghan nation is slowly emerging. The most important region that is still essentially tribal lies along the eastern frontier with Pakistan. A variety of tribes and clans, mostly Pushtuns, inhabit this mountainous borderland on both the Afghanistan and Pakistan sides. Many migrate seasonally across the international boundary. These peoples, among the most intractable and militant in the world, have been slow to recognize the authority of the central governments under whose jurisdiction they theoretically reside. The northwestern frontier region was a major trouble spot in the old Indian Empire of Great Britain, and Peshawar, at the foot of the Khyber Pass on the Indian side, became a famous British garrison town. More recently, this region has been an important source of friction between Afghanistan and Pakistan. Partially the friction has been due to border incidents, but mainly it has grown out of proposals that the Pushtun-inhabited areas of Pakistan be incorporated in a separate state ("Pushtunistan"), either independent or affiliated with Afghanistan. Such proposals, sponsored or at least encouraged by Afghanistan, have been vigorously and firmly opposed by Pakistan.

## ETHIOPIA AND SOMALILAND

East of the Sudan section of the Nile Basin a great volcanic mountain mass rises steeply from the desert. Much of this mountainous area, the heartland of the empire of Ethiopia, lies above 10,000 feet and one peak reaches 15,158 feet. The highland receives heavy rains during the summer half of the year rather than the winter rain characteristic of mediterranean climatic areas. Important Nile tributaries such as the Blue Nile, the Sobat, and the Atbara rise here (map, p. 301). Temperature conditions vary from tropical to temperate as elevation increases. Thus crops varying from bananas, coffee, and dates through oranges, figs, and temperate fruits to cereals can be produced without irrigation. Large expanses of upland pasture a variety of livestock, primarily cattle and sheep.

Ethiopia, together with Eritrea, is inhabited by an estimated 22 million people, of very diverse racial and cultural characteristics. Although dark-skinned, most of the population is descended from the Hamitic or Semitic branches of the Caucasian race. It is estimated that about 57 percent of the population, including the politically dominant Amhara peoples, adheres to the Coptic Christian faith,[17] a very ancient branch which penetrated Ethiopia from Egypt, where there is still a sizable Coptic minority. The rest of the population is divided between the Moslem faith and a variety of more primitive pagan beliefs. This diverse population is held in relatively loose political union under the emperor of Ethiopia, whose seat is in Addis Ababa (450,000), the only sizable city in the country. Tribal forms of life remain important, and disputes are still often settled on a private basis with the rifle. Probably 95 percent of the empire's population is illiterate.

East of the mountain mass of Ethiopia, and partly included within the empire, lower plateaus and coastal plains descend to the Red Sea, the Gulf of Aden, and the Indian Ocean. Extreme heat and aridity assert themselves at these lower levels, and nomadic or seminomadic Moslem tribesmen make a poor living from camels, goats, and sheep. Precarious forms of irrigated agriculture are carried on in scattered oases.

Ethiopia and its borderlands constitute a very marginal part of the Middle East. The latter is especially true of the rainy tropical Ethiopian highlands. However, the arid lowland sections possess many typically Middle Eastern characteristics, and the entire area has had important cultural and historical links with the core of the Middle East in Egypt, the Fertile Crescent, and Arabia.

## ▶ *European Imperialism*

European powers seized coastal strips of this territory in the latter nineteenth century. Britain was first with British Somaliland in 1882, then France annexed French Somaliland in 1884, and lastly Italy asserted dominance over Italian Somaliland and Eritrea in 1889. The strategic importance of these holdings along the Suez–Red Sea route and adjacent to the independent native state of Ethiopia is obvious. Their economic importance is negligible.

Italy attempted to extend its domain from Eritrea over the much more attractive and potentially valuable land of Ethiopia in 1896, but the Italian forces were annihilated by the Ethiopian tribesmen at Aduwa. Forty years later, in 1936, a second attempt was successful. Hopes of developing the country's potential wealth and of using it as an outlet for surplus Italian population were frustrated in World War II, when the Italian empire in eastern Africa was conquered by British forces in 1941. Ethiopia was restored to independence and Eritrea was federated with it in 1952. Italian Somaliland was returned to Italian control to be administered as the Trust Territory of Somalia under the United Nations, pending independence in 1960. The Somali Republic was proclaimed on July 1, 1960. It includes not only the former Italian territory, but former British Somaliland as well. The British territory was granted independence at the same time and chose to unite with Somalia. However, the people of French Somaliland, in a 1958 referendum, indicated their desire to remain in a de-

---

[17] The estimates cited for total population and adherence to Coptic Christianity are probably too high. The figure of 22 million for total population is a 1959 conjectural estimate by the Ethiopian government. Other estimates place the total as low as 13 million or even 10 million or less. No census has ever been taken. The estimate of 57 percent for Coptic Christians was taken from the 1959 *Encyclopedia Britannica Book of the Year*. According to other sources the figure may be as low as 33 to 40 percent.

pendent relationship to France for the present. Influential elements among the Somali peoples advocate the formation of a "Greater Somalia" which would include the three Somaliland units plus substantial parts of Ethiopia and possibly some of Kenya. Claims to Ethiopian areas rest primarily on seasonal use of these lands by Somali graziers who migrate with their livestock across the international boundary. Needless to say, the Ethiopian government takes a poor view of these proposals to annex portions of its territory.

### ▶ Problems of Ethiopian Development

Ethiopia has substantial resources, including a fair amount of known mineral wealth. But its resource base remains largely undeveloped, though the emperor's government, with foreign assistance, is doing what it can. A primitive transport system whose best parts are the 3000 miles of good road built by the Italians during their occupation is a major factor in keeping the country isolated and undeveloped. The French-built railroad from the port of Djibouti (city proper, 31,-000) in French Somaliland to Addis Ababa (map, p. 323) lacks feeder lines and has never proved as successful as hoped, although a substantial part of the coffee which comprises Ethiopia's major export does move through the port. An estimated 50 to 60 percent of the empire's foreign trade now moves through the small Eritrean ports of Massawa and Assab. Both have highway connections with the interior, and a rail line extends inland from Massawa to the northern highlands via the Eritrean capital, Asmara (130,000) (map, p. 323). Most routes into the Ethiopian heartland are mere trails, though Addis Ababa is accessible by scheduled air services from Aden, Khartoum, and Nairobi. Radio-telegraph communication to and from Ethiopia was only established in 1947. Under such circumstances one of the Middle East's and the world's areas of potential wealth remains in isolation and backwardness, though it should perhaps be added that the isolation probably had something to do with its remaining in independence during most of the colonial age.

15

# Introduction to the Orient

The Orient (East) is used in this book as a regional name for the countries occupying the southeastern quarter of Eurasia. Besides mainland countries extending from India and Pakistan to Korea, the Orient, as herein defined, also includes an arc of island countries stretching for thousands of miles between Ceylon and Japan (map, p. 334).

## REGIONAL GROUPS OF COUNTRIES

For convenience in study in the chapters that follow, the countries of the Orient are divided into a number of regional groups on the basis of such factors as (*a*) proximity, (*b*) environmental, economic, and cultural similarities, (*c*) political relationships, and (*d*) historical ties.

1. The *countries of the Indian subcontinent* include India, Pakistan, and the disputed area called Kashmir (map, p. 334); the small Himalayan states of Nepal, Bhutan, and Sikkim; and the tiny Portuguese colonial possessions of Goa, Damão, and Diu. Ceylon is often included with this group, although it is considered with Southeast Asia in the present treatment.

2. The *countries of Southeast Asia* include (*a*) Burma, (*b*) Thailand (Siam), (*c*) the units that formerly comprised French Indochina—South Vietnam, Cam-

Terraced rice fields are the most characteristic and best known type of rural landscape in the Orient. The terraces in this view are located on the mountainous island of Java in the East Indies. (Information Office of the Republic of Indonesia.)

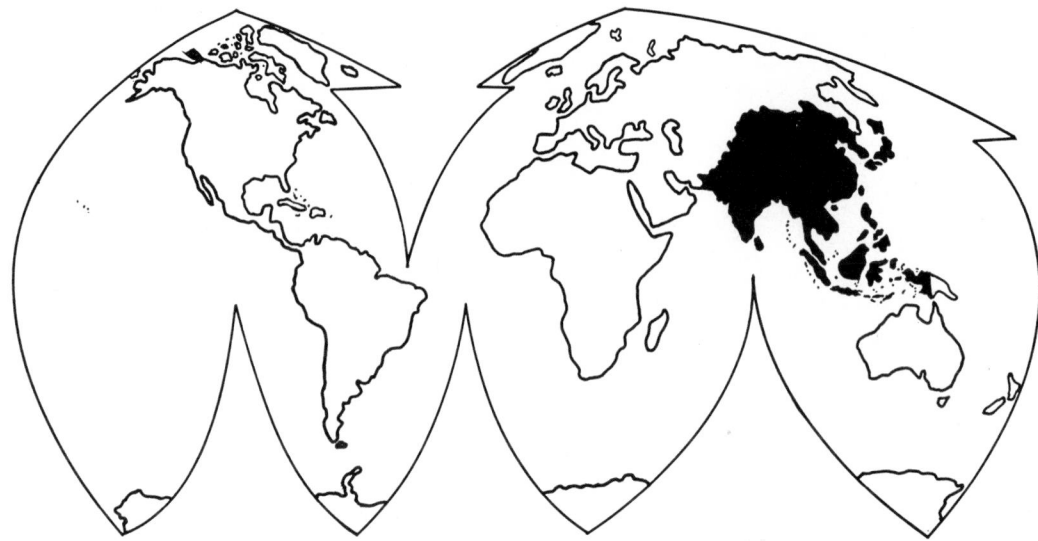

Location of the Orient. (Boggs Equal Area Projection, copyright A. J. Nystrom and Co.)

bodia, Laos, and the Communist satellite state of North Vietnam, (*d*) Malaya, (*e*) the large island country of Indonesia, (*f*) the smaller island countries of Ceylon and the Philippines, and (*g*) a scattering of minor European island dependencies, including the internally self-governing state of Singapore, affiliated with Great Britain; Sarawak, Brunei, and North Borneo, comprising British Borneo; Portuguese Timor; and Netherlands New Guinea.

3. The *countries of the Chinese realm,* as considered herein, include Communist China, Nationalist China (Taiwan [Formosa] and smaller islands), the Mongolian People's Republic or Outer Mongolia (placed in this group for convenience and because of its historical associations with China), and the European coastal possessions of Hong Kong (British) and Macao (Portuguese), which are largely Chinese in population.

4. Japan is placed for convenience with its former colony of Korea, now divided between North Korea (Communist) and South Korea (non-Communist).

## THE COLONIAL BACKGROUND OF THE ORIENT

Modern European penetration of the Orient began at the end of the fifteenth century. The early comers established trading posts and gradually extended political control over limited areas near the coast. In the eighteenth and nineteenth centuries the pace of annexation quickened, and large areas came under European sway. By the end of the nineteenth century Great Britain was supreme in India, Burma, Ceylon, Malaya, and northern Borneo; the Netherlands possessed most of the East Indies; and

France had acquired Indochina and a number of small holdings around the coasts of India. Meanwhile Portugal, the supreme colonial power of the Orient in the sixteenth century, had been displaced from her early holdings with the exception of Macao, a part of the island of Timor, and Goa and two other small holdings on the west coast of India. China, though retaining a semblance of territorial integrity, was forced to yield possession of strategic Hong Kong to Britain in the mid-nineteenth century and to grant special trading concessions and extraterritorial rights to various European nations and the United States. At the end of the century the Philippines, dominated by Spain after the mid-sixteenth century, passed into American control. The only Oriental countries of any importance to escape domination by the Western powers during the colonial age were: (1) Thailand, which formed a buffer between British and French colonial spheres in Southeast Asia; (2) Japan, which withdrew into almost complete seclusion in the seventeenth century, but emerged in the latter nineteenth century as the first modern, industrialized Oriental nation, and soon acquired a colonial empire of its own; and (3) Korea, which also followed a policy of isolation from foreign influences from the early seventeenth century until 1876, when a trade treaty was forced on it by Japan.

During the age of European expansion the Orient constituted an extraordinarily rich colonial area from which Western nations extracted vast quantities of such valuable commodities as rubber, sugar, tea, copra, palm oil, spices, and tin, and in which Western manufacturers found large markets for cheap textiles, metalwares, and other inexpensive types of goods. Westerners also found the Orient a fertile field for investment in plantations, factories, mines, and transportation, communication, and electric power facilities.

### ▶ Decline of Colonialism in the Twentieth Century

Western dominance of the Orient was ended in the twentieth century by a complex chain of circumstances, including (1) the weakening effects of conflicts among the Western nations in the two world wars, (2) the rise of Japan to great-power status and its successful, though temporary, military challenge to the West in the early stages of World War II, and (3) the rise of anticolonial movements in areas subject to European control. World War II ended Western colonialism in China, and after the war all colonial possessions in the Orient, whether European (map, p. 35), American, or Japanese, gained independence, except for a few minor units listed earlier. The latest unit to become an independent nation was Malaya in 1957.

In the Orient, and particularly in China, the twentieth century has been an age of revolution, war, and general turmoil. Today military action and other forms of open violence are less frequent. But the region is a major focus in the world-wide cold war, and it harbors other serious conflicts, such as the Kashmir issue (p. 362) and continuing rebellions against government authority in Indonesia (p. 382). Resolution of these problems seemed, at the time of writing, a very distant prospect.

## THE VARIED PHYSIOGRAPHIC SETTING

The stage on which the Oriental drama is being enacted is a complex intermingling of many types of topography—high, rugged mountains, arid plateaus and basins, humid hill lands and river plains, and a vast number of offshore islands rising from the floor of shallow seas. Although the picture is extremely complicated in detail, a certain order appears if the surface features of the Orient are conceived of as three concentric arcs or crescents of land—an inner arc of high mountains, plateaus, and basins; a middle arc of lower mountains, hill lands, and river plains; and an outer arc of islands and seas (map, p. 335).

### ▶ The Inner Highland

The inner highland of the Orient is composed of the highest mountain ranges on earth, interspersed with plateaus and ba-

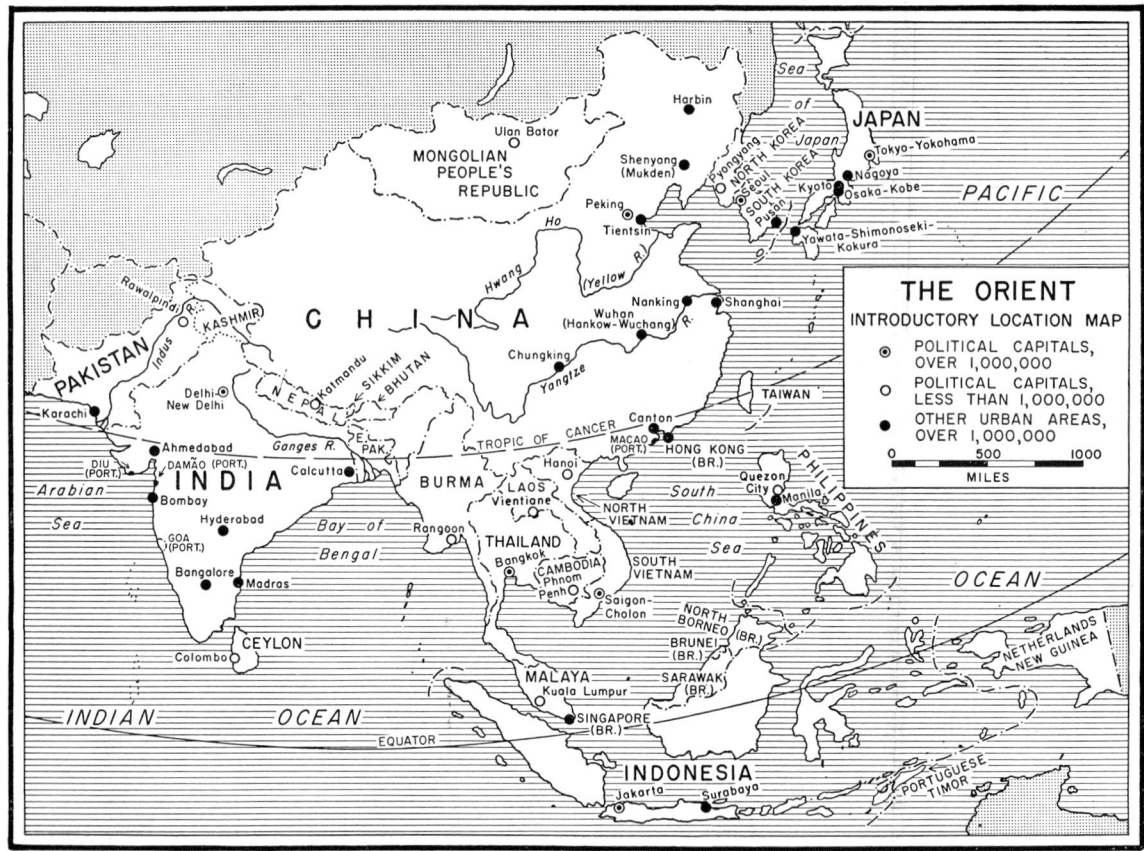

Introductory location map of the Orient. Provisional boundaries within Korea and Vietnam are shown by dashes.

sins. At the south the great wall of the Himalaya, Karakoram, and Hindu Kush mountains overlooks the north of the Indian subcontinent. At the north, the Altai, Tien Shan, Pamirs, and other mountains separate the Orient from the Soviet Union. Between these mountain walls lie the sparsely inhabited Tibetan Plateau, over 15,000 feet in average elevation, and the dry, thinly populated basins and plateaus of Sinkiang and Mongolia.

### ► River Plains and Hill Lands

The area between the inner highland and the sea is principally occupied by river flood plains and deltas, bordered and separated by hills and relatively low mountains. The major components of the topography include (1) the immense plain of northern India, built up through countless ages by the Indus, Ganges, and Brahmaputra rivers, (2) the hill lands of peninsular India, geologically an ancient plateau, but largely hilly in aspect, (3) the plains of the Irrawaddy, Chao Praya (Menam), Mekong, and Red rivers in peninsular Southeast Asia, together with bordering hills and mountains, (4) the hill lands and small alluvial plains of southern China, (5) the broad alluvial plains along the middle and lower Yangtze River in central China and the mountain-girt Red Basin on the upper Yangtze, (6) the large delta plain of the Yellow River and its tributaries in North China, backed by loess-covered hilly uplands, and (7) the broad central plain of Manchuria, almost completely enclosed by mountains with low to moderate elevations. The floor of the Red

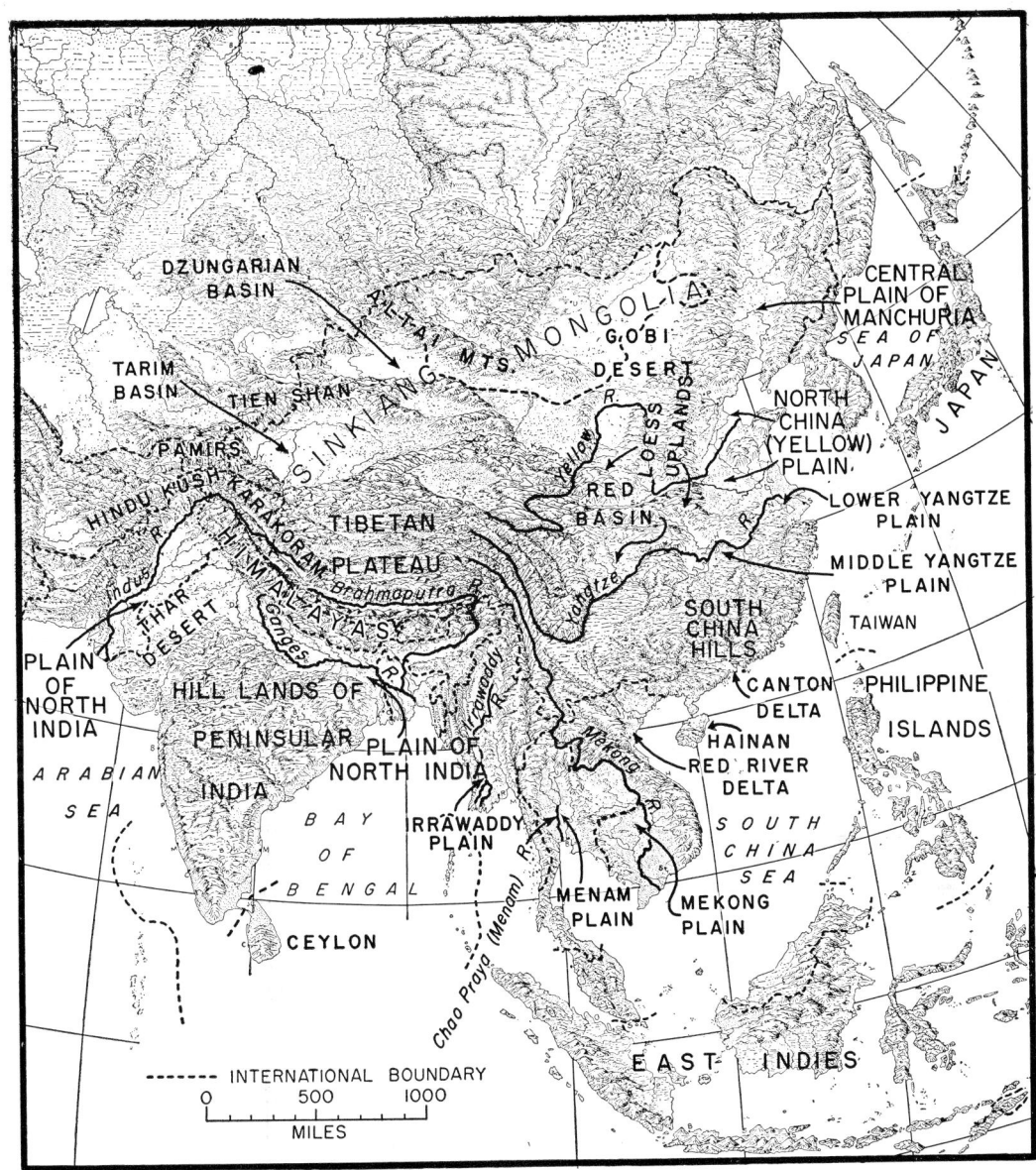

Major landforms of the Orient. (Base map is a portion of A. K. Lobeck's Physiographic Diagram of Asia, copyright Geographical Press, a division of C. S. Hammond & Company.)

Basin and the central plain of Manchuria are structural rather than river-made plains, and are rolling or hilly in aspect rather than flat.

### ▶ Offshore Islands and Seas

Offshore, a fringe of thousands upon thousands of islands, mostly grouped in great archipelagoes, borders the mainland. On these islands high interior mountains with many volcanic peaks are flanked by broad or narrow coastal plains where most of the inhabitants live. Three major archipelagoes include most of the islands—the East Indies, the Philippines, and the Japanese Archipelago. Ceylon, Taiwan, and Hainan are large islands not included in an archipelago. Between the archipelagoes and the mainland lie the China Seas, and, to the north, the Sea of Japan. At the southwest the Indian peninsula projects southward between two immense arms of the Indian Ocean—the Bay of Bengal and the Arabian Sea.

# THE PATTERN OF CLIMATES AND VEGETATION

In detail the climatic, like the physiographic, pattern is one of almost endless variety. However, two unifying elements are present throughout most parts of the Orient inhabited by any considerable number of people. These are (1) the dominance of warm climates and (2) a characteristic monsoonal regime of precipitation.

### ▶ *Temperature and Precipitation*

In the parts of the Orient where most of the people are found, temperatures are tropical or subtropical and the frost-free season ranges from around 200 to 365 days. The principal exceptions are found in northern sections of China, Korea, and Japan. Here summers are warm to hot in the lowlands, but the growing season is generally less than 200 days and winters are often severely cold. The arid, sparsely populated basins and plateaus of Sinkiang and Mongolia also have a continental type of climate with warm summers and cold winters. The higher mountain areas and Tibetan Plateau have highland climates varying with the altitude and latitude. Permanent snowfields and glaciers are found at the higher elevations.

Annual precipitation varies from near zero in the Tarim Basin of Sinkiang to an average of more than 400 inches in parts of the Khasi Hills of northeastern India. A monsoon climate, or at least a climate with monsoon tendencies, prevails nearly everywhere in the populous middle arc of plains and hills, and in many parts of the islands as well. Technically a monsoon is not, as some people imagine, a violent downpour of rain with accompanying winds and lightning (though such are often its effects), but is simply a current of air blowing fairly steadily from a given direction for several weeks or months at a time. Although conditions vary from place to place, the Orient is broadly characterized by two monsoons: a summer monsoon blowing from the sea to the land and bringing high humidity and rain, and a winter monsoon blowing seaward and bringing little or no rain and cool or cold, clear weather. The characteristic features of the monsoonal type of climate, then, are (1) the seasonal reversal of wind direction, (2) the strong summer maximum of rainfall, and (3) the long dry season, typically lasting for most or all of the winter half year.

### ▶ *Types of Climate*

Seven main types of climate in the Orient are customarily recognized in climatic classifications—tropical rain forest, tropical savanna, humid subtropical, humid continental, steppe, desert, and highland (front end-paper climatic map).

#### Tropical Rain Forest

The rainy tropical climates of the Orient are found along or relatively near the equator. Consequently, high temperatures are experienced throughout the year in the lowlands. There is a complete absence of frost, and the year-round growing season offers the maximum possibilities for agriculture from the standpoint of temperature. However, the high temperatures and heavy rain promote rapid leaching of mineral nutrients and destruction of organic matter, with the result that most soils in the rainy tropics are relatively infertile despite the thick cover of deep-rooted trees and grasses they often support. Two main types of humid tropical climate, each associated with characteristic forms of vegetation, are recognized. These are (1) tropical rain forest climate and (2) tropical savanna climate.

The *tropical rain forest climate* is typically found in lowlands within 5° or 10° of

# TABLE 15

## CLIMATIC DATA FOR SELECTED ORIENTAL STATIONS

| STATION | COUNTRY | LATITUDE TO NEAREST WHOLE DEGREE | ELE-VATION ABOVE SEA LEVEL (FEET) | TYPE OF CLIMATE | AVERAGE TEMPERATURE (DEGREES F TO NEAREST WHOLE DEGREE) | | | AVERAGE PRECIPITATION | | |
|---|---|---|---|---|---|---|---|---|---|---|
| | | | | | ANNUAL | JANUARY | JULY (OR WARMEST MONTH) | ANNUAL TO NEAREST INCH | PERCENT OCCURRING APRIL–SEPTEMBER (TO NEAREST WHOLE PERCENT) | PERCENT OCCURRING JUNE–SEPTEMBER (TO NEAREST WHOLE PERCENT) |
| Karachi | West Pakistan | 25°N. | 13 | Desert | 77° | 67° | 85° (June) | 8″ | 78% | 74% |
| Delhi | India | 29°N. | 718 | Tropical savanna | 77° | 58° | 92° (May, June) | 27″ | 88% | 84% |
| Bombay | India | 19°N. | 37 | Tropical savanna | 81° | 76° | 86° (May) | 72″ | 97% | 96% |
| Madras | India | 13°N. | 22 | Tropical savanna | 83° | 76° | 90° (May, June) | 49″ | 36% | 31% |
| Calcutta | India | 24°N. | 21 | Tropical savanna | 79° | 67° | 87° (May) | 63″ | 87% | 75% |
| Mandalay | Burma | 22°N. | 250 | Tropical savanna | 82° | 70° | 90° (April) | 35″ | 74% | 55% |
| Singapore | Singapore | 1°N. | 16 | Tropical rain forest | 80° | 78° | 82° (May) | 93″ | 46% | 31% |
| Jakarta | Indonesia | 6°S. | 26 | Tropical rain forest | 79° | 78° | 79° | 71″ | 29% | 15% |
| Canton | China | 23°N. | 29 | Humid subtropical | 73° | 57° | 85° (August) | 61″ | 81% | 58% |
| Shanghai | China | 31°N. | 23 | Humid subtropical | 59° | 38° | 81° | 45″ | 69% | 53% |
| Wuhan | China | 31°N. | 121 | Humid subtropical | 63° | 40° | 86° | 50″ | 72% | 47% |
| Chengtu | China | 31°N. | 1611 | Humid subtropical | 62° | 43° | 79° | 39″ | 90% | 79% |
| Peking | China | 40°N. | 125 | Humid continental | 54° | 25° | 80° | 24″ | 93% | 84% |
| Shenyang (Mukden) | China (Manchuria) | 42°N. | 141 | Humid continental | 47° | 11° | 78° | 28″ | 84% | 71% |
| Harbin | China (Manchuria) | 46°N. | 526 | Humid continental | 39° | −1° | 73° | 19″ | 86% | 73% |
| Tokyo | Japan | 36°N. | 19 | Humid subtropical | 57° | 37° | 78° (August) | 60″ | 61% | 44% |
| Hakodate | Japan | 42°N. | 13 | Humid continental | 46° | 26° | 69° (August) | 46″ | 57% | 45% |
| Kashgar | China (Sinkiang) | 40°N. | 4296 | Desert | 55° | 23° | 80° | 3″ | 62% | 41% |
| Ulan Bator | Outer Mongolia | 48°N. | 4347 | Steppe | 28° | −11° | 63° | 8″ | 86% | 30% |
| Gyantse | China (Tibet) | 29°N. | 13,110 | Highland | 42° | 24° | 58° | 12″ | 97% | 90% |

the equator. A rainfall of at least 30 to 40 inches, often 100 inches or more, is spread throughout the year so that every month has considerable rain. Average temperatures vary only slightly from month to month; Singapore, for example, exhibits a difference of only 4° between the warmest and coolest months. Monotonous heat prevails the year round, although excessively high temperatures of 95° or 100°F or more are seldom or never experienced. Some relief is afforded by a drop of 10° to 25° in the temperature at night, and conditions are more pleasant along coasts subject to periodic sea breezes.

The tropical rain forest produced by the climatic conditions described above is characteristically a thick forest of large broad-leaved evergreen trees, mostly hardwoods, from 50 to 200 feet in height, and forming an almost continuous canopy of foliage. The trees are often entangled in a mass of vines, and dense undergrowth is found wherever sufficient light penetrates to the ground.

Tropical rain forest climate and vegetation are characteristic of most parts of the East Indies, the Philippines, and the Malay Peninsula. Rain forest vegetation is also found in certain other areas which experience a dry season, but in which the precipitation of the rainy season is sufficiently heavy to promote a thick growth of trees. Such areas are found (1) along the west coast of India south of Bombay and along the south coast of Ceylon, (2) along the west coast of Burma, extending northward to the delta of the Ganges and Brahmaputra rivers in India and East Pakistan, (3) along the east coast of Indochina, and (4) in parts of the northern Philippines.

### Tropical Savanna

Although the *tropical savanna climate,* like the tropical rain forest climate, is characterized by high temperatures the year round, this climate type is customarily found in areas farther from the equator, and the average temperatures vary somewhat more from month to month. However, the most striking and important difference between the two climate types lies in the fact that the savanna climate has a well-defined dry season, lasting in some areas for as much as six or eight months of the year. The annual precipitation is less, on the average, than in the rain forest climate, but it is the seasonal distribution of the rain rather than inadequate total precipitation which represents the principal handicap for agriculture. The savanna climate is typical of the greater part of the Indian subcontinent and Ceylon, the interior of Burma, practically all of Thailand, all of Indochina except the east coast, and eastern Java and smaller islands to the east. Much larger areas of this climate type are found in Africa and Latin America and a smaller area in northern Australia.

In the Orient the characteristic natural vegetation associated with the savanna climate is a deciduous forest of smaller trees than those found in the tropical rain forest. The forest growth deteriorates to scrub in the drier areas. Tall, coarse tropical grasses, the most common vegetation form in the African and Latin American savannas, are found in only limited areas, and even there are thought to have been produced by repeated burning of forest growth during the dry season. In parts of Southeast Asia long-continued burning has fostered pure stands of certain tree species peculiarly resistant to extinction by fire. Among these are a number of economically valuable types, especially teak, which is exploited on a considerable scale in Burma and Thailand. In the more densely populated and long-settled parts of the Oriental savanna lands the natural vegetation has been so modified by centuries of human occupation that the original conditions are difficult or impossible to determine.

### Climates Outside the Humid Tropics

The climate of southern China (including the Yangtze Valley), southern Japan, and extreme southern Korea is customarily classified as *humid subtropical*. This climate type is characterized by warm to hot summers, mild or cool winters with some frost, and a frost-free season lasting 200 days or longer. The annual rainfall of 30 to 50 inches or more is fairly well distributed throughout the year, although monsoonal tendencies produce a dry season in some areas. The natural vegetation, now largely removed over extensive areas (especially in China), is a mixture of evergreen hardwoods, deciduous hardwoods, and conifers. A generally comparable climate occurs in the southeastern part of the United States, although rainfall is more evenly distributed through the year in the latter area.

The northern part of China proper, most of Korea and Manchuria, and northern Japan have a *humid continental* type of climate marked by warm to hot summers, cold winters with considerable snow, a frost-free season of 100 to 200 days, and less precipitation than the humid subtropical areas. Most areas experience a definite dry season in winter. The predominant natural vege-

tation is a mixture of broad-leaved deciduous and coniferous trees, although prairie grasses are thought to have formed the original cover in parts of North China and Manchuria. Many aspects of the humid continental climate of the Orient are duplicated in comparable latitudes of eastern North America, though the American areas lack the dry season in winter. The Orient has the long-summer subtype of humid continental climate except for northern Manchuria and extreme northern Japan, which have the short-summer subtype.

*Steppe and desert climates,* whose characteristics have been previously described in chapters 11 and 13, are found in Sinkiang and Mongolia and in parts of western India and West Pakistan. A severe *highland climate* characterizes Tibet and adjoining mountain areas. Some of the higher mountains in the East Indies are also best classified as having highland climates.

Climatic data for representative stations in the Orient are presented in Table 15.

## POPULATION AND ECONOMY OF THE ORIENT

Approximately half of the world's people live in the Orient. They range from some of the most primitive tribes on earth in the remoter highlands to peoples such as the Indians and Chinese who have been civilized for thousands of years and are the possessors of rich and varied cultures. Mongoloid peoples form a majority in China, Japan, Korea, Burma, Thailand, Cambodia, North and South Vietnam, and Laos, but the majority of the people in India, though darker skinned than Europeans, are considered to belong to the Caucasian race, and brown-skinned Malays or kindred peoples form a majority among the native inhabitants of the Malay Peninsula, the East Indies, and the Philippines. This cursory survey does little justice to the tremendous variety of racial stocks found in the region as a whole.

The picture with respect to religion is also complicated. Hinduism is dominant in India, although many other religions are practiced, while the Moslem faith is dominant in Pakistan, most parts of the East Indies, parts of the southern Philippines, parts of outer China, and among the native Malays of the Malay Peninsula. Various forms of Buddhism are dominant in Burma, Thailand, Cambodia, Laos, Tibet, and Mongolia. Ceylon and Nepal divide between Buddhism and Hinduism. The Chinese are hard to categorize, even if effects of Communist rule in mainland China are disregarded. Among them, Buddhism, Confucianism, and Taoism have all exerted an important influence, often in the same household. The same general situation has prevailed in Korea and Vietnam. In Japan religious affiliations have been divided between Buddhism and the strongly nationalistic religion of Shintoism. The Philippines, with a large Roman Catholic majority, is the only Christian nation of the Orient, though Christian groups are found in various other areas such as Korea, India, and Indonesia. Oriental religions (excepting the Moslem religion and Christianity, which are not indigenous to the region) may be broadly described as contemplative in nature, emphasizing meditation rather than active work for social betterment, and seeking converts with much less vigor than Christianity or Islam. Veneration of ancestors is a prominent feature, especially among the Chinese, Vietnamese, and Koreans. Often an elaborate ritual for everyday living is followed, this being particularly characteristic of the Hindu religion. The more primitive hill tribes of the Orient are largely Animists.

## ▶ Distribution of Population

The densest populations of the Orient are found, generally speaking, on river and coastal plains, although surprisingly high densities occur in some hilly or mountainous areas. The higher mountains and the steppes, deserts, and some areas of tropical rain forest are very sparsely inhabited.

Most countries in the Orient have experienced large increases in population during recent centuries, and especially since the beginning of the nineteenth century. Rural densities of 500 to 1000 persons per square mile are fairly common, and some of the more fertile irrigated areas support 2000 persons per square mile or even more. At present, high rates of population increase are found in many areas of the Orient, and a number of Oriental countries—notably India, Japan, Pakistan, Indonesia, and China—are faced with serious problems of population support. Should present rates of population growth continue for a considerable period, the problem of finding enough food for so many millions will become increasingly critical.

## ▶ Means of Livelihood

Japan was the first country of the Orient to develop modern types of manufacturing on a really large scale. But Communist China and India also have important industries and, like Japan, both countries are expanding their industrial output. These giant countries, by far the largest in the world in population, are much better supplied with mineral resources than Japan, and they have cheaper labor. But Japan's labor force is more skilled, and Japan has been shifting more and more to types of industry requiring skilled labor. The remaining countries of the Orient lag far behind the three leaders in industrial development, though at least one of them, Indonesia, has sufficient natural resources to support a large expansion of industry.

For the Orient as a whole, agriculture remains the dominant source of livelihood. Even in Japan, the nation which has the smallest proportion of its population in agriculture, well over a third of the labor force is agricultural. A number of major types of agriculture may be distinguished in the Orient. Two types, plantation agriculture and shifting cultivation, are discussed in some detail in Chapter 17 on Southeast Asia, the part of the Orient in which these forms of agriculture are the most prominent. In the steppes and deserts of outer China, the Mongolian People's Republic, and West Pakistan, nomadic or seminomadic herding and oasis farming are practiced. Over large sections of the Orient, most farmers make a living by cultivation of small rain-fed or irrigated plots worked by family labor. (In Communist-held areas, collectivized agriculture is replacing the traditional family farms.) Large amounts of hand labor are applied to the land (photo, p. 342), and production is generally of a semisubsistence character. This type of agriculture, which is often referred to as intensive subsistence agriculture, is built around the growing of cereals, although other types of crops are raised. Where natural conditions are not suitable for irrigated rice, such grains as wheat, barley, millet, grain sorghums, or corn are raised. However, irrigated rice is the grain which yields the largest amount of food per unit of area where conditions are favorable for its growth, and this crop is the agricultural mainstay in the areas inhabited by a large majority of the Orient's people.

## ▶ Importance of Rice in the Oriental Economy

The nature and significance of rice growing in the Orient is briefly presented in the following selection by Smith and Phillips: [1]

The old adage that bread is the staff of life is a striking example of the ease with which a half-truth is perpetuated as a universal verity. The fact is that hundreds of millions of healthy and industrious men have never seen bread as we in the Occident know it, but that is no sign that these men are savage, barbarian, or heathen. Throughout the Orient from India to Japan, teeming millions obtain their carbohydrate from rice, which is low in gluten and will not make light bread. . . .

Since rice does not make light bread because it lacks the gluten, the Oriental boils the grain and eats it in that form. He flavors it with a bit of meat or fish if he can afford it; or uses curry, a hot seasoning preparation made in endless varieties. With peas and beans and some greens, rice furnishes almost the entire nourishment for hundreds of millions of people. Peas and beans are widely grown by almost all Eastern peoples who raise rice, and they are the substitutes for meat, milk, and cheese of the West, while the starch of rice is the substitute for bread, potatoes, and many puddings as well. . . .

### The Rice Environment

Among the environmental factors affecting rice production, water supply is most important, for the great bulk of all rice is grown under irrigation, the rice fields being submerged under approximately 6 inches of fresh, slowly moving water for at least 75 days. While the amount of water needed in a given area varies with such factors as rate of evaporation, relative humidity, and soil conditions, a total of 45 to 65 inches of water is generally required for rice production. . . . Furthermore, rice requires a mean temperature of more than 70°F during the growing season of 4 to 6 months. Hence, rice is a product of the tropics and subtropics, most of it being grown in regions of reeking humidity with frequent, almost daily rains. . . .

Level land is obviously essential for irrigation, and where it is lacking man must create it artificially as he has done by laboriously building terraces on the steep hillsides in many parts of Japan, China, the Philippines, and the East Indies. Although rice is grown on a variety of soils, there must be an impervious subsoil to prevent the loss of valuable irrigation water by seepage. Ideal soil conditions are found on many an alluvial plain, where a topsoil of fertile and friable silt has been deposited above a layer of impervious clay.

Although rice is now produced in the tropic and subtropic lands of every continent, 95 percent of the world's crop is grown each year in southern and eastern Asia. . . .

### The Technique of Rice Growing

Lowland rice must be grown by irrigation, and the devices used in fitting and keeping the land for this service are among the greatest monuments of human diligence in the world. . . . In Ceylon, for example, the railway that goes from the seacoast to the highlands goes through an irrigated plain divided by low banks into ponds of small area—rice fields, each of which has by great labor been leveled so that the water may be of uniform and proper depth for rice growing. As the railroad climbs the slopes of the hills the rice patches continue, with smaller area and higher banks, turning at last into a giant flight of gentle water steps, one of the most beautiful landscapes that the world possesses. . . .

The common treatment of . . . lowland rice is alternately to flood it and draw off the water during the early periods of its growth. It is kept under water during a large part of its development, the water being entirely drawn off as it ripens. The water must not become stagnant, and to keep it in motion it is the

---

[1] J. Russell Smith and M. Ogden Phillips, *Industrial and Commercial Geography,* 3d ed. New York: Holt, Rinehart and Winston, 1946. Pp. 428–434. Authors' footnotes and all headings except one have been omitted. One heading has been added and one word italicized in editing. Used by permission of the authors and the publisher.

A Japanese peasant harvests a rice crop near Tokyo. (Foreign Agricultural Service, U. S. Department of Agriculture.)

common practice on the hillsides to lead a stream to the top terrace, and let the water pass from terrace to terrace down the slopes. . . .

The labor of rice growing often involves the raising of plants in small seed beds and transplanting them in little bunches to the rice field itself. This work, as most of the other work in connection with terrace-grown rice, can be done only by hand. The small fields make it impossible to use such machinery as reapers and at times even the ox and water buffalo. . . .

When the Asiatic rice field is finally drained, the ripened grain is usually cut by hand, tied up in bundles, and allowed to dry. To accomplish this in moist places, it is often necessary to put the sheaves upon bamboo frames. It is usually threshed by hand with the aid of some very simple devices. One of these is a board with a slit in it. Drawing the rice through the slit pulls the grains from the heads and allows them to fall into a receptacle. The grain at this stage is called *paddy* because of a close-fitting husk not unlike that which protects the oat kernel. As with oats, these husks cause the grain to keep much better than when the husk is removed and the final husking of rice for home use is usually deferred until the time of use approaches. Among the Oriental people the husking of the paddy to prepare it for food is a daily occurrence, commonly done by hand. One of the commonest sounds throughout the East . . . is the pounding of a heavy mallet or pestle as it falls into a vessel full of paddy in the process of pounding the grain and loosening the husk.

# The Indian Subcontinent

The northern reaches of the Indian Ocean are split into two enormous bays—the Bay of Bengal and the Arabian Sea—by a triangular peninsula which thrusts southward for a thousand miles from the main mass of Asia. To the north the peninsula is bordered by the alluvial plain of the Indus and Ganges rivers, beyond which lie ranges of high mountains (map, p. 335). The entire unit—peninsula, alluvial plain, and fringing mountains—is often called the Indian subcontinent. Today it is occupied by the five countries of India, Pakistan, Nepal, Bhutan, and Sikkim, plus three small Portuguese possessions—Goa, Damão, and Diu [1]—along the west coast of the peninsula (map, p. 344). India and Pakistan are by far the largest countries in area and population. Nepal, Bhutan, and Sikkim are small states [2] on the southern flank of the Himalaya Mountains. They have strong economic and political ties with India, and Bhutan and Sikkim are under formal Indian protection. The three Himalayan states are mountainous, sparsely populated, and difficult of access. Until recent years they have been of

[1] The three units combined occupy a reported 1619 square miles and had an estimated population of 649,000 in 1959. Goa comprises around nine tenths of the total area and population of Portuguese India.

[2] Area estimates in square miles: Nepal 54,362; Bhutan 19,305; Sikkim 2744. Population estimates (mid-1959): Nepal 9,044,000; Bhutan 660,000; Sikkim 150,000.

Making cow-dung cakes, India's most common cooking fuel. The number of cakes in the photo indicates a commercial rather than a household operation. (Foreign Agricultural Service, U. S. Department of Agriculture.)

little importance in world affairs, but in 1959 were involved in border disputes with Communist China. The latter country claimed territory in all three states as well as in Himalayan sections of India and Pakistan. The large island of Ceylon off the southeast coast of the Indian peninsula is often included with India and Pakistan in regional groupings. However, in many respects Ceylon is more similar to the countries of Southeast Asia, and is considered with them in Chapter 17.

The Indian subcontinent is entirely enclosed on its landward borders by mountains. Its northern boundary lies in the highest ranges in the world, the Himalaya and the Karakoram. From each end of this massive wall, lower flanking ranges trend south-ward, to the Arabian Sea on the west and the Bay of Bengal on the east. Until 1947 it was customary to refer to the entire area now included in India and Pakistan as "India." It was for well over a century the most important unit in the British colonial empire. Then in 1947 it gained freedom, but in the process became divided along religious lines into two sovereign nations, the predominantly Hindu nation of India and the Moslem nation of Pakistan. Both countries have remained within the Commonwealth of Nations as republics which recognize the British monarch as the head of the Commonwealth and symbol of Commonwealth unity, but not as the titular head of their respective governments.

## IMPORTANCE OF INDIA AND PAKISTAN

### ▶ Population and Area

India and Pakistan are among the most influential of the many nations that have gained independence since World War II.

Political units of the Indian subcontinent. Pakistan is indicated by diagonal lines and the three Himalayan states of Nepal, Bhutan, and Sikkim by a dot pattern. The three units of Portuguese India are shown in black. The future status of Kashmir, disputed between India and Pakistan, remained undecided at the time of writing.

While many factors are involved, one important element contributing to their influence in world affairs is their large size. Both are among the largest countries of the world in population, and both occupy sizable areas. Of the two countries, however, India is much the larger, being in fact the second country of the world in population and the seventh country in area. India's estimated population in 1959 was around 400 million, as opposed to about 87 million for Pakistan; her area of about 1,174,000 square miles compares with approximately 365,000 square miles for Pakistan (population and area figures exclude the disputed state of Kashmir). But Pakistan, though it is much smaller than India, ranks seventh among the world's countries in total population, and is the second largest Moslem country, after Indonesia. Pakistan's population is divided between the two widely separated provinces of (1) East Pakistan, with about 49 million people inhabiting 54,500 square miles, and (2) West Pakistan, with 37 to 38 million people occupying slightly more than 310,000 square miles.

## ► Economic Importance and Potentialities

The subcontinent's production of goods and services is not impressive if it is measured on a per capita basis. But the total output of certain commodities is very great, and a considerable potential exists for economic development. India is a more important country economically than Pakistan and her resources are much greater. She is one of the world's largest producers of textiles (mostly cotton or jute) and ranks third in the Orient, after Japan and Communist China, as a producer of iron and steel. Her proven reserves of high-grade iron ore amount to one fifth of the estimated world total and are larger than those of any other country. She also has abundant coal reserves, though comparatively little of her coal is suitable for coking. She ranks second to the Soviet Union as a producer of manganese and second to the United States as a producer of mica, is an important producer of salt, and a minor producer of various other minerals. Pakistan's mineral resources are relatively meager, but do include substantial reserves of natural gas, salt, and chromite and small deposits of other minerals, including oil and low-grade coal. Both countries have sizable reserves and a modest but growing production of hydroelectric power. India's reserves and production are much larger than Pakistan's. The annual production of agricultural commodities in the two countries bulks large in sum total, but is dangerously small in terms of the enormous number of people to be supported. There are few important agricultural exports, though India is the world's largest exporter of tea and Pakistan is the largest exporter of raw jute and a sizable exporter of raw cotton.

Some further characteristics and aspects

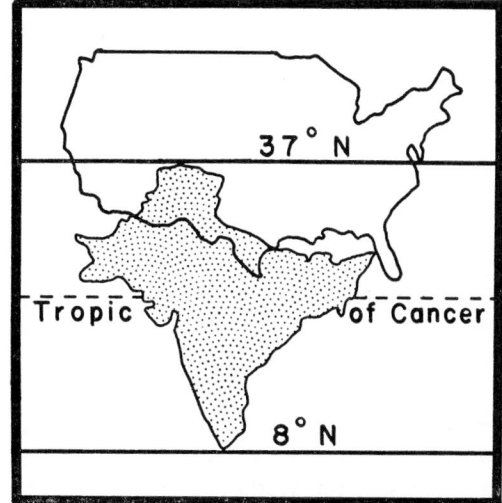

The Indian subcontinent compared in latitude and area with continental United States.

of the subcontinent are summarized in the following selection from an important book on India and Pakistan by a regional specialist on South Asia, W. Norman Brown: [3]

The population figures show that the subcontinent has a large labor supply. Not only is the source practically inexhaustible; Indian labor also has a tradition of skill celebrated in Europe since the times of classical Greece and Rome. Five centuries ago India was producing wares which induced technically less advanced Europe to seek a water route to that land. Hence the discovery of America! Early in the war in 1942 a United States Technical Mission to then unpartitioned India reported that, given a living wage, the Indian workman stood up well in comparison with industrial workers of Western countries.

## ► Intellectual Achievements and Potentialities

Besides economic potentiality, India and Pakistan have the prospect of significant intellectual accomplishment. In the Indian subcontinent flourish today two of the world's greatest his-

---

[3] Reprinted by permission of the publishers from W. Norman Brown, *The United States and India and Pakistan*. Cambridge, Mass.: Harvard University Press, Copyright, 1953, by The President and Fellows of Harvard College. Pp. 3–14. All headings and one editorial footnote have been added, and more recent statistical material has been inserted in brackets in a few places without compromising the sense of the original.

toric civilizations—the native Indian and the imported Islamic. Of these the first has existed for more than four and a half thousand years. Islam, though younger in India, is the heir to a thousand years more of civilization in the Near East. Both of these have been supplemented in the subcontinent by Europeanism since it established itself militarily and politically in the latter half of the eighteenth century. Thought in India has never been static, nor has social custom. As Jawaharlal Nehru repeatedly points out in his *Discovery of India* (1946), it is just the adaptability of Indian civilization to new ideas and its conjunction of intellectualism with imagination which have enabled it to modify or abandon outworn institutions and maintain its vitality and strength by developing new ones. It is this same adaptability which makes India and Pakistan potentially strong for intellectual development in the modern world. It is reasonable to expect that in the future, as in the past, the Indian subcontinent will be intellectually creative and will rank with Europe and America in scientific, social, and humanistic accomplishment. It may rival, though not duplicate, the great Western nations. . . .

### ▶ Elements of Weakness

But along with these potential sources of strength, India and Pakistan have serious elements of weakness. One is the conflict between the Islamic and Hindu communities which has now separated the subcontinent into two political entities and may lead to further strife. There are perilous divisions within each country between majority and minority social groups, between linguistic groups, between geographical regions. Today the economy of each is weak. Poverty is general, and sudden disaster can produce a famine, local or widespread according to the circumstances. The population problem is critical. Before these two countries can realize their potentialities, they must get these various problems under control.

## A LAND OF VILLAGES

India and Pakistan live today, as they have done in the past, primarily by means of agriculture, with relatively little supplement from industry. The imbalance is shown by the small number of industrial workers. Modern factories in the two nations employ only around 2 million persons, or by the most liberal interpretation of "factory" perhaps 2.5 million. This is about one half of 1 percent of the total population. Whether you travel in the subcontinent by rail, automobile, or air, you emerge suddenly from one of the few large cities to proceed for hundreds of miles across open country, dotted with drab little villages, lightened by only an occasional whitewashed Hindu shrine or Muslim [Moslem] mosque. Here and there you come to a small town. There is nothing to compare with the Atlantic coastal stretch of almost continuous urbanization from Boston to Wilmington or with some other American industrial areas, as around Pittsburgh and Chicago.[4] . . .

Most of the people . . . live in the more than 650,000 villages, which are settlements of less than 5000 population, averaging about 520 each. Of the villagers much the greater part (about 70 percent of the total population) are cultivators of the adjacent land; the others supply services or pursue handicrafts (weaving, pottery, metal work, oil pressing, or other). The country, as one sees it, consists of clusters or even long stretches of tiny fields, streaked with inarable land and jungle. Except at a few centers like Calcutta, Bombay, Madras, Jamshedpur, Asansol, Ahmedabad, Kanpur (Cawnpore), Sholapur, Karachi [map, right], factory chimneys are solitary or absent. . . . In the hills and mountains, where agriculture is more difficult, villages are fewer and smaller. In the deserts . . . they are still scarcer.

## THE PERENNIAL PROBLEM OF WATER SUPPLY

Agriculture in almost every part of India and Pakistan has to depend upon a scanty or fickle water supply, and the possession of water is a perennial and never fully solved problem. Nowhere else do so many people put so much labor into getting water; and nowhere else is

---

[4] *Editorial Note.* Only an estimated 9 percent of India's population and 5 percent of Pakistan's lived in metropolitan areas of 100,000 or over in 1955.

In the United States the comparable metropolitan percentage in 1956 was about 58.

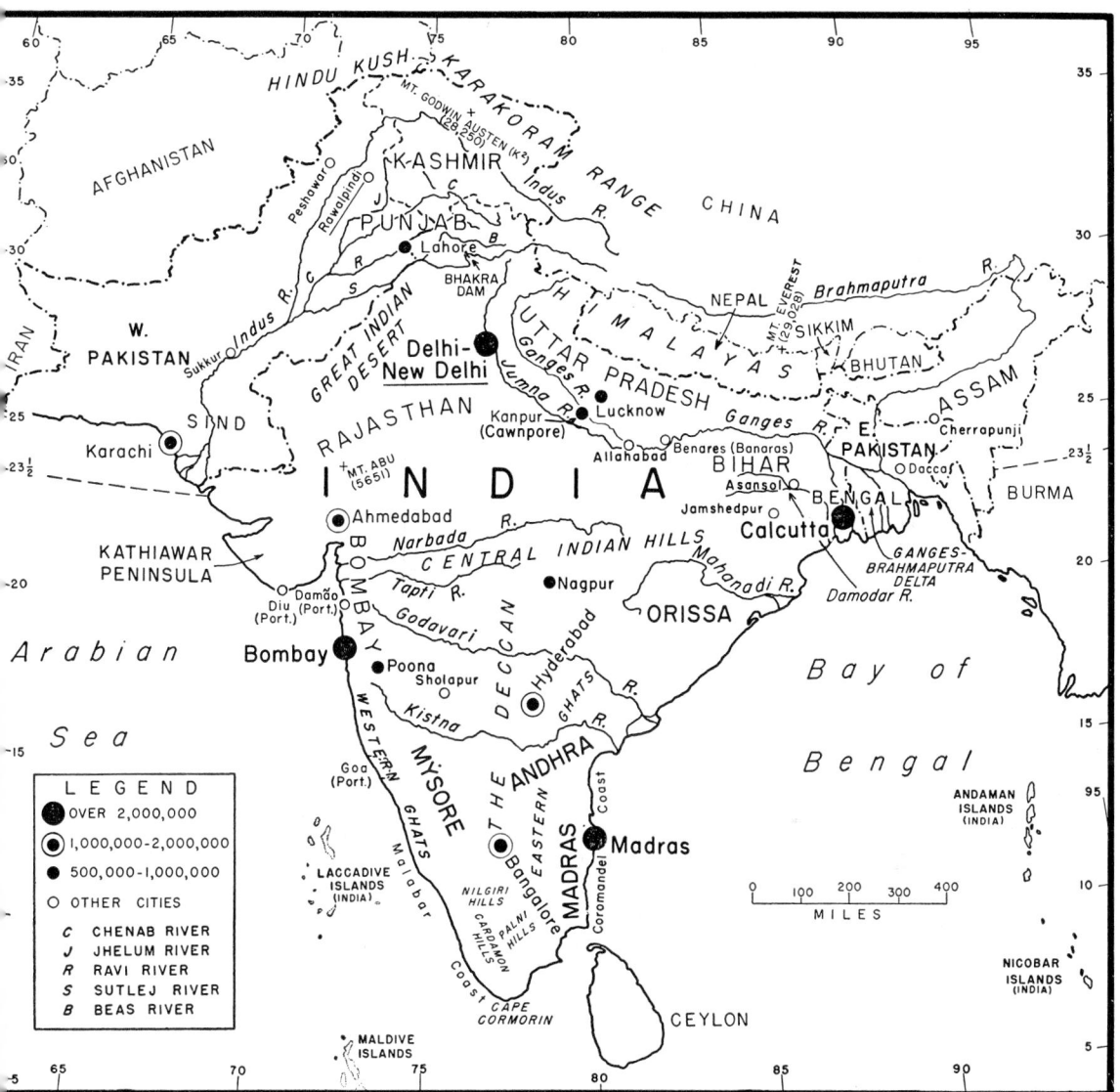

Index map of the Indian subcontinent. National capitals of India and Pakistan are underlined. The Maldive Islands, southwest of the Indian peninsula, are a sultanate under British protection. City-size symbols on the map are based on metropolitan-area estimates.

the problem of getting it more dramatic. In a region where great rivers can be used for irrigation, such as the Punjab or Sind, the water is impounded by huge dams or barrages and led off through canals. The major outlets are large; from these run off smaller canals, and from these still smaller ones, and so by graduated decrease until the water finally reaches the fields through minute capillary-like distribution. For part of the year many of these channels must be cut off, to save the water until it is needed later. At the latter time the peasants are busy throughout the day opening the sluices leading to their land so as to get the maximum flow during the hours for which they have contracted and to direct the water first to one part of their farms and then to another. This is the easiest of India's ways of using human labor to water fields, and the most certain. The rivers of north India are largely fed by the melting snows of the Himalayas and the rain that falls upon their southern ranges during the annual summer monsoon. At that time the clouds, after crossing the plains, have to rise, are cooled, and so are made to condense and precipitate their moisture. The flow of water in the rivers fluctuates from year to year, but in no year does it cease entirely. Hence, peasants who live in regions where there are river-fed irrigation systems are usually better off and less subject to crop failure and famine than those who must rely upon other sources.

In many parts of India and Pakistan the farmer gets water for his fields from a well. In north India he may use a great Persian wheel, filling the air with an interminable creaking, which dips an endless chain of earthenware pots into the water, raises them above ground level, and empties them into a trough from which the water flows through runlets to the land. A blindfolded camel or a pair of bullocks operates the mechanism, treading a tiny circle all day long while a man or boy stands by to keep them moving. Elsewhere a peasant may use a buffalo or a bullock or a pair of bullocks, which alternately raise and lower a leather sack into the water. There is a ramp built up to the well, rising above its mouth some six feet or more. Along it the bullocks tread forward and backward, relaxing the rope to which the sack is tied, and so letting it fall, then, when they reverse, raising it to the wooden crossbeam at the high end of the incline, where it is emptied into a channel to flow away. It takes one man to empty the sack, another to drive the bullocks. Very poor peasants who own no bullocks and cannot arrange to use those of a neighbor may operate such a well with only human labor,

India's cheapest commodity, drawn from the ranks of the family.

In still other areas peasants raise the water with a sweep, like an Egyptian *shaduf*. This is a seesaw-like apparatus with a leather sack or an earthenware pot at one end of the beam and a counterpoise balanced at the other. All day long a man may walk back and forth along the beam, first lowering the container into the well and then raising it to the top, where another man empties it into a runway. Or at the extremity of the sweep there may be a bamboo pole with the vessel fastened to its end. A man stands beside the well forcing the pole down until the vessel is submerged, then letting it go so that the counterpoise can raise it to the surface. In south India one may see a channel or ditch full of water, into which two peasants, often women, jointly dip a shallow scoop, rhythmically swinging it back and forth between them, lifting the water and emptying it in a higher channel through which it flows to the fields.

Throughout the land there are hundreds of thousands of "tanks," or artificial ponds, which are filled by the annual rains and serve in the dry season for irrigation, washing, even drinking. It is important to keep these tanks in good working order. Silt must not be left to accumulate; plants, such as the rapidly spreading water chestnut, must be prevented from choking them and absorbing the water supply. A tank has to be cleaned out regularly. But when it is cleaned, it is necessary to do the work carefully, so as not to dig out the bottom and let the water seep away. . . .

## PHYSICAL GEOGRAPHY OF THE SUBCONTINENT

What are the facts about the subcontinent's topography, its fertile plains, its river systems, its mountainous areas, its deserts, its basic water supply? [Maps, pp. 335 and 347.]

### ▶ The Outer Wall of High Mountains

The subcontinent is shaped roughly like a quadrangle—or, more precisely, like a pentagon, though the fifth side is disproportionately short. One long point of the figure is the Deccan peninsula projecting sharply southward into the Indian Ocean, with the Arabian Sea on its west and the Bay of Bengal on its east. The rest is mountain-bound. Along the northwestern side, now held by Pakistan, is a protective barrier of [mountains] and desert, generally difficult for

armies or peoples on the trek, yet penetrable at various points, and providing the chief means of ingress to India by land throughout recorded history. The northern side is a concave arc of lofty mountains, containing the world's highest peaks. . . . These ranges are geologically young and they and the nearby plains are disturbed by frequent tremors and occasional disastrous earthquakes, such as those in . . . Assam in 1950. On the east the short fifth side is the Burma frontier, whose jungle-covered mountains and dangerous marshes are all but impassable.

### ▶ The Northern Plain

Inside the northwestern and northern walls is the great plain of the subcontinent. It starts at the Arabian Sea with the peninsula of Kathiawar in the present Republic of India, and extends, first, slightly west of north to Sind in Pakistan. There it bends to a little east of north and continues for about 700 miles to the Himalayas, including all of Western Pakistan except some mountain areas. It then turns eastward into India, to follow a curved course below the Himalayan chain, crossing the breadth of the country and coming to an end against the hills of Assam and Eastern Pakistan and the coast of the Bay of Bengal.

This plain varies from 80 to 200 miles in width. In its sweeping course it contains the greatest of India's river systems. In the west is the Indus, which rises on the northern side of the Himalayas, flows westward behind them to round their end, separating them from the Karakoram and Hindu Kush ranges, and then drives inside the northwestern frontier down to the sea. The Indus is fed by the five rivers of the Punjab ("Land of Five Streams"), one of which (the Sutlej) also rises north of the Himalayas not far from the source of the Indus, but, unlike it, finds a route directly through them. The four others (Jhelum, Chenab, Ravi, Beas) rise in the range and flow directly to the lowlands. In the upper Punjab the moderate rainfall and the irrigation based upon its rivers support an extensive agriculture. Farther south, in the lower Punjab and Sind, rainfall is scanty, varying from ten to twenty inches annually and in many places being even less. Here agriculture is impossible except with the aid of irrigation. This has been practiced for millennia, but never on a scale to support a large population. Today there are great systems of irrigation in this region, and others are under construction or planned. East of the long course of the Indus is the Great Indian [Thar] Desert. . . .

The northern part of the Great Indian Plain, often called Hindustan, contains the Ganges-Jumna (Jamna) river system, which only a low rise of ground separates from the Indus system. The soil of this region is a deep alluvial deposit. Its two main rivers, the Ganges and the Jumna, rise on the lower side of the Himalayas and curve southeast in gradually converging arcs until they unite at Allahabad. From there the Ganges continues eastward to Bengal, absorbing many tributaries, to join the Brahmaputra. This last, like the Indus and the Sutlej, rises on the northern side of the Himalayas, but, as though to polarize the Indus, flows eastward to turn and circle the eastern end of the mountain chain, where it finds an opening, reverses itself, and flows southwest. It and the Ganges unite and form an immense delta.

Their waters reach the Bay of Bengal through many mouths, steadily depositing silt, and today as for millennia in the past continually projecting the land area into the bay.

The part of the northern plain east of the Punjab, already favored by its rivers, is in normal years also well watered by seasonal rains. It is the most desirable part of India and has always been the goal of invaders. Its population density [averages between 600 and 700] per square mile and, though it comprises only about [one fifth] of the subcontinent's total area, it contains about two fifths of its total population.

## ▶ Peninsular India

Below [south of] the northern plain is a complex highland, the upper end of which is embraced by . . . two descending extremes of the plain. Along its northern part are various ranges of low hills, of which the highest peak, Mount Abu, is 5651 feet in elevation. These make the Central Indian terrain difficult to penetrate and permit it to support only a moderately dense population. Indian literature has for 2500 years spoken fearfully of the wild jungles and the primitive peoples in this area. . . .

Still farther south is the part of the plateau known specifically as the Deccan ("South"), which comprises most of the triangle of peninsular India. This tableland (varying from about 1000 to 2500 feet in elevation) tilts gently from west to east. Its great rivers rise on the western side, flow eastward across it, and empty in the Bay of Bengal. It is not well watered, either by streams or by rainfall, and much of its area is rocky or has soil of only inferior quality. Nevertheless it supports [between 200 and 300] persons to the square mile.

The Deccan is bordered on east and west by low ranges of mountains known as Ghats ("Steps"). The Western Ghats, a kind of seaboard scarp, which have a few peaks of approximately 5000 feet but average around 3000 feet, descend in thickly forested, bold declivities to the seaboard. The southern part of this shoreline, known as the Malabar coast, is one of the best-watered, most fertile, and most thickly populated parts of India, having over 800 persons to the square mile. On the other side of the peninsula the Eastern Ghats, averaging about 1500 feet in altitude, are less picturesque. They lead down to another well-watered, productive, and thickly inhabited plain, wider than that on the west and known as the Coromandel coast. The central plateau terminates in clusters of hills called the Nilgiris ("Blue Mountains") and Palni, which respectively have peaks as high as 8640 and 8841 feet. Finally, . . . at the extreme south, are the Cardamon Hills. Beyond these last is Cape Comorin, the southernmost point of India, east and south of which lies the fragrant island of Ceylon. . . .

## ROLE OF THE MONSOON RAINS

The most important climatic feature of the subcontinent is the annual southwest monsoon, which brings "the rains" and gives India 90 percent of its heaven-dispensed water. So impressive has this phenomenon been upon India's consciousness that in her languages the commonest words for year primarily mean "rain" or "rainy season." . . .

. . . . . . . . . . .

If "the rains," that "annual gamble" from the southwest, are "normal" and widespread, the subcontinent is prosperous. That is, people do not actually suffer starvation; the government can collect the land revenue; the peasantry do not have to borrow from the village moneylenders at a ruinous rate of interest and may even do something toward reducing the principal of their debts. But if the rains are scanty in any area or fail, not only do the fields get no direct water from heaven; the sources of irrigation dwindle too. Rivers fall; the village tanks are not replenished; the water table is lowered; wells dry up. So, too, if in northern India, the rains are too full and make the rivers flood, as in 1950, seed may be washed out, cattle carried off, villages destroyed, and ruin come upon the peasantry and their land. Where there is irrigation from snow-fed streams, as in the Punjab, the case is not so desperate, for the mountain slopes always get a share of rain, which ultimately collects in the rivers. Elsewhere the inevitable result is poor crops or none at all. Agriculture stops; food is exhausted; there follows "distress," "scarcity," or "famine"; and relief must be brought in from outside. Such conditions have been reported since the third century B.C., just after India's historical records start; the case has not been different since.

### ▶ The Wet Monsoon

The southwest or wet monsoon is at its height during the months from June to September, and most parts of the subcontinent receive the bulk of their annual rainfall during those months (Table 15, p. 337). Two main arms of this monsoon can be discerned. One arm, approaching from the west off the Arabian Sea, strikes the Western Ghats and precipitates heavy rainfall on these mountains and the coastal plain at their base. But the amount of rain diminishes sharply in the interior Deccan to the east of the mountains. Here the annual precipitation over a sizable area is barely sufficient for unirrigated agriculture and in some years is so low as to result in serious crop failures.

The second major arm of the monsoon, approaching from the Bay of Bengal, brings moderate amounts of rain to the eastern coastal areas of the peninsula and heavy precipitation to the Bengal delta region (Ganges-Brahmaputra delta) and the northeastern Indian state of Assam. Exceptionally heavy rainfall occurs on the forward slopes of low mountains that rise behind the delta. One climatic station, Cherrapunji in the Khasi Hills on the border between Assam and East Pakistan, has an average annual rainfall of 452 inches (over nine tenths of which occurs in the summer half-year), and thus ranks with a station on the island of Kauai in the Hawaiian group as one of the two spots with the greatest annual rainfall yet recorded on the globe. Part of the moving air in the Bay of Bengal arm of the wet monsoon passes up the Ganges Valley and precipitates moisture that diminishes with some regularity in total amount from east to west. Both major arms of the monsoon bring some rainfall to West Pakistan, but the total is so small as to result in semiarid or desert conditions in most areas.

### ▶ The Dry Monsoon

The monsoon of the winter half-year is often called the northeast monsoon, though it blows generally from the west over most of the northern plain. The wind is often northeasterly, however, over the peninsula, the

Bay of Bengal, and the Arabian Sea. To most parts of the subcontinent this monsoon brings dry weather, with occasional light rains in areas outside the tropics. An exception is found in the far south of the peninsula, where the heaviest rainfall of the year occurs along the eastern coast and in adjacent interior uplands during the period October–January. This precipitation is brought by retreating maritime air of the summer monsoon and by continental air of the winter monsoon which has accumulated moisture in its passage over the Bay of Bengal. In addition to widespread drought, the winter monsoon brings cooler weather to the subcontinent, especially in the north. But a period of stifling heat is experienced in the spring before the onset of the rainy season.

## THE EXTENT AND EFFECTS OF POVERTY

Standards of living in the Indian subcontinent are among the lowest in the world. The extent and effects of the subcontinent's poverty have been summarized by Brown: [5]

The bulk of the village population gets only the most meager living in terms of food, clothing, and shelter. Urban factory labor lives no better, possibly worse. Without seeing Indians in their villages, towns, and cities, it is difficult for a Westerner to visualize the extent and effect of their poverty. And if the average American visitor wants to remain sensitive to the conditions in which the masses of the people live, it is well for him not to stay in the country long. Very quickly the want, the disease, the discomfort, the misery, become only accepted facts.

[In the middle 1950s the United Nations estimated the average individual diet in India to be 1890 calories a day and in Pakistan 2000—against a needed 2400 to 3000 calories. In 1946 the government reported that the average diet] was "ill balanced" as well as low and it estimated that 30 percent of India's families were seriously undernourished. In prewar years, with food supply at "normal," the Director of the Indian Medical Service . . . estimated that 41 percent of the people were "poorly nourished," that is, endured continued semistarvation. . . .

For clothing a gauge may lie in the consumption of cotton textiles—almost all clothing in India and Pakistan is of cotton. The average for personal clothing and household purposes combined was about [12 yards in India and 7 yards in Pakistan in 1956]; . . . the United States [consumed about six times as much cotton cloth per person as India in that year, plus large amounts of cloth made from wool, synthetics, and other fibers].

Housing is equally inadequate. In the villages most dwellings are made of mud and wattle or sun-dried brick, crowded together in an irregular huddle, affording little protection from the winter cold, the burning heat of summer, and the torrents of the rainy season. The average floor space per person in the villages is impossible to determine. In industrial urban areas surveys in 1938 showed it to be less than 28 square feet in Bombay, about 43 square feet in Ahmedabad, about 24 square feet in Sholapur. Most urban workers with their families were living in one-room tenements; in 1931 in Bombay 74 percent, in Karachi 58, in Kanpur (Cawnpore) 63; in London at the same time it was 6.0 percent. Often the quarters were without a chimney or a window, with no lights or water supply, and no sanitary arrangements. Conditions can hardly be better now, since living costs have gone up more rapidly in intervening years than wages, and the urban population has increased, while little new housing has been erected.[6] Every city, at least during the present century, has had a large number of

[5] Reprinted by permission of the publishers from Brown, *op. cit.*, pp. 15–17. Two editorial footnotes have been added. More recent statistical material has been inserted in brackets in three places without compromising the sense of the original.

[6] *Editorial Note.* A UN source, citing the Indian Ministry of Works, Housing, and Supply, says that in 1951 it was estimated that 2.5 million additional houses would be required to give each household in India a separate house. Later it was estimated that the shortage would be at least twice as great by 1961 despite construction of several million new houses during the intervening period. The same source, citing the United Nations Housing Seminar in Denmark, 1956, country monograph on Pakistan, says: "In Pakistan, according to the 1951 census, only 1.7 million families out of 14 million lived in well-built houses. The rest were living in huts or in temporary tenements, or had practically no shelter at all." Both citations from United Nations, *Economic Survey of Asia and the Far East, 1958*, p. 154.

people with no housing at all, who sleep each night in the open.

In typical village and urban dwellings furniture scarcely exists. A house, or hut, has a fireplace consisting of a few bricks or stones or molded clay set to form three sides of a rectangle over which a pot or pan can be placed; it may also contain a few metal cooking vessels and some primitive implements for farming or the pursuit of a handicraft. That is likely to be all. Scavenging is a function of the village dogs. With these basic handicaps to health go heavy incidence of disease and paucity of preventive and curative medicine.

The combined effect of poor diet, insufficient clothing, substandard housing, lack of medical resources, is a high mortality rate.[7] . . . The brevity and ills of life in India have often been held responsible for her preoccupation with religion, emphasis upon family organization, and intense desire to have progeny and have it early in life, thus conducing to early marriage. In our time they look like an invitation to extremist remedies, such as communism or any other that claims to have a quick cure for social ills.

For some five millennia man in the Indian subcontinent has not merely held his own against the disadvantages which nature puts upon him, but has searched out and utilized means to maintain a life of high achievement in the arts of civilization. If on the spiral of history South Asia once was more accomplished in those arts than the West but now is less so, it may again reach a position of equality. That, at least, is the hope of many citizens of India and Pakistan. But the two young nations started life after a wearying struggle to achieve independence, and a destructive conflict between Hindus and Muslims, the ill effects of which still continue. With no time granted for recuperation, they have had to attack their basic living problems, build new sources of national strength, and assume international responsibilities.

The "basic living problems" which India and Pakistan must attack are among the most difficult and pressing to be found anywhere in the world. Though the various problems are closely interrelated, they may be classified for convenient discussion under the headings of agricultural problems, industrial problems, problems of social relations, and population problems. In the following discussion the major problems are viewed against the general economic and social order and regional articulation of the subcontinent.

## AGRICULTURAL CHARACTERISTICS AND PROBLEMS

From the standpoint of total production of agricultural commodities the Indian subcontinent is clearly one of the world's outstanding agricultural areas, as indeed it has to be to support its immense population even at the present low level of subsistence. It accounts for one tenth or more—in some cases much more—of the annual production of at least seven or eight of the world's major crops and it has over one fifth of the world's cattle. Its enormous cattle population is of limited benefit, however, as will be seen.

### ► *Major Crops of the Subcontinent*

**Major Food Grains**

Somewhat more than half of the crop land in India and Pakistan is devoted to a group of major food grains which furnish most of the calories in the meager diet of the people. In order of acreage these include (1) rice, (2) the combined acreage of various millets and sorghums, and (3) wheat, a poor third in acreage but a much stronger third in total yield. Rice is the leading crop

[7] *Editorial Note.* Different estimates of the annual crude death rate in India for the period 1950 to 1955 vary from about 15 to about 28 deaths per thousand population, and in Pakistan from about 12 to about 30 per thousand. Estimates in the upper part of these ranges seem more likely, and compare with a rate of approximately 9.5 in the United States for the same period. Life expectancy at birth in India and Pakistan is estimated at around 35 years; in the United States at around 71 years. Figures on life expectation in India and Pakistan are scaled sharply downward by infant mortality rates estimated at about 200 per 1000 live births. See United Nations, *Report on the World Social Situation, 1957,* pp. 14–23.

of the subcontinent in both acreage and production. It occupies over 20 percent of the crop land of India and over 40 percent of the much smaller cropped area of Pakistan. The total rice production of the two countries combined amounts to more than one fourth of the world total. Rice is generally preferred as a food over other grains by the subcontinent's people, and under favorable conditions it gives a markedly higher food yield per unit of land than other cereals. Thus it generally dominates agriculture where there is sufficient water and level land. The main rice-producing areas include (1) the delta area of Bengal and the lower Ganges Valley—areas in which unusually heavy monsoonal rainfall is supplemented by floods—and (2) the coastal lowlands fringing both the eastern and western sides of peninsular India. These rice-growing areas are the most productive agricultural sections of the subcontinent, but are not necessarily the best fed, as they are also the most densely populated areas.

Millets and sorghums are grown principally in areas of marginal water supply, where a low rainfall cannot be supplemented by irrigation. The average yield of these grains per unit of land is relatively low—perhaps one third that of rice. Some millets appear to be more nutritive than rice, but rice is generally preferred over them as a food. In the Republic of India the annual production of millets and sorghums combined amounts to about one fifth of the world total, and the total acreage devoted to these crops is greater than the acreage in rice. But they are relatively unimportant in Pakistan, and rice exceeds them in acreage within the subcontinent as a whole. Millets and sorghums dominate the agriculture of large areas in the interior of peninsular India where rainfall and irrigation water are too limited for other grains to thrive. They are supplemented, however, by patches of irrigated rice in local areas where water is more abundant. Millets and sorghums are associated in general with less

productive and less populous areas than those that depend primarily on rice. But even these areas often have an average population density of 200 or more per square mile. In such areas these crops provide a basis for life that other grains could not.

Wheat, the third great food crop of the subcontinent, is grown principally on the northern plain in a belt extending from the Punjab to the middle Ganges Valley. It is the most important food crop of West Pakistan and adjoining parts of India, occupying a larger acreage in those areas than any other crop. Precipitation decreases markedly along the northern plain from east to west until steppe and semidesert conditions are reached in the Punjab, which produces more wheat than any other region of equal size in the subcontinent. (It may be noted that the Punjab formed a single province in the Indian Empire but is now politically divided between India and Pakistan, with much the greater part of the total area and wheat acreage being in Pakistan.) Thus wheat is of greatest importance in some of the driest farming areas of the subcontinent. It is produced, however, not by extensive machine methods, as in semiarid parts of Anglo-America or Australia, but by intensive cultivation of small irrigated holdings. Water is supplied by a system of irrigation dams and canals that may well be the world's largest. Originally a product of British governmental and financial enterprise, this irrigation system is still being extended. During the last 70 years or so, a rapid colonization of the new irrigated lands has taken place. Thus wheat-growing areas which were sparsely populated before the irrigation system was built have now become intermediate in population between the heavily populated rice lands and the millet and sorghum lands of the subcontinent, and the wheat surpluses that the new irrigated sections were able to provide at first have practically vanished. However, the average yield of wheat per acre in the Punjab is nearly twice the average yield of millets and sorghums for the subcontinent as a whole, and the average population density of the Punjab is still well below that of the rice lands. Thus the Punjab is a relatively well-fed and prosperous part of the subcontinent.

**Minor Food Crops**

Minor food crops in the subcontinent are legion. Outstanding among these are various kinds of peas and beans and a variety of oilseed crops. Peas and beans are widely grown over the subcontinent and supply vegetable protein in an area where meat is not plentiful. These legumes grow reasonably well under unfavorable conditions of soil and climate, and they benefit the soil by adding to its nitrogen content. Oilseeds are also widely produced, although the main crop in this group, peanuts, is concentrated largely in peninsular India. Oilseed crops supply cooking oil for the households of the subcontinent and are a considerable export item. Corn, barley, sugar cane, coconuts, bananas, spices, and a long list of other minor crops are grown. The over-all magnitude of the subcontinent's agricultural production is reflected in the fact that the total output of one of these "minor" crops, sugar

Immense quantities of low-grade cane sugar are produced for household use in the Indian subcontinent. The bullocks in the photo are supplying motive power for a small sugar-cane press. The crushed cane pulp in the foreground will be used for fuel. (Foreign Agricultural Service, U. S. Department of Agriculture.)

cane (photo, left), amounts to well over one tenth of world production and ranks India second only to Cuba as a cane producer. The middle Ganges plain is the most important producing area.

### Industrial and Export Crops

Cotton, jute, and tea are the principal crops grown in the subcontinent for industrial use or export. India has the largest cotton acreage of any country in the world, although her average yield per acre is so low that she ranks only fourth in total cotton production. Indian cotton is a small-farm crop, grown mainly in the interior Deccan on certain soils that are unusually retentive of moisture and produce a crop without irrigation. India's large textile industry absorbs most of the country's production of raw cotton and requires supplementary imports, part of which come from Pakistan. Small farmers growing cotton by irrigation in the Punjab and the lower Indus Valley make Pakistan a considerable producer, though its total output is much smaller than India's. With a much smaller textile industry, however, Pakistan is an important exporter of raw cotton.

Two thirds or more of the world's jute, the principal raw material for burlap and gunny sacking, is produced annually in the Ganges-Brahmaputra delta region. The canelike jute plant is grown in several feet of water and requires a long growing season with high temperatures. Its production also requires much hand labor. Thus it is well suited to the delta region, which is tropical, practically amphibious, and settled by a dense agricultural population. The plant became the commercial mainstay of the area in the nineteenth century, after British entrepreneurs had developed the necessary technology. The Ganges-Brahmaputra delta lies in the former British province of Bengal, which was partitioned between India and Pakistan at the end of British rule. Most of the jute-growing areas went to East Pakistan, while the jute-manufacturing plants,

which had developed in the Calcutta area, went to India. Since partition, India has markedly increased the production of raw jute on its side of the border, though its total output is still far less than that of Pakistan, and it imports sizable quantities of raw fiber from the latter country. Pakistan supplies around nine tenths of the world's total exports of raw jute, and nearly half of its export revenues come from this source.

Of the three major commercial crops in the subcontinent, only tea is exported from the Republic of India on a sizable scale. But in tea growing and exporting India leads the world, accounting for more than one third of world production and exports. Tea is India's largest single export. Unlike cotton, jute, and most other crops of the subcontinent, tea is principally a plantation crop. The plantations were developed and are still mainly owned by British interests. Production centers in the northeastern province of Assam, with a secondary center in the mountainous Nilgiri "Hills" and adjacent mountainous sections in the far south of peninsular India. Development of tea plantations in both Assam and south India was favored by the availability of lands which were lightly occupied, reasonably fertile and well-drained, and supplied with ample moisture by a heavy rainfall.

### ▶ General Aspects of the Agricultural Situation

The huge and varied agricultural production of the subcontinent must, unfortunately, be balanced against the fact that approximately one sixth of the world's people live there and support themselves primarily by farming. The average production per man and per acre is abysmally low, despite the pressing need for food that is indicated by chronic undernourishment of large segments of the population (probably the majority) in India and Pakistan, coupled with periodic famines in various areas.

The magnitude of the subcontinent's food problem is perhaps not fully apparent until it is realized that the average inhabitant is more poorly fed today than was the case some decades ago. It has been estimated that in 1941 the production of food grains in the Indian Empire was still at the same general level that it had been in 1921, despite the fact that population had increased during this period from 306 to 389 million. An estimate for the Republic of India indicates that total food production in the area which India now occupies increased about 23 percent between 1936–1938 and 1956–1957, but that during the same period population increased by about 29 percent. Thus the trend of *per capita* food production in both these periods was downward, though increasing food imports appear to have maintained the average diet in India and Pakistan as a whole at approximately the same low level as in the 1930s. A hopeful element in the situation may lie in the fact that most of India's reported increase in food production has taken place since 1950, after a long period of relative stagnation or decline. This may conceivably portend a new pattern for the future. However, there is considerable evidence that much of the increase was really due to improved or changed methods of statistical reporting, together with better than average weather conditions between 1950 and 1956–1957.

### ▶ Low Productivity of the Individual Farmer

The shortage of food and the extreme degree of rural poverty over the subcontinent are closely related to the individual farmer's lack of productivity. One of the reasons for the latter is the small size of farms. In the years between 1891 and 1941 the average size of farm in that part of the subcontinent for which statistics are available decreased from 2.23 acres to 1.90 acres, and this trend has apparently continued. Many "farms" total less than a single acre. Many peasants have been detached completely from the land and have come to form a growing landless rural "proletariat."

Even if the individual farmer were able to make the most of his small holding his total production could not be large, but this is far from the case. His time is often wasted in traveling between parts of his holding which are widely separated, for fragmentation of farms into numerous small, separated plots has been the rule. Cases are recorded where one acre has been split among the holdings of sixteen different cultivators. The efficiency of his labor is decreased by lack of adequate equipment. It has often been noted that the plows of many farmers in the subcontinent are no more than iron-shod sticks which merely scratch the soil rather than turn it over. Tillage is retarded in some areas by lack of adequate draft power, despite the huge number of cattle, principally oxen and water buffaloes, whose primary function is to serve as draft animals. The Hindu prohibition on the killing of cattle and the lack of scientific animal husbandry combine to keep great numbers of useless animals alive which compete with work animals for the sparse forage. A large but undernourished and relatively ineffectual animal population is the result.

On his small holding the farmer of the Republic of India obtains some of the world's lowest crop yields. Rice yields in India appear to be among the lowest in the Orient—approximately half the average yield in China and one fourth the average yield in Japan per unit of land. Wheat yields averaging 10 to 11 bushels per acre are the lowest for any major producer and among the lowest anywhere. Yields in Pakistan are generally somewhat better than in India, but still below the world average. Such low yields are the result of poor techniques of cultivation, lack of scientific seed selection, moisture deficiencies, and the poverty of the soil. Most of the soils now in use have been intensively worked for many centuries

come in reconciling the aims and aspirations of sharply divided groups within their respective countries, as well as in creating satisfactory relations between the two new countries themselves.

## ▶ Religious Divisions and Conflicts

The major social divisions within the subcontinent are in religion and language. Of these, religious divisions have generally appeared the more important and have received more attention. The most serious division has been between the two major religious groups, the Hindus and the Moslems. Hinduism is a religion native to the subcontinent and was the dominant religion at the time Islam made its appearance. It has continued to have the largest number of adherents. Hindus are estimated to number about 350 million at the present time as compared with around 110 million Moslems.

Islam made its appearance in the subcontinent as a proselytizing and conquering religion in the eighth century A.D. Periodic later invasions penetrated the relatively weak northwestern frontier until at the peak of Islamic power in the sixteenth and seventeenth centuries the Mogul Empire dominated most of the subcontinent. British penetration of India was aided by the internal disintegration of this Moslem empire in the eighteenth century.

Seldom have two large groups with such differing beliefs lived in such close association with each other. To Islam's uncompromising monotheism and insistence on uniformity in religious beliefs and practices, polytheistic Hinduism opposes the view that a variety of religious observances is consistent with the differing natures and social roles of human beings. To Islam's essential intolerance of all other faiths, Hinduism opposes an essentially tolerant attitude. To Islam's belief in its divine mission to convert all men to the true religion, Hinduism opposes the belief that proselytizing is essentially useless and wrong. To Islam's democratic belief in the essential equality of all believers, Hinduism opposes a social system founded on the inequalities of caste. To Islam's use of the cow as food and for sacrifice, Hinduism opposes the view that the cow is an especially sacred animal and must under no circumstances be killed. The exuberant and noisy celebrations of the Hindu faith are a great contrast to the austere and silent ceremonials of Islam. Bloodshed has sometimes resulted when a Hindu parade with its jingling bells and firecrackers disturbed the solemnity of Moslems gathered for a particularly sacred religious rite.

The antagonism to be expected between such differing groups was intensified when the formerly subordinate Hindus came, under the British occupation, to dominate most Indian business as well as the civil service. Many Moslems feared the results of being incorporated into a single state with the Hindu majority, and their demands for political separation led to the creation of two independent states from the Indian Empire rather than one. The creation of Pakistan in two widely separated parts was due to the distribution of the main areas of predominantly Moslem population at the time of partition. Immediately preceding and following partition violence broke out between the two peoples on a huge scale, and hundreds of thousands of lives were lost in wholesale massacres before the new governments could establish control. Mass migrations between the two countries involved some 12 million people, most of whom became a burden on the country of their choice until they could be resettled and integrated into the life of their new communities, a task not yet entirely finished.

Partition of the subcontinent has left a minority of a few million Hindus in East Pakistan and probably 40 to 50 million Moslems in India. In addition, India has religious minorities of some importance in about 9 million Christians, living mainly in the south of the peninsula, and about 7

Cows, held sacred by Hindus, may frequently be seen on the sidewalks and streets of Indian cities. Those in the photo are on the sidewalk of a business street in Calcutta. (John Morgan of the Charleston, W. Va., *Gazette*.)

million Sikhs, concentrated mainly in the Punjab. Smaller numbers of Jains, Parsees, Jews, and Buddhists are present, mainly in India. Perhaps the most significant, though not the largest, of these groups is the Parsees. Though numbering only somewhat over a hundred thousand, mainly in Bombay, this group has attained wealth and economic power in India far out of proportion to its numbers. The Parsees derive originally from Persia, although the group has been in India for more than a thousand years. Their religion is the ancient Persian faith of Zoroastrianism.

## ▶ The Kashmir Question

The great religious conflict of the subcontinent between Moslems and Hindus has now been principally transmuted into a problem of international relations between India and Pakistan. Cooperation, especially in the economic sphere, is in the interest of both nations, but a heritage of ill will has yet to be overcome. Relations between the two countries are particularly disturbed by the fact that partition cannot yet be regarded as complete, since the fate of an important part of the subcontinent still hangs in the

4. Occurrence in some areas of uplifted coral platforms which weather into a superior soil.

A few areas of Southeast Asia exhibit fairly dense populations without any corresponding soil superiority. Such areas are ordinarily characterized by a plantation type of agriculture based on crops adapted to poor soils, such as rubber.

Side by side with the present areas of dense settlement, some of which are seriously overcrowded, are sizable areas still undeveloped despite the fact that they apparently are capable of supporting large populations. Their development must wait until the need for their utilization becomes sufficiently great and the available resources sufficiently large to encourage large-scale clearing of forests, draining of swamps, and construction of irrigation systems. It also must await the initiative and resourcefulness of a sufficient number of people who are willing to leave established homes and accept the risks of pioneering in areas often plagued by relatively low and undependable rainfall and/or malaria.

The typical inhabitant of the present areas of permanent sedentary agriculture is a subsistence farmer whose main crop is wet rice, grown with the aid of natural flooding or by irrigation. In some drier areas unirrigated millet or corn, the latter especially in Indonesia and the Philippines, take the place of rice. The major crop is supplemented, to a degree tending to vary positively with the pressure of population, by secondary crops which can be grown on land not suited for rice or other grains. Prominent secondary food crops include coconuts, yams, cassava, beans, and garden vegetables. If the year is a good one, a portion of the produce may be sold, and some farmers grow a secondary crop such as tobacco, coffee, or rubber primarily for sale. Fish are an important component of the food supply and a considerable source of income, not only along the coasts but also inland along streams and lakes. Many fish are harvested from artificial fish ponds.

## ▶ The Role of Commercial Agriculture

Subsistence production in Southeast Asia exists side by side with an important development of commercial agriculture, directed mainly toward supplying commodities for export. The region is one of the world's major supply areas for tropical plantation crops as well as a supplier of surplus rice to other parts of the Orient. These commercial elements in Southeast Asian agriculture are principally the result of Western colonial enterprise in the region.

European imperialism in Southeast Asia began in the sixteenth century. Until the nineteenth century, however, the principal interest of the newcomers lay in the region's strategic location on the route to China, and they were generally content with effective control over scattered patches of land along the coasts and with gleaning for trade such surpluses of value as the native economies happened to offer. But during the nineteenth century increasing populations and an expanding technology in Europe and North America greatly enlarged the demand for products of tropical agriculture. Consequently, effective European political control was forcibly extended over almost the whole of Southeast Asia, and European capital and knowledge were applied to bring about a rapid increase in production for export. Certain indigenous commodities, such as copra and spices, were given increased emphasis, and a number of entirely new crops were introduced, a case in point being the rubber seedlings smuggled out of Brazil in 1876 and introduced into Malaya in 1879.

The usual method of introducing commercial production was to establish large estates or plantations managed by Europeans but worked by indigenous or imported Oriental labor. Development of these large commercial farming enterprises was assisted not only by the favorable climate, but also by the availability of land in a relatively empty part of the Orient and by the amphibious nature of the topography, which made possible a close dependence on cheap, efficient, and easily established transportation by water. The major difficulty to be overcome was in most cases the recruitment of an adequate labor force from a population already fully engaged in food production and not sufficiently pressed by poverty and hunger to be easily attracted from the communal life of the villages into labor for wages on the plantations. The eventual solution to the latter problem in many areas was large-scale importation of contract labor from India and China.

Plantation activity came to have widespread repercussions on the economic life of the natives themselves, for many native farmers and ex-estate laborers learned by example and entered commercial production on their own account. Even shifting cultivators could plant a few rubber trees and return when the trees reached the producing stage, 7 to 10 years later, to tap them for latex if the price warranted. Smallholders of the foregoing types now command an important share in the export production of most plantation commodities.

Many different plantation-type commodities have been produced in Southeast Asia on a medium to large scale at one time or another. Wide fluctuations have occurred from time to time in the crops grown, the centers of production, the amounts exported, and the prosperity of the producers. These shifts have been occasioned by such factors as fluctuating world demands, intraregional and interregional competition, changing political conditions, and the occasional ravages of plant diseases. This general situation has prevailed not only in Southeast Asia but in plantation areas throughout the tropical world. Excluding rice, the major agricultural exports from Southeast Asia together with the main producing countries at the present time are indicated in Table 17. A smaller development of some of the major commodities listed in the table has occurred in various Southeast Asian countries other than those indicated. In addition, a variety of other products such as tobacco, kapok, cinchona (the natural source of quinine), spices, and sisal enter the total export picture. In the supply of some of these lesser commodities such as kapok, cinchona, and certain spices, Southeast Asia is the world's leading region.

Political convulsions since 1941 have effected great changes in the commercial

TABLE 17

EXPORTS OF MAJOR SOUTHEAST ASIAN PLANTATION-TYPE AGRICULTURAL
COMMODITIES

| COMMODITY | APPROXIMATE PERCENT OF WORLD EXPORTS ORIGINATING IN SOUTHEAST ASIA | PRINCIPAL EXPORTING COUNTRIES IN SOUTHEAST ASIA WITH APPROXIMATE PERCENTAGE OF WORLD EXPORTS |
|---|---|---|
| Rubber | 85–95 | Malaya: 35–45 <br> Indonesia: 25–35 |
| Tea | 35–45 | Ceylon: 30–40 <br> Indonesia: 5–10 |
| Copra | 80–90 | Philippines: 50–60 <br> Indonesia: 10–20 |
| Coconut oil | 60–70 | Malaya: 20–30 <br> Philippines: 20–30 |
| Palm oil | 30–40 | Indonesia: 20–30 |
| Sugar | 5–10 | Philippines: 5 |
| Abaca | 85–95 | Philippines: 85–95 |

agriculture of this region. Especially notable has been the great decline and only partial recovery of Indonesian export production as a consequence of war and revolution, coupled with the new government's emphasis on increased production of food for use within the country. Prior to World War II Indonesia was second only to Cuba as a sugar exporter and second only to the United States as a tobacco exporter, but postwar exports of both of these commodities have been relatively insignificant.

## ▶ Commercial Rice Farming

One very significant aspect of Western influence on the economy of Southeast Asia has been the stimulation of commercial rice farming in certain areas that were formerly unproductive. The development of plantation agriculture, mining, and trade provided a market for rice by bringing into existence a large class of people who worked for wages and had to buy their food. During the same period Western economic, medical, and sanitary innovations helped bring about an enormous increase in Oriental population generally and a growing demand for food. Western technology made possible the bulk processing and movement of rice, and aided in the development of drainage, irrigation, and flood control facilities needed to produce it on a large scale in areas previously undeveloped. As a consequence of these developments an Asian pioneer movement took place into certain areas capable of greatly expanded rice production. Among these latter areas three have gained outstanding importance in commercial rice growing: the deltas of the Irrawaddy, Chao Praya, and Mekong rivers, located in Burma, Thailand, and South Vietnam and Cambodia, respectively (map, p. 376).

Almost impenetrable swamps and uncontrollable floods had kept these deltas thinly settled previously, as other swampy areas in Southeast Asia are today, but adequate incentives and methods for pioneering have turned them into densely settled areas within the past century. Despite growing populations, the farms in these areas are larger than is common in the Orient, and the surplus of rice is such that 60 percent or more of the world's total rice exports generally originate in the three deltas. In the years before World War II Burma ranked first among the world's rice exporters, generally accounting for about a third of the world total, and was followed by Thailand and French Indochina (which then controlled the Mekong delta), each supplying approximately 15 percent of world exports. Unsettled conditions in Burma and Indochina during the war and postwar periods led to a serious decline in rice production and exports. Indochina's production and exports were still far below prewar levels in the late 1950s. Thailand, on the other hand, has experienced fewer political and military difficulties and has been able to greatly expand its output and exports of rice. In 1957 Burma accounted for 31 percent and Thailand for 28 percent of the world's total rice exports, while the combined exports of Cambodia and South Vietnam (which share the Mekong delta) amounted to an additional 7 percent of the world total.

These exports of the basic food of the Orient go mainly to India, Pakistan, Japan, and Hong Kong, or to other nations within Southeast Asia. City populations, especially near the coast, and laborers in plantation and mining areas are the principal consumers of imported rice. The vital need for such imports to make up for deficiencies in domestic production has given Burma, Thailand, and the lower Mekong states great significance in the eyes of other Oriental nations, and indirectly in the eyes of all nations interested in Oriental affairs. Nor is that significance lessened by the fact that full development has not yet been reached in any of the surplus rice-producing areas.

### ▶ Production and Reserves of Minerals

Southeast Asia has considerable mineral wealth, much of which remains essentially unexploited. Tin and petroleum are the principal minerals to be exploited thus far. This region produces and exports about half of the world's tin: 25 percent from Malaya, 15 percent from the islands of Bangka and Billiton in Indonesia, and most of the rest from southern Thailand. Oil is produced on the islands of Sumatra, Java, and Borneo in Indonesia, the region's main producing country, as well as in British Borneo, Burma, and Netherlands New Guinea, but the total regional production amounts to only about 2 percent of the world total. However, added significance is given to Southeast Asian oil by the possibilities of expansion and its status as the most important source between the Persian Gulf and California.

About 3 percent of the world's bauxite is produced in the Riouw Archipelago of Indonesia or in Malaya, and about 10 percent of its chromite in the Philippines. Iron ore is fairly abundant in the region. It is exported from Malaya and the Philippines in relatively small quantities, and is worked on a very small scale in Thailand and North Vietnam. In addition, there are present in the region, and often worked on at least a minor scale, a great range of other mineral resources: gold and silver; the alloys tungsten, nickel, and manganese; the major non-ferrous metals lead, zinc, and copper; and others.

Production of minerals thus far has been almost entirely for export, with western Europe, Japan, and the United States representing the principal markets. Use of Southeast Asian mineral resources for industrialization within the region itself would face the handicap of a shortage of coal suitable for large-scale metallurgy. Lignite is present, especially in Burma and Thailand, and low-grade bituminous coal is mined in Sumatra, Borneo, and the Philippines, but the only metallurgical coal known to exist in quantity in the region is the anthracite of North Vietnam. Electricity produced from low-grade coal and lignite and by utilization of the region's sizable resources of water power, although a necessity for future industrial development, could hardly replace metallurgical coal in heavy industry. Nevertheless, Southeast Asia appears to have the resources for a considerable expansion of both mining and manufacturing, in addition to its undoubted and perhaps more important potential for further expansion of agriculture. But like most underdeveloped areas, this region faces serious problems in securing the necessary labor, capital, and markets to make economic expansion a success.

## DISTINCTIVE QUALITIES OF THE INDIVIDUAL COUNTRIES

While the countries of Southeast Asia have many broad similarities, each also has its own distinctive qualities. Each exhibits a different combination of environmental features, native and immigrant peoples, economic activities, and culture traits. Many of the dominant characteristics and problems of these countries are the outcome of 400 years of European imperialism, but in no two countries have the influences and results of imperialism been the same. The following brief portraits of the major countries in the region will perhaps be sufficient to give an idea of the distinctive characteristics of each.

### ▶ Ceylon

The island of Ceylon consists of a coastal plan surrounding a knot of mountains and hill lands in the south central part. Most of the people live either in the wetter southwestern portion of the plain, in the hilly areas of the south center, in the dry Jaffna Peninsula of the north, or in a limited area on the east central coast. Coconuts and rice are the major crops of the low southwestern coast and Jaffna Peninsula, while tea and rubber plantations dominate the economy of the uplands. Colombo (829,000; unless otherwise noted, city populations in this chapter are metropolitan area estimates), in the southwest, is the capital, chief port, and only large city.

Centuries of recurrent invasion from India were followed by Portuguese domination in the early sixteenth century, Dutch in the seventeenth, and British from 1795 until 1948. In the latter year Ceylon was granted independence as a dominion in the British Commonwealth. This eventful history plus the island's long-standing commercial importance on the sea route around southern Asia has given Ceylon a polyglot population. The two major ethnic groups, distinguished from each other by language and religion, are the predominantly Buddhist Sinhalese, making up about 70 percent of the population, and the Hindu Tamils, constituting about 20 percent. The Tamils, whose main center of settlement is the Jaffna Peninsula, are descendants of early invaders and more recent imported laborers from southern India. In addition to the numerically superior Sinhalese and Tamils, there is a remnant of Arab population and the Burghers, descendants of Portuguese and Dutch settlers. About 10 percent of the people are Moslems and about 5 percent Roman Catholics. In the interior a few thousand tribesmen known as Veddas practice shifting cultivation. There is some antagonism among the various ethnic groups; in recent years the Sinhalese majority and the Tamils have often been at odds politically, and rioting between the two groups has occurred.

The economy of Ceylon is rather highly commercialized, with three export crops—coconuts (1,230,000 acres), rubber (665,-000 acres), and tea (573,000 acres)—occupying over half of the land under cultivation. Most of the remaining acreage is in rice, but the production is insufficient to feed the growing population of Ceylon, and considerable amounts of rice are imported. Much potential agricultural land is currently unused, and the government is attempting to reduce food imports by expanding rice production through the establishment of modern irrigation works. Relatively prosperous export industries and stable political conditions seem to favor these and other forward-looking projects. However, an increase in the island's total population from 5.3 to 9.6 million since 1931 has considerably aggravated the food problem.

### ▶ Burma

Burma centers in the basin of the Irrawaddy River and includes surrounding uplands and mountains. Within the basin are two distinct areas of dense population: the Dry Zone, around and south of Mandalay (city proper, 190,000), and the Delta, focusing on the capital and major seaport of Rangoon (city proper, 775,000). The Dry Zone has been the historical nucleus of Burma. The annual rainfall of this area (35 inches at Mandalay) is exceptionally low for Southeast Asia and there is a dry season of about 6 months (Table 15). The people are supported by mixed subsistence and commercial farming, with millet, rice, cotton, beans, peanuts, and sesame as major crops. During the past century the Dry Zone has been surpassed in population by the Delta, where a commercial rice-farming economy now supplies most of the country's exports. The Irrawaddy River forms a major artery of transportation uniting these two core areas.

The native Burmese, most of whom live in the Irrawaddy Basin, number only about 70 percent of the country's total population. Prior to World War II around 1 million Indians (about equally divided between Hin-

Index map of the Southeast Asian mainland

cent of its total population adhering to this religious faith.

Burma was conquered piecemeal by Great Britain in three wars between 1824 and 1885. In 1948 it abandoned all formal ties with Britain and became an independent republic. Japanese conquest and Allied reconquest in World War II were succeeded by a period of civil war following the establishment of an independent Burma. At one time no less than eight different rebellions were in progress. Communist agitation has been an important cause of disaffection, and also ethnic separatism, especially among the Karens. The country is being gradually reduced to order, but its economy has been badly damaged. Shipments of rice, principally to India, Japan, Malaya, and Indonesia, currently account for more than three fourths of all exports by value.

## ▶ *Thailand*

Thailand, formerly known as Siam, centers in the delta of the Chao Praya River, often referred to as the Menam (a Thai word meaning river; the full name as used in Thailand is Menam Chao Praya). The annual floods of this river irrigate the commercial rice production that forms the mainstay of the country's economy. More than nine tenths of all cultivated land in Thailand grows rice, and this one product constitutes almost three quarters of all exports by value. Rubber, accounting for about one fifth of total export value, tin, and teakwood are the other main exports. On the lower Chao Praya in the most densely populated part of the country is the capital, main port, and only large city, Bangkok (1,484,000). Areas outside of the delta region are more sparsely populated, largely by sedentary farmers, although some shifting cultivators are present. These areas include mountainous territories in the west and north, inhabited mainly by Karens and a variety of mountain tribes, and the dry Korat Plateau to the east, populated by the Thai and related Laotian and Cambo-

dus and Moslems) lived in the Delta as laborers, merchants, moneylenders, and owners of farm land, much of it rented to Burmese tenants. The number of Indians is apparently less at present due to a homeward migration to India during the war. The Shan Plateau to the east is inhabited by two distinct groups, each accounting for between 5 and 10 percent of the country's population—the Shans to the northeast and the Karens to the southeast and in the delta of the Salween River. Some of these people eke out a meager livelihood by shifting cultivation in the hills, although the majority are plain and valley dwellers growing irrigated rice. A variety of hill-dwelling tribes inhabit the Arakan Mountains of the west and the northern highlands. Most of these people are shifting cultivators. Burma is predominantly a Buddhist country, with over 80 per-

dian peoples. To the south in the Kra Isthmus, a part of the Malay Peninsula, live some 700,000 Malays. An estimated 95 percent of the population of Thailand adheres to the Buddhist faith, the only significant exception being the Malays, who are Moslems.

The Thai monarchy enjoys the distinction of being the only Southeast Asian country to preserve its independence throughout the period of Western colonialism. Its success appears to have been largely due to its position as a buffer between British and French colonial spheres. A number of border territories were lost, however, mostly inhabited by peoples related to the Thai, and the government of the country has exhibited irredentist tendencies for many years. In return for Thailand's cooperation during World War II, the Japanese allowed the country to take over certain border territories from neighboring countries, but these areas were lost again at the end of the war. Recently there have been border disputes with Cambodia and Laos, not explicitly centering, however, on irredentist claims.

The major ethnic minority of Thailand is Chinese. About 3 million Chinese are resident in the country and are claimed as citizens both by Thailand and by China. The Chinese control much of the country's rice trade and other business, and have extensive interests in the rubber plantations and tin mines of the Malay Peninsula section. This situation has roused a considerable amount of ill feeling on the part of the Thais, and makes the loyalty of the Chinese a matter of considerable importance. Thus far, however, Thailand has escaped serious civil conflict, just as it escaped serious involvement in World War II.

▶ *Vietnam, Cambodia, and Laos*

North and South Vietnam, Cambodia, and Laos are conveniently discussed together, as they are the states which emerged when the former French possession of Indochina disintegrated under Communist and nationalist pressure in 1954. The areas they occupy were conquered by France in stages between 1858 and 1907. In the process, the French extinguished an Annamite empire covering the approximate territory of present-day Vietnam, and defeated the Chinese, whom the Annamese called to their aid. Subsequently two sizable areas—Laos (in 1893) and western Cambodia (in 1907)—were taken from Thailand.

Three distinct regions—Tonkin, Annam, and Cochin China—have long been recognized in the territory now occupied by Vietnam. Tonkin, the northern region, includes the heavily populated delta of the Red River and a surrounding frame of sparsely populated mountains. Annam, in the center, includes the sparsely populated Annamite Cordillera and numerous small, densely populated pockets of lowland along its seaward edge. Cochin China, to the south, is mainly comprised of the Mekong River delta, which has a fairly high density of population. When France attempted to regain control of Indochina after the Japanese occupation of World War II, it was confronted with a strong and militant nationalist movement armed and led by Communists. Eight years of warfare resulted in French defeat in 1954. Vietnam was partitioned between the Communist North (the "Democratic People's Republic of Vietnam"), including Tonkin and northern Annam, and an independent non-Communist South (the Republic of Vietnam), occupying Cochin China and southern Annam.

Cambodia and Laos also became independent non-Communist states as French colonial control ended. Except for Cambodia's short and commercially little developed sea front on the Gulf of Siam (map, p. 368), these two states occupy interior, but very different, regions. Cambodia is comprised principally of plains along and to the west of the lower Mekong River, although it has mountainous fringes to the northeast and southwest. Laos is a very mountainous unit which borders every other country on the Indochinese Peninsula and also Communist China. A sparsely populated, poorly organized, and weak state, Laos has been an object of considerable concern to other non-Communist countries (including the United States), which have feared that it might succumb to pressures from the two Communist states which border it.

A number of different peoples inhabit the four states. However, each state is dominated by a particular people. Nine tenths of the 29 million people in North and South Vietnam belong to the group traditionally known as Annamese, although Vietnamese is now the more common and preferred term. They are closely related to the Chinese in language and general culture, practicing ancestor worship and honoring the precepts of Confucius. Cambodians comprise a majority in their own state (estimated population about 5 million) and also form a considerable minority in adjacent Cochin China. More than a million Thais are distributed almost evenly between Laos, where they form the dominant group, and the mountains of Tonkin. Both Cambodians and Thais are predominantly Buddhist in religion. A variety of primitive tribes in the mountains of Vietnam and Laos aggregate more than a million people. A final element in the four states is comprised of approximately half a million Chinese. Specializing in trade, they have an economic importance far out of proportion to their numbers. Most Chinese are found in the larger cities: Saigon-Cholon (2,000,-000) in South Vietnam, Hanoi (265,000) and Haiphong (186,000) in North Vietnam, Phnom Penh (392,000) in Cambodia, and Vientiane (80,000) in Laos (all figures are estimates for city proper).

France's colonial administration, centered in Saigon and Hanoi, proved relatively ineffective from the standpoint of economic development, though it did succeed in opening the Mekong delta for commercial rice production. Economic functions connected with the rice industry, plus French administrative functions, were largely responsible for the development of Saigon-Cholon as French Indochina's only city of truly large size. The city is located in the eastern part of the Mekong delta. During the period of French control a number of other commercial crops besides rice were introduced in Indochina, both into native small-farm production and into plantation agriculture. None of these attained a really large export production. The area's substantial mineral resources were developed either on a small scale or not at all.

Since independence the four states have followed varying economic paths as they have attempted to recover from the extensive damage inflicted by eight years of conflict and to reach higher levels of national power and public welfare. South Vietnam and Cambodia have concentrated largely on resuscitating and expanding their agriculture, settling new or abandoned lands, and rebuilding their rice exports. Both states have received large amounts of American economic aid. Laos has received, at least on a per capita basis, even more massive American support, but its domestic economy remains relatively primitive, and its international trade, which includes a tiny export of tin, is very scanty. North Vietnam is developing its economy along Communist lines and with Chinese and Russian support. Agriculturally it is the most crowded and hard pressed of the four Indochinese states. But it contains the largest reserves of known mineral wealth—including the best coal deposits in Southeast Asia plus some iron ore, tin, zinc, and other minerals—so that its industrial resources may eventually compensate for its overcrowded agricultural lands.

### ▶ Malaya and Singapore

The small island of Singapore, narrowly separated from the southern tip of the moun-

Communist accession to power in 1949, except in a few scattered areas; and they are still poorly developed in relation to the country's vast size and population despite spectacular growth under the Communist regime. Inadequate transportation has been one of several important handicaps to the development of large-scale industry.

China has been almost continuously involved in wars and revolutions since 1911, although there has been no large-scale fighting since the conclusion of the Korean war in 1953. For about a century prior to World War II it was dominated by various other nations and at times was virtually reduced to a colonial status—a fact which was, and is, bitterly resented by many Chinese. Their resentment has perhaps been intensified by the fact that China is a very old and proud country with a long record of achievement in many fields, although prior to recent years the Chinese did not share to any great degree in the scientific and technological advances which have been so marked a feature of Western culture in modern times.

The foregoing facts have gained added significance for the world at large with the emergence of mainland China as a military power under Communist rule and allied with Soviet Russia. The full meaning of this development has yet to be unfolded, but there can be no doubt that Communist China has become an extremely important factor in world affairs. In the Korean war, which the Communist Chinese entered late in 1950, this Asian country put troops in the field whose performance against a modern Occidental army removed any lingering doubts as to the ability of Asians to make effective use of modern weapons and methods of warfare. Thus under the new Communist regime, China, which had been largely a negative quantity as a military nation in modern times, suddenly thrust itself upon world attention by force of arms. Since then, the country's economic base has been undergoing rapid development, thus adding to China's power potential; and its foreign policy has frequently had a belligerent, aggressive tone. This policy impinges directly on the many different countries or colonies which have a common land frontier with China (map, p. 388); and it is a factor of major consequence in world affairs generally.

## HISTORICAL BACKGROUND

In order to understand the significance of China's new role in the world, a certain amount of historical perspective is needed. This perspective, up to the beginning of war with Japan in 1937, is briefly supplied in the following selection: [2]

### ▶ Early China

The foundations of Chinese history go back many centuries before the Christian era. The unification of the people into an empire came in the third century B.C. Since that time there have been many dynasties, some of them dynas-ties of conquering rulers leading nomadic peoples from the north, some of them native rulers. There were period of weak central government characterized by wars between feudal states. The area known as China has shrunk and grown with the changing fortunes of these dynasties. Under the Mongol rulers of the Yuan dynasty (1280–1367) the boundaries of China were extended to the borders of Europe and encompassed Manchuria, Korea, Indochina, Burma, and Tibet. The Ming dynasty (1368–1644) that followed the Mongol rule was under native sovereigns and in this period some of the conquests of the Mongols were lost. Manchu rule replaced the Mings in 1644 in another period of aggres-

---

[2] *Geographical Foundations of National Power* (Army Service Forces Manual M 103–3). Washington: Government Printing Office, 1944. Pp. 1–3.

One footnote has been omitted and two headings added. Some passages have been updated by words inserted in brackets.

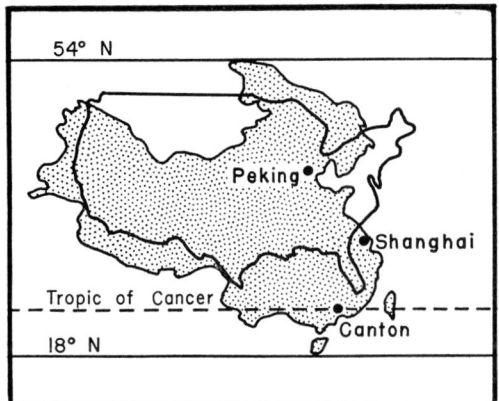

China compared in latitude and area with the continental United States.

sive expansion. Under this rule the boundaries again extended into Tibet, Central Asia, and other areas lost during the Ming dynasty. Much of this territory was very loosely held and allegiance amounted to sending tribute to the Imperial Court at stated times. The Republic of China dates from 1911. In the revolution that brought about this change of dynasty native control was re-established. However, China was subjected to almost continuous civil war from the Revolution [to the outbreak of war with Japan in 1937]. . . .

The civilization that grew within the areas known as China was of a very high order. Learning was held in great regard, and officials were scholars, appointed to their posts under a democratic examination system that was fairly well developed as early as the sixth century. Literature, philosophy, poetry, and the arts flourished and rose to high levels of excellence. An ingenious handicraft system produced objects of great beauty and delicacy as well as sturdy objects for daily use.

Transportation and communications were well organized and amazingly swift. Post offices were set up at short intervals along the main roads and letters were carried by relays of riders on horseback so that the Emperor in Peking was informed within a very few days of events occurring on the outer edges of his empire. This stage post system began in the Han period before the Christian era. Public inns also served the main highways and were open freely to all who had occasion to travel, and there were stores of fodder for the horses. Some of the more important roads were paved with stones. In the Sui dynasty in the sixth century the Grand Canal was built to connect the north and the south. It was rebuilt in the thirteenth cen-

tury by the great Khublai Khan to improve communications between the capital and the Yangtze Valley and to facilitate the administration of the empire. Great use was made of the rivers as means of internal communication. The Yangtze and its tributaries were then, as they are now, important factors in the life of the nation.

The Chinese felt no need of the outside world. Their civilization was superior to that of neighboring lands and was drawn upon and borrowed from by those lands. It reached also into the outside world and influenced distant cultures. Japan took from China her written language and much of her art and literature and industry. Korea also drew heavily on Chinese culture. China gave the world silk and paper and many medicines, the art of printing, the magnetic needle, gunpowder, and many other things. Chinese philosophy reached far beyond the widest borders of the empire.

## ▶ Contacts with the West

Influences from the outside world did come in and affect Chinese culture. Some of these influences came in by way of the conquering barbarians from the North; some came through peaceful trade; some were brought back by Chinese forces that had moved into the outer regions in the waves of empire expansion. Buddhism came from India and Christianity from the West, and they have had a wide and deep influence upon Chinese thinking and upon Chinese art. China also received many gifts from the outside, including cotton, which has become the primary fiber of her economy. By the eleventh or twelfth century, the use of the compass brought more sailing ships to China's shores, and by the sixteenth century contact with Europe by sea had become frequent.

China's self-sufficient economy had little interest in these first visitors from the West and the trade that they wanted. Even later, when the British East India Company tried to develop a trade, because they wanted China's tea and silk, pottery, lacquer, and cotton cloth, there was little besides silver that they could use in exchange—silver and a few luxuries and trinkets like watches and clocks. Their woolen cloth could find no market. The Chinese were not interested in the staple products of the West. America traded ginseng and silver for China's silk and teas in the early trade.

The Chinese were not eager for trade with the West. They erected a barrier to commerce comparable to the Great Wall they had built against the northern invaders in the first years

Soviet Middle Asia. Sinkiang has deposits of coal, petroleum, iron ore, and other minerals. A large expansion of mining and associated manufacturing is planned for the region and apparently well under way.

Economic development in Sinkiang, especially the improvement of transportation, may well serve important Chinese political purposes by tying this remote area more closely to China's core area. The population is predominantly Moslem and of non-Chinese Turkic stock, and has often been restive under Chinese rule. In addition, the region has at times been a debatable territory between China and Russia. It has tended to be drawn into the economic orbit of Russia by the close proximity of Russian rail connections. Sinkiang is now formally ruled by China as an "autonomous region" (the Sinkiang Uigur Autonomous Region), but it is quite possibly under a tighter control by the Chinese central government than it has ever been in the past.

## ► Mongolia

Although it is not politically united, the area north of the Great Wall of China and west of Manchuria, extending northward to the southern border of the USSR, is customarily referred to as Mongolia. This region contains extensive mountainous sections, particularly along its borders with Sinkiang, the USSR, and Manchuria, but also has large plains and long, narrow, mountain-rimmed basins which are occupied by desert or dry grassland. The plains areas are known locally as *gobis,* and have given their name to the Gobi Desert, which occupies much of Mongolia. A large part of Mongolia is included in the Mongolian People's Republic, often referred to as Outer Mongolia. Although the latter area has traditionally been considered a part of China, since 1924 it has been a separate country organized along Soviet lines and under strong Soviet influence. It includes an area of about 626,-

Herding sheep at the base of arid mountains in Sinkiang. Note the sparse pasturage. (Eastfoto.)

000 square miles but is estimated to have only around 1.1 million people.

The part of Mongolia nearest the Great Wall is known as Inner Mongolia and is definitely a part of China. Parts of Inner Mongolia are desert, but immediately north of the Great Wall is a belt of grassland which receives enough rain in wet years for a precarious agriculture. For centuries Inner Mongolia, like other grassland areas along the dry margins of world agriculture, has been a zone of competition and conflict between grain farmers on the one hand and graziers with their flocks and herds on the other.

Prior to World War II Inner Mongolia was considered to include four provinces immediately north of the Great Wall with an aggregate area of approximately 400,000 square miles and a total population of perhaps 7 million. However, the Communist government of China has now established an Inner Mongolian Autonomous Region which includes the major portion of the old Inner Mongolia and also includes areas detached from the western part of what was formerly considered to be Manchuria. This new Autonomous Region had a 1953 census population reported at 7.1 million, four fifths of whom were Chinese. Much of the population is concentrated in irrigated areas along the great northern bend of the Hwang Ho.

## HUMID CHINA

Humid China, the core region of the country, includes the densely settled parts of China south of the Great Wall, and also includes Manchuria. The 18 ancient provinces of China south of the Wall (reduced to 17 in 1959) are often referred to by outsiders as "China proper," although the Chinese themselves do not employ the term. China proper includes two major divisions, North China and South China, which differ from each other in various physical, economic, and cultural respects. Although each area exhibits much variety from place to place, South China may be characterized in general as subtropical, humid, and hilly or mountainous, with irrigated rice as the main crop, while North China is continental, subhumid, has larger stretches of level land, and depends mainly on nonirrigated grain crops other than rice. The North Chinese are typically taller, heavier, more purely Mongoloid, wear warmer clothing during the cold winters, and are popularly considered to be somewhat slower in thought and action and less excitable by nature than the inhabitants of South China. Many more languages and dialects are current in South China than in North China (mainly localized in the hilly coastal districts between Shanghai and Canton), although the majority of Chinese in both areas speak regional varieties of the same basic language. Farms are larger, streets and roads wider in North China, and oxen or camels are the characteristic draft animals rather than the water buffalo of South China.

The two major regional divisions are briefly described in the following selection: [6]

### ▶ North China

North China is subhumid, average annual precipitation ranging from 17 inches in the Loess Upland to 21 inches in the North China Plain. But owing to the very high variability from year to year the area is subject to famine from droughts and floods. The winters are cold, the summers hot. . . . The people depend on wheat, millet, and kaoliang (a sorghum), as their primary food. The great plain of the un-

[6] *Geographical Foundations of National Power, op. cit.,* pp. 1 and 6–8. One footnote has been omitted and one heading added.

ruly Yellow River (Hwang Ho) dominates the region and is densely populated. Chinese civilization originated and developed in this area. . . .

North China . . . comprises two very different subregions: (1) the uplands of the interior and (2) the great alluvial plain of the Hwang Ho, or North China Plain, with the included uplands of Shantung.

### The Uplands

The Hwang Ho (Yellow River), which rises in Tibet, drains the western portion of the uplands; thence it makes a great swing far to the north into the steppes of Mongolia, where it turns back south through the uplands, only to make a right angle bend to the east, 200 miles before flowing out into the plain. The upland area as a whole was the historic frontier zone between China proper and the dry lands of inner Asia. Much of the region is covered with deep deposits of loess, which the Chinese descriptively call "Yellow Earth," an exceedingly fine-grained but fertile soil, laid down by the wind. The scarce and unreliable rainfall renders agriculture precarious, however. In periods of drought famine occurs. Conversely, when a series of years brings more than average rain, much of the steppe borderland can be tilled, and farmers push out into it. . . .

### The North China Plain

The North China Plain [Yellow Plain] is an immense complex delta. The Hwang Ho shifts its course from time to time, reaching the sea first to the north and then to the south of the Shantung hills. Numerous [other streams] and ditches cross the Plain. These waterways are shallow and most of them are fordable and they have generally been diked in an effort to keep them within bounds during flood season. As the [Hwang] deposited silt and debris, the dikes were built higher and higher to keep above the rising water level until the bed of the stream in many sections is above the level of the surrounding country. This situation placed the residents of the area in a precarious position. Few rivers are subject to such violent floods as the Hwang. Hardly any of its waters, shallow and full of shifting sand bars, are navigable for large craft.

The country is so dry that it is a yellow and dusty land except during spring and early summer. There is generally sufficient rain, however, to bring crops to bearing without irrigation. . . .

### ▶ South China

South China is a different world from that of the North. Its abundant rainfall and warmer climate make it lush and green at times of the year when North China is parched with drought or withered with cold. Much of South China is hilly or mountainous. The principal lowlands are the three large basins drained by the Yangtze River and the smaller Canton delta section.

### The Yangtze Basins

The three Yangtze basins are set off from each other by narrows in the river valley. The Lower Basin is a delta merging with that of the Hwang Ho. The Middle Basin is likewise largely built up of river sediments and is flat, low, and dotted with lakes. The soil of these two basins is not quite as fertile as that of the North China Plain, but the more abundant rainfall insures a good crop every year and provides water for the irrigation of rice, which cannot be extensively grown farther north because of the long, cold winters. The third or Red Basin lies farther upstream [in the province of Szechwan; it is] separated from the Middle Basin by a mountain wall through which the river has cut a deep gorge. The Red Basin stands several hundred feet above the Middle and Lower basins and is a land of hills, among which lies the highly productive Chengtu plain.[7]

The Yangtze basins are set off from North China by a combination of barriers. On the east the many rivers and lakes of the delta flats form a considerable obstacle. Farther west, first a range of hills and then the Ch'in Ling (Tsinling) mountains, which rise to more than 10,000 feet, mark the border zone. These barriers are crossed by minor trails in many places, but the main highways . . . are few and have remained little changed since the beginning of China's history. Even the construction of canals and railroads has not altered the pattern of the principal connecting routes. . . .

Throughout its course in China proper the Yangtze River is broad, deep, and, in places,

---

[7] *Editorial Note.* The Basin of Szechwan or Red Basin contains one of the largest concentrations of population in China, currently estimated at 50 to 60 million people. Nature has provided comparatively little level land in the basin, but rice and other crops are grown in enormous numbers of small fields on terraced hillsides.

swift. It is [an important element in] the Chinese communication system. The lower part of its course is paralleled by railroads, but the river itself constitutes the sole through connection between the three basins. It has always carried naval vessels as well as trading ships. Large ocean craft can ascend to Nanking at all seasons. Ships drawing ten feet of water can continue, at all seasons, to [Wuhan], the metropolis of the Middle Yangtze Basin, and river craft drawing seven feet can ascend to Ichang at the foot of the gorge. Chungking, 1300 miles from the river mouth, is [accessible by] small power vessels. The gorge between Chungking and Ichang is hazardous because of rocks, whirlpools, and the swift current, and specially constructed, powerful steamers are required for its navigation. . . .

**The Canton Delta**

The principal river of China's far south is the Hsi, or West, River, a shorter stream than either the Hwang or the Yangtze. Its course is through uplands, except where its delta merges with those of lesser streams to form the Canton delta, a densely populated lowland, smaller in area than those farther north. This lowland, which is separated from the Yangtze by a wide belt of hills and low mountains, was not finally incorporated into China until the time of the Tsin and Han dynasties, nearly 1000 years after the basins of the Hwang Ho and Middle and Lower Yangtze had been consolidated. . . .

**The Hill Lands**

The coastal zone between the deltas of the Yangtze and the Hsi is so difficult to penetrate that it was not annexed to China until the third century A.D. The range of relief is between 1500 and 2500 feet, although some peaks rise to 6000 feet. The rivers are short, swift, and unnavigable, and each basin constitutes a unit isolated except on the seaward side. The size of the towns at the river mouths is limited by the productivity of the basins they serve. Agriculture is restricted to small and scattered valley lands. The coast is dotted with fishing hamlets. This is the only section of China in which the people have taken much interest in seafaring.

Most of Yunnan, the southwesternmost province of China proper, is a deeply dissected plateau some 6000 feet high. In the long history of the southward advance of the Chinese, it was the area most recently penetrated. Many primitive groups still live there unassimilated to the Chinese way of life. . . .

## ▶ Cities of Humid China

Relatively few large cities exist in China, considering the enormous population total of the country. The lack of great metropolitan areas is largely a reflection of the predominantly rural character of China, the country's relatively small foreign trade, and the underdeveloped status of Chinese industry. By far the largest city, and second largest in all Asia, is the major seaport and industrial center of Shanghai (6,204,000), located on a navigable tributary of the Yangtze near the mouth of the latter stream. Three other cities with a million people or more are spaced along the Yangtze. They include (1) Nanking (1,091,000), the capital of Nationalist China prior to 1937 and again from 1945 to 1949, (2) the conurbation of Wuhan (Wuchang, Hankow, and Hanyang, combined population 1,427,000), and (3) Chungking (1,773,000) in the Red Basin, the capital from 1937 to 1945. Two other cities numbering more than a million are found near the northern edge of the North China Plain. They are Peking (2,768,-000), the capital before 1911 and again since 1949, and the important seaport of Tientsin (2,694,000), located around 70 miles to the southeast of Peking. South of the Yangtze the only "million city" of China is the seaport of Canton (1,599,000) in the Hsi delta. A few tens of miles to the south of Canton are the small Portuguese possession of Macao (estimated population 215,000 in 1959) and the vastly more important British colony and entrepôt of Hong Kong (estimated population 2,857,000 in 1959) (see photo and caption, right). Both of these European possessions are overwhelmingly Chinese in population.

A number of large cities in Manchuria are described in the following section.

## ▶ Manchuria

Manchuria is the part of Humid China north of the Great Wall. To the west are the Mongolian steppes and deserts; to the

able to intercede, Japan was able to extort from China numerous economic and political privileges throughout southern Manchuria, placing that area definitely within a Japanese "sphere of interest," though leaving China still the legal sovereign.

6. The Caroline Islands, Marshall Islands, and Mariana Islands. These Pacific island groups were former German possessions, except for the island of Guam in the Marianas, an American possession since 1898. When World War I broke out in Europe, Japan joined the Allied side and seized the German holdings in the Orient and the Pacific north of the equator. The peace settlements after the war confirmed Japanese occupancy of the islands under a mandate of the League of Nations. While the other major powers were embroiled in Europe, Japan was able, in addition, to exert pressure successfully on China for increased economic privileges, especially in Manchuria, Inner Mongolia, and northern China proper. Although Japan had occupied former German-controlled territory in China on the Shantung Peninsula, she was induced by Chinese and international pressure to evacuate that area in 1922.

7. Manchuria. Conquered in the course of hostilities with China lasting from 1931 to 1933. Manchuria became the Japanese protectorate of "Manchukuo." At the same time further Japanese privileges were extorted in Inner Mongolia and northern China proper.

8. Most of northern, central, and coastal China proper. These areas were overrun in 1937 and 1938. The war with China which Japan precipitated in 1937 continued, however, until 1945 without additional significant Japanese gains. Instead, Japan found it difficult to control the territory already conquered due to steadily increasing guerrilla warfare by the Chinese.

9. French Indochina. Occupied without resistance during 1940 and 1941, after the conquest of France by Germany.

10. The empire was brought to its greatest extent by a series of rapid conquests between December 1941 and the summer of 1942, after the Japanese had entered World War II. These conquests included Guam and Wake islands, the Philippines, Hong Kong, Thailand, Burma, Malaya, Singapore, the East Indies, much of New Guinea, the Admiralty, Bismarck, Solomon, and Gilbert islands, and part of the Aleutian chain.

After 1942 Japan was generally in retreat, and 1945 found her shorn of the overseas territories acquired during nearly 70 years of successful imperialism. The motives of Japanese expansionism were mixed, including a tradition of national superiority and "manifest destiny," the desire of military officers to aggrandize themselves and gain complete control of the Japanese government, and a desire on the part of various elements in Japan to gain assured markets for Japanese goods and assured sources of materials. Though the methods of gaining them may have been illegitimate, the desire for materials and markets was solidly based on need. Expansion of industry and population on an inadequate base of domestic natural resources has made Japan vitally dependent on sales of industrial products outside the homeland. Such sales provide the principal funds with which the country purchases the imported foods, fuels, and materials that it requires for its large and growing population and its expanding industries. In its dependence on foreign markets and supplies Japan obviously resembles the United Kingdom.

## THE JAPANESE HOMELAND

Japan is a nation of some 92.7 million people (1959 official estimate) occupying four main islands and numerous smaller islands with an aggregate area of approximately

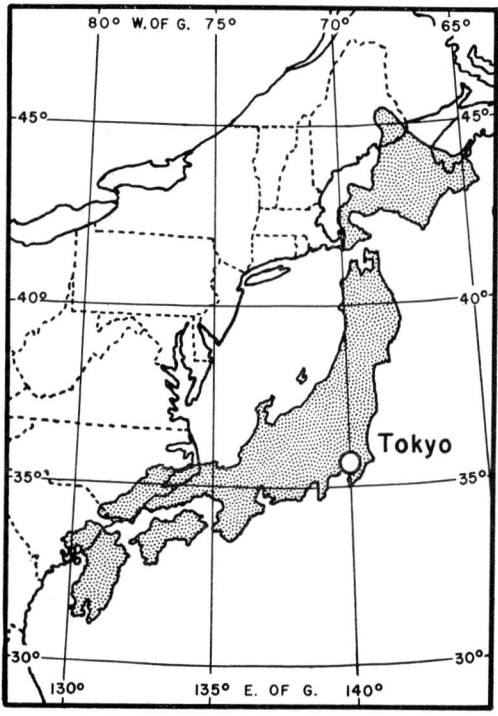

Japan compared with the eastern United States in latitude and area. (After a map by E. O. Reischauer.)

142,800 square miles. The Japanese homeland is briefly described in the following selection: [1]

The homeland of Japan proper consists of four large volcanic islands—Honshu, Hokkaido, Shikoku, and Kyushu [map, p. 408]—and several hundred smaller islands in the same arc-shaped chain.

. . . Honshu, the largest island, has an area a little less than the combined areas of New York and Pennsylvania but with [two and one half times] their population. Hokkaido, lying in about the same latitude as Maine [map, above], has approximately the same area and [five] times the population. Shikoku, in the general latitude of South Carolina, has less than one fourth the area but double the population. Kyushu, between the same parallels as Georgia, has one fourth the area and [three and one half] times the population. . . .

## ▶ Climate and Basic Natural Resources

The climatic conditions in Japan proper are not altogether comparable to those of points in corresponding latitudes in the eastern United States. On the whole, the winters are colder in Japan and the annual precipitation is heavier. This may be accounted for partly by the presence of a cold current which extends farther south in winter than in summer on both sides of the Japanese islands, and by their position in the path of the monsoon winds. Within the islands, differences in latitude produce marked climatic differences, and the great variation in altitude produces much local diversity irrespective of latitude. Along the southern and southwestern shores the climate is humid and subtropical; the winters are mild and the summers uncomfortably hot and oppressive. North of Tokyo the winters grow progressively colder. . . . Seasonal variations are particularly marked in the north and in the interior basins.

Nature was not generous to the Japanese. In a country where [2 out of 5] people engage in agriculture, nearly five sixths of the land is too rugged for cultivation. The Japanese have been able partially to supply themselves with rice and other cereals, but only by the most intensive use of the arable soils. Forests cover [more than] half the land surface but do not supply all the kinds of wood needed. The many varieties of fish in the adjacent seas furnish a large part of the protein food consumed in Japan, as well as a valuable export.

. . . The hydroelectric energy generated from the mountain streams of Japan compensates only in part for the lack of petroleum and the poor quality of the coal. The raw materials for heavy industry are far from abundant. [Half or more of the country's requirements of nearly all the metals, including iron, must be imported.] The cotton textile and rubber manufacturing industries are wholly dependent on foreign sources of raw cotton and raw rubber. . . .

## ▶ Contrasts between North and South

The contrast between areas north and south of the 37th parallel is in part due to differences in

[1] *Geographical Foundations of National Power* (Army Service Forces Manual M 103–2). Washington: Government Printing Office, 1944. Pp. 125–131. Six headings have been omitted and two headings slightly altered. Population figures and comparisons quoted in original source have been brought up to date. One editorial note has been added. The spelling of "Kwanto Plain" has been altered to read "Kanto Plain." Some changes in italicizing have been made and supplementary material has been supplied in brackets in several places.

climate and in part to the earlier settlement of the south. Southern Japan was settled early in the Christian era. There, particularly around the shores of the Inland Sea, the features considered typical of the Japanese landscape are found: a dense population living in lightly constructed dwellings, tiny farms, with fields of paddy rice on the bottomlands, small terraced fields on the hill slopes, and tea gardens and mulberry groves on the uplands. The settlement of the north began much later and proceeded gradually, in spite of the pressure of population and the scarcity of arable land in the south. The expansion of manufacturing after 1868 has been much more significant in the south, and the concentration of population in the lowlands there has been greatly augmented.

▶ *Highlands and Lowlands*

About three quarters of the area of Japan proper is composed of hill land or mountains of which the slopes are usually too steep and the soils too thin for normal cultivation. Scores of volcanic cones in various stages of activity provide some of the highest elevations. The mountain streams are short, swift, shallow, and generally unnavigable. They are chiefly important as sources of hydroelectric power and irrigation water for the populous lowlands.

The typical Japanese plain is an isolated area of alluvial soil deposited by rivers in mountain basins or by rivers and waves in coastal indentations. There is no continuous lowland belt along the shores of the islands. Because of shallowness and divided channels, the lowland streams are of little use for navigation, but their elevated beds make gravity irrigation simple. . . .

The marginal lowlands at the heads of bays or other openings upon the sea contain most of the arable land, most of the population, and the centers of trade, industry, and political and cultural life. Those of the north are less fully developed than those of the south.

▶ *Japan's Core Area*

The core area of Japan . . . is an irregular zone about 800 miles long, extending westward from the Kanto Plain through Nagoya to Osaka and thence along both shores of the Inland Sea to northwestern Kyushu [map, p. 408].

The Kanto (Tokyo) Plain has an importance in the national life comparable in many ways to that of the English Lowland and the Paris Basin. . . . [Tokyo, the national capital, is the largest city in a metropolitan agglomeration which, including Japan's leading seaport, Yokohama (photo, p. 406), and various other satellite and surburban areas, numbered an estimated 11,350,000 in 1955. Only the New York metropolitan area exceeds the Tokyo-Yokohama area in population.] The Kanto Plain on which [the Tokyo agglomeration] stands is the largest lowland in Japan (2500 square miles). . . . Tokyo and Yokohama, both on tidewater, [together with their suburbs] comprise the [leading] industrial center of Japan and the commercial center not only for the plain itself, but for all of northern Japan.[2] The regions to the north and west are tapped by a network of railroads. . . .

South of the Kanto Plain the *Sun-en Coastal Strip* runs along the Pacific shore. This lowland, composed of rather small, isolated deltas separated by spurs of rocky hills, has been for several centuries a thoroughfare between Kyoto and Tokyo. It is traversed by the famous old Tokaido highway and the modern railroad. The mild winters and heavy precipitation in summer have favored the cultivation of mandarin oranges and tea. Half of the Japanese tea crop is grown there and is refined, blended, and packed in the castle town of Shizuoka [city proper, 33,000].

The *Nobi (Nagoya) Plain* which lies at the head of Ise Bay, 160 miles west of Tokyo, is second only to the Kanto Plain in area. Although third in importance as an industrial center, it [is very densely populated]. The harbor of Nagoya [1,500,000] is shallow and silted, and the city, unlike Tokyo and Osaka, lacks a connecting deep-water port.

Farther west, the *Kinki District* at the eastern end of the Inland Sea has the longest record of compact human habitation and contains the earliest capitals. The district is the [second] industrial area of the nation today and the site of three of the largest cities—Osaka, Kyoto, and Kobe.

Osaka [metropolitan area, with Kobe, 6,405,000] is 230 miles west of Tokyo on the bayhead delta of the broad, diked Yodo River and its numerous tributaries. Like Tokyo, the

---

[2] *Editorial Note.* Yokohama developed originally as a deep-water port for Tokyo, which was handicapped by a shallow harbor. However, the harbor of Tokyo itself has now been improved to accommodate most deep-sea vessels. The two cities form a diversified industrial center. Lighter industries predominate, but there is a considerable amount of heavy industry. In parallel fashion, Kobe developed as the deep-water port for Osaka and has now coalesced with it to form a continuous urban and industrial area.

city has a network of canals and a shallow, silted harbor. Many of its modern Occidental buildings are supported on piles or metal drums. Its facilities for water transportation have contributed to the industrial pre-eminence of modern Osaka. So, too, have its excellent rail facilities, its level expanse of plain, and its large labor supply.

Kobe is on deep water, 16 miles down the bay from Osaka. Like Yokohama, its rival deep-water port, Kobe was brought into existence by the demands of the modern commercial and industrial era. It has become a relatively important manufacturing center, specializing in metal industry, especially shipbuilding. . . . The coastal strip on which it is built is too narrow to allow much industrialized settlement, however.

Inland Kyoto [1,437,000], the capital from 794 to 1869, has been little changed by the Industrial Revolution. Large factories are forbidden by law. The city retains much of its ancient splendor, making it a center in peacetime for millions of pilgrims and tourists. The handicrafts of the feudal period—the making of lacquer, porcelain, bamboo articles, cloisonné, bronze, and silk textiles—survive as cottage and workshop industries.

Along the deeply indented shores of the *Inland Sea* there are innumerable alluvial lowlands and river deltas. The sea is, in its way, as historic and beautiful as the Mediterranean. Settlements crowd the diminutive plains and adjacent hill slopes. The density of population and the scarcity of arable land have led to the artificial terracing of the hillsides, sometimes to elevations of several hundred feet. . . . The toil of generations of a single family is recorded in the stones or terraces inclosing a bare half acre of good loam. . . .

The sea varies from 20 to 40 miles in width. . . . Hundreds of small intercoastal and inter-island boats [carry] on a thriving local trade, and the entire length of 230 miles [is] traversed by trans-Pacific steamers and coastwise freighters plying between the coal fields of northern Kyushu and the factories of the eastern cities.

The Northern Kyushu Coastal Strip . . . extending . . . west from . . . the Strait of Shimonoseki holds the greatest concentration of heavy industry in Japan. [At least 3 million people live in a string of medium-sized industrial cities extending from Moji through Fukuoka (659,000) to Nagasaki (334,000). The greatest single agglomeration is formed by the iron and steel center of Yawata, largest in Japan, plus Kokura, Moji, and two other cities on Kyushu, and the city of Shimonoseki on the Honshu side of the narrow Strait of Shimonoseki. Most of the coal for the industries of northern Kyushu] is supplied by the Kyushu mines. Other raw materials—some coking coal . . . , iron ore, pig iron, steel scrap, petroleum, etc.—are brought in by sea. Coal from the Kyushu fields and steel for fabrication are sent out by the Inland Sea route to the Osaka and Nagoya industrial areas and even to Tokyo.

## JAPAN'S POPULATION AND ECONOMY

Although a little smaller in area than the state of California, Japan is the world's fifth most populous country. A population aggregating more than half that of the entire United States must be supported in a nation whose total acreage of cultivated land amounts to only about 24,000 square miles —approximately the area of the state of West Virginia. No other important country approaches the over-all Japanese figure of approximately 3860 people to be supported per cultivated square mile. Furthermore, the Japanese population is currently increasing at a rate of approximately a million a year, and should reach a total of over 100 million by 1970. Although land reclamation on a considerable scale appears possible, the best lands of Japan are already fully occupied, and there seems no real prospect of counterbalancing the rise in population simply through bringing additional land into cultivation. Japan must already import about a fifth of its total food requirements as measured in calories, and could not feed even its

A winter scene in the mountains of western Honshu near the Sea of Japan. The buildings in the picture belong to a hot-spring and ski resort. (Japan Travel Bureau.)

present population from home production except at the barest starvation levels.

A century and a half ago Japan, already a crowded land, had a population now estimated at around 30 million. However, increases in the population were kept in check by disease and starvation and by the almost universal practices of abortion and infanticide.

A rapid growth of population after 1868 was made possible by industrialization, which provided exports of manufactured goods with which to purchase imported food. Industrialization also undergirded the rising military power that enabled Japan to build an empire and thereby to gain assured markets and assured sources of food and industrial materials. Today the country no longer has an empire to exploit, but it must still continue to import foods, fuels, and materials and to find ways to pay for them in the face of stiff competition from other industrial nations in export markets.

Under these conditions it is not surprising that the Japanese are emphasizing additional measures to help solve their food problem, including (1) maximization of agricultural output and (2) birth control. Food production, measured by total calories, had regained prewar levels by the early 1950s, and by the late 1950s was over 40 percent higher. A major factor in the increase was the expansion of irrigated rice acreage. This was accomplished largely at the expense of other cereals, which generally yield no more than half the caloric value of irrigated rice per unit of land. Increased fertilization and the reclamation of a moderate amount of new farm land have been other measures contributing to the rise in agricultural production. Meanwhile, Japan's birth rate of the 1930s has been halved, possibly portending a stabilization of the population within a few decades. Government encouragement of birth control and the country's very rapid urbanization have probably been important factors contributing to the decline of the birth rate.

## ▶ Agriculture and Fisheries

Even for Japan to supply four fifths of its current caloric needs from domestic production has required an intensive agriculture giving some of the world's highest yields, together with associated development of the world's largest fishing industry. More than nine tenths of all cultivated land is devoted to food crops. Irrigated rice is the basic crop nearly everywhere, including most parts of the northern island of Hokkaido. Wherever conditions of climate, water, and soil will permit—which includes the greater part of the irrigated acreage south of 38°N.—double cropping, or the planting of a second crop on the same field following the rice harvest, is practiced. In limited areas of the south where the growing season is unusually long, irrigated rice is grown as the second crop. However, in most areas rice is followed by winter wheat or winter barley, and in some cases by vegetables or white potatoes. Only an estimated 57 percent of the total cultivated area of Japan is irrigated. Crops grown in unirrigated fields include a variety of grains, among which barley and wheat occupy the largest acreages. Various kinds of beans and peas, of which soybeans are the most important, stand next to the grains in acreage planted, and these are very closely followed by potatoes: white potatoes in northern Honshu and Hokkaido, and sweet potatoes in southern Honshu, Kyushu, and Shikoku. Most of the common vegetables are also grown. Double cropping is practiced on nonirrigated as well as irrigated fields wherever possible. Intertillage—the growing of two or more crops simultaneously in alternate rows—is common. Most Japanese farms have at least a few fruit trees. Persimmons, pears, and apples are the most common fruits, although mandarin oranges are widely grown along the Pacific and the Inland Sea south of about 37°N. Specialty crops grown in certain areas include mulberry trees, used for feeding silkworms, and in addition such crops as tea, sugar cane, tobacco, peanuts, flax, hemp, pyrethrum, and peppermint. Sugar beets are raised in Hokkaido, and along the Inland Sea are grown the reeds used for making mats which provide the universal floor covering in homes throughout Japan. On the whole, the variety of Japanese agricultural production belies the customary picture of Japan as almost exclusively a rice-growing country. Nevertheless, rice is a basic component of every Japanese meal, and provides about two thirds of the total calories in the Japanese diet.

Probably no nation surpasses Japan in over-all intensiveness of agricultural development. Farms average only 2 acres in size, except in Hokkaido with its harsher climate, where the average rises to 11 acres. In order to feed his family the Japanese farmer must utilize every means of extracting the highest possible yields from the scanty acreage at his disposal. The prevailing conditions are pictured in the following selection from an important book on Japan by Edwin O. Reischauer: [3]

Japanese methods of agriculture, involving as they do an immense amount of arduous hand labor, seem primitive and inefficient to most Americans. With our simple faith in machinery we often feel that mechanization of agriculture in Japan would not only save labor but would also increase production. Unfortunately, saving labor in a densely populated land like Japan means nothing unless the labor saved can be profitably employed in other tasks, and the concept that production can be increased by mechanizing farming is a complete fallacy as far as Japan is concerned. Tractors are used to a slight extent in the island of Hokkaido, but they are of little use in the narrow hillside terraces and tiny paddy fields that make up so much of Japan's farm land. And even on the broader stretches of flat fields, mechanization of the sort common in this country would on the whole decrease the yield rather than increase it. Machines have not been invented which till the soil as effectively as the great Japanese hoe with its two-foot blade. Nor have machines been invented which can equal the skill and loving care

of the individual farm wife transplanting rice seedlings by hand. It would be as practical to mechanize the growing of flowers around an average suburban home in this country as to mechanize a Japanese farm. Japanese farming is really gardening, with the prolific farmer and his family lavishing as much work and care on each square yard of their land as an American family would on its prize flower bed. . . .

Actually, Japanese farming stands at a high level of achievement, given the special relationship of man to land existing in Japan. The tools and techniques used, while recklessly extravagant of manpower, make the most of every cultivable scrap of land, which is as it must be wherever men are overabundant and land is scarce. Machines are used on a small scale for certain farm tasks but only where they do not reduce the yield. With government aid, better seeds have been developed and are utilized widely. Most important of all, fertilizer, which is essential to make Japan's infertile and overworked soil produce, is used lavishly and when available in close to maximum quantities, considering the cost of fertilizers, which has in recent years risen to about 20 percent of the total cost of agricultural production in Japan. While chemical fertilizers [are used in great quantities] the most universally available and therefore most widely used fertilizer in Japan . . . still is night soil. In the tight Japanese economy nothing can be wasted. As the cities grow, they require more food, but at least they produce in return more night soil with which to grow more crops and incidentally to impart that unfortunate olfactory atmosphere to Japan's farm lands which contrasts so sharply with their pleasant visual impression.

More than nine tenths of the total calories in the Japanese diet are supplied by starchy foods, including rice, other grains, and potatoes. Livestock products are of very minor importance, although dairying has been developed to some degree in Hokkaido. Fish are the principal source of protein and along with rice are an important element in most Japanese meals. A variety of valuable food fish are present in the waters surrounding Japan, and Japanese fishermen range widely throughout the North Pacific Ocean. The an-

[3] Reprinted by permission of the publishers from Edwin Oldfather Reischauer, *The United States and Japan*. Cambridge, Mass.: Harvard University Press, Copyright, 1950, 1957, by The President and Fellows of Harvard College. Pp. 58–59.

nual fish catch considerably exceeds that of any other nation in both tonnage and value.

## ▶ Importance of Forestry and Wood Products

The varied local environments of Japan support a wide range of valuable tree species, including broad-leaved evergreens in southern Japan, a mixture of broad-leaved deciduous and conifers in central and northern Honshu and southern Hokkaido, and conifers in northern Hokkaido and at higher elevations farther south. About three fifths of the entire country is forested, and the Japanese, short of mineral resources, make use of wood in almost endless ways. The largest single use of wood is for fuel, accounting for about two thirds of all the wood consumed in Japan. The significance of forestry and wood industries in Japan has been described by Reischauer: [4]

Next to men and the power resources of coal and water, wood is probably Japan's greatest natural resource. With over half the land devoted to forest, Japan is among the more heavily forested of the civilized countries of the world and unquestionably the most heavily forested of the populous lands. Her poverty in agricultural land has meant a larger proportion of terrain preserved from the farmer's hoe. The country is rugged, but little of it is too high for forest growth, and relatively warm temperatures throughout most of the forest lands plus ample rainfall everywhere mean excellent growing conditions.

But the ratio of men to forest land in narrow Japan, while not so disastrous as the ratio of men to agricultural land, is precarious. The per capita acreage of forest land is only about [one sixth] that of the United States. With timber lands so limited and with so little else to treasure, the Japanese have been forced to tend their forests with a care undreamed of in a land like ours, which has been more bountifully provided by nature. Up until the outbreak of war with China, attempts were made to cut no more than the annual growth, and reforestation over the years had gradually expanded the forest area. In the three southern islands, artificially planted forests account for about one fifth of the total, making curious patterns of symmetri-

cal rows of conifers, like some great corn field, in the mountain fastnesses of Japan. Careful cutting and planting practices have spread over the hills a patchwork pattern of different types and sizes of timber, resembling the patchwork patterns of agricultural land. The ratio of men to land in Japan has left man's imprint even on her wild mountains and rugged hills.

Japan is almost as dependent on a maximum yield from her forest lands as from her farms. While far richer in wood than are many of the lands of Asia and Europe, she depends upon her wood supply for greater and more vital services than does any other nation. The chief of these is for building material. . . . Despite tile, thatch, or tin roofs, mat floors, paper and glass sliding partitions, and walls made in part of mud plastered on bamboo lattice, wood forms the framework and bulk of the building materials in every house. The frequency of serious earthquakes throughout the land makes the utilization of stone or brick for houses somewhat hazardous. Lightly built wooden houses will sway safely with the motion of the tremor, where more rigid walls of stone or brick crack and fall. . . .

As an industrialized nation, Japan needs huge quantities of wood for railroad ties, telegraph poles, and mine timbers. The petty handicraft uses of wood and bamboo, which must be classed with it as a forest product, are numberless. Short of other materials, the Japanese use wood and bamboo for a thousand things for which we can afford to employ more costly materials. Japanese buckets may not be oaken but they are still made of wood. Simple wooden chopsticks take the place of our more complicated cutlery. Bamboo, an unbelievably versatile material, turns up in hundreds of surprising and ingenious uses. Japan also depends on wood, normally converted into charcoal, for what little heating her houses have and for cooking fuel whenever city gas supplies, made from coal, are not available. The Japanese, by holding their hands and wrists over charcoal braziers or by placing their feet in or close to specially designed heating devices, derive a considerable amount of warmth and cheer from a tiny spot of heat in an otherwise frigid house. . . .

And over and above these direct uses of forest products is the growing demand for wood pulp. The Japanese have had a famous paper industry for about a thousand years and have developed some ingenious uses for paper. Pasted on sliding partitions and screens, it is an impor-

---

[4] Reprinted by permission of the publishers from Reischauer, *op. cit.* Pp. 74–77.

# PART 6
## *The Pacific World*

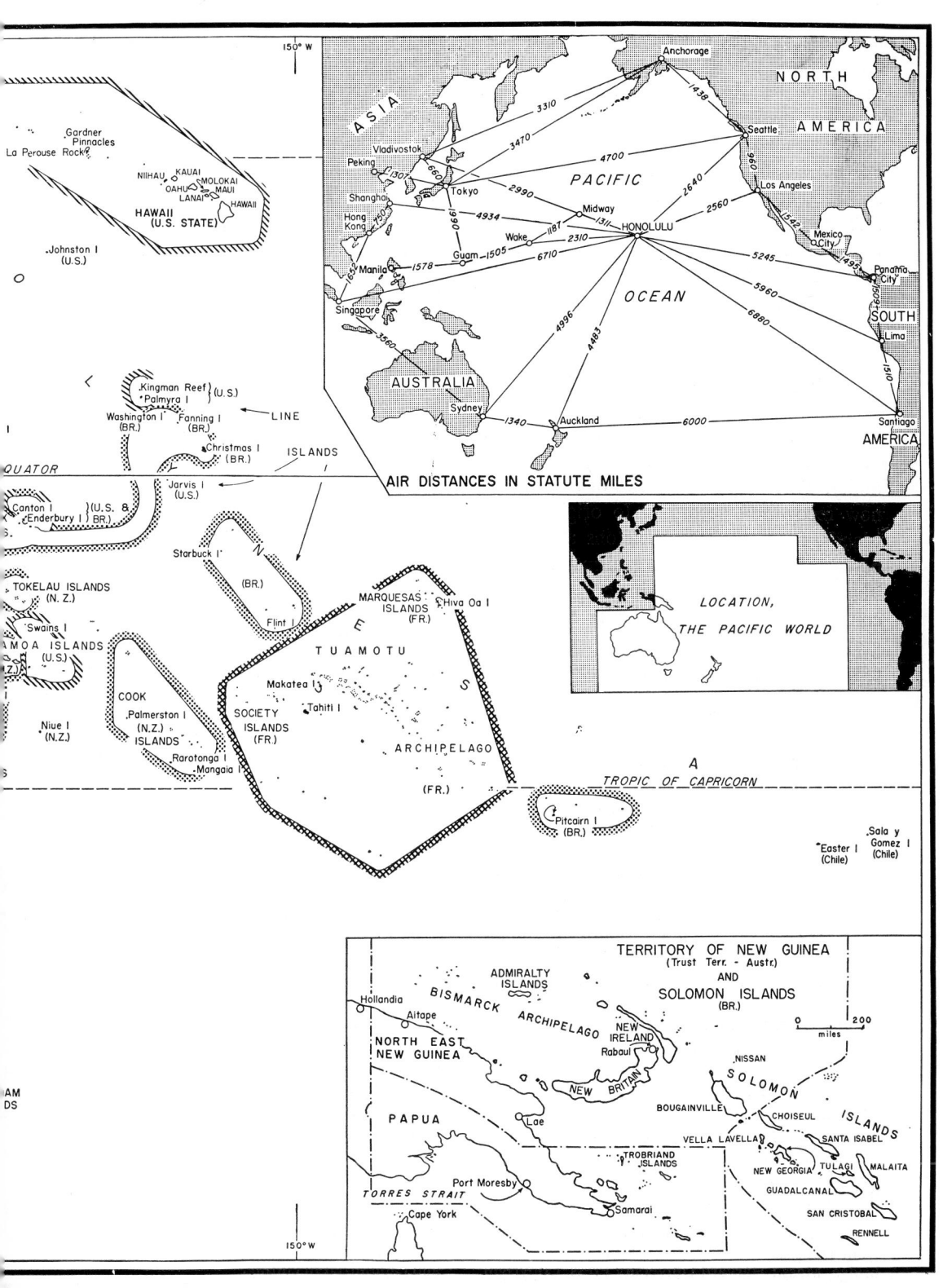

AIR DISTANCES IN STATUTE MILES

LOCATION,
THE PACIFIC WORLD

TROPIC OF CAPRICORN

TERRITORY OF NEW GUINEA
(Trust Terr. - Austr.)
AND
SOLOMON ISLANDS
(BR.)

mixing with earlier immigrants, settled Micronesia and probably Polynesia, as well as mixing with other peoples in the more complex amalgam of Melanesia.

Over a long period the Micronesians and Polynesians became relatively distinct from each other and relatively homogeneous throughout their separate spheres. The people of each area came to speak dialects of a single basic language and to share many features of a common culture. In Melanesia, on the other hand, complex and varied mixing of successive migrant groups has led to an extremely confused racial and cultural pattern. Racially the Negroid element is generally dominant, though often diluted by other elements. A variety of languages and dialects are found, and anthropologists have distinguished literally hundreds of fairly distinct cultures. Some of the tribes, especially in the remote interiors of the larger islands, are extremely primitive.

## TYPES OF ISLANDS

The almost countless islands scattered across the Pacific vary widely in size, type, and utility. Three main categories of islands are now recognized according to origin: coral islands, formed of the skeletons and living bodies of small marine organisms; volcanic islands, formed by submarine eruptions; and continental islands. These major categories, grouped into further subclasses, have been described as follows by an American anthropologist, Douglas L. Oliver, in an outstanding book on the Pacific islands: [3]

From man's point of view, physical setting consists of several elements: the form of the land and the nature of the soil, the quality of the climate, the types and dispositions of plants, and the presence of animal life. In Oceania these components are variously combined to produce seven major types of islands, differentiated according to the limits they imposed upon the islanders and their primitive technologies:

1. *Treeless Atolls or Coral Islands* (typical examples are Canton, Johnston, and Howland islands). Grass and herbs provide survival food for castaways and small parties of fishermen, but the lack of good soil and drinking water renders these land specks unsuitable for permanent native settlements. Sea birds and fish abound and, if drinking water were present, human life could be sustained indefinitely on these islands; but for the most part the vegetation-loving Oceanic natives have avoided them. On the other hand, the very conditions which discouraged native settlers and made these islands bird refuges resulted in the deposit of valuable guano fertilizer and produced ready-made runways for twentieth-century aircraft.

2. *Dry-forest Atolls or Coral Islands* (typical are most of the Marshall and Ellice islands, and many of the Tuamotus and northern Cooks). Strand flora, together with some arable soil and fresh water, make these islands habitable for limited numbers of people; rich marine resources supplement the scanty vegetable and fruit diets. However, overpopulation is a constant threat, and crowded native communities have sought solutions in mass emigration and in infanticide. Yet despite the paucity of resources on these islands, some communities have developed intricate and aesthetically pleasing arts and crafts, utilizing every material at their disposal. They have, moreover, appeared to compensate for the limitations imposed upon their economies by evolving exceedingly complex institutional relations.

3. *Luxuriant, Moist Atolls or Coral Islands* (typical examples are the Gilbert and Tokelau islands, Swains Island, Fanning, Ebon, Ulithi, and Nissan). These are the lush and beautiful "tropical isles" of romantic novel and motion picture. They have sufficient soil to support cultivation of taro and bananas, in addition to the coconut palms and breadfruit also grown on the dry islands.

4. *Raised-coral Islands* (typical examples are Makatea, Niue, Ocean, Nauru, Angaur, Peleliu, and Fais). These islands were formed out of successive elevations of old coral reef and are

---

[3] Reprinted by permission of the publishers from Douglas L. Oliver, *The Pacific Islands.* Cambridge, Mass.: Harvard University Press, Copyright 1951 by The President and Fellows of Harvard College. Pp. 12–14. Italicized portions numbered and capitalized in editing.

Some of the wilder aspects of Melanesia are portrayed in this view from Papua, the southeastern quarter of the large island of New Guinea. Note the luxuriant, tangled growth of the tropical rain forest rising above the long thatched hut occupied by members of an entire village. (Australian News and Information Bureau.)

composed of limestone covered by thin layers of soil which support low and dense stands of dry-land flora (medium-sized trees, small trees, shrubs, vines, ferns, and so forth). Rough pitted limestone surfaces and tangled growth make these islands difficult to cross. Fresh water in the form of springs and streams is usually lacking, and cave pools or rain-catchment basins provide drinking water. Coconuts and other food plants grow fairly well in the scattered pockets of soil, but frequent droughts are a menace to native agriculture. Since many of these islands contain rich phosphate deposits, they have assumed an economic value far surpassing that of any other kind of island of comparable size.

5. *Unweathered Volcanic Islands* (typical examples are the northern Marianas and Niuafo'ou). Because weathering of these islands has not progressed far, there is considerably less soil on them, and hence less vegetation, than on

the "older" weathered volcanic islands. Most forest growth is limited to the valleys and the ridges are covered with grasses and smaller plants. Native populations can and do thrive in moderate numbers on these islands; usually the little soil present is rich and supports luxuriant growths of coconuts and other food plants.

6. *Weathered Volcanic Islands* (typical examples are the Hawaiian, Society, and Samoan islands). These islands, some of them rising thousands of feet above sea level, contain many kinds of environment: wide strands, brackish and fresh water swamps, gentle and steep slopes, extensive lava fields, and so forth. They are subjected to great variation in rainfall. Plant life is extremely varied. Nearly every kind of growing thing or growing condition needed by man to develop complex technologies is to be found. Minerals alone are lacking.

Certain "mixed" islands, including Guam, Saipan, Rota, and Mangaia, possess characteristics of both weathered volcanic and raised-coral settings.

7. *"Continental" Islands* (New Guinea, Viti Levu, New Caledonia, Espiritu Santo, Guadalcanal, Bougainville, New Britain, New Ireland, and most other large islands in the Melanesian archipelagoes). These islands are formed of continental rocks complicated by volcanic intrusions and possess even wider varieties in environment and plant life than the volcanic islands. Their richer, mineral-bearing soils support nearly every kind of vegetation. Their high mountains, dense forests, and broad swamps have encouraged the existence of numerous isolated native communities, favoring the development of cultural and even racial diversity.

## ▶ *"High" and "Low" Islands*

A somewhat simpler distinction is commonly made between the "high" and "low" islands of the Pacific. Some of the characteristics of these two types of islands are elaborated in the following selection by an American geographer, Otis W. Freeman: [4]

In the Pacific one of the most distinctive things . . . is the difference between "high" and "low" islands. The "high" islands, mostly of volcanic origin, abound in food as compared with the "low" islands of coral origin. The mountainous islands are large in proportion to the land area of coral atolls, have a variety of trees, plenty of water, fertile soil, and can support considerable populations. The low islands have few plants except the coconut palm, little or no drinking water, scanty soil, and each coral isle can support few inhabitants. . . .

The major seaports of the mid-Pacific are located on the larger islands. No city of real size and importance is built on a coral atoll, although such localities may serve as first class air and sea bases. Only Honolulu [500,000] and [four] cities in New Zealand exceed 100,-000 in population. Hilo [24,000] on Hawaii, Noumea [22,000] in New Caledonia, Suva [37,000] on Fiji, Papeete [17,000] on Tahiti, and Apia [18,000] on Samoa are smaller cities of importance as seaports and commercial centers. [Population figure for Honolulu is a 1960 census figure for the standard metropolitan area; figures for the other cities are estimates for the city proper.] The high islands in the trade winds are generally healthful and a con-siderable tourist trade exists in Hawaii and to a less extent in Fiji and Tahiti. Health conditions in the wet tropical islands of the Solomons and New Hebrides are not so favorable, malaria and many other diseases being prevalent. . . .

On the volcanic islands large sugar plantations have been developed by the Americans on Hawaii, the British at Fiji, and the Japanese on [prewar] Saipan in the Marianas. . . . In none of these islands were the natives numerous enough or willing to work on the plantations so that outside labor had to be imported. In Hawaii Chinese and Portuguese were first used but today Japanese and Filipinos mostly do the work. In Fiji, Indians, mostly of the Hindu faith, were brought in and now [outnumber] the native Fijians. At Saipan the Japanese brought in their own people. The natives . . . produce little for sale from the land—most of their farming is of a sustenance nature.

On the high islands the natives originally lived in villages rather than on individual farms, and the custom is still generally followed. Each valley commonly supported a village which by preference was located on the beach or as close to the sea as the topography permitted. . . .

As mentioned, a variety of food could be produced on the high islands. . . . Pigs furnished most of the meat to supplement the starchy foods, fruit, and fish. The seedless breadfruit, plantain, taro, yam, and sweet potato were the chief native sources of starch. These have now been supplemented by arrow-root, cassava, and improved varieties of bananas. Sugar cane, coffee, [cacao], papaya, mango, lime, orange, lemon, shaddock, and ginger are among the useful plants introduced by Europeans. Cattle and goats are found on the larger islands where grasslands exist. . . .

### Coral Atolls

The "low" islands are made of coral and usually have an irregular ring shape around a lagoon. Such an island is called an atoll [(photo, p. 427)]. Generally the coral ring is broken into many pieces, separated by channels leading into the lagoon, but the whole circular group is commonly considered one island, although quite often individual names are given to the larger islets. . . . The coral atolls are wholly within the tropics as the reef-forming organisms can only survive in warm waters.

Two leading theories have been advanced to account for the coral atolls. That of Charles

[4] Otis W. Freeman, "The Pacific Island World." *Journal of Geography*, v. 44 (1945), pp. 22–28.

Used by permission of the author and the *Journal of Geography*. City populations added in editing.

Darwin has three stages: (1) the coral builds a fringing reef around a volcanic island, (2) the island slowly sinks and the coral reef is built upward and forms a barrier reef separated by a lagoon from the shore, (3) the volcanic island has sunk out of sight and a lagoon occupies the former land area whose outline is reflected in the roughly oval form of the atoll. . . . Another theory is that of Sir James Murray who would have the coral forming a reef on the outer limits of a shallow submarine platform. Likely most such platforms would result from erosion of a volcanic island, so would have the approximately oval shape of a volcanic peak.

No matter how they may have been formed, the geographer finds that the atolls have similar characteristics wherever they occur, although in size they vary. Many are only a few miles in diameter, while a few huge affairs up to 50 to 100 miles across occur. . . . Some coral islands lack the central lagoon, which has either been filled to become land or the island itself has been elevated enough for the feature to disappear. . . .

. . . The greatest concentration of atolls is in the Tuamotu Archipelago (also called the Paumotu, Low, and Dangerous Archipelago). The atolls of the Marshalls are arranged in two parallel chains, an eastern and a western. The Gilbert, Ellice, and Tonga islands are atolls, as are the Union (Tokelau), Cook, and Phoenix groups. In addition there are many isolated low isles of coral. . . . Frequently the atolls follow an arcuate course and rise at intervals from a submarine platform or uplift, likely a zone of volcanic activity. . . . While the barrier reefs of the atolls protect ships in the lagoons from currents and waves, they are themselves a great danger to navigation, especially as charts of Polynesia and Micronesia are often incomplete

Fishing is a basic means of livelihood throughout the Pacific islands. This view shows native fishermen in the Trobriand Islands, east of New Guinea, arriving at a beach where part of their catch will be bartered for yams (center foreground) raised by inland villagers. Note the characteristic outrigger canoes. (Australian News and Information Bureau.)

and inaccurate. . . . Occasionally some atoll is completely overwhelmed by a hurricane and the giant waves associated with it that may wash entirely over the low land and destroy most of the palms and inhabitants. . . .

The soil of the low islands is broken from the coral by the waves and winds. It is thin and poor, and few plants except coconuts can grow on it or withstand the infiltration of the salt sea into the ground water supply. On the more barren islands, coconuts, the rather poor fruit of the pandanus, and fish are the only available foods. Sometimes the natives by much labor construct a garden of artificially fertile soil. Within a stone wall or pit . . . all available plant waste and other refuse is collected to supply needed humus to the sterile coral sand. . . .

The most significant animal life on the low islands consists of birds. . . . Birds have some-times been slaughtered for their feathers, and both eggs and birds are eaten, although they have a fishy flavor. However, the most valuable product of the birds is guano and indirectly phosphate rock. On the low islands in the trade winds, rain is too scanty to wash away the bird droppings and other refuse which accumulate and change to the brownish guano that is a valuable fertilizer because it is high in nitrogen and phosphorus. On some islands, notably Nauru and Ocean, just south of the equator, the phosphorus from the guano has interacted chemically with the coral limestone to form phosphate rock. This is quarried and exported to the temperate zone to use on depleted soils. Nauru and Ocean islands, together with Christmas Island, 2000 miles to the east, supply [about one twentieth] of the world's output of phosphate rock.

## RELATIONS WITH THE WEST

Europeans began to visit the Pacific islands early in the Age of Discovery. Spanish and Portuguese voyagers were followed by Dutch, English, French, and, later, American and German. Many famous names are connected with Pacific exploration, including those of Magellan, Tasman, Bougainville, La Perouse, and Cook. By the end of the eighteenth century virtually all of the important islands were known.

For a long period the European governments exercised only nominal control over the islands, and the natives were subjected to the unrestrained abuses of whaling crews, sandalwood traders, indentured labor contractors ("blackbirders"), and other adventurers. On island after island European penetration presented the dismal spectacle of decimation of the natives and disruption of their cultures. The intruders introduced new diseases, alcohol, opium, forced labor, and firearms which greatly increased the slaughter in tribal wars. Although the introduction of better tools and medicines, as well as the work of missionaries and the belated attempts of the imperial governments to give the natives a "new deal" must be entered on the other side, the balance sheet for four and a half centuries of Western influence in the Pacific islands does not reflect much credit on the outsiders.

In recent times Western personnel and capital have been attracted to the islands by mining and plantation agriculture. Although in general the islands are notably deficient in mineral resources, there are some exceptions. The phosphate resources have already been described. In addition, gold has been found in the Solomons, the Fijis, and, especially, New Guinea. The French island of New Caledonia is particularly outstanding in mineral reserves and exploitation, with producing deposits of nickel, chrome, cobalt, and iron ore.

## A "COCONUT CIVILIZATION"

Most tropical plantation crops have been attempted in the islands at one time or an-other, with varying degrees of success. However, two crops—sugar and coconuts—have gained much greater importance than any others. Of the two, sugar leads in value of production, but coconuts are by far the more widespread and fundamentally important in the lives of the people. The growing of coconuts and the trade in copra provide a common denominator for a large part of the island world, which has been said with considerable justice to have a "coconut civilization." The latter is described in the following selection by Douglas L. Oliver: [5]

South Seas sugar statistics are far more impressive in tonnage and in value than those of the South Seas coconut, but sugar's influence is limited to Hawaii, Fiji, and prewar Saipan-Tinian, and only whites and immigrant Asiatics benefit directly from it. The influence of the coconut, however, stretches from Truk to Tonga and from Hiva Oa to Hollandia, and directly or indirectly affects the life of nearly every islander in this vast area. . . .

Coconuts require year-round warm temperature, a well-drained soil, and plenty of moisture and sunlight; they grow best of all in low altitudes near the coast. The palm grows out of the mature, fallen nut, and requires from eight to ten years to reach the bearing stage. After that it lives for nearly 80 years and bears nuts at the rate of about 50 a year for 60 or 70 years.

The mature nut consists of a hollow kernel of oily white meat, one half inch thick, encased in a hard woody shell. Around this is a fibrous husk one half to two inches thick. The cavity of the unripe nut is filled with a thin "milk," a nutritious and refreshing beverage with a tangy taste. As the nut matures, this "milk" is absorbed into the coconut meat, which when dried and removed from the shell becomes the copra of commerce.

Throughout Oceania the coconut leads a double life. In one way it is a source of food, shelter, and income which helps support native life nearly everywhere. In another way, however, it has been the instrument by which white men have done most to change native life.

To islanders the milk of the unripe coconut is a prized beverage, the only one, in fact, on many islands lacking potable water or rain catchments. The meat is scraped from the shell and eaten either by itself or mixed into puddings of taro and yams and sago. Or, the oil is squeezed from the meat and used as a food, an unguent, or a cosmetic. The hollowed shell becomes a flask, a clean-scraped shell a cup or a spoon or a material for carved ornaments. Cord is manufactured from the fibrous husk; furniture, utensils, and building timbers from the tough trunk. Leaves are used to thatch huts or weave baskets; and even the pith of the palm is eaten when for some drastic reason the palm is felled. On islands nearer to Asia's influence, the sugar-rich sap is drawn off by tapping the flower bud and is allowed to ferment into inebriating toddy. To deprive an islander of his coconut palms is to take away much of the basis of his living. Even the white man's world would be a much poorer place without them.

From the copra of commerce oil is expressed to produce margarine, cooking and salad oils, fine soap, and cosmetics. Copra cake, the residue after most oil has been expressed, is an important stock food rich in protein. Coir mats and rugs are manufactured from the fibrous husks, and coconut-shell charcoal is the best vapor absorbent known, especially valuable for absorbing industrial odors, for recovering gasoline and benzol from the air, and for use in gas masks. In the manufacture of soap, coconut oil plays a unique role; it hardens well, and its highly soluble acids possess exceptional lathering qualities, even in salt water. It has consequently become a favorite for toilet and salt-water soaps and for soap chips. And, in addition to all these, consider how empty life would be without coconut pie!

But most of these good things are end products, processed in factories thousands of miles from the islands. With the exception of a few tons of coconuts used in the local manufacture of desiccated coconut and some locally used cooking oils, most palm products leaving the islands do so in the form of copra.

Copra is merely coconut meat removed from the shell and dried sufficiently for shipping. To obtain it, mature nuts may be picked from the palm or they may be collected after they have fallen. Then the whole coconut is split in half and the meat either immediately cut out of the shell or allowed to dry a bit before removal. Excess moisture must then be removed from the meat by some method of drying, and the resulting copra bagged in hundred-pound sacks for overseas shipment.

### ▶ Organization of the Copra Industry

In 1957 the Pacific islands, exclusive of the Philippines and Indonesia, accounted for

---

[5] Reprinted by permission of the publishers from Oliver, *op. cit.*, pp. 135–136.

Loading bags of copra and drums of coconut oil for export at the wharves in Suva, the capital and principal port of the Fiji Islands. (British Information Services.)

some 8 percent of the total world production of copra by weight, as compared with 40 percent for the Philippines, 22 percent for Indonesia, and 8 percent for Ceylon. Despite the relatively minor role of Oceania on a world basis, however, copra production is of the utmost local importance on most of the islands, frequently being the leading industry in employment, value of product, and general effect on the lives of the islanders. The organization of the industry varies a great deal from one island or island group to another, but in general three principal types of production can be distinguished: by natives, by small planters, and by large corporations.

1. *Native production* is of some impor-tance in the copra industry of every island group and is the dominant form of production in many groups. Natives gather the nuts, prepare the copra, and sell it to mid-dlemen for marketing. The middleman is generally the local storekeeper and is usu-ally either a Chinese or a white man. He in turn disposes of the copra to larger firms for overseas shipment.

2. *Small-planter production* involves the "independent" operation of a single plantation by one of the many white men who have come into the islands for this purpose. Such a plantation will ordinarily comprise plantings amounting to several hundred acres of trees, and will employ up to a hundred workers living in barracks. The workers are usu-

ally natives but are sometimes imported Asians. Often the plantation is quite isolated. The small-planter type of enterprise is declining due to high production costs and hazards, coupled with widely fluctuating world prices which the planter can do nothing to control and against which he generally has little by way of a financial reserve. Planters complain of a chronic shortage of labor and its lack of efficiency, which they maintain is partly due to government regulation of working conditions, including wages. In addition, their position is made more precarious by a plenitude of diseases and insect pests capable of seriously damaging the groves and sometimes not even susceptible of control by organizations having much greater resources than those of the small planter.

3. *Production by large corporations* has been of increasing importance. British concerns are generally the most important, but those of a number of other nations are also in the field. Outstanding names are Lever Brothers, Burns Philip Company, Ltd., and W. R. Carpenter Company, Ltd. Such concerns own many separate plantations and usually operate such facilities as shipping lines, stores, and warehouses. They may, as in the case of Lever Brothers, have worldwide interests. Their financial resources apparently allow them to operate successfully in an industry becoming more and more difficult for the small planter.

# Australia and New Zealand

The basic kinship of Australia and New Zealand is widely recognized and is indicated in common usage of the term "Anzac countries" to refer to the two collectively. This kinship is derived from similarities in population, cultural heritage, political problems and orientations, type of economy, and location.

Both Australia and New Zealand are prod-ucts of British colonization and are strongly British in ancestry and culture.[1] The Australians and New Zealanders speak English, live under parliamentary forms of government, claim the British sovereign as their own, attend schools patterned after those of Britain, and attend the Anglican Church in greater numbers than any other. Both countries, like Britain, are socialistic "welfare

[1] Both New Zealand and Australia contain surviving minorities of prewhite native inhabitants. The primitive Negroid inhabitants of Australia were slaughtered or driven into outlying areas by the whites. Today they number about 75,000, in contrast to an estimated 300,000 at the beginning of white settlement in 1788. Efforts are being made to preserve this remnant, found mainly on reservations in the tropical north, but the decline in numbers is still continuing. In New Zealand the native inhabitants were the Maori, a Polynesian people. Not so primitive as the Australian aborigines, and more warlike, their hold on the land was broken only by a bloody war between 1860 and 1870. At present the Maori, who seemed destined for extinction about 1900, are achieving something of a renaissance. Their numbers have increased from 40,-000 at the turn of the century to 150,000 today. While still something of a depressed group in New Zealand, their economic and social situation is much better than that of the apparently vanishing Australian natives, and they are being increasingly integrated, both socially and biologically, with the rest of New Zealand's population.

Vast areas of grazing land are found in the central lowlands of Australia. The above photo of sheep grazing was taken in northwestern New South Wales. (Australian News and Information Bureau.)

440

states," with comprehensive social security standards and benefits, although in the development of this aspect of their societies Australia and New Zealand actually preceded Britain and were world pioneers along with the Scandinavian countries. Both Australia and New Zealand have exceptionally high standards of living, ranking generally in a class with the United States and Canada in this regard.

Although they are independent nations, loyalty to Britain is an outstanding characteristic of the Anzac countries. Their loyalty is expressed in their membership in the Commonwealth of Nations and was plainly evident at the outbreak of both world wars, which Australia and New Zealand entered immediately in support of Britain. However, since World War II, when a threatened Japanese assault on their homelands was mainly frustrated by American forces, the two countries have also sought closer relations with the United States. Close international ties with strong and friendly outside powers, especially naval powers, are extremely important to the Anzac countries due to their

small populations and remote insular locations, far distant from other Western and white nations. Australia's 10 million people plus New Zealand's 2.3 million (1959 estimates for both countries) amount to a smaller total than the population of the New York metropolitan area. In view of this fact, it is understandable that the two countries look with some apprehension at the awakening masses of the neighboring Asian countries to the north, whose teeming and land-hungry populations stand in striking contrast to the comparative emptiness and material abundance of Australia and New Zealand.

Australia and New Zealand are also tied closely to Britain and the United States by trade. Basic to the economies of both countries are exports of a few primary products, principally wool, with wheat a poor second, in the case of Australia and wool, meat, and dairy products in the case of New Zealand, coupled with extensive imports of manufactured goods. This vital trade is carried on largely with the United Kingdom, and secondarily with other industrialized nations (Table 19).

### TABLE 19

#### PRINCIPAL TRADING PARTNERS OF AUSTRALIA AND NEW ZEALAND

| | AUSTRALIA | | NEW ZEALAND | |
|---|---|---|---|---|
| Percent of exports [a] to | United Kingdom | 27 | United Kingdom | 56 |
| | Japan | 13 | United States | 15 |
| | France | 9 | France | 6 |
| | New Zealand | 7 | All others | 23 |
| | United States | 6 | | |
| | All others | 38 | | |
| Percent of imports [a] from | United Kingdom | 41 | United Kingdom | 53 |
| | United States | 13 | Australia | 17 |
| | West Germany | 5 | United States | 7 |
| | All others | 41 | All others | 23 |

SOURCE: *United Nations Yearbook of International Trade Statistics*, 1958.
[a] Percentages are based on total value, 1958.

# PHYSICAL AND CLIMATIC CHARACTERISTICS OF AUSTRALIA

Australia is not only a country, but an island continent with an area, including the off-

shore island of Tasmania, of nearly 3 million square miles. It is exceeded in area by only five countries: the Soviet Union, Canada, China, the United States, and Brazil. However, most of the continent is very sparsely populated, and in terms of total population Australia is a relatively small country. The sparseness of Australia's population and its concentration into a comparatively small part of the total land area are closely related to the continent's physical characteristics, among which aridity (accentuated by high temperatures and rapid evap-

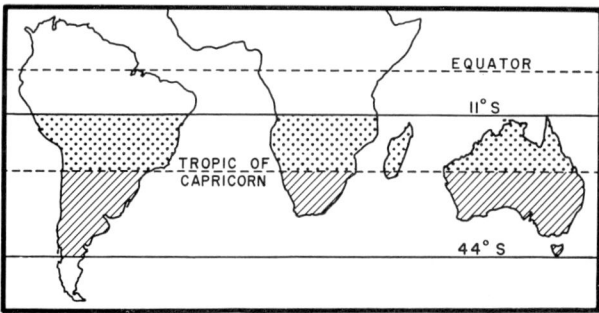

Australia compared in latitude and area with southern Africa and southern South America.

oration) and low average elevation are outstanding. On the basis of climate and relief, Australia may be divided into four major natural regions: (1) the humid eastern highlands, (2) the tropical savannas of northern Australia, (3) the "mediterranean" lands of southwestern and southern Australia, and (4) the dry interior (map, facing page).

### ▶ The Humid Eastern Highlands

Australia's only major highlands extend along the east coast from Cape York to southern Tasmania in a belt 100 to 250 miles wide. Although complex in form and often rugged, these highlands seldom reach elevations of 3000 feet. Their highest summit and the highest point in Australia is Mount Kosciusko, which attains only 7316 feet. The highlands and the narrow and fragmented coastal plains at their base constitute the only part of Australia which does not experience a considerable period of drought each year. However, although on-

shore winds from the Pacific bring appreciable rain each month, the strong relief reduces the amount of agricultural land in this most favored of Australia's climatic areas. South of Sydney and at higher elevations to the north the climate is commonly classified as marine west coast (humid marine), despite the location. North of Sydney higher summer temperatures change the classification to humid subtropical, while still farther north, beyond approximately the parallel of 20°S., hotter temperatures and greater seasonality of rain cause essentially subhumid conditions.

### ▶ Tropical Savannas of Northern Australia

Northern Australia, from near Broome on the Indian Ocean to the coast of the Coral Sea, receives heavy rainfall during a portion of the (Southern Hemisphere) summer season, but experiences almost complete drought during the winter six months, or more, of the year. This highly seasonal distribution of rainfall is essentially the result of monsoonal winds which blow onshore during the summer and offshore during the winter. The seasonality of the rainfall, combined with the tropical heat of the area, has produced a savanna vegetation of coarse grasses with scattered trees and patches of woodland. The effect of the long season of drought in reducing agricultural possibilities is compounded by the poverty of the soils and by a lack of highlands sufficient to nourish large perennial streams for irrigation. The alluvial and volcanic soils which support large populations in some tropical areas are almost completely absent in northern Australia.

### ▶ "Mediterranean" Lands of Southwestern and Southern Australia

The southwestern corner of Australia and the lands around Spencer Gulf have a mediterranean or dry-summer subtropical type of climate with subtropical temperatures, winter rain, and summer drought. In winter the Southern Hemisphere belt of the westerly

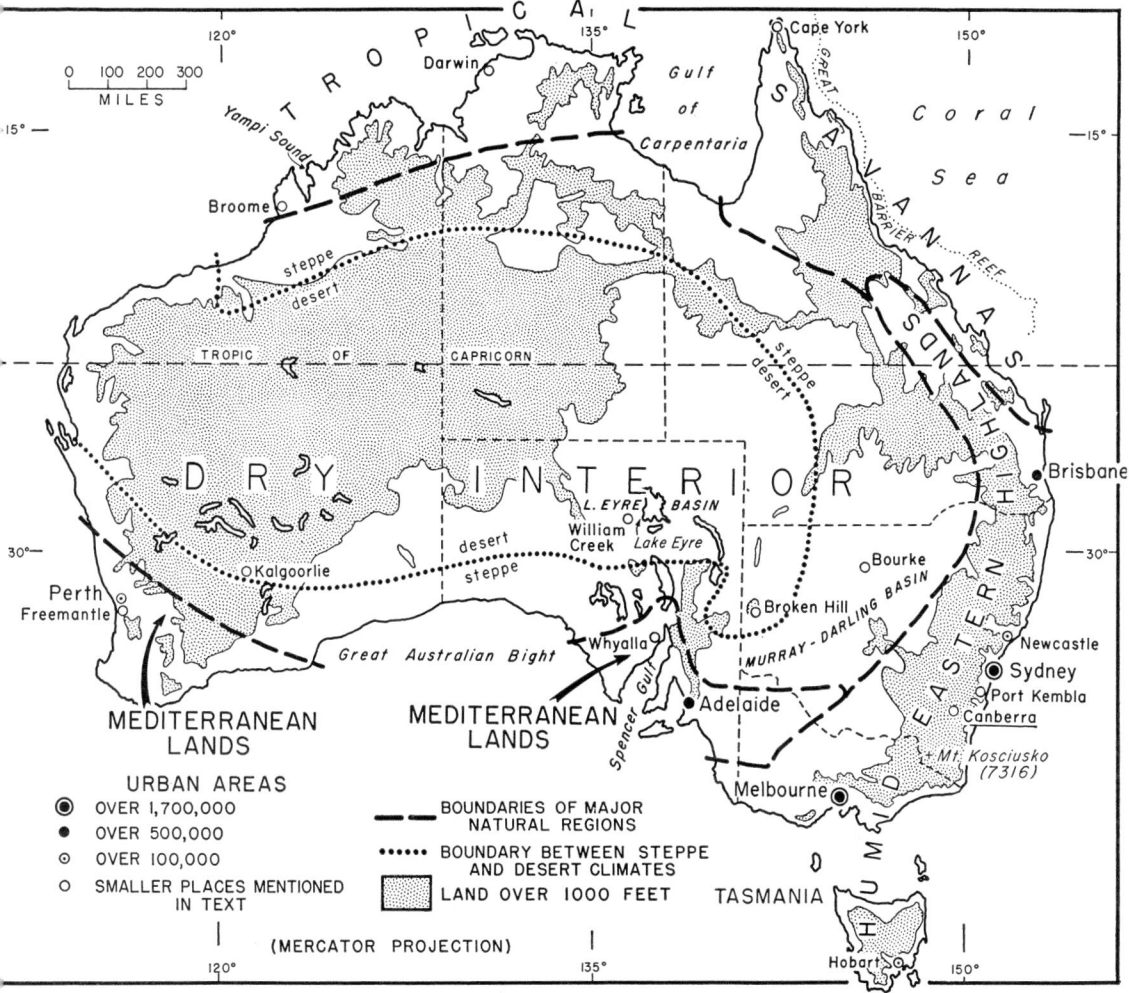

Major natural regions of Australia. The national capital is underlined. City-size symbols are based on 1958 estimates for the city proper.

winds shifts far enough north to affect these districts, while in summer this belt lies offshore to the south and the land is dry. Crops introduced from the mediterranean lands of Europe generally do well in these parts of Australia, but the agricultural possibilities of the Australian areas are limited by the lack of high highlands to catch moisture and supply irrigation water to the lowlands.

### ▶ The Dry Interior

The huge interior of Australia is desert, surrounded by a broad fringe of semiarid grassland (steppe) which is transitional to the more humid areas around the edges of the continent. Altogether, the interior desert and steppe cover more than half of the continent, and extend to the coast in the northwest and along the Gulf of Carpentaria and the Great Australian Bight. This tremendous area of dry land is too far south to get much rain from the summer monsoon, too far north to benefit from rainfall brought by the westerlies in winter, and is shielded from Pacific winds by the eastern highlands. Here again the lack of highlands is unfortunate from a climatic point of view. Approximately the western half of Australia is occupied by a vast plateau of ancient igneous, metamorphic, and hardened sedimentary rocks, but its general elevation is only 1000 to 1600 feet and its few isolated mountain ranges are too low to materially influence the climate or supply perennial streams for irrigation. To the east, between the plateau and the eastern highlands, the land is still lower in the great central lowland which stretches across the continent between the Gulf of Carpentaria and the Great Australian Bight. The effect of elevation on the climate is shown by the fact that the lowest part of this lowland and of Australia, the Lake Eyre Basin, is the driest part of the continent. Another part of the lowland, however, the Murray-Darling Basin, contains Australia's only major river system and has the most extensive development of irrigation works on the continent.

Temperature and precipitation data for the four major natural regions of Australia are presented in Table 20.

### ► The Small Proportion of Arable Land

One very important result of the widespread seasonal or total aridity and of the occupation of most of the only truly humid area by highlands is that Australia offers very little good agricultural land relative to its total area. Although some estimates place the proportion of potentially cultivable land as high as 15 percent of the total, the Australian government now classifies only about 2 percent of the land as arable with another 1 percent "potentially productive." Some 4 percent is classed as forest and woodland, while about 46 percent is classed as meadows and pastures and about 47 percent as wasteland. These figures give Australia an arable area which is only about one fourteenth as large as the arable area of the United States, a country of comparable size, and is actually less than that of a number of countries with a small fraction of Australia's total area, such as France, Spain, Poland, and Italy.

The distribution of population in Australia generally follows that of arable land. Thus most of the country's small population is found in the humid eastern highlands and coastal plains, especially in the cooler south; in the areas of mediterranean climate; and in the more humid grasslands adjoining the southern part of the eastern highlands and the mediterranean areas.

## AUSTRALIA'S ECONOMY AND POPULATION

Australia is one of a few countries in the world which are highly industrialized and at the same time important exporters of raw materials and food. There is an obvious similarity to the United States and Canada in this respect. But Australia, despite employment of a larger proportion of its labor force in industry than the United States, is predominantly an importer of manufactured products rather than an exporter like the United States. In the latter respect Australia is more like Canada, although Australia is more industrialized in proportion to the size of its population than is Canada. There are various other points of similarity between these two countries. Both are large countries with relatively small populations. In both, the population is mainly distributed around the periphery, a fact related to the large amounts of poor and undeveloped land which both possess in the interior. Both countries have a disproportionately high rank in world trade, both have close connections with Britain and with the United States, and both have high standards of living. One important difference, however, lies in the fact that Australia is able to produce a greater variety of foodstuffs than is Can-

# TABLE 20

## CLIMATIC DATA FOR SELECTED AUSTRALIAN STATIONS

| NATURAL REGION, CLIMATE TYPE, AND STATION | LATITUDE TO NEAREST WHOLE DEGREE | ELEVATION ABOVE SEA LEVEL (FEET) | AVERAGE TEMPERATURE (DEGREES F TO NEAREST WHOLE DEGREE) | | | PRECIPITATION | |
|---|---|---|---|---|---|---|---|
| | | | ANNUAL | JANUARY (OR WARMEST MONTH) | JULY (OR COOLEST MONTH) | ANNUAL AVERAGE TO NEAREST INCH | MONTHS AVERAGING LESS THAN ONE INCH OF PRECIPITATION |
| Humid eastern highlands | | | | | | | |
| Humid subtropic | | | | | | | |
| Brisbane | 27°S. | 134 | 69° | 77° | 59° | 45″ | 0 |
| Marine west coast | | | | | | | |
| Melbourne | 38°S. | 114 | 59° | 68° (Feb.) | 49° | 26″ | 0 |
| Tropical savannas | | | | | | | |
| Darwin | 12°S. | 97 | 83° | 86° (Nov.) | 77° | 61″ | 5 (May–Sept.) |
| Cape York | 13°S. | 69 | 79° | 80° | 76° (Aug.) | 82″ | 5 (June–Oct.) |
| Mediterranean areas | | | | | | | |
| Adelaide | 35°S. | 140 | 63° | 74° (Feb.) | 53° | 21″ | 2 (Jan., Mar.) |
| Perth | 32°S. | 210 | 65° | 74° (Jan., Feb.) | 55° | 35″ | 5 (Nov.–Mar.) |
| Dry interior | | | | | | | |
| Bourke | 30°S. | 92 | 69° | 85° | 52° | 15″ | 2 (July–Aug.) |
| William Creek | 29°S. | 250 | 69° | 83° (Jan., Feb.) | 53° | 5″ | 12 |

ada because of greater environmental variety. Canada, for example, has no tropical or subtropical climates.

## ▶ Agriculture and Ranching

The sectors of the Australian economy which regularly produce a surplus for export are grazing, agriculture, and mining. Such a result seems a logical outgrowth of a situation where 10 million people have at their command the natural resources of an entire continent, albeit a poor continent from the standpoint of agriculture. The existence of large and dependable markets for Australian primary products in Europe, the United States, and elsewhere, coupled with cheap and efficient transportation by sea to those markets, and the possession by the Australian people of the necessary technical skills and equipment to exploit the continent on an extensive basis, utilizing a minimum of labor and a maximum of land and equipment, makes the emphasis on surplus production and export of primary commodities seem even more logical. Australian agricultural and pastoral output per man has been estimated to be twice that of the United States.

### Sheep and Cattle Ranching

Sheep ranching has always been the most important of Australia's rural industries (photo, p. 440). When the first settlement was planted at Sydney in 1788, the intention of the British government was merely to establish a penal colony, with the expectation that enough agriculture would be carried on to make the colony self-sufficient in food and perhaps provide a small surplus of some products for export. While self-sufficiency proved difficult to obtain in the early days due to the poverty of the leached soils around Sydney, it was soon discovered that sheep did well. At the time the market for wool was rapidly expanding with mechanization of the woolen textile industry in Britain. Thus, Australia found its main export staple in the early years of the nine-

teenth century. Sheep graziers rapidly penetrated the interior of the continent, and by 1850 Australia was already the largest supplier of wool on the world market, a position it has never lost.

Sheep raising has been tried practically everywhere in Australia that there seemed to be any hope of success. Much of the interior has been found too dry, parts of the eastern mountain belt too rugged and wet, and most of the north too hot and wet and with too coarse a forage in summer. Thus the sheep industry has become localized. It is concentrated mainly in a crescentic belt of territory which follows roughly the gentle western slope of the eastern highlands from the northern border of New South Wales to the western border of Victoria. New South Wales has over 40 percent of the Commonwealth's sheep, and Victoria between 15 and 20 percent. Beyond the main belt of concentration the sheep industry spreads on poorer pastures north almost to the Gulf of Carpentaria and west into South Australia. A minor area of production rims the west coast from about latitude 16°S. to beyond Perth, with the greatest concentration relatively near the latter city. The sheep ranches or "stations" in Australia vary in size from a few hundred to many thousands of acres. They are generally larger on the poorer pasture lands, that is, outside the main belt of production.

The main product of the Australian sheep stations is wool. The importance of wool in the country's economy is indicated by the fact that it ordinarily constitutes 40 to 50 percent of the total value of all Australian exports. Its importance to the world is indicated by the fact that Australian wool normally amounts to about a quarter of the total world production and over half of the total production of high-quality Merino wool. In addition, Australia has been able, since the development of refrigerated transport, to export considerable quantities of mutton and lamb.

Lands in Australia which have not been

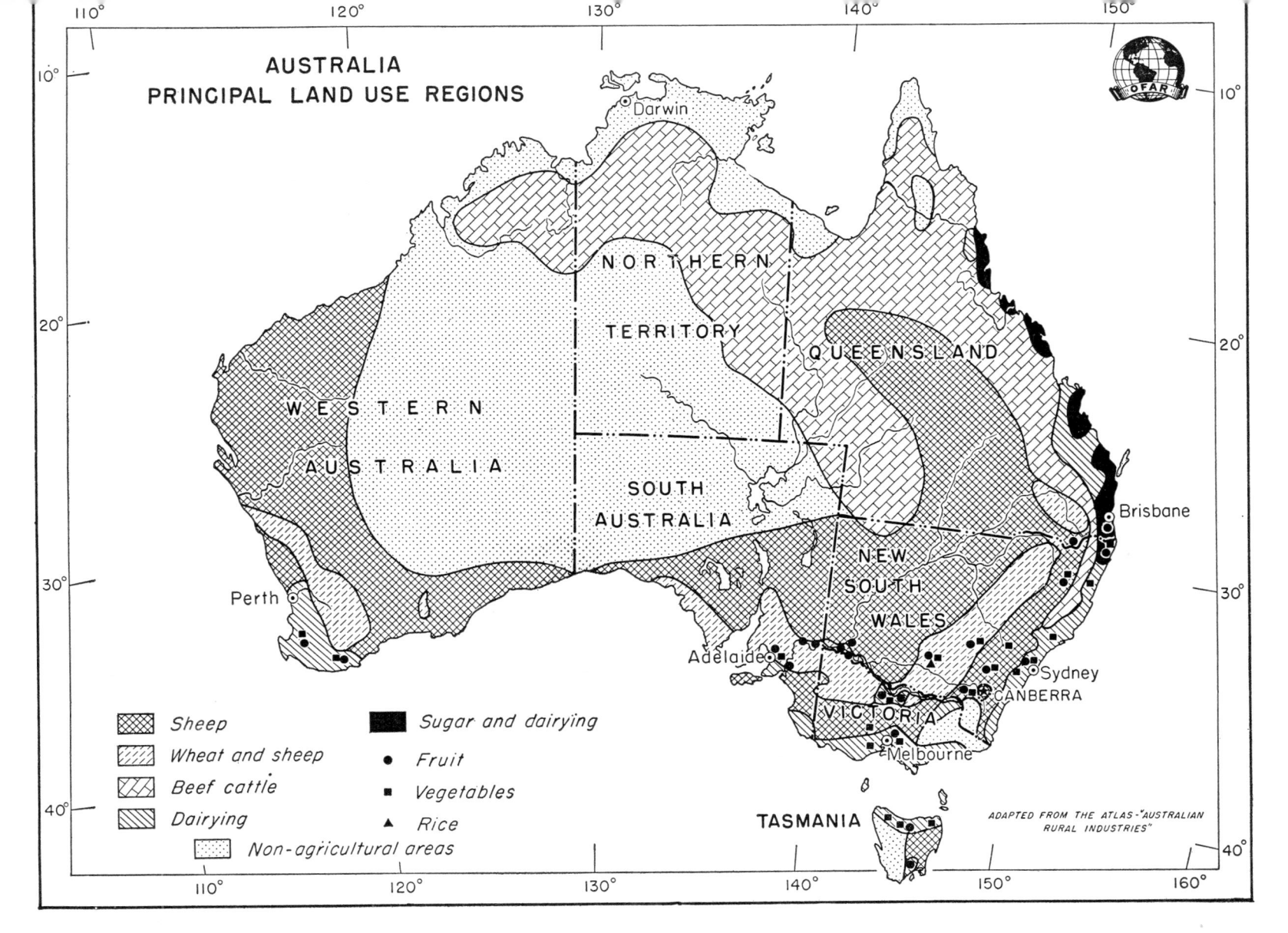

AUSTRALIA
PRINCIPAL LAND USE REGIONS

Legend:
- Sheep
- Wheat and sheep
- Beef cattle
- Dairying
- Non-agricultural areas
- Sugar and dairying
- Fruit
- Vegetables
- Rice

ADAPTED FROM THE ATLAS "AUSTRALIAN RURAL INDUSTRIES"

found suitable for sheep or for a more intensive form of agriculture are generally devoted to cattle ranching. Such lands include particularly those of the north, with hot, humid summers and coarse forage. The main belt of cattle ranching extends east-west across the northern part of the country (map, p. 447). The greatest concentration is in Queensland, which contains over half of the cattle, other than dairy animals, in Australia. On many of the remote ranches, especially in the Northern Territory, the labor force is composed of remnants of the black aboriginal population of Australia.

The beef cattle industry is not as important to Australia as the sheep industry. It is difficult to market first-class beef from a remote tropical area. Variability in weather, poor pasturage in the dry season, tropical insect pests and diseases, and drives of hundreds of miles to market are among the factors that retard the industry. Nevertheless, Australia supplies its own needs for beef, and exports appreciable quantities of meat as well as hides for tanning.

### Wheat Farming

After wool, wheat, including flour, is Australia's most important export, generally supplying 5 to 10 percent of all exports by value. As in the case of wool, wheat surpluses are largely a reflection of Australia's aridity and low density of population. In contrast to wool, however, wheat production did not begin as the result of a search for export staples. Wheat was the key crop in early attempts to make the settlement at Sydney self-sufficient. The soils along much of the coastal margin of Australia are leached and poor, though capable of much improvement through application of fertilizer. In the early years the colony almost starved as a result of wheat failures, and the problem of grain supply was not really solved until the development of the colony, now the state, of South Australia. There, fertile land and a favorable climate were found near the port settlement of Adelaide, so that wheat could be

grown and shipped by sea to other coastal points.

In the decade of the 1860s, Australia passed from a deficit to a surplus position in grain production. Thereafter, wheat farming expanded rapidly. Among the factors making this expansion possible were (1) the development of the mechanical reaper and other types of machinery suited to extensive wheat farming, (2) the building of railroads inland from the ports, (3) scientific work in plant breeding and soil fertilization, (4) the enactment of legislation under which some of the large grazing estates were divided into smaller farms, and (5) an expanding European market. The main belt of wheat production spread from the eastern coastal districts of South Australia into Victoria and New South Wales, generally following the semiarid and subhumid lands which lie inland from the crests of the eastern highlands. Thus the main wheat belt has come to occupy nearly the same position as the main belt of sheep production (map, p. 447). In fact, the two types of production are very often combined in this area. A second, less important wheat belt has developed in the southwestern corner of the continent inland from Perth. The combined exports from these two areas have normally been sufficient to give Australia high rank among the world's wheat exporters, after the United States, Canada, and sometimes Argentina and/or the USSR. It should be emphasized that Australian wheat production is an extensive and highly mechanized form of agriculture, characterized by a small labor force, large acreages, and low yields per acre, although very high yields per man.

### Dairy Farming

Though not as important as grazing or wheat farming for the export trade, dairying is now the leading type of agriculture in Australia in terms of employment. It has developed mainly in the humid coastal plains of Queensland, New South Wales, and Victoria (map, p. 447). Originally oriented entirely toward the local market, it has been mainly a response to the striking urbanization of the country's coastal districts and the necessity of a relatively high return per acre to defray the expense of clearing heavily forested land. Dairying has now become well established as the dominant type of farming in most of these coastal areas and regularly produces an export surplus beyond the requirements of Australia itself.

### Fruit Growing

When Australia was settled, it was found not to have any native fruits of commercial value. Consequently, the fruit-growing industry which now exists is based entirely on plants transplanted to the Australian environment. The range of climates allows production of both tropical and mid-latitude fruits, the most important items being pineapples from Queensland, bananas from New South Wales and Queensland, citrus fruits mainly from New South Wales, grapes for wine and table use produced under irrigation in the Murray Basin and near Adelaide, and apples and pears produced especially in Tasmania and Victoria. The home market is abundantly supplied with fruit, and there is normally a substantial export.

### Sugar Production

Australia is also an export sugar producer, though at a cost. Sugar production was begun on the coastal plain of Queensland in the middle of the nineteenth century to supply the Australian market. Laborers were imported from Melanesia to work in the cane fields on what often amounted practically to a slave basis. When the Commonwealth of Australia was formed in 1901 by union of the six states (New South Wales, Victoria, Queensland, South Australia, Western Australia, Tasmania), Queensland was required to repatriate the imported "Kanaka" laborers in the interest of a "white Australia." However, since it was felt that production costs would be considerably raised by the use of exclusively white labor, the Com-

monwealth gave Queensland in return a high protective tariff on sugar. Operating behind this protective wall, the sugar industry has prospered in a tropical area where it was once argued that no white man could survive for very long at manual labor in the fields. Most of the original large estates have been divided into family farms worked by individual white farmers. This system of agriculture is very unusual for a commercial cane-sugar area. The Queensland sugar area is also unusual in the fact that it is probably the most thoroughly tropical area yet settled by white men doing hard manual work without benefit of native labor.

### ▶ Urbanization and Industrialization

While grazing and agriculture produce the great bulk of Australia's exports, most Australians are city dwellers, and the high degree of urbanization is one of the country's outstanding characteristics. In June 1958 the populations of the five largest cities were estimated as follows: Sydney 2,016,000; Melbourne 1,726,000; Brisbane 555,000; Adelaide 544,000; and Perth, including its port, Freemantle, 382,000 (estimates are for city proper). Thus 38 percent or two out of every five Australians were in the two largest cities, and 53 percent in one of the five largest cities. When smaller cities and towns are added the Australian population may be counted as well over 70-percent urban.

It will be noted that all of the five largest cities are seaports and that each is the capital of one of the five mainland states of the Commonwealth. One of the reasons for the striking degree of urban development and its concentration in the port cities is the heavily commercial nature of the Australian economy. A large proportion of the production from the country's rural areas is destined for export by sea. In addition, much of Australia's internal trade moves from port to port by coastal steamer. Growth of the respective capital-city ports has been further stimulated by the fact that each state originally built its own individual rail system focusing on its

A view of Melbourne, Australia's second largest city and port. The railroad yards in the center lie between the wharves and the downtown business district of the city. (Australian News and Information Bureau.)

particular port. Since the different states used different gauges in building their rail lines, necessitating expensive break of bulk at or near state frontiers, each major port tended to effectively dominate the business of its own state. (The rail system is now being changed by substitution of a standard gauge throughout the Commonwealth.)

Among other things, the high degree of urbanization in Australia is indicative of a high degree of industrialization. A relatively small labor force is needed for the extensive forms of agriculture and grazing which are characteristic of Australia. As a means of supporting an increased population, the Australian government has encouraged industrial development. The latter has been viewed as highly desirable, not only as a means of giving Australia a population more in keeping with the size and resources of the continent, but also as a means of providing more adequate armaments for defense and of securing greater stability through a more diversified and self-contained economy.

The rise of industry was facilitated by the formation of the Commonwealth, which gave a unified internal market and tariff protection for developing industries. Industrial progress has also been facilitated by the fact that the continent was able to provide many of the natural resources needed for the development of manufacturing. Australia produces many different economic minerals in at least small quantities. The most serious deficiencies appear to be in petroleum (the first major oil strike was made in 1953) and in the fertilizer minerals of nitrate, phosphate, and potash. The deficiency in fertiliz-

PART 7

*Africa*

# Introduction to Africa

Recent decades have seen a world-wide surge of interest in the awakening continent of Africa. Although many facets of African life have drawn attention, the world's interest has focused primarily on the continent's mineral wealth, its racial and tribal problems, its drive for political independence, and its increasing modernization.

Africa has long been famous for its gold and diamonds, and it still leads the world in the production of these minerals. But today it is the *diversity* of Africa's mineral wealth that is attracting more and more attention. The continent is a major producer of copper, cobalt, chromium, manganese, platinum, phosphate, and uranium; is a significant producer of iron ore, tin, vanadium, lead, zinc, silver, and asbestos; has large bauxite, petroleum, and natural gas reserves, all in an early stage of development; and has, in its southern reaches, impressive reserves and a substantial production of coal. A variety of other minerals are produced; for some of them, such as the rare metal columbium (used in making alloys that will withstand extreme heat), Africa is the world's leading source. Large unexploited reserves of a great many valuable minerals are known to exist.

But Africa's minerals, important as they are, attract less attention from day to day than its racial, tribal, and colonial problems. Frictions and tensions between Europeans and native Africans or Arabs are the most

An African village near Juba in the zone of tropical savanna climate of the Sudan republic. The village, in its thorn-bush enclosure, is on the bank of a good-sized river. But the photo was taken at the height of the dry season, and the stream bed reveals no trace of water. (Photograph from R. U. Light: *Focus on Africa*, American Geographical Society.)

familiar issues, but many others exist. Prior to World War II, most of Africa was controlled by Europeans. Only a handful of independent nations existed; the remaining units were possessions of European colonial powers. In these possessions, Europeans were a privileged class both socially and economically. But since the war, a spectacular drive for independence by African peoples has remade the political map of the continent and is bringing great changes in its social and economic order. From 1945 through 1960 no less than 23 independent nations emerged from a colonial status (map, p. 35). At the time of writing (early 1961), other units were moving toward independence. Thus in most of Africa, European colonialism is passing off the scene and local nationalism (perhaps better described as "Africanism" in many instances) is emerging as the dominant political force. Meanwhile a far-reaching modernization of Africa's economic, social, and cultural life is in progress. It is centered in the rapidly growing cities, but its influence is spreading to every corner of the continent.

## AREA, POPULATION, AND MAJOR AREAL DIVISIONS

Africa is the largest in area of the major world regions discussed in this book. Its 11.7 million square miles (including Madagascar) make it more than three times as large as the United States. But much of it is sparsely populated. The continent's total population in 1959 was estimated at 236 million, giving an average density of about 20 per square mile, as compared with a population of 179.3 million or slightly less than 50 per square mile for the United States according to the 1960 census. Five main areas of comparatively dense population exist in Africa (map, p. 12). They are (1) lands bordering the Gulf of Guinea in West Africa, particularly Nigeria and the southern parts of Ghana, Dahomey, and Togo (for locations of political units, see map, p. 466), (2) the Nile Valley in Egypt and the Sudan, (3) the coastal fringes of northwestern Africa in Algeria, Morocco, and Tunisia, (4) the East African highlands, particularly the highlands of Ethiopia and the region surrounding Lake Victoria in Kenya, Uganda, Ruanda-Urundi, and Tanganyika, and (5) the eastern and southern coasts and high interior plateaus (High Veld) of South Africa. Each of the foregoing regions is a key area in the political and economic geography of Africa. A few areas in Africa containing smaller concentrations of people are notable centers of mining and/or transportation and European influence. Prominent among these are (1) the Katanga mining region of the former Belgian Congo and the adjoining Copperbelt of Northern Rhodesia (map, p. 467), (2) the Salisbury-Bulawayo mineralized axis in the highlands of Southern Rhodesia, and (3) the ocean and rail gateway to the Congo Basin formed by two seaports and two political capitals: the port of Matadi and capital city of Léopoldville in the former Belgian Congo, and the port of Pointe Noire and capital city of Brazzaville in the former French Congo. Area and population data for the individual political units of Africa are given in Table 21.

Africa falls broadly into the two major divisions of North Africa, the Arab-Berber realm of the continent, which is mostly comprised of desert or steppe with a fringe of mediterranean climate in northwestern coastal sections; and Africa south of the Sahara, or Negro Africa, which is predominantly an area of tropical and subtropical grassland or scrub forest, but with sizable areas of tropical rain forest and of dry lands, including some areas classed as desert. Since North Africa has already been considered in some detail in Chapters 13 and 14, major attention in the present two chapters will be focused on sub-Saharan Africa.

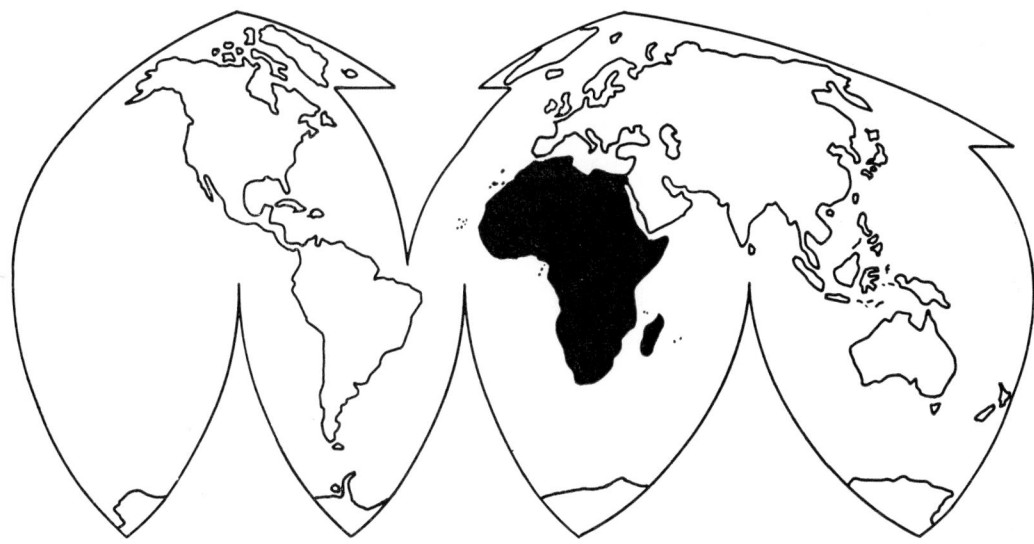

Location of Africa. (Boggs Equal Area Projection, copyright A. J. Nystrom & Co.)

## HISTORICAL BACKGROUND

By European or American standards, most parts of Africa were still extremely backward at the end of the nineteenth century. This was least true of the northern and southern extremities. Parts of northern Africa have been civilized for thousands of years, and by 1900 the more desirable parts of South Africa had been occupied by Europeans. However, at the dawn of the twentieth century the vast spaces of interior tropical Africa were still primitive and little known. The isolation of much of Africa from contact with more advanced areas until comparatively recent times was due to a combination of factors. Among these were (1) the presence of the great Sahara Desert barrier in North Africa, making difficult the penetration of tropical Africa by land from the north, (2) the inhospitable character of the African shoreline, which is exceptionally regular, thus lacking protected harbors and is bordered in many places by extensive sandbars and/or thick tropical forests (including considerable stretches of mangrove swamp) or desert, (3) the character of African rivers, which are generally shallow and

full of sandbars near their mouths and are blocked inland at varying distances by falls and rapids, thus rendering difficult penetration of the interior by water, (4) the hot, humid climate and the many diseases encountered by outsiders in the coastal areas, (5) the hostility of many African tribes, due in considerable part to slave-trading by Europeans, Americans, and Arabs, and (6) the lack of readily apparent sources of wealth in the interior which would justify the risks of penetration.

Although Westerners did not penetrate the deep interior to any marked degree until the last half of the nineteenth century, a fringe of trading posts and of way stations to service passing ships began to be established around the Atlantic and Indian Ocean coasts of the continent early in the colonial period. The articles of trade in greatest demand by Europeans were slaves and ivory. Slave-trading, primarily by Arabs, was already extensively developed at the beginning of the European colonial age, but it was greatly intensified when the establishment of mines and plantations in the Ameri-

# TABLE 21

## AFRICA: AREA AND POPULATION DATA

| POLITICAL UNIT | POLITICAL STATUS (EARLY 1961) | AREA (THOUSAND SQUARE MILES) | POPULATION (MILLIONS: 1959 ESTIMATES) [a] | DENSITY (PER SQUARE MILE: TO NEAREST WHOLE NUMBER) |
|---|---|---|---|---|
| Portuguese Africa [b] | | 799.9 | 11.95 | 15 |
|   Angola | Overseas province | 481.4 | 4.55 | 9 |
|   Mozambique | Overseas province | 302.3 | 6.31 | 21 |
|   Portuguese Guinea | Overseas province | 13.9 | 0.57 | 41 |
|   São Tomé and Principe | Overseas province | 0.37 | 0.064 | 172 |
|   Cape Verde Islands | Overseas province | 1.6 | 0.195 | 125 |
|   Madeira Islands | Administered as districts of Portugal | 0.31 | 0.267  (1950) | 867 |
| Spanish Africa | | 117.0 | 1.27 | 11 |
|   Ifni | Overseas province | 0.58 | 0.053 | 92 |
|   Spanish Sahara | Overseas province | 102.7 | 0.019 | 0.2 |
|   Rio Muni | Overseas province | 10.0 | 0.165 | 16 |
|   Fernando Po | Overseas province | 0.79 | 0.045 | 57 |
|   Places of Spanish sovereignty in Morocco [c] | Administered with Spain | 0.082 | 0.15 | 1768 |
|   Canary Islands | Two provinces of Spain | 2.8 | 0.85 | 302 |
| Republic of the Congo | Independent republic (former Belgian colony) | 905.4 | 13.84 | 15 |
| Ruanda-Urundi | Belgian trust territory | 20.9 | 4.78 | 229 |
| Independent republics of French Community | | 2891.2 | 29.42 | 10 |
|   Islamic Republic of Mauritania | Independent republic | 419.2 | 0.73 | 1.7 |
|   Republic of Senegal | Independent republic | 76.1 | 2.57 | 34 |
|   Republic of Mali [d] | Independent republic | 464.9 | 4.33 | 9 |
|   Republic of the Niger | Independent republic | 459.0 | 2.56 | 6 |
|   Republic of the Upper Volta | Independent republic | 105.8 | 4.03 | 38 |
|   Republic of the Ivory Coast | Independent republic | 124.5 | 3.12 | 25 |
|   Republic of Dahomey | Independent republic | 44.7 | 1.75 | 39 |
|   Gabon Republic | Independent republic | 103.1 | 0.43 | 4 |
|   Republic of the Congo [e] | Independent republic | 132.0 | 0.81 | 6 |
|   Central African Republic [f] | Independent republic | 238.2 | 1.19 | 5 |

| | | | | | |
|---|---|---|---|---|---|
| Republic of Chad | Independent republic | 495.8 | 2.63 | | 5 |
| Malagasy Republic (Madagascar) | Independent republic | 227.8 | 5.28 | | 23 |
| Overseas departments and territories of France | | | 929.9 | 11.51 | 12 |
| Algeria [g] | 17 overseas departments | 919.6 | 10.93 | | 12 |
| Réunion | Overseas department | 0.97 | 0.32 | | 334 |
| French Somaliland | Overseas territory | 8.5 | 9.07 | | 8 |
| Comoro Islands | Overseas territory | 0.84 | 0.185 | | 221 |
| Independent states of the Commonwealth of Nations | | | 1221.5 | 55.58 | 46 |
| South Africa | Independent state [b] | 472.7 | 14.68 | | 31 |
| South West Africa | Former mandated territory integrated with South Africa | 317.7 | 0.55 | | 1.7 |
| Nigeria | Independent federation | 339.2 | 33.66 | | 99 |
| Ghana | Independent republic | 91.8 | 6.69 (1960) | | 73 |
| British dependencies | | | 1525.7 | 36.43 | 24 |
| Cameroons | Trust territory | 34.1 | 1.62 | | 48 |
| Sierra Leone | Colony and protectorate [c] | 27.9 | 2.28 | | 82 |
| Gambia | Colony and protectorate | 4.0 | 0.29 | | 72 |
| Kenya | Colony and protectorate | 225.0 | 6.45 | | 29 |
| Tanganyika | Trust territory | 361.8 | 9.08 | | 25 |
| Uganda | Protectorate | 94.0 | 6.52 | | 69 |
| Zanzibar and Pemba | Protected sultanate | 1.02 | 0.304 | | 298 |
| Bechuanaland | Protectorate | 275.0 | 0.34 | | 1.2 |
| Basutoland | Colony | 11.7 | 0.67 | | 57 |
| Swaziland | Protectorate | 6.7 | 0.28 | | 41 |
| Mauritius [j] | Colony | .72 | 0.62 | | 863 |
| Federation of Rhodesia and Nyasaland: | | | | | |
| Southern Rhodesia | Self-governing colony | 150.3 | 2.86 | | 19 |
| Northern Rhodesia | Protectorate | 288.1 | 2.36 | | 8 |

[a] Estimates for many African political units vary widely; some official estimates—for example, the one cited for Ethiopia—may be grossly inflated. The United Nations estimated in 1959 that the total population of Africa was 236 million—a figure substantially smaller than the sum total of individual estimates shown in this table. Africa's area is about 11.7 million square miles; its average population density was about 20 per square mile in 1959.

[b] Apparent discrepancies in totals and averages in this table are due to rounding of figures.

[c] See footnote j, Table 13, p. 277.

[d] Formerly French Sudan.

[e] Formerly Middle Congo.

[f] Formerly Ubangi-Shari.

[g] See footnote i, Table 13.

[h] Scheduled to become a republic outside the Commonwealth of Nations on May 31, 1961.

[i] Scheduled for independence on April 27, 1961.

[j] Figures exclude small island dependencies of Mauritius in the Indian Ocean.

## TABLE 21 (Continued)

| POLITICAL UNIT | POLITICAL STATUS (EARLY 1961) | AREA (THOUSAND SQUARE MILES) | POPULATION (MILLIONS: 1959 ESTIMATES) | DENSITY (PER SQUARE MILE: TO NEAREST WHOLE NUMBER) |
|---|---|---|---|---|
| Nyasaland | Protectorate | 45.4 | 2.77 | 61 |
| Federation totals | | *483.8* | *7.99* | *17* |
| Arab League states | | 2252.6 | 52.40 | 23 |
| Egypt | Southern Region of United Arab Republic | 386.1 | 25.37 | 66 |
| Sudan | Independent republic | 967.5 | 11.39 | 12 |
| Libya | Independent kingdom | 679.4 | 1.17 | 1.7 |
| Tunisia | Independent republic | 48.3 | 3.93 | 81 |
| Morocco | Independent kingdom | 158.6 | 10.55 | 67 |
| Other independent states | | | | |
| Ethiopia [k] | Independent empire | 457.3 | 21.80 | 48 |
| Somali Republic [l] | Independent republic | 246.2 | 2.00 | 8 |
| Guinea | Independent republic | 94.9 | 2.71 | 29 |
| Cameroun | Independent republic | 166.8 | 3.23 | 19 |
| Togo | Independent republic | 22.0 | 1.12 | 51 |
| Liberia | Independent republic | 43.0 | 1.25 (1956) | 29 |

[k] See footnotes *e* and *f*, Table 13.
[l] See footnote *g*, Table 13.

Improved health services are gradually being brought to tropical Africa. The government nurse above is instructing a group of expectant mothers in Ghana regarding the proper care of the newborn child. (British Information Services.)

cas created a vast new market for slaves. One of the motives which led several European governments to claim territory in the interior of tropical Africa during the last quarter of the nineteenth century was a desire to stop this traffic at its source. Penetration of the interior was pioneered by a series of important journeys of exploration which began in the 1850s. These expeditions were undertaken by missionaries, traders, adventurers of various sorts, and in some cases government officials. Once the main outlines of inner African geography were revealed, a scramble for colonial territory took place among the European powers, beginning about 1881. By 1900 Africa had become predominantly a region of European dependencies—a status it retained for more than half a century.

## AFRICAN PROBLEMS

Recent decades have not only witnessed a transition from European colonialism to independence in many African countries, but they have also seen notable changes in the general conditions of African life. Improved standards of health and literacy among African peoples have resulted from the work of government agencies (photo, above) and

Christian missions. Better transportation facilities, particularly a wide extension of roads and airways, have made possible the marketing of farm products, including perishable items, from formerly inaccessible areas. The development of village stores has made available to millions of Africans a variety of European and American manufactured goods. Modern factories employing African labor have been established in a considerable number of urban centers, and improved agricultural techniques have been introduced in many areas. Today it is becoming increasingly difficult to find African peoples who are still essentially outside the range of Occidental influences.

The foregoing changes have affected some African peoples and areas much more than others. Not all of the effects have been favorable: for example, one result of better transportation and increased opportunities for employment in mines and factories has been a drift of Africans from tribal villages to overcrowded slum areas in towns and cities, often in numbers too great for the local job market to absorb. Nor has the total impact of change been sufficient as yet to lift Africa above its current status as one of the major underdeveloped regions of the world. Africa still shares many of the customary problems of such regions, including (1) a high incidence of illiteracy, poverty, hunger, and disease, (2) native customs, attitudes, and forms of social organization which tend to hinder the development of a modern economy, (3) inadequate overall facilities for transportation and communication, and (4) a lack of domestic capital which could be used to foster increased agricultural and industrial production and thus to raise the standard of living. Other problems arise from a heavy dependence on outside markets. Like most other underdeveloped regions, Africa's place in the commercial world is basically that of a producer of foodstuffs and raw materials for sale outside the region. In the world markets where African goods are sold, there is a considerable fluctuation in demand and in prices over a period of years. Whenever the market is glutted and prices are low, unemployment and severe distress may result in African producing areas where farmers have come to rely on cash returns from commercial production. Finally, there are problems of racial and tribal friction, which are among the most serious of all African problems at the present time, especially in certain areas such as South Africa and the former Belgian Congo.

## THE DIFFICULT AFRICAN ENVIRONMENT

Many of the problems of Africa are due to the presence of a natural environment which is difficult to manage, particularly by peoples equipped with a primitive technology. This environment varies considerably from place to place, but its broad outlines are relatively simple.

### ▶ Surface Configuration

Most of the continent is essentially comprised of a vast plateau, or more precisely, a series of plateaus at successive elevations. The plateau surfaces, predominantly level to rolling, are hollowed by shallow river basins, such as those of the Congo, Zambezi, and Orange. The principal areas of lowland plain are found in a narrow band around the coasts, averaging 20 to 100 miles in width, though in places considerably wider. Inland from the coast, abrupt or ragged escarpments mark the transition to the plateau, which customarily lies at an elevation of 1000 feet or higher. In southern and eastern Africa the general elevation rises to 2000 or 3000 feet, with considerable areas lying at 5000 feet or higher (inset map, p. 467). The principal belt of highlands occupies roughly the eastern third of the continent, from South Africa northward to Ethiopia. It is in this part of Africa that the largest numbers of Europeans are found. A great many live at altitudes of 4000 feet or higher, as indicated by the elevations of several important cities containing substantial European populations: in South Africa, Johannesburg (5700 feet) and Pretoria (4400); in Southern Rhodesia, Salisbury (4800) and Bulawayo (4400); in Kenya, Nairobi (5500).

In the highland belt of eastern Africa are located the highest mountain peaks and the principal lakes of the continent. The principal mountainous areas are found in (1) Ethiopia, (2) the general region of the East African lakes, and (3) the eastern part of South Africa. The loftiest summits lie within a radius of 250 miles from Lake Victoria (map, p. 467); they include mounts Kilimanjaro (19,565 feet) and Kenya (17,-040), which are volcanic cones, and Mount Ruwenzori (16,795), a remnant of an ancient plateau surface.

Lake Victoria (26,828 square miles), the largest lake in Africa, is surpassed in size among inland waters of the world only by the Caspian Sea and Lake Superior. Other large lakes found in East Africa include lakes Tanganyika, Nyasa, Kyoga, Albert, and several others (map, p. 467). Although these lakes, particularly Lake Victoria, are used considerably for local water transportation and to some extent as connecting links in long-distance transportation routes, their total traffic is only a tiny fraction of that carried by the Great Lakes of North America.

Aside from the discontinuous mountain zone in eastern and southern Africa, the most extensive area of high mountains is the Atlas Mountains of northwestern Africa, described briefly in Chapters 13 and 14.

One of the most spectacular features of Africa's physical geography is the Great Rift Valley, a steep-walled trough extending from Mozambique northward to the Red Sea and the valley of the Jordan River in south-western Asia (map, p. 467). The Rift Valley has several branches and much of it is occupied by lakes, rivers, seas, and gulfs. It contains most of the larger lakes of Africa, although Lake Victoria, located between two of its principal arms, is a conspicuous exception.

▶ *African Rivers*

The physical structure of Africa has significantly influenced the character of African rivers. The main rivers rise in interior uplands and descend by stages to the sea. At various points they descend abruptly, particularly at plateau escarpments, so that their courses are interrupted by rapids and waterfalls. These often block navigation a short distance inland from the sea. In addition, the navigation of many African rivers is hindered or prohibited by low water at certain seasons and by shallow and shifting delta channels. Among the important rivers which have built deltas are the Nile, Niger, Zambezi, Limpopo, and Orange. The Congo River, in contrast, has scoured a deep estuary 6 to 10 miles wide, which can be navigated by ocean vessels for a distance of about 85 miles to the seaport of Matadi in the former Belgian Congo. The Congo is used more for transportation than any other African river. A few miles above Matadi navigation is blocked by rapids, and goods must be transshipped by rail a distance of 230 miles to Léopoldville. Above that city the Congo and its major tributaries are navigable for long distances by river steamers and barges, although the continuity of transportation is broken in places by falls and rapids which are bypassed by rail (map, p. 467) or road. The character of water transportation on the Congo system is generally representative of Africa's inland waterways, which are discontinuous and interconnected by rail or highway in a manner not duplicated in any other continent.

The frequent falls and rapids of African rivers have a more positive side. They represent a great potential reservoir of hydro-

**AFRICA**
POLITICAL UNITS AND
URBAN AREAS
(POLITICAL CAPITALS UNDERLINED)

- ◉ 1,000,000 OR OVER
- ● 500,000 - 1,000,000
- ◌ 250,000 - 500,000
- ○ SELECTED SMALLER PLACES

0    400    800
MILES

**POLITICAL STATUS -- 1960**

POLITICAL
AFFILIATION

INDEPENDENT
COUNTRIES
- COMMONWEALTH OF NATIONS
- FRENCH COMMUNITY
- ARAB LEAGUE
- OTHER INDEPENDENT COUNTRIES
- FEDERATION OF RHODESIA AND NYASALAND

DEPENDENCIES
- BRITISH
- SOUTH AFRICAN
- FRENCH
- PORTUGUESE
- SPANISH
- BELGIAN

The mineral symbols on the right-hand map show the main producing areas as of 1960. A given symbol sometimes marks two or more closely-spaced areas. Notations of oil in Libya and of natural gas in Algeria show areas where the principal discoveries have been made. None of these areas was reported to be producing on a commercial basis as of late 1960. No symbol is shown for the famous uranium mine at Shinkolobwe near Jadotville in the Katanga mining region of the former Belgian Congo, as the mine is reported to be inactive. The principal sources of data concerning minerals were (1) George H. T. Kimble, *Tropical Africa*, 2 vols. (New York: Twentieth Century Fund, 1960), (2) *Oxford Regional Economic Atlas, The Middle East and North Africa* (London: Oxford University Press, 1960), (3) John H. Wellington, *Southern Africa: A Geographical Study*, 2 vols. (Cambridge: At the University Press, 1955), pp. 119–166, (4) Joseph E. Williams, ed., *The Prentice-Hall*

in early 1961) have been found in the neighboring country of Libya. In addition to phosphate and iron ore, Morocco produces ferroalloys, lead, and several other metals, and Tunisia produces lead.

*East Africa* has been relatively unimportant in mineral production. However, Tanganyika has large diamond mines; large deposits of copper are now being mined in Uganda; and both Kenya and Uganda have substantial, though undeveloped, deposits of iron ore.

Mineral production in Africa has been primarily in the hands of large European corporations. Modern, large-scale methods are employed in extracting and processing the ores for export. Managers and overseers at the mines are mainly Europeans, and native Africans or Arabs are employed as workers (photo, left).

## THE AFRICAN PEOPLES AND THEIR ECONOMY

Among the peoples who inhabit the African continent, excepting 5 to 6 million Europeans and somewhat less than a million Asians (mainly Indians), those south of the Sahara exhibit Negroid characteristics in varying degree, while those north of the desert and in Egypt are basically Caucasoid and speak languages, principally dialects of Arabic or Berber, which are quite distinct from the languages of Negro Africa. In the east-west grassland belt known as the Sudan, in the Sahara, and in the East African highlands and coastal areas, there has been considerable mixing of Negroid and non-Negroid peoples over a long period.

Most of the peoples of Negro Africa belong to one of two broad groupings: (1) the Bantu, most of whom live south of the equator or (2) the Guinea Coast and Sudanese peoples. The *Bantu peoples* speak languages

This celebrated picture, published previously in a collection of outstanding photographs called *The Family of Man* (New York: Simon and Schuster for the Museum of Modern Art, 1955), shows a Bushman hunter in the desolate Kalahari semidesert of Bechuanaland preparing to dispatch a cornered gemsbok. Africans who live primarily by hunting form a tiny minority of the continent's population, and their numbers, like those of the animals that support them, are dwindling. For a perceptive recent account of Bushman hunters in the Kalahari region, see Elizabeth Marshall Thomas, *The Harmless People* (New York: Knopf, 1959). (Life Photo by N. R. Farbman.)

belonging to the same language family, though individual languages are often different enough to be mutually unintelligible. The *Guinea Coast and Sudanese peoples,* in contrast, speak a great variety of languages; in fact, the areas of forest and grassland they inhabit have often been termed a linguistic "shatter belt," comparable to parts of Melanesia in the confused pattern of languages. These peoples have attained a somewhat higher level of development than most other Negroid peoples of Africa. Most of the African political units that gained independence between 1945 and 1960 are found in parts of the continent that they inhabit.

Three minor and relatively primitive Negroid groups, the Pygmies, Bushmen, and Hottentots, deserve mention. The *Pygmies,* averaging around 4½ feet in height, are found principally in the tropical rain forests of the Congo Basin. Formerly most Pygmies lived by hunting, using poisoned arrows, and by gathering roots, nuts, fruits, and other food in the forest. Today, however, most of them are farmers, although their food supply is still augmented by gathering and hunting. The *Bushmen,* found primarily in the Kalahari region of southwestern Africa, are also below average in height, although a little taller than the Pygmies. They are nomadic hunters, using poisoned arrows and spears (photo, p. 475), and constructing crude temporary shelters as they move about in search of game. They are expert trackers and stalkers of wild animals, and are also skilled in finding water. The latter is of vital importance in the semidesert country where they live. Like the Pygmies they are gatherers as well as hunters; their diet includes such items as roots, honey, gum from acacia trees, ant eggs, ostrich eggs, lizards, and locusts.

The *Hottentots* have nearly been eliminated as a separate people. The remnants live mainly on tribal reservations in South West Africa. They are primarily herdsmen, raising sheep, goats, and long-horned cattle. They live in semipermanent villages of oval huts built about a central open space. The village is surrounded by a thorn fence, and the animals are driven within the enclosure at night for protection. This type of village, known as a *kraal,* is often found among pastoral peoples of sub-Saharan Africa. Both the Hottentots and the Bushmen formerly ranged widely over southern Africa, but most of the lands they utilized were taken over by Europeans or by Bantu tribes pushing in from the north at roughly the same period that the Europeans began to move inland from the Cape of Good Hope.

### ▶ *African Agriculture*

The peoples of the Guinea Coast live principally by tilling the soil and growing tree crops such as the cacao tree and the oil palm. Some tribes among the Sudanese peoples are also cultivators, some are herdsmen, and many are both. The same is true of the Bantu. Some of the chief characteristics of the native agricultural and pastoral economy of Africa have been described as follows by L. D. Stamp: [2]

Along the Mediterranean borders we find an agriculture established from very early times, with cattle, the plow, cereals and Mediterranean fruits—especially barley, wheat, olives, figs and the grape. Southward toward the desert margins nomadic pastoralism based on sheep replaces cultivation; in the deserts cultivation is limited to oases, and human life depends on date palms and camels.

South of the deserts in the semiarid open lands of the Sudan are again pastoralists depending for their livelihood on cattle and sheep. Southward, with increasing rainfall and a modest rainy season, there is again some cultivation, precarious, and dependent mainly on sorghum and millet. Cultivation is by the hoe; use of the plow remains unknown.

The area of intermediate rainfall of the savanna between the steppes of the desert margins

---

[2] Stamp, *op. cit.* Pp. 147–151. Used by permission of the author and the publishers.

which are too dry and the forests of the equatorial margins which are too wet is favorable to cultivation. Large villages are the rule [photo, p. 457]; there have been in the past empires of considerable size. Dependence for food is on millet and corn (maize); latterly on groundnuts [peanuts] on the uplands and rice along the rivers. Tobacco is grown, sometimes cotton; kola nuts are gathered. Often cattle are bred, sometimes sheep and horses, and among the cultivators or mixed farming communities are tribes almost exclusively pastoral.

Unfortunately, where the rainfall becomes more reliable and where mixed farming should reach its maximum intensity, we encounter the "fly belts" where the tsetse fly virtually eliminates domestic animals. Here the basis of life becomes the yam, manioc, banana, and palm oil, with cocoa as a "cash crop" now developed to a great extent in [Ghana] and elsewhere.

As the closer forest is reached, villages are smaller, population sparser and patches of cultivation (shifting cultivation) more scattered.

On the plateaus of East Africa, and formerly in South Africa, the balance is somewhat different. The settled cultivators tend to be less numerous and subordinate to the aggressive, often warlike, pastoral tribes. It is here that wealth has come to be measured in head of cattle, independently of quality; indeed the cattle have little more practical value than the gold bars we civilized people bury in our vaults. Madagascar differs somewhat from the continental mainland in that cattle breeding is there associated with rice cultivation. . . .

### Shifting Cultivation

The system of agriculture commonly though somewhat misleadingly known as "shifting cultivation" is practiced through a very large part of tropical Africa. As a system it is better described as "land rotation" or "bush fallowing." In those areas inhabited by sedentary farming peoples, each village or settlement has proper to it a tract of surrounding land. The tract is probably only loosely defined except where settlements are close and population dense. In a given year the villagers working together as a community will clear a part of this village land, cutting and burning the woodland or scrub and then planting the crops appropriate to the climate and soil of the area. In due course the crops are harvested communally and the land used for a second and perhaps a third year. It is then abandoned, and a fresh tract of the village land is cleared. The abandoned land quickly becomes covered with a second-growth woodland

or scrub. In due course the clearings reach a full cycle, and if a given tract has been allowed to "lie" fallow for about fifteen years it may be regarded as fully rested. Bush clearing is largely man's work. There is also surrounding the village itself, often as a series of enclosed gardens or "compounds" attached to individual huts, the "women's land," cultivated regularly to afford a supply of vegetables for the pot. Often the kokoyams, peppers, beans, melons, bananas, etc., are scarcely grown at all in the open farmland. The women's land is enriched by house sweepings, ashes, refuse and manure afforded by chickens, goats and human beings.

The system has often been condemned as wasteful of natural forest, of land and of labor. But it has many good points. The natural forest is probably second growth of little value anyway. The land cleared in small patches protected by surrounding woodland escapes the evils of soil erosion, and its nutrient status temporarily enhanced by the ashes of the burnt bush is maintained by the fallowing, the soil not being exposed to the atmosphere long enough for serious oxidation. Expenditure of labor is minimized by burning, and no attempt is made to remove large stumps. The cultivation is by hand—by hoeing—so the stumps do not constitute the obstacles there would be if the plow were used. We may accordingly agree with Lord Hailey when he says that shifting cultivation is "less a device of barbarism than a concession to the character of a soil which needs long periods for recovery and regeneration."

### Peasant Farming in Low-latitude Africa

At least two thirds of the people of Africa depend directly on agriculture for a livelihood. In many parts of the continent, particularly in low-latitude areas, the proportion is much higher than this. Most crops and livestock produced on farms of native Africans are grown for the use of the cultivators and their families or for a purely local sale. In other words, these farmers operate in large measure on a subsistence or semisubsistence basis. However, the proportion of cash crops grown for export or for sale in urban centers has been increasing in recent years. This has been partly the result of taxation and other governmental pressures, but has also been due to the desire of Africans for cash with which to purchase manufactured goods or food. In some parts of tropical Africa, such as Nigeria and Ghana, a class of peasant cultivators has developed which is heavily dependent on the sale of cash crops. In southern Nigeria and southern Ghana, the cacao tree and the oil palm are the main sources of cash income for these farmers. Between 60 and 65 percent of the world's annual exports of cocoa beans come from Africa, as do approximately two thirds of all exports of palm oil and nine tenths of all exports of palm kernels. Most of this production originates on small farms in western and central Africa.

Large quantities of cotton and peanuts are produced for cash sale on farms in the tropical savannas and steppes. The Sudan and Uganda are the largest cotton producers in tropical Africa. The Sudan's production comes largely from irrigated tracts in a desert climate. Nigeria is the largest producer of peanuts, though large quantities are grown by a number of units in former French West Africa, and smaller quantities by other countries that share the tropical savanna or steppe climate.

### Commercial Plantation Farming

Only in scattered areas of tropical Africa have large commercial plantations become well established. Some of the largest plantations are corporate enterprises in the former Belgian Congo, with palm oil and palm kernels as major products. The Firestone Company, an American concern, has developed large rubber plantations in Liberia. On the whole, however, commercial plantations have been little developed in West Africa. In British East Africa sisal, which yields a hard fiber used for making twine and rope, is an important plantation crop. Africa produces and exports between 60 and 65 percent of the world's supply. Tanganyika is the leading producing and exporting country in Africa and in the world. Tea is produced on European estates in the highlands of Kenya, Nyasaland, and several other countries; however, African production of this crop is less than 5 percent of the world total. Coffee is widely grown in tropical Africa, both on European holdings and on African farms. The continent normally accounts for somewhat more than 15 percent of world production and exports. In Southern Rhodesia, tobacco, grown primarily on European farms, is the main cash crop and agricultural export.

### Farming in Areas Outside the Tropics

In the parts of Africa that lie outside the tropics, much of the farming by Africans or Arabs is on a subsistence or near-subsistence basis. But these sections of Africa also have a considerable development of commercial agriculture. It is carried on primarily by Egyptian cotton growers in the Nile Valley (who produce about half of Africa's cotton), by European growers of livestock, grain, fruit, and sugar cane in South Africa, and by European or Arab fruit growers (citrus, grapes, olives) in Algeria, Morocco, and Tunisia. Most European farms in Africa, whether in the low latitudes or middle latitudes, are worked by African or Arab labor.

### ▶ The Importance of Livestock

Many Africans are pastoral. However, most Africans who live by tilling the soil also keep some animals, even if only goats and poultry. The significance of livestock in the life of the African is portrayed in the following selection: [3]

> Many [African peoples] rely largely on cattle. This is especially true of the . . . Basuto, Bechuanas, Hereros, Watusi, Masai, Gallas, Nilotic Negroes, and Fulbes, some of whom have become so dependent on cattle that if the latter were destroyed their whole economic and social order would be disrupted and even their religion affected.

---

[3] H. L. Shantz, "Agricultural Regions of Africa. Part I—Basic Factors." *Economic Geography,* v. 16 (1940), pp. 126–128. Used by permission of *Economic Geography.*

Masai herdsmen with their animals in the crater of an enormous extinct volcano (Ngorongoro Crater) in Tanganyika. Wild animals may be seen grazing on the floor of the crater in the distance. Africa's increasing cattle population is steadily constricting the habitat of wild species. (Edgar Monsanto Queeny.)

It is difficult to overestimate the importance of domestic animals in the lives of the African natives. While wives represent to some extent real property or estates, cattle, sheep, and goats represent currency. In many tribes wives are secured only by the payment to the woman's family of a certain number of animals, say 30 goats or sheep or 10 cattle. . . . This is even the practice in the essentially crop-producing tribes of the Bantu peoples. Among the tribes such as the Watusi, Masai, and others which are dependent on cattle for their daily food, the whole social, economic, and religious pattern of their society is dependent on cattle. . . . These are extreme cases, but even in a crop-raising tribe such as the Kikuyu sheep or goats constitute the basis of the most important social and economic events in the life of the individual. . . .

Cattle, sheep, and goats occupy the greater part of the African continent. They are absent or scarce in the extreme deserts . . . and the heavy tropical forest or coarse high grass savannas of the Congo and the Guinea Coast.

With these exceptions, they are distributed over the remainder of the continent. . . .

The great grasslands between the tropical rain forests and the deserts and the mountain grasslands of central and southern Africa were occupied by cattle-raising peoples. They dominate the adjacent agricultural tribes and often hold within their organization a dependent group of soil tillers. The Masai of East Africa depend entirely on cattle [photo, above] which they milk and bleed for their daily food. So close is this relationship that they cannot migrate without their herds. Moreover, they regard these cattle as almost a divine gift and husband them as carefully as they would their own children. The same can be said of the Banyoro and the Watusi. Each animal has a name, the herds are often carefully sorted as to color, and the greeting of the nobles of the tribe asks first about the welfare of the cattle, then about the welfare of the wives and children.

The great grasslands support the herds throughout the year in most places, and there is no set migration. In the drier portions migrations are often forced by lack of grass for the herds. . . .

Sheep and goat herdsmen have ranged nearer the deserts and been probably more nomadic than the cattlemen. . . . The goat and the chicken have been a boon to the less favored [tribes]. Everywhere, even in the dense forests of tropical Africa, these animals constitute a part of the diet of the agricultural [tribes]. . . . One seldom sees a native moving without the accompanying coop with chickens inside or tied to the outside, and goats are generally tethered also.

One of the major needs of Africa is the development of strains of grasses suited to African conditions which will be more nutritious for livestock than the native grasses now present. The latter are often coarse, tough, and not very nutritious, so that the carrying capacity of the native grasslands is relatively low. Considerable work with grasses has been done by government experiment stations in Africa, with results that seem promising. It is conceivable that Africa may eventually become a major exporter of livestock products, provided better grasses can be widely introduced, the menace of the tsetse fly brought under control, and the tribesmen induced to take an interest in improving the quality of their herds, rather than thinking of them in terms of mere numbers. At present the largest exports of livestock products are from European farms and ranches in South Africa.

prised of secondary forests, often of poor quality, interspersed with grasslands. Sierra Leone has gained some note in recent times as an exporter of high-grade iron ore and diamonds. The same is true of its neighbor, the Republic of Liberia, which bears a broad resemblance to Sierra Leone in size, physiography, climate, vegetation, and types of production. Each of these units was originally established as a haven for freed slaves, Sierra Leone under British auspices in the late eighteenth century and Liberia under American auspices in the early nineteenth century. Liberia has some notable rubber plantations developed by the Firestone Company, and rubber is by far the largest export by value, with iron ore second and diamonds third. Diamonds, iron ore, palm kernels, and coffee are the main exports of Sierra Leone.

Sierra Leone's capital, largest city, and main port is Freetown (77,000), located on an excellent natural harbor. Monrovia (45,-000) is the capital and largest city and port of Liberia. It has an artificial harbor, constructed with American aid. The Bomi Hills iron-mining district lies about 40 miles to the northwest of the city. Two new iron-mining areas are being developed in widely separated interior sections of Liberia, one in the extreme north and the other in the southeast.

Gambia, a British colony and protectorate, occupies a 20-mile-wide strip of savanna grassland and woodland extending inland for 300 miles along either side of the Gambia River. The major commercial product, peanuts, supplies more than nine tenths of all exports by value.

### ▶ British East Africa

The countries of British East Africa include the colony and protectorate of Kenya, the United Nations trust territory of Tanganyika, the protectorate of Uganda, and the protectorate of Zanzibar and Pemba, an island sul-

tanate off the coast of Tanganyika. Physically, the mainland units consist of a lowland along the coast of Kenya and Tanganyika, rising to interior plateaus which exceed 5000 feet over an extensive section in southwestern Kenya as well as in some sections of the adjoining units, particularly Tanganyika. A tropical savanna type of climate prevails, with temperatures considerably moderated by altitude in the higher interior lands. The vegetation cover is comprised of woodlands interspersed with areas of grass and bushland. Much of northern Kenya and some parts of northern Uganda are very dry and desertlike.

Most parts of Kenya and Tanganyika and sizable areas in Uganda have an average population density of less than 25 per square mile. The principal areas with a greater-than-average density are found (1) in a fairly broad belt surrounding Lake Victoria, (2) in the highlands of Kenya around Nairobi, and (3) in fairly small, discontinuous areas along the coast of Tanganyika and extreme southern Kenya.

The overwhelming majority of the population in Kenya, Tanganyika, and Uganda is comprised of African tribes; among the better known of these are the Kikuyu and Luo tribes of Kenya and the Baganda tribe of Uganda, the pastoral Masai tribe of Kenya and Tanganyika, and the prosperous, coffee-growing Wachagga tribe on the slopes of Mount Kilimanjaro in Tanganyika. European, Asian (mainly Indian), and Arab minorities exist in all three units. Population elements were estimated in 1958 as follows: [7]

| | *Kenya* | *Tanganyika* | *Uganda* |
|---|---|---|---|
| Africans | 6.1 million | 8.8 million | 5.7 million |
| Asians | 165,000 | 81,000 | 58,000 |
| Europeans | 65,000 | 21,000 | 9,600 |
| Arabs | 35,000 | 21,000 | 2,100 |

Kenya represents the principal area of European settlement. Most Europeans are

---

[7] Margery Perham, "White Minorities in Africa." *Foreign Affairs*, v. 37 (July 1959), p. 639.

concentrated in the volcanic southwestern highlands. About 4000 European families in Kenya operate plantations which produce the bulk of the country's exports. Coffee and tea are the most prominent items in a considerable list of export commodities. Nairobi (197,500), located toward the southeastern edge of the main area of European settlement, is the capital of Kenya and the largest city in British East Africa. The city has one of the most important international airports in tropical Africa. Nairobi is connected by the Kenya–Uganda Railway with Uganda and with the seaport of Mombasa (85,000) on the Indian Ocean (map, p. 467). Mombasa, the most important port in British East Africa, handles nearly all of Kenya's foreign trade and sizable amounts of trade for neighboring countries. It has an excellent deepwater harbor.

Kenya attracted much notice in the early 1950s as a result of terrorist activities by a secret native society, the Mau Mau, whose avowed purpose was to oust the European population. The Mau Mau were principally members of the Kikuyu tribe of cultivators. Numerous atrocities, partially against Europeans and their livestock but mainly against Africans friendly to Europeans, created a serious state of emergency, and British troops were brought in to restore order. The Mau Mau uprising has left a heritage of suspicion between Africans and Europeans in Kenya which is complicating the country's progress toward independence.

Tanganyika, with a smaller European, Asian, and Arab population than Kenya, and more harmonious relations among its racial groups, appears to be proceeding uneventfully toward independence. Dar es Salaam (129,000) is the capital, largest city, and main port. Only in 1956 did it acquire a modern deep-water harbor. Tanganyika's main rail line, the Central Tanganyika Railway, extends from Dar es Salaam to Kigoma on Lake Tanganyika. A branch line reaches Lake Victoria, and another branch extends to a mining area at Mpanda (map, p. 467).

Tanganyika's exports, like Kenya's, consist primarily of agricultural commodities, and, as in Kenya, the greater part of the export value is supplied by European plantations. Sisal, most of which is produced on large plantations in northeastern Tanganyika, is by far the leading export. It accounts for roughly half of the country's exports by value, and moves to overseas markets through the port of Tanga (38,000) or through Dar es Salaam. Tanganyika is the world's largest producer and exporter of sisal.

The landlocked protectorate of Uganda, almost purely African in population, is notable for the greater-than-average prosperity of its African peoples. This prosperity is based primarily on two major export crops, cotton (photo, p. 3) and coffee, which are grown almost exclusively by African farmers and supply about two thirds of the total value of exports. The protectorate has long been administered with African interests paramount. The largest urban place is Kampala (60,000), the capital of the Buganda kingdom. This kingdom, the homeland of the Baganda tribe, is the most prominent element in the political structure of Uganda. Suspicion, jealousy, and fear of the Baganda by other African peoples has been one of several internal stresses that have interfered with Uganda's progress toward independence. The town of Entebbe (8500) on Lake Victoria is the center of British administration in Uganda. Jinja is a textile center in eastern Uganda. Its mills are supplied with electricity from a hydroelectric power station at the Owen Falls Dam on the Nile River.

The island protectorate of Zanzibar and Pemba, once a major slave-trading center, is today chiefly renowned for large plantations which produce the bulk of the world supply of cloves. The plantations are owned by Arabs or Indians. The largest racial element in the protectorate's population, however, is comprised of Africans.

British East Africa has experienced a

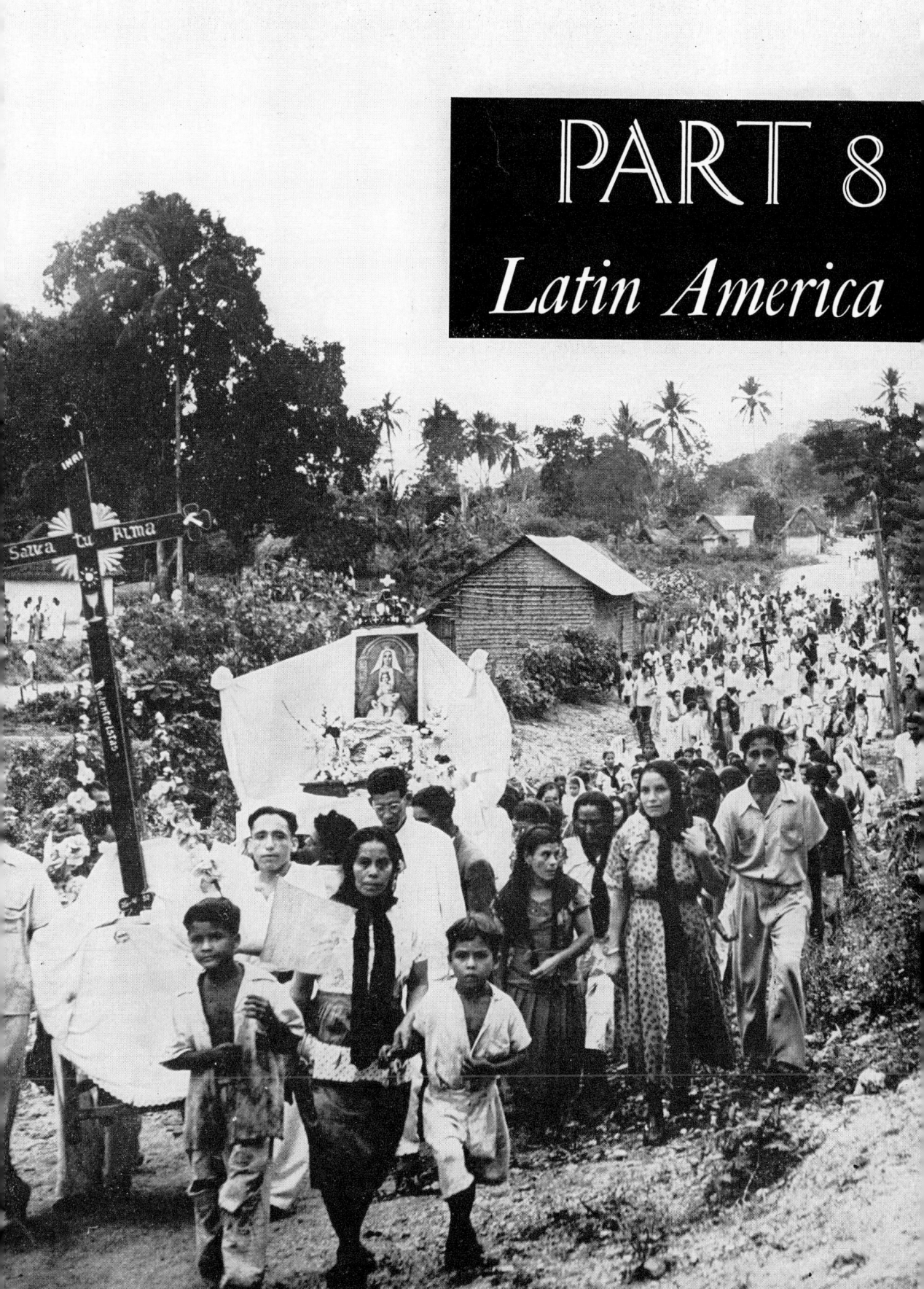

# PART 8
## Latin America

# Introduction to Latin America

The land portion of the Western Hemisphere to the south and southeast of the United States has come to be known as Latin America (maps, pp. 516 and 518). Both the name of this region and its ways of life reflect the importance of culture traits inherited from the Latin-European nations of Spain, Portugal, and France. Spanish is the prevailing language in 18 of the 20 Latin American republics, the exceptions being Brazil and Haiti where, respectively, Portuguese and French are used. Roman Catholicism, also a heritage from Mediterranean Europe, is the main religious faith of the region and is the official religion in

some nations. The feudalistic *hacienda,* or large estate, transplanted from Spain and Portugal, is perhaps better preserved in parts of Latin America than in the countries of origin. Nor are all the ties with Latin Europe indirect: newcomers from Portugal, Spain, and Italy are very prominent in Latin American immigrant lists.

It should not be assumed that the transplanting of European cultures to Latin America has been achieved without essential modification or that a uniform culture prevails today throughout the region. Many Latin American culture traits are a heritage from native Indians, imported Africans, or

Native Indians constitute a major population element in several Latin American countries. These Indian coffee-pickers in Guatemala are engaged in separating the ripe red coffee berries from the immature green ones. (Foreign Agricultural Service, U. S. Department of Agriculture.)

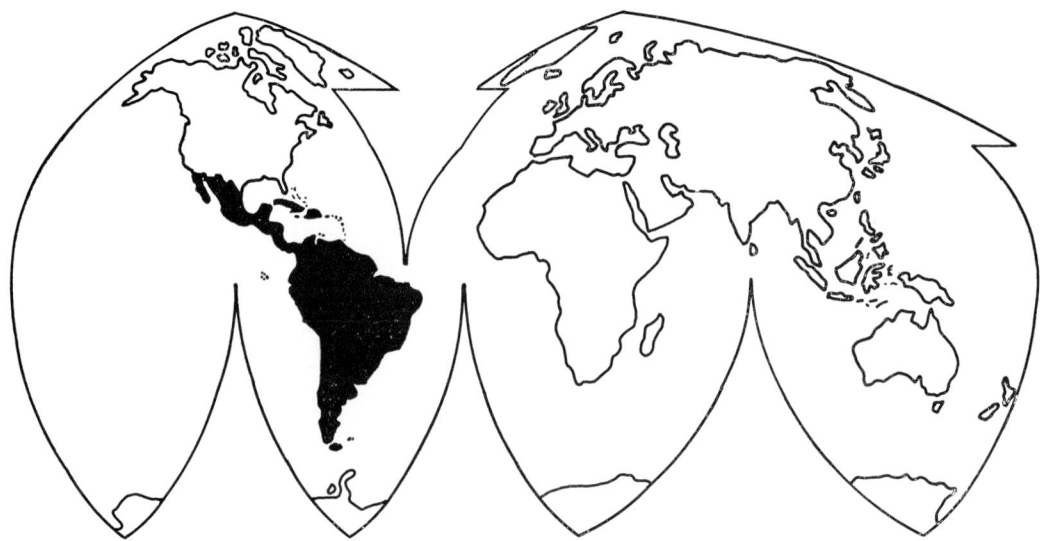

Location of Latin America. (Boggs Equal Area Projection, copyright A. J. Nystrom & Co.)

other non-European groups, and the cultural impress of these groups has varied unequally from one part of Latin America to another. Nevertheless, many features of a common Latin culture are discernible in most parts of the region, and the civilization of Latin America as a whole stands in recognizable contrast to that of Anglo-America, which has primary roots in Great Britain and in Germany, the Scandinavian countries, and other countries of northwestern continental Europe.

## PHYSICAL DIMENSIONS

With a land area of slightly more than 7.9 million square miles, Latin America is outranked in size by Africa, the Soviet Union, Anglo-America (including Greenland), and the Orient. However, its maximum latitudinal extent of more than 85 degrees or nearly 5900 statute miles is greater than that of any other world region, and its maximum east-west measurement, amounting to more than 82 degrees of longitude, is by no means unimpressive. Yet Latin America is not so large as these figures might suggest, for its two main parts are offset from each other.

The northern part of the region, known as Caribbean or Middle America, trends sharply northwest from the north-south oriented continent of South America. The latter continent is thrust much farther into the Atlantic Ocean than is the Caribbean realm or its northern neighbor, Anglo-America. In fact, the meridian of 80°W, which intersects the west coast of South America in Ecuador and Peru, passes through Pittsburgh, Pennsylvania (inset map, p. 518). Africa lies less than 2000 statute miles east of Brazil.

## DIVERSITY OF LATIN AMERICAN PEOPLES AND CULTURES

Statistics on physical size and shape, however, do not answer the basic questions of significance. What is Latin America? How many people live there and what are they like? What are their political, economic, and social viewpoints? Are they the masters of their own destiny? What is the character of the land they live upon? In short, how does Latin America fit into the world pattern of major regions?

### ▶ Variations in Population Density in Latin America

The total population of Latin America was estimated at 200.5 million in 1959, as compared with a total of 179.3 million people for the 50 states of the United States according to the 1960 census. But as Latin America embraces well over twice the area of the United States, its over-all population density is correspondingly less, amounting to 25 per square mile in 1959, as compared with an average over-all density of some 50 per square mile for the United States in 1960. However, the Latin American population is more unevenly distributed than that of the United States. Some sections of Latin America exhibit rural population densities which are much heavier than any to be found within areas of comparable size in the United States. On the other hand, a much larger proportion of Latin America is sparsely inhabited. At present the populations in both Latin America and the United States are growing through natural increase at very rapid rates, with the estimated over-all rate of increase in Latin America being somewhat the higher.

### ▶ Political Diversity

The 200 million people of Latin America are organized into political units that vary tremendously in size and political status. Most of the population is contained in the 20 independent republics. These countries broke away from European control in the nineteenth century. In most of them, democratic processes have developed very slowly, and dictatorships of various kinds are still common. The republics vary in size from gigantic Brazil, which occupies more than a third of the total Latin American land

area and boasts nearly a third of its total population, down to tiny El Salvador, which possesses only .1 percent of the land area, though containing a disproportionately high 1.2 percent of the aggregate population. The remainder of Latin America's population is found in units that are affiliated politically with the United Kingdom, France, the Netherlands, or the United States. All of these are located in the Caribbean region or adjoining parts of northern South America. Most of them are even smaller than El Salvador in area, population, or both. The different units vary a great deal in their precise relationships to the overseas nations with which they are linked. Most of them, however, have much latitude in handling their internal affairs. Area and population data for the individual political units of Latin America are given in Table 27, pages 520–521.

### ▶ Economic Diversity

The people of Latin America are supported primarily by various forms of subsistence and commercial agriculture, supplemented in some areas by mining, manufacturing, and trade. Between one half and three fifths of the total population live on a subsistence, hand-to-mouth basis within a self-contained economic orbit that has little contact with foreign commerce and exchange. However, the economy of Latin America also reflects —with marked variations from area to area —the presence of the foreign investor. Large amounts of foreign capital have been invested in oil wells and refineries, factories, mines, transportation lines, commercial plantations, and other sources of profit. Most of the invested capital is from the United States, which has placed between 25 and 30 percent of its private long-term foreign investment in Latin America. Investments from West Germany are increasingly important. Britain and France also have investments in Latin America, but these are small and account for declining percentages of the total foreign investment in the region.

Factories and other enterprises financed directly by Latin American private or public capital represent still a third ingredient in the economic structure. Often such capital is borrowed from sources outside the country concerned.

### ▶ Ethnic Diversity

The inhabitants of this region do not evince much ethnic uniformity. In only three nations—Argentina, Uruguay, and Costa Rica—have European strains been preserved on a large scale with little admixture by Indians or Negroes. (Scattered districts in other political units are predominantly European.)

Native Indians comprise more than half of the total population in the highland nations of Guatemala, Bolivia, Ecuador, and Peru, as well as in the lowland country of Paraguay. They are also a major population element in southern Mexico and El Salvador. In outlying areas, especially in the basin of the Amazon River and in Panama, scattered lowland Indian tribes live more or less apart from the world about them.

The Negro is found in greatest numbers on the islands and along the hot, wet coastal lowlands of Caribbean America and areas near by. Except in Puerto Rico, Cuba, and the Dominican Republic, nearly all Caribbean islanders are Negroes. On the mainland, the east coast of Brazil between Cape São Roque and Salvador and the northern hinterland of Rio de Janeiro have sizable Negro populations, as do small districts in French Guiana, Surinam (Dutch Guiana), British Guiana, Venezuela, and Panamá. A major concentration of Negroes is found along the lower valley of the Magdalena River and on the Caribbean coast of Colombia.

In most of Latin America, however, mixed bloods predominate. Most of the region exhibits a primary mixture of Spanish and native Indian stocks, resulting in a heterogeneous group known as *mestizos*. Mixed bloods of Negro-native Indian ancestry are usually termed *zambos*. European-Negro mixtures, or *mulattoes*, are fewer in number and are found chiefly in the Caribbean units that are affiliated with overseas nations.

## SIMILARITIES AND DIFFERENCES BETWEEN LATIN AMERICA AND OTHER MAJOR WORLD REGIONS

From the foregoing description one can infer that Latin America is an unusual amalgam of ideas, pursuits, and men. Yet this region is very much a part of the world geographic pattern, possessing characteristics which, however altered, tend to recur in other parts of the world. In fact, a comparison of Latin America with each of the other world regions considered in the present volume reveals many interesting and significant similarities and differences.

### ▶ Latin America and the Soviet Union

In over-all political and economic organization Latin America is unlike the Soviet Union. It is not, in other words, a unitary block of land controlled by a single dictatorial government and undergoing rapid and sometimes ruthless economic development according to a preconceived plan. Yet certain instructive comparisons can be made between recent economic developments in Latin America and the USSR. For example, in Mexico a government-enforced program of land reform has been introduced during the past five decades. Its primary objective has been the breaking up of large estates and redistribution of the property among the many landless peons.

By subdividing large holdings Mexico is making an appeal to man's inherent love of the land and is trusting that the new responsibility will, with government aid and ad-

# TABLE 27

## LATIN AMERICA: AREA AND POPULATION DATA

| POLITICAL UNIT [a] | POLITICAL STATUS (EARLY 1961) | AREA (THOUSAND SQUARE MILES) | | POPULATION (MILLIONS: 1959 ESTIMATES) | | DENSITY (PER SQUARE MILE: TO NEAREST WHOLE NUMBER) |
|---|---|---|---|---|---|---|
| *Caribbean America* [b] | | | *2024.6* | | *85.54* | *42* |
| Mexico | Independent republic | | 760.3 | | 33.30 | 44 |
| Guatemala | Independent republic | 42.0 | | 3.65 | | 87 |
| El Salvador | Independent republic | 7.7 | | 2.52 | | 326 |
| Honduras | Independent republic | 43.3 | | 1.89 | | 44 |
| Nicaragua | Independent republic | 57.1 | | 1.42 | | 25 |
| Costa Rica | Independent republic | 19.7 | | 1.13 | | 57 |
| Panama [c] | Independent republic | 28.8 | | 1.03 | | 36 |
| Totals: Central American republics | | | 198.6 | | 11.63 | 59 |
| Colombia | Independent republic | | 439.5 | | 13.82 | 31 |
| Venezuela | Independent republic | | 352.1 | | 6.51 | 18 |
| Panama Canal Zone | United States military reservation | 0.55 | | 0.057 | | 103 |
| British Honduras | British colony | 8.9 | | 0.090 | | 10 |
| British Guiana | British colony | 83.0 | | 0.550 | | 7 |
| Surinam (Dutch Guiana) | Autonomous unit of Netherlands kingdom | 55.1 | | 0.255 | | 5 |
| French Guiana | Overseas department of France | 35.1 | | 0.030 | | 0.85 |
| Totals: Mainland affiliates of overseas nations | | | 182.7 | | 0.98 | 5 |
| Cuba | Independent republic | 44.2 | | 6.47 | | 146 |
| Haiti | Independent republic | 10.7 | | 3.46 | | 323 |
| Dominican Republic | Independent republic | 18.8 | | 2.89 | | 154 |
| Totals: Island republics | | | 73.7 | | 12.82 | 174 |
| Puerto Rico | Self-governing commonwealth affiliated with the United States | 3.4 | | 2.35 | | 683 |
| U. S. Virgin Islands | United States dependency | 0.133 | | 0.030 | | 226 |
| Bahama Islands | British colony | 4.4 | | 0.140 | | 32 |
| West Indies [d] | Semi-independent federation of British colonies | 8.0 | | 3.21 | | 401 |
| British Virgin Islands | British colony | 0.067 | | 0.008 | | 119 |

| | | | | |
|---|---|---|---|---|
| Guadeloupe [e] | Overseas department of France | 0.687 | 0.264 | 384 |
| Martinique | Overseas department of France | 0.426 | 0.270 | 635 |
| Netherlands Antilles [f] | Autonomous unit of Netherlands kingdom | 0.371 | 0.195 | 526 |
| Totals: Island affiliates of overseas nations | | 17.5 | 6.47 | 369 |
| *Native Indian countries of South America* | | *1183.2* | *19.83* | *17* |
| Bolivia | Independent republic | 424.2 | 3.42 | 8 |
| Peru | Independent republic | 496.2 | 10.52 | 21 |
| Ecuador [g] | Independent republic | 105.7 | 4.17 | 39 |
| Paraguay | Independent republic | 157.0 | 1.72 | 11 |
| *Brazil* | Independent republic | *3287.2* | *64.22* | *20* |
| *Countries of the southern mid-latitudes* | | *1431.3* | *30.88* | *22* |
| Argentina | Independent republic | 1072.7 | 20.61 | 19 |
| Chile | Independent republic | 286.4 | 7.47 | 26 |
| Uruguay | Independent republic | 72.2 | 2.80 | 39 |
| Grand totals | | 7926.3 | 200.47 | 25 |

[a] The Falkland Islands, a British colony in the South Atlantic located somewhat more than 400 miles to the east of Argentina and claimed by that country, are not included in the table. Area of the Falklands (excluding Antarctic dependencies): 4618 sq. mi.; estimated total population, about 2250 in 1958.

[b] Apparent discrepancies in totals and averages in this table are due to rounding of figures.

[c] Figures do not include the Canal Zone.

[d] About 85 percent of the population of the West Indies federation is contained in the three most populous units: Jamaica (4411 sq. mi.; est. pop. 1,671,000; density 379/sq. mi.), Trinidad and Tobago (1980 sq. mi.; est. pop. 817,000; density 413/sq. mi.), and Barbados (166 sq. mi.; est. pop. 239,000; density 1436/sq. mi.).

[e] Includes two main and five lesser islands.

[f] Includes Curaçao, Aruba, Bonaire, and three smaller island units.

[g] Figures include the Galapágos Islands, a dependency of Ecuador.

vice, result eventually in higher yields per unit of area and a higher standard of living per person. In the Soviet Union, where the former private holdings have been amalgamated into large collective farms or state farms, the stated objectives—higher agricultural production and a higher standard of living—are the same as in Mexico. The methods, however, are quite different. The Soviet leaders have placed their dependence in a collectivized system of agriculture controlled from above and fitted into an over-all economic plan for the entire nation. Private ownership of farm land has been abolished (though each family is allotted a garden plot to till as it sees fit), and farming has been made to resemble more and more a factory type of enterprise. Land reform in Mexico has also proceeded according to a plan—but a plan which depends for success on giving each peon access to land—*his* land. He may or may not own it outright and he owns neither the water nor mineral rights to it (these being reserved by the government), but he has the right of access to it as long as he cares for it properly. Nearly 2 million peon families have thus been granted access to land within the past 45 years. Some have acquired private holdings, but many are members of *ejidos*—communities whose members may till, but usually not own, their individual plots of land.

### ▶ Latin America and Europe

In political organization Latin America bears a certain resemblance to Europe. Each of these world regions contains a large number of individual political units which vary widely in population, area, mode of governance, and other respects. However, unlike some nations in Europe, no Latin American country can boast a world-wide political and economic system with lifelines reaching over the globe toward raw materials and markets in outlying nations and political dependencies. Several of the Latin American republics have small island possessions,[1] but these are trivial when compared with the remaining overseas dependencies of Great Britain or France, not to speak of the many former colonies that are still aligned with Britain or France in the Commonwealth of Nations and French Community. Far from being generators of economic power, the republics of Latin America, as well as the politically dependent or semidependent units, exhibit a high degree of economic dependence on the United States and Europe. Most of the trade of Latin America, for example, is with the latter two areas.

### ▶ Latin America and Anglo-America

Latin America bears a certain resemblance to Anglo-America in the nature and arrangement of its major topographic features. The major land mass within each of these world regions exhibits a gross physical pattern of high rugged mountains with associated plateaus and basins at the west, lower and generally older highlands and uplands at the east, and broad plains in the center. In each case more than half of the central region of plains lies within the drainage area of a single river system—the Amazon system in Latin America and the Mississippi-Missouri system in Anglo-America.

In political and economic respects, however, these New World regions are very different. The two massive, stable political units of Anglo-America—the United States and Canada—stand in marked contrast to the fragmented political order and notorious governmental instability of Latin America. The tremendous economic productivity and

---

[1] The principal island possessions of the Latin American republics include the Galápagos Islands (Ecuador) and Easter Island and Sala y Gómez (Chile), all in the Pacific Ocean. In recent years Argentina has contested British claims to the Falkland Islands, in the Atlantic. Argentina and Chile have claims to portions of Antarctica.

general prosperity of the Anglo-American nations place them in a different class from the underdeveloped and often poverty-stricken political units which comprise most of Latin America.

## ▶ Latin America and the Orient

Latin America, like the Orient, is in part a region of heavy population pressure, primitive or intensive subsistence agriculture, poverty, and hunger.

### Population Density

At first glance the region does not appear overpopulated, for its average population density of 25 per square mile is several times less than the average density in Europe or the Orient. Yet the tiny island of Barbados, a member of The West Indies,[2] contains a reported 1436 persons, chiefly rural, per square mile—a density comparable to that of the more heavily populated rural areas of the Orient. Also in the Caribbean realm are other, not so extreme, examples: Puerto Rico, a self-governing commonwealth voluntarily associated with the United States, has 683 persons per square mile, and Martinique, an overseas department of France, has 635 per square mile. Additional political units whose population densities exceed the over-all average in the Orient include the Netherlands Antilles; the French isle of Guadeloupe; most of the other members of The West Indies (besides Barbados); the United States Virgin Islands; and the republics of El Salvador and Haiti.

There are, of course, political units in Latin America which are very sparsely populated. French Guiana, for example, has an average density of less than 1 person per square mile. Between these extremes, the larger countries occupy a position resembling that of the region as a whole: Argentina has approximately 19, Brazil 20, Chile 26, and Mexico 44 inhabitants per square mile.

### Population Distribution

In its general pattern of population distribution Latin America differs somewhat from the Orient and from all other world regions. The Latin American pattern is one of heavy density in and around coastal cities (if local climatic handicaps, insects, diseases, and other liabilities are not too serious), a marked pressure in and near high mountain urban centers—in many cases, the capital of a country—and corridors of moderate to heavy concentration along the outlet routes from the mountains to the sea. There are, of course, variations and exceptions; yet the pattern is sufficiently consistent that nearly every political unit consists of a well-defined population core (or cores) with an outlying sparsely populated hinterland.[3] In other words the total area of each country differs considerably from the total occupied area, with exceptions in the case of Uruguay, El Salvador, Haiti, Puerto Rico, and most small island units. In Brazil over three fourths of the total land area is essentially without inhabitants other than aboriginal tribes. Most Brazilians live along the

---

[2] The West Indies, which came into being in 1958, is a quasi-autonomous federation of British-affiliated island units. It is expected eventually to achieve complete independence within the Commonwealth of Nations. The federation is comprised of the following islands (inset map, p. 539): (1) Jamaica, (2) Barbados, (3) Trinidad and Tobago, (4) Antigua, Montserrat, St. Kitts, Nevis, Anguilla, and three lesser islands, all in the Leeward Islands group, (5) Dominica, Grenada, St. Lucia, St. Vincent, and some smaller islands, in the Windward Islands group, and (6) two former dependencies of Jamaica: the Cayman Islands and

the Turks and Caicos Islands. The temporary capital of The West Indies is Port-of-Spain, Trinidad; its permanent capital will be in a city to be constructed on that island. Two other British-affiliated island units in the West Indian region—the British Virgin Islands and the Bahama Islands—do not belong to the federation and continue to be held by the United Kingdom as individual colonies.

[3] More detailed treatment of this idea, with excellent maps, may be found in R. S. Platt, *Latin America: Countrysides and United Regions*. New York and London: McGraw-Hill Book Company, Inc., 1942.

eastern seaboard south of the city of Recife. Nearly seven tenths of the Argentine population is clustered in Buenos Aires or the adjacent humid pampa—an area containing slightly more than one fifth of Argentina's total land. Almost one half of Mexico's population is found in several mountain basins and valleys clustering around Mexico City —a district representing less than one seventh of the country's entire area.

### Widespread Poverty

Like most residents of the Orient, the great majority of Latin Americans are poor (photo, right). An inadequate, yet noteworthy, indicator of this poverty is the per capita national income of selected countries. According to one source—and sources differ appreciably—this amount is about $460 per year in Argentina, $360 in Chile, $230 in Brazil, $220 in Mexico, and $120 in Peru. The same source cites a figure for the United States of $1870.[4] But income comparisons between the United States and Latin American countries must be made with great caution, because the measurement and comparison of national incomes is subject to wide margins of error for at least two reasons. (1) National income includes the value of produce consumed by farmers in their own households, and this is impossible to calculate accurately. (2) In calculating the figures cited above, Latin American currencies have been converted into United States dollars by the international exchange rates of the respective Latin American countries. It is well known that a United States dollar, thus converted into a Latin American currency, will often buy more in Latin America than it buys in the United States. Usually it will buy very much more of those goods and services which are consumed by the rank and file of Latin Americans. Thus the figures above do not indicate that Americans are, on the average, four times as rich as Argentin-

ians and over fifteen times as rich as Peruvians; but we can say with assurance that compared to Americans the people of Argentina are poor, and those of Peru very poor.

### ► Latin America and the Pacific World

Like the Pacific World, Latin America is comprised of a series of islands and a continental area supporting, all in all, a comparatively sparse population. The comparison can be carried still further. Like Australia, the largest land unit of the Pacific World, South America is a continent in which the most densely populated areas are situated on or near coasts, the interior being sparsely peopled. However, the settlement possibilities of the two continents differ. Australia possesses neither an Amazon River providing easy access to the interior nor a natural environment over most of its area which, by present standards, can be occupied successfully by more than small numbers of people. In short, Australia's unpopulated expanses are chiefly desert. In contrast, over 80 percent of Brazil, a country somewhat larger than Australia, may eventually be occupied, although at present only about 25 percent is used effectively—even for such extensive practices as the pasturing of livestock.

Ethnically, Latin America and the Pacific World offer some interesting contrasts. The islands of Latin America are occupied almost wholly by descendants of immigrants from Europe or Africa, the native Indians having been driven off or exterminated long ago. The islands of the Pacific World, however, except New Zealand, the Hawaiian Islands, and the Fiji Islands, are settled principally by native peoples who have lived for centuries in their present habitats. The mainland of Latin America is populated by an amalgam of native Indians, Africans, Europeans, and other ethnic groups; but the mainland of the Pacific

---

[4] All data from: Statistical Office of the United Nations, *Per Capita National Product of Fifty-five Countries: 1952–1954*. New York: United Na- tions, 1957. P. 8. This source equates national product with national income.

World—Australia—is occupied almost entirely by descendants of European, mainly British, immigrants, the aborigines having been killed or driven to inaccessible places by the early European settlers.

There are also political and economic similarities between these two world regions. Both are governed, with few exceptions, by Europeans or descendants of Europeans. In each case most of the inhabitants are citizens of independent countries and yet must depend economically upon foreign commerce—primarily with Anglo-America and Europe—to take away surplus raw materials (chiefly from the farm or mine) and to supply certain manufactured goods. Each is an outlying part of the commercial world, the cores of which are found in the industrialized areas lying on either side of the North Atlantic Ocean.

### ▶ Latin America and the Middle East

Like the Middle East, Latin America is a region that derives much of its regional unity from the nigh-omnipresence of a single religion—the Moslem faith in the Middle East and Roman Catholicism in Latin America. Each faith is dominant in most parts of its region. In Latin America, Ro-

The rural poverty which afflicts much of Latin America is well exemplified in this photograph, taken in Venezuela. The farm family in the picture is engaged in planting a field of upland rice. With a sharpened stick the farmer digs holes into which his wife drops the rice seeds. (Standard Oil Company, N. J.)

man Catholicism is the accepted religion of the upper classes, and is the official state religion in some countries. In somewhat altered form it filters down to the majority of the people, who tend to observe not only Catholic rites but also those learned from their native Indian or African forebears. This is particularly true in the communities of the native Indian.

The relationships between church and state in Latin America vary from country to country. The basic issues appear to be (1) the control of educational facilities, (2) the control of the marriage ceremony, and (3) continued exercise by the church of certain rights and property titles held during the colonial period—rights and titles whose validity has been challenged, with varying degrees of vigor, by the various national governments since independence.

## COMPARISONS BETWEEN LATIN AMERICA AND AFRICA

Thus Latin America contains features or combinations of features which have counterparts in the Soviet Union, Europe, Anglo-America, the Orient, the Pacific World, and the Middle East. But perhaps the greatest number of similarities, especially of a locational, climatic, and economic nature, exist between Latin America and Africa.

▶ *Similarities in Shape and Location*
Perhaps the most apparent similarity between Latin America and Africa is that of general shape. The major land mass of each assumes the form of a triangle with the apex pointing toward the South Pole. Moreover, in each case that land mass is connected to an even larger continent to the north—*i.e.,* to North America and Eurasia respectively —by an isthmus which man has found it advantageous to canalize. There are also other similarities of location: north of the major land mass in each region is a sea— the Caribbean and the Mediterranean— which tends to separate it from, and concomitantly to provide shipping lanes to, its poleward neighbor. And, in either case, that northern continental neighbor is the home of a busy industrial society which has established strong political and/or economic ties with the region to the south. Thus Latin America tends to lie predominantly within the overseas economic orbit of the United States and Africa within that of northwestern Europe.

The economic ties between Latin America and Africa and the industrialized regions to the north are associated with the fact that both Latin America and Africa are located predominantly in the lower latitudes, and hence are able to produce tropical crops which are in demand in Anglo-America and Europe but cannot be produced in quantity in the latter regions because of climatic handicaps.

▶ *Similarities and Differences in Landforms*
Both Latin America and Africa are characterized by pronounced differences in elevation from one part of the region to another. However, contrasts in elevation are much greater in Latin America than in Africa. Nowhere in the latter continent is there a prominent low-lying plain series like that of the Orinoco-Amazon-Paraná-Paraguay—the river plains which dominate the interior of South America and separate the older, lower highlands of the east from the rugged Andes of the west. With high mountains, too, Latin America is the more generously endowed. This is evidenced by the nearly continuous Andes, Sierra Madre, and associated mountains which extend from northern Mexico to Tierra del Fuego (maps, pp. 539 and 552, and back endpaper landform map). Between the latitudes of 30°N and 40°S these mountains reach prevailing heights of at least 5000

feet above the sea. Within the Andes proper the highest crests exceed 9000 feet for over 3500 miles from northern Colombia and Venezuela to central Chile and Argentina. The latter's Mount Aconcagua—with an altitude of 22,835 feet that marks the highest point of the Western Hemisphere—is in the southern portion of this more rugged Andean belt. In Central America, the West Indies, and Mexico, mountains reaching higher than 9000 feet are found in northern Panama, Costa Rica, Guatemala, the Dominican Republic, and Mexico—in the last of these, especially near the capital city. Thus Latin America has very extensive areas of high mountains. But in Africa, mountains of comparable elevation are limited to a few comparatively small and erratically distributed ranges or isolated peaks.

### ▶ Similarities in Types of Climate

In general, the types of climate and associated vegetation in Latin America as recognized in climatic classifications duplicate those of Africa. The differences most readily apparent are the much larger proportion of desert climate in Africa and the greater prevalence of middle latitude and high highland climates in Latin America. (See maps, pp. 539 and 552, and end-paper climatic map.)

### Humid Tropical, Subtropical, and Marine Climates of Latin America

The *tropical rain forest climate* in the massive center of Latin America tends to be—like its African counterpart—located at or near the equator. However, the Latin American area of this climate type is somewhat larger than the African area, reaches farther poleward in the Northern Hemisphere, and its coastal segments are mainly found on the east coast, rather than on the west coast as in Africa. On either side of this tropical rainy climate—as in Africa—is found the *tropical savanna climate*, which in Latin America extends erratically to the vicinity of the Tropic of Cancer in the

Northern and the Tropic of Capricorn in the Southern Hemisphere. Still farther poleward in the eastern portion of South America is found a sizable area of *humid subtropical climate*. Its Northern Hemisphere counterpart lies north of the Mexican border in southeastern United States. These three climate types—tropical rain forest (photo, p. 528), tropical savanna (photo, p. 529), and humid subtropical—characterize most of Latin America. Of the others, perhaps the most idyllic is a small strip of *mediterranean* or *dry-summer subtropical climate* in central Chile. To the south in Chile is a strip of *marine west coast (humid marine) climate* bordered by bleak, rainy, windswept, glaciated, essentially uninhabited mountain country.

### Dry Climates of Latin America

The Latin American climates discussed above are those of more or less orderly, repetitious arrangement. One may expect to find generally similar climates in generally similar positions on all major land masses of the world. However, there are also in Latin America climates which are due at least partially to the presence of high landforms. These include some of the region's dry climates and, of course, its mountain highland climates.

The dry climates, especially those of the arid and semiarid sections of Mexico (and southwestern United States) are to be associated partially with the global pattern of orderly climatic arrangement, and partially with local mountains and uplands. A glance at a climate map will reveal dry lands in generally similar positions in Africa (both north and south of the equator) and in Australia. However, the high mountain ranges on either side of the northern Mexican plateau, meeting in the vicinity of Mexico City, cannot be entirely overlooked in a consideration of causes for this particular area of dry land. The aridity of the dry lands of Argentina is largely the result of their location in the rain shadow of the

A clearing in tropical rain forest on the Pacific lowlands of Ecuador. Subsistence crops are grown among the stumps in front of the house, while pigs and chickens find shelter under the house. The family food supply is rounded out from a small orchard of orange trees in rear of the house, and by hunting, fishing, and gathering of nuts, fruits, and other foods in the forest. (Foreign Agricultural Service, U. S. Department of Agriculture.)

Andes. They have counterparts in other sections of the world only where high ranges of mountains happen to block the path of prevailing winds and hence to cause a deficiency of rainfall on the lee side. In the west-coast tropics and subtropics of South America, the Atacama and associated deserts cannot be explained so simply; for shifting winds, cold offshore currents, and other complexities—as well as the Andes Mountains—are important to climatic conditions there. However, the mountains serve to restrict this area of desert to the coastal strip.

### High Upland and Highland Climates of Latin America

Although the lowlands and low uplands of Latin America are extensive and support sizable populations in some countries, the highlands and high uplands are also very important to man's use of this region. They are significant not only for the mineral resources they contain but also—chiefly because of their cooler temperatures—as habitats for settlement, particularly in the otherwise persistently hot lands. To immigrants or descendants of immigrants from the middle latitudes such conditions have been especially attractive, for they resemble somewhat the climates from which the settlers came. However, the annual range of temperatures is much lower than in the middle latitudes. For example, Quito, Ecuador —an extreme case—records an average temperature of 54 or 55 degrees Fahreinheit every month of the year.

These upland and highland climates

change markedly with increased elevation, and hence are subject to classification into vertical zones. Although each of the four basic weather and climatic elements—temperature, pressure, humidity, and winds—varies with altitude, temperature is the primary criterion for zonal classification. At least three major zones are commonly recognized in the higher lands of Latin America: the *tierra caliente* (hot country); the *tierra templada* (cool country); and the *tierra fría* (cold country).

Rising from the previously discussed lowland climates, the *tierra caliente* zone of hot, wet conditions reaches to approximately 3000 feet above sea level at or near the equator, and to slightly lower elevations in parts of Mexico and other areas near the margins of the tropics. It is, in effect, an upward projection of these lowland climates, from which it has never been satisfactorily isolated by geographers and climatologists. Thus it is the environment of nature's rain forest or tropical savanna and man's rice, sugar cane, and cacao. It tends also to be the zone of the truly tropical plantation—whether owned locally or abroad—and of the Negro, zambo, and mulatto worker. In the islands of Caribbean America, it is the zone of major urban units, containing all of the cities of 100,000 or over.

The *tierra caliente* merges almost imperceptibly into the *tierra templada*. Although sugar cane, cacao, bananas, oranges, and other lowland products reach their respective uppermost limits at some point in this higher level, the *tierra templada* is most notably the zone of the coffee tree. Indeed, some scholars use the criterion of effective coffee culture as the dividing line from the *tierra caliente*. In the *tierra templada* coffee can be grown with relative ease; at lower altitudes the crop encounters difficulties occasioned by excessive heat and/or moisture. The upper limit of this zone—approximately 6000 feet above sea level—tends also to be the upper limit of European-induced plantation agriculture in Latin America. In its distribution the *tierra templada* flanks the rugged western mountain cordilleras and, in addition, is the uppermost climate in the lower uplands and highlands to the east. The broad-leaved

Sparsely settled ranching country in the tropical savannas of eastern Colombia. The isolated *mestizo* family on this cattle ranch may not see other human beings for months at a time, aside from the relatively primitive Vichada Indians who come to the ranch to trade. (Standard Oil Company, N. J.)

evergreen trees of its moister, hotter sections tend to resemble those of the *tierra caliente*. This is especially true of the eastern flanks of the high mountains. In its poleward margins, however, broad-leaved trees are replaced to some degree by coniferous evergreens. In such places as the highlands of Brazil or Venezuela where there is less moisture, scrub forest or savanna grasses appear—the latter generally requiring the more water.

In brief, the *tierra templada* is a prominent zone of European-induced settlement and of commercial agriculture. Urban as well as rural settlement is very much in evidence: of Latin America's cities of 100,000 or over about a fourth are in or very near the *tierra templada*. Two of the region's metropolises exceeding 1,000,000—São Paulo and Caracas—are in this zone, while another—Mexico City—lies just above it. Others, like Rio de Janeiro, which are themselves situated at lower elevations, maintain close ties with predominantly residential or resort towns found in these cooler temperatures.

The *tierra fría,* or cold country, may be distinguished from the other zones by two criteria. First and perhaps most important in an agricultural region like Latin America, it is a zone where frost occurs. As one might expect, frosts are only occasional in the zone's lower reaches at approximately 6000 feet above the sea, but are much more frequent at higher elevations. The second criterion refers to type of economy: in contrast to the Europeanized *tierra templada,* the *tierra fría* tends to be the habitat of a subsistence, native Indian economy—most extensive in Peru and Bolivia but also present in Ecuador, Colombia, Guatemala, El Salvador, and Mexico. The upper limit of the *tierra fría* is generally placed at about 10,000 feet above sea level for locations near the equator, and at lower elevations toward either pole. This line is usually drawn on the basis of two criteria: (1) the upper limit of agriculture, as rep-

resented by such hardy crops as potatoes, barley, or the locally important cereal quínoa; and (2) the upper limit of natural tree growth. Above are the alpine meadows, sometimes called *paramos;* still higher there may or may not exist barren rocks and snow or ice.

The *tierra fría* tends to be a last retreat and the major home of the native Indian and is characterized by small permanent settlements and by what Europeans or Americans might consider rather primitive ways of life. It is chiefly rural, containing only seven of nearly a hundred cities in Latin America that number 100,000 or over. However, nature has placed here certain valuable minerals like tin and copper which have attracted modern types of large-scale mining enterprise into the *tierra fría* of Bolivia and Peru as well as some other Latin American countries.

Climatic data for representative Latin American stations are given in Table 28.

### ▶ Latin American Minerals

Latin America is a large-scale producer of a somewhat shorter list of important minerals than is Africa. However, Latin America's mineral production is very significant to the outside nations that purchase most of it, despite the rather small number of key minerals that bulk large when viewed in a world perspective. The region's bauxite, for example, is critically important to the industrial economies of the United States and Canada. Currently, Latin America's known mineral resources of greatest consequence include iron ore, petroleum, bauxite, tin, copper, nitrate, sulfur, and silver. Supplies of good coal, especially coking coal, are almost entirely lacking.

Deposits of high-grade *iron ore* in the eastern highlands of Brazil and Venezuela are the largest known in the Western Hemisphere and are among the largest in the world. Lesser and yet noteworthy producing deposits occur in northern Mexico, north-central Chile, and southern Peru. Venezuela

## TABLE 28

### CLIMATIC DATA FOR SELECTED LATIN AMERICAN STATIONS

| STATION | COUNTRY | LATITUDE TO NEAREST WHOLE DEGREE | ELEVATION ABOVE SEA LEVEL (FEET) | TYPE OF CLIMATE | AVERAGE TEMPERATURE (DEGREES F TO NEAREST WHOLE DEGREE) | | | PRECIPITATION | |
|---|---|---|---|---|---|---|---|---|---|
| | | | | | ANNUAL | COOLEST MONTH | WARMEST MONTH | ANNUAL AVERAGE TO NEAREST INCH | NUMBER OF MONTHS WITH LESS THAN 1 INCH OF RAIN |
| Monterrey | Mexico | 26°N. | 1752 | Steppe | 71° | 57° | 83° | 20″ | 3 |
| Bridgetown | Barbados | 13°N. | 181 | Tropical rain forest | 79° | 77° | 80° | 54″ | 0 |
| Caracas | Venezuela | 11°N. | 3418 | *Tierra templada* | 69° | 65° | 71° | 33″ | 3 |
| Cuidad Bolívar | Venezuela | 8°N. | 125 | Tropical savanna | 82° | 79° | 84° | 37″ | 3 |
| Manaus | Brazil | 3°N. | 147 | Tropical rain forest | 81° | 80° | 83° | 65″ | 0 |
| Cuiabá | Brazil | 16°S. | 541 | Tropical savanna | 80° | 75° | 82° | 55″ | 2 |
| São Paulo | Brazil | 24°S. | 2690 | *Tierra templada* | 64° | 58° | 69° | 52″ | 0 |
| Rosario | Argentina | 34°S. | 98 | Humid subtropical | 63° | 49° | 77° | 35″ | 0 |
| Mendoza | Argentina | 33°S. | 2625 | Desert | 61° | 47° | 75° | 8″ | 10 |
| Santiago | Chile | 33°S. | 1706 | Mediterranean | 56° | 46° | 67° | 14″ | 7 |
| Valdivia | Chile | 39°S. | 16 | Marine west coast | 53° | 46° | 60° | 105″ | 0 |
| Lima | Peru | 12°S. | 512 | Desert | 66° | 61° | 73° | 2″ | 12 |
| La Paz | Bolivia | 17°S. | 12000 | *Tierra fría* | 49° | 44° | 53° | 23″ | 4 |
| Quito | Ecuador | 0° | 9350 | *Tierra fría* | 55° | 54° | 55° | 42″ | 0 |

is by far the largest Latin American producer of iron ore, followed by Brazil, Chile, and Peru.

*Petroleum* is significant in the Caribbean Sea–Gulf of Mexico area, particularly in northern Venezuela (the leading producing region by far), northeastern Colombia, the central Gulf coast of Mexico, and the island of Trinidad. Other fields exist (1) along the Peruvian-Ecuadorian coast, (2) along the Atlantic margins of Patagonia in Argentina, (3) along the eastern piedmont of the Andes in northern Argentina and southern Bolivia, (4) on the east coast of Brazil near Salvador, and (5) in the Chilean part of Tierra del Fuego. The large sedimentary basins east of the Andes, shared by Brazil and several other South American countries, may contain sizable petroleum deposits not currently known.

Most of the region's production of *bauxite* —the major source material for aluminum —comes from Jamaica, Surinam (Dutch Guiana), or British Guiana. The deposits in all of these countries are located relatively near the sea.

Most of the known reserves of *tin* in Latin America are in the Andes of Bolivia, and that country is the region's only significant producer.

Low-grade but comparatively abundant *copper* deposits occur in the Atacama Desert of northern Chile and the arid and semiarid sections of Mexico. Additional reserves of copper are found in the Andes, especially in the mountainous sections of

Chile and Peru. Chile is overwhelmingly the largest copper producer in Latin America, and was the world's second largest producer in 1958 (after the United States).

Chile contains the only sizable reserves of natural *nitrate* that have ever been exploited commercially on a grand scale. Like the lower grades of copper, these are in the Atacama Desert.

Since 1955, Mexico has become a major source of native *sulfur*. Only the United States produces more. The main fields, like those of the United States, border the Gulf of Mexico. They lie in the vicinity of Veracruz.

The *silver* of Mexico, Peru, and Bolivia is principally found in mountains or rough plateau country. These countries, in the order named, are by far the largest Latin American producers of silver, and Mexico is the largest producer in the world. Mexico's deposits are mainly in the dry northern and north-central sections of the country.

► *Similarities in Economic Activities*
Since both Latin America and Africa are outlying regions in the world's economy, their basic industries serve principally to supply the wants of their own inhabitants and to furnish certain raw materials and foods to more highly industrialized areas. In both regions agriculture is the leading livelihood industry.

**Latin American Agriculture**

In Latin America as a whole, agriculture employs between 50 and 60 percent of the total labor force. The percentage of the labor force that is employed in agriculture is declining rather rapidly in some countries but scarcely at all in others. There is an appreciable range in the proportionate current importance of agriculture among the various countries. For example, Argentina has only one fourth of its total labor force in agriculture, whereas over four fifths is so engaged in Guatemala or Haiti. In other countries the figure is between these two extremes.

The systems of agriculture vary. In some tropical lowland areas, particularly in Caribbean America, single-crop commercial plantations owned by companies or syndicates dominate the scene. The capital to establish these enterprises has come principally from Anglo-America or Europe. Most plantations grow sugar cane or bananas. Sugar plantations are especially prominent in the Caribbean islands, while banana plantations are found principally in Central America. A considerable amount of subsistence farming by individual families is carried on in plantation areas, often on plantation-owned land.

But despite the importance of commercial plantations in some areas, the bulk of Latin America's farm production is accounted for by individually owned and community-owned agricultural holdings belonging to citizens of the respective countries in which these properties are located. Community-owned lands, reflecting native Indian traditions, are especially well represented by the previously described *ejidos* of Mexico (see p. 540) and by some settlements in the two major Latin American concentrations of native Indians—one in northern Central America and southern Mexico inhabited by descendants of the Mayas, Aztecs, and neighboring peoples and the other in the middle Andes of Peru and neighboring countries, containing descendants of the Incas. Unlike the *ejidos,* most of the native Indian communally held lands support a predominantly subsistence form of agriculture.

Most individually owned holdings are of Latin European origin. They may be large *haciendas* (Spanish) or *fazendas* (Portuguese) such as are found in some form in nearly all Latin American nations, or they may be small holdings like those of Costa Rica. Agricultural production on the large estates, whether called *haciendas, fazendas,* or by some other name, involves the employment of large numbers of landless, often illiterate, workers. In some areas these workers are traditionally bound to the estate, and in others they are free to move at will. In actual fact, most of them remain on the estate. The estate owner is well educated—often in Europe. He is usually a citizen of the country in which his property is located. He may have a residence in a city in addition to that on the estate. He may also be engaged in business, or one of the professions, leaving the direction of the estate to a carefully chosen manager. Although one estate may produce several commodities commercially, there is a tendency toward specialization in only one or two. All in all, such estates produce a sizable proportion of the coffee, sugar, cotton, henequen, livestock products, and other Latin American agricultural commodities entering world markets.

Types of production on small individual holdings vary with owner and place. The more active small farmers, like those of Costa Rica, tend to grow coffee, cotton, and other commercial specialties as well as subsistence crops of corn, beans, sorghums, and vegetables. Other, more inefficiently managed holdings tend to concentrate on subsistence crops only. Various land-reform programs in Latin America are resulting in an increased number of small private holdings and collectives and a decreased number of large estates.

Not only does agriculture employ the majority of Latin America's people; it is also responsible for most of the region's exports. Of the 20 independent countries in the region, all but Venezuela, Bolivia, and Chile now export a larger value of agricultural commodities than of products from other livelihood industries. Coffee, sugar, cotton, meat, cacao, wheat, bananas, wool, and corn are among the major agricultural products leaving the region.

### Mining as a Source of Livelihood

The significance of mining to Latin America is not easily appraised. In terms of labor force it is comparatively unimportant, for the highly mechanized mining industry seldom employs more than 4 percent of the total labor force of a Latin American country. Since mining ventures are largely financed and usually managed by outside interests in order to get raw materials for the industrial economies of Anglo-America and Europe, few of the extracted products reach the Latin American people. However, revenues from mining—whether in the form of income, property, export tariff, or other taxes—are very important to some Latin American governments.

Some of the area's mining activities are of considerable importance on a world basis. For example, in 1958 over 14 percent of the world's petroleum output by volume and nearly 4 percent of its iron ore originated in Venezuela. About 20 percent of all silver, 19 percent of all sulfur, 9 percent of all lead, and 7 percent of all zinc was extracted in Mexico. About 29 percent of all bauxite came from Jamaica, 14 percent from Surinam, and 8 percent from British Guiana. Approximately 14 percent of all copper and essentially all natural nitrate came from Chile. Nearly 12 percent of all tin was mined in Bolivia.

### The Increasing Importance of Manufacturing

In both Latin America and Africa, manufacturing industries are making an increasingly important contribution to national economies. In fact, the industrial revolution which we so often place in the latter part of the eighteenth century is only now beginning to reach effectively to these outlying world regions. In a sense, a frontier— or a series of frontiers—of industrialization is migrating over them, just as the now legendary frontier of settlement in the United States once shifted westward. A leading authority on Latin America, Professor Preston E. James, has characterized this change as follows: [5]

---

[5] Preston E. James, *Latin America*, third ed. New York: The Odyssey Press, 1959. Pp. 52–57. Used by permission of the author and the publisher.

This book is highly recommended as a standard, up-to-date, very readable, and comprehensive work on the geography of Latin America.

The history of the Occidental world during the last few centuries has been involved with the impact of the new *industrial society* and the older *pre-industrial society*. This is what we call the industrial revolution. Beginning in Western Europe the new way of living, coupled with enormously increased productivity in all forms of economic activity through the use of controlled inanimate power, has gradually transformed whole sections of Europe and America. In some instances the transformation has taken place by gradual evolution; in not a few instances it has been accompanied by violence and warfare, both civil and international. The rapid increase in the need for raw materials of all kinds has produced the present intense rivalry for the control of the productive regions, especially of the sources of power. The English-speaking peoples, who were the first to adopt the new way of living, were able to gain control of about 75 percent of the developed power resources of the world; and the challenge to this control lies behind the present international turmoil. In Latin America, the impact of the industrial society with the traditional pre-industrial society is now going on. Where the industrial way of living has become established, a new and still more profound line of cleavage has been formed across all the previous diversities of Latin-American society.

The fundamental characteristics of the industrial society should be reviewed briefly. The use of controlled inanimate power changes the emphasis from production by cheap labor to production by machines—or, in terms of economics, capital investment assumes a position of preponderant importance, and the owners of capital rather than the owners of land assume places of the highest prestige and political power. Production is enormously increased, not only total production, but also per capita production. This leads to specialization and exchange, and hence to interdependence over wide areas. Trade is transformed from a small-scale exchange of luxury goods or specialties to a large-scale exchange of staples, and as a result communities are no longer supported by the products of the territories immediately surrounding them, but from a wide variety of producing areas, most of them beyond the control of the community which absorbs the products. With life organized on such a pattern society reaches a much higher standard of material comfort than any previous society has been able to reach; but this standard can be maintained only if a nation accepts the fact of wide geographical interdependence, turns away from provincial isolation, and cooperates with other nations in the maintenance of a stable financial structure of money and credits.

The industrial society brings profound changes in the details of human life. Prestige, we repeat, is to be gained through the ownership of capital which brings power, rather than through the ownership of land which brings security. Life becomes more speculative, less certain, but with rewards for the successful which are in a material way far beyond anything the world has offered before. There comes a notable change in the time concepts. With the increased tempo of life the vague concepts of pre-industrial society, such as *por la mañana, por la tarde,* must be given up for more precise concepts, such as 9:45 A.M. or 3:10 P.M. Behavior of all sorts becomes more standardized. The picturesqueness of provincial costumes disappears under a uniform cover of blue denim overalls; people from Patagonia to Labrador watch the antics of Mickey Mouse; local differences in manners and customs are modified by the impact of the new patterns of life. In the big cosmopolitan centers of Latin America life follows the same routine as in North American or European cities—this uniformity is apparent in styles of architecture, styles of dress, forms of work and recreation—in short, the whole aspect of life is changed from its variegated pre-industrial base to a uniformity repeated in all the Occidental urban centers.

These changes affect the distribution of people. As long as coal remains the chief source of power, manufacturing industry is carried on at the lowest cost in large concentrated units. People gather together in great cities—cities greater than any that the world ever knew before, cities of more than a million inhabitants. Although the use of electric power may have the effect of spreading manufacturing industry over a wider area, thus transforming the life in smaller towns and villages, the large concentrations of city people still perform more efficiently the urban functions of commerce and administration. These cities are still dependent on the productivity of the land for their support, but the land base has been greatly extended; and as a result the means of transportation which tie the cities together must be greatly elaborated.

The urban-industrial way of living has come to Latin America from outside, not by slow evolution from the earlier pre-industrial base. In parts of Europe and in Anglo-America where the cities and the urban life developed out of the rural background there is a certain normal relationship between the size of the city and the productivity of its rural hinterland. . . . In Latin America one finds cities which have become industrial and commercial centers with an industrial way of living, but which bear little relationship in size or in function to the rural districts back of them. The contrast between the cities and the rural districts is enormous: the average tourist who journeys by boat or airplane from one city to another scarcely catches a glimpse of the Latin America which is traditional, and which is still dominant in terms of area and numbers of people.

Urban-industrial growth has appeared at various places in Latin America. The largest developments of this cosmopolitan life center in Buenos Aires, Rio de Janeiro, São Paulo, Santiago, Lima, Mexico City, Caracas, and Habana [Havana]—all cities of a million or more people, all thoroughly modern metropolises, with a way of living entirely familiar to metropolitan dwellers throughout the Occidental world. Modern industrial development has appeared also in many smaller cities throughout Argentina, Chile, Brazil, Colombia, Venezuela, Mexico, and Cuba. Yet the industrial productivity of all Latin America is still very small compared with that of the United States or of Western Europe.

The Latin American countries which have the largest output of factory-made goods are Argentina, Brazil, Mexico, and Chile. Also prominent in this regard are Peru, Cuba, Uruguay, Colombia, and Venezuela. Over 15 percent of the total labor force in the four most active nations is now composed of factory workers, engaged chiefly in the production of processed foods, textiles, and fabricated metal products for home markets.

## ▶ Similarities in Over-all Patterns of Settlement and Transport

Both Latin America and Africa tend to have a "rim" pattern of settlement. In other words, the main concentrations of people tend to be found around or relatively near the coasts. The principal exceptions are certain interior highlands which support dense, or moderately dense, populations. In both regions, large areas of sparsely occupied land, peopled by erratically distributed aboriginal tribes, exist in the interior. Most countries in both regions touch the sea; in Latin America only Bolivia and Paraguay do not. Large cities, with few exceptions, lie on or near the sea or at high elevations.

Land transportation is poorly developed in most parts of Latin America and Africa. Rail lines reach inland from seaports in many places, but in only a few sizable areas has a reasonably dense web of railroads developed (map, p. 555). Highways, also, are in an immature stage of development. Few roads are hard-surfaced, and many are passable only with difficulty. This is particularly true in the rainier climates of the low latitudes. In both regions, the airplane is becoming increasingly important as a carrier—not only of specialty items but also of meat and other staples.

## SOME IMPORTANT DIFFERENCES BETWEEN LATIN AMERICA AND AFRICA

Similarities between Latin America and Africa should not be overstressed. Many of the apparent similarities are only superficial. The two regions exhibit profound differences in racial composition, in historical relationships, and in cultural heritage. The independent countries of Latin America have had much more experience in self-government than most independent African countries. Racial segregation and strife is less of a problem in Latin America than in Africa, due to the fact that many Latin American ethnic groups have tended to mingle through intermarriage.

There are also important environmental differences. Latin America has a larger area of mountain lands and of low-lying river plains and smaller areas of plateau and upland than does Africa. In addition, Latin America projects farther into the Southern

Hemisphere and thus gains access to a larger area of humid middle-latitude climates. Africa has no effective counterpart of the rich pampas of Argentina, Uruguay, and southern Brazil, nor of the marine west-coast climatic area of southern Chile.

## SUMMARY OF SOME MAJOR LATIN AMERICAN CHARACTERISTICS

Latin America is a highly diversified region. Particularly in its landforms, climates, political arrangements, and population patterns, it is one of the most diverse of the eight world regions.

It is a region which does not use its natural and human resources as efficiently as do more highly industrialized regions elsewhere. Between 50 and 60 percent of its labor force depends upon some form of agriculture for a livelihood, yet the region produces only about one tenth of the world's farm output. Many of its farmers have no knowledge of modern agricultural techniques, and most Latin American governments lack adequate capital to promote a revision of farming practices.

It is a region in which population increase is pronounced—particularly in the poorer, less developed sections such as most islands in Caribbean America.

It is also a region which depends markedly upon the industrial societies of Anglo-America and Europe with respect to exports, imports, and investment of capital. This dependence is currently being decreased, especially in the economically stronger countries, by the development of local manufacturing plants—of which many are sponsored by the respective national governments. In these countries a long-established landed aristocracy now sees its traditional rights, privileges, and power threatened by a rising merchant and factory class.

Finally, it is a region with potentialities for further development. They tend to take one of four primary forms: (1) the establishment of more factories in the region; (2) the breaking up of large landed estates into smaller parcels which can be worked by owners or quasi-owners; (3) the opening up of new agricultural and grazing lands, particularly in the interior of South America; (4) the intensified utilization of mineral resources, for domestic consumption wherever possible. Whether these potentialities can be realized at a rate concomitant with the rapid increase in population numbers remains to be seen.

# Latin American Regions

One of many possible ways of subdividing Latin America for purposes of study results in a major northern realm known as Caribbean or Middle America; a second region comprised of the predominantly native Indian countries of Ecuador, Peru, Bolivia, and Paraguay; a third consisting of giant Brazil; and, finally, mid-latitude South America—cored by Argentina, with the smaller country of Chile flanking its western border and still smaller Uruguay situated to the northeast. These regional subdivisions will be discussed in the order named. Area and population totals for each regional group of countries, as well as for individual countries, are given in Table 27 on pages 520–521.

## CARIBBEAN AMERICA

The northernmost of the four major Latin American realms is Caribbean or Middle America. Broadly conceived, it includes (1) the large mainland nations of Mexico, Colombia, and Venezuela, (2) the small Central American republics of Guatemala,

The downtown business and administrative district of Bolivia's largest city and *de facto* capital, La Paz. The city lies in a valley beneath the rim of the central Andean plateau or Altiplano, marked by the irregular skyline in the background. In the foreground is a spacious avenue—the only one in La Paz. Such a thoroughfare is frequently found in the central part of the larger Latin American cities. (Foreign Agricultural Service, U. S. Department of Agriculture.)

El Salvador, Honduras, Nicaragua, Costa Rica, and Panama, (3) the mainland units of British Honduras, British Guiana, Surinam (Dutch Guiana), French Guiana, and the Panama Canal Zone, all affiliated politically with overseas nations and dependent in varying degree on those nations, and (4) the numerous islands, large and small, in the Caribbean Sea or near it. Among the insular political units, only Cuba, which encompasses all of the largest island, and Haiti and the Dominican Republic, which share the second largest, are independent nations.

## ▶ Variations in Size and Population Density among the Component Political Units

Caribbean America is comprised of 12 independent countries and 13 political units that are affiliated with foreign nations (map, right, and Table 27).[1] These units vary greatly in size, shape, and intensity of human settlement and use. The largest unit, Mexico, has an area of 760,336 square miles and a population of 33,304,000. The smallest independent country, El Salvador, has only 7722 square miles, but has a population of 2,520,000. The population density of Mexico—approximately 44 people per square mile—is about equal to that of all Caribbean America. The density in El Salvador, on the other hand, amounts to 326 per square mile.[2] However, the greatest variations in population density are found in the units affiliated with overseas nations.

British Guiana, the largest of these in area, has some 83,000 square miles, a population estimated at 549,000, and a density of only 7 persons per square mile. The tiny colony of the British Virgin Islands, by contrast, includes a total of only 67 square miles and an estimated population of only 8000, but has an average population density of 119 persons per square mile. There is still more to the story: French Guiana has a density of less than 1 per square mile, whereas Barbados in The West Indies has more than 1400 per square mile. In appraising these statistics, the student should remember that the people of Caribbean America are predominantly rural. By way of comparison, the average population density of highly industrialized United States was 50 per square mile according to the 1960 census.

In the remainder of this section, the numerous political units that comprise Caribbean America are grouped for discussion as follows: (1) Mexico, (2) the Central American republics, (3) Colombia and Venezuela, (4) the mainland units affiliated with overseas nations, (5) the island republics, and (6) the island units affiliated with overseas nations.

## ▶ Mexico

The following are striking characteristics of Mexico: (1) nearly one half of its people live in, around, or between Mexico City (3,900,000)[3] and Guadalajara (530,000); (2) almost one third of the total population is native Indian, and most of the rest is

---

[1] It should be noted that one of the 13 units affiliated with overseas nations is The West Indies, a federation comprised of a considerable number of individual British-affiliated units. The latter vary among themselves with regard to the degree of political control that is still exerted by the United Kingdom. (See footnote, p. 523.)

[2] Area and population figures cited for Latin American political units in this chapter are from United Nations sources (see first footnote, Table 1, p. 11). Population figures are mid-1959 estimates. Other sources give the area of El Salvador as 8260 square miles. If the United Nations estimate for total population is used along with the alternate estimate for area, El Salvador's population

density becomes 305 per square mile or somewhat smaller than that of the Republic of Haiti (10,714 square miles; 3,464,000 population; density of 323 per square mile).

[3] Most population figures cited in this chapter for cities with populations of 100,000 or over are metropolitan area estimates from the publication *The World's Metropolitan Areas* (see pp. 62 and 594). Figures for a small number of cities not shown in that publication have been added from other sources. All figures for cities under 100,000 are from other sources. Such sources often do not state whether a figure cited pertains to the city proper or to the metropolitan area. Presumably it is for the city proper in most cases.

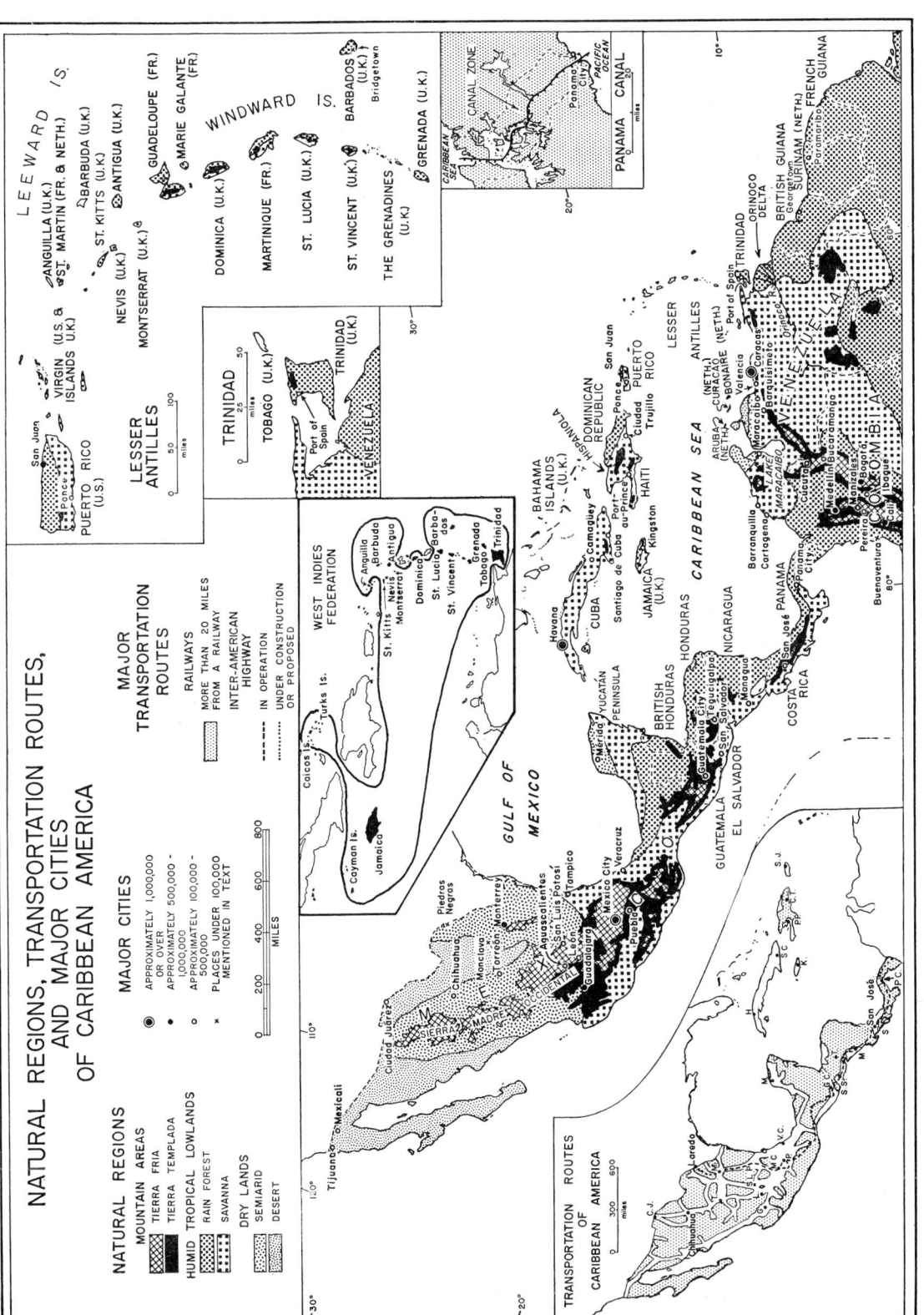

The city-size symbols are based on metropolitan-area estimates.

*mestizo;* (3) the proportion of the labor force that is employed in agriculture (54 percent in 1956) has been declining for many years and is smaller than in most Latin American political units; and (4) nearly three fifths of all tilled land grows corn, chiefly for human consumption.

## Agriculture

Mexicans are a people who prize agricultural land. Three major types of agricultural holding are represented.

1. Properties owned by entire communities, whether allotted to (but not owned by) individual heads of families or, in rare cases, worked communally, are called *ejidos*. Unlike the other holdings, the *ejido* system can be traced to native Indian ways of life. An average *ejido* worker has at his disposal 45 acres of land, of which slightly less than one fourth is in crops. The *ejidos* are most numerous in areas of dense population near Mexico City, but also are found in irrigated areas farther north, as well as in the Yucatán peninsula and in the south. There are now over 18,000 *ejidos* in Mexico. Although they occupy only slightly over one fourth of all exploited land, they encompass well over half of all cultivated land. This means that a very high proportion of the privately owned land in Mexico is in forest, pasture, or other noncrop use.

2. Small private holdings have various names: *solar* (if containing fewer than 2½ acres); *granja* (if involving from 2½ to 12½ acres; and *rancho* (if covering from 12½ to 2500 acres). These are far more numerous than the *ejidos,* amounting to over one million holdings. They occupy much of the remaining irrigated land but only about one fifth of all exploited land.

3. Individual *haciendas,* the feudalistic, large-scale private holdings, contain over 2500 acres and in some cases over 100,000 acres. They are scattered throughout the country, but are found in largest numbers in the semiarid northeast. Before the 1910 revolution *haciendas* contained nearly all

of Mexico's exploited land and as late as 1940 encompassed possibly 60 percent. Their share of the total exploited land is still appreciable, but they contain only a very small portion of all cultivated land. The dominance of the *hacienda* in Mexican life is over.

Shortly before World War I, Mexico instituted a state-enforced agricultural reform program which recently has slowed but is still continuing. Its major objective has been the breaking up of *haciendas* into small units. The estates usually are left with no fewer than 250 acres of land, including the central buildings. Approximately 2 million peon families have been granted access to land through this movement. Most of these are members of *ejidos*. Although mistakes have been made—the initial subdivisions, for example, were too small—the program appears to have effected a wholesale transfer of land title without a serious decline in production and without major bloodshed.

In addition to corn, the primary subsistence crops include beans, wheat, rice, and barley. These crops occupy over three quarters of Mexico's crop land—most of it in the *tierra templada* and lower *tierra fría* climates of the heavily populated central section. Yields per acre are low, although they have improved somewhat in recent years. Corn, for example, averages less than 15 bushels per acre as compared with over 45 bushels per acre for the United States. Mexico is one of the larger Latin American producers of tobacco, citrus fruits, vegetables, cane sugar, oilseeds, and meat (primarily beef). Most of this production is utilized within the country, although exports of a few commodities are fairly sizable.

Cotton, grown principally in the dry north under irrigation, is of increasing importance to both home and foreign markets. It has been Mexico's leading export for several years. The country's second most important agricultural export is coffee, grown in scattered districts throughout the southern half of Mexico, but primarily to the east of

Mexico City. Mexico is Latin America's leading cotton exporter and ranks third in coffee exports (after Brazil and Colombia).

## Manufacturing

Measured by labor force, manufacturing is far less significant than agriculture, accounting for only about one sixth of the nation's total employment. Many of the workers are in handicraft industries. However, the total output of manufactured goods has been growing quite rapidly in recent years, especially the output of production goods such as iron and steel, chemicals and chemical fertilizers, machinery, and cement. Manufacturing now exceeds agriculture in value of product. The principal modern manufacturing plants are found in two general areas: (1) the central region, in which labor-oriented and market-oriented industries (*e.g.,* cotton, woolen, and rayon textile plants; tobacco-processing plants) predominate, and (2) the dry lands of the north, in which the chief industries are raw material oriented (*e.g.,* concentrating and smelting mills for production of iron and steel, lead, zinc, copper, silver, and other metals). Except for iron and steel production, most of these latter industries are more a branch of mining than of manufacturing, as their primary function is to enrich the ores sufficiently that they can be shipped elsewhere for further manufacture.

Of major importance to Mexico is the northeastern iron and steel industry centered at Monterrey (500,000) and the much smaller city of Monclova. Most of the iron ore and coal are brought from fields that lie within a radius of 300 miles from Monterrey. This northeastern region—which also includes a plant manufacturing steel from scrap iron at Piedras Negras on the Rio Grande—produces more than four fifths of Mexico's iron and steel output. The production is insufficient for the country's needs, however, and steel in various forms is one of Mexico's larger imports.

## Mining

Only about 2 percent of Mexico's labor force is engaged in mining. This figure does not convey accurately the importance of the mining industry, for many of the mines are highly mechanized and thus employ comparatively few workers. Mined products comprise an important part of Mexico's exports. The leading commodities, of which most are exported in semifinished form, are lead (refined), zinc (concentrates and refined metal), copper (refined metal and concentrates), petroleum (largely refined), silver (largely refined), and sulfur (Frasch process).[4] Mexico's silver production, though of comparatively minor importance to the country's total economy, is the highest in the world. It amounts to about one fifth of the average annual world production. The mining industry of Mexico is financed largely by investment from foreign countries.

## Minor Livelihood Industries

Among minor livelihood industries are commercial fishing (along both coasts) and tourism. Shrimp from coastal waters of the Gulf of Mexico are a prominent export. Most of the tourists come from the United States. In return, a migratory counterflow occurs annually—not of tourists, but of laborers seeking farm work. Of the estimated 50,000 to 400,000 such workers moving northward and returning each year, a large share are "wetbacks" who cross the Rio Grande or the land frontier to the west in a manner strictly informal. The strength of this movement indicates the disparity in standards of living between the United States and Mexico and dramatizes the key problems of Mexico—a low standard of living, a rapidly increasing population, and

[4] In the Frasch process, underground deposits of practically pure sulfur, often deeply buried, are melted and forced through pipes to the surface, where the molten sulfur flows into vats and solidifies.

a dearth of local capital for exploitation of its natural resources.

The general economic status of Mexico is not unlike that of most other Latin American political units, particularly those of the Caribbean area. In most parts of Caribbean America the bulk of the people support themselves by subsistence or semisubsistence farming. A few commercial export crops or mined products are grown or extracted in scattered localities, mainly with the aid of foreign capital. In most countries one or two primary commodities dominate the export lists, as shown in Table 29.

### ▶ The Central American Republics

Economically, the Central American republics are miniatures of Mexico—except that they have even less local capital and fewer exploitable minerals. Systems of land use vary. The predominant subsistence or semisubsistence farming is most evident in the native Indian settlements of northern Guatemala and adjacent areas and least perceptible in Costa Rica, where a society of small farmers—relatively unmixed descendants of Spaniards—works most of the land. Coffee, the predominant mainland crop for export, is grown on both small and

**TABLE 29**

**DOMINANT EXPORT COMMODITIES OF THE CARIBBEAN AMERICAN REPUBLICS**

| COUNTRY | COMMODITY AND PERCENT OF TOTAL EXPORTS BY VALUE, 1958 |
|---|---|
| Mexico [a] | Cotton, 26; coffee, 11 |
| Guatemala | Coffee, 77; bananas, 8 |
| El Salvador | Coffee, 73; cotton, 16 |
| Honduras | Bananas, 53; coffee, 19 |
| Nicaragua | Cotton, 39; coffee, 38 |
| Costa Rica | Coffee, 52; bananas, 33 |
| Panama | Bananas, 58; fresh shrimp, 27 |
| Colombia | Coffee, 77; petroleum, 17 |
| Venezuela | Petroleum, 91; iron ore, 5 |
| Cuba | Sugar and molasses, 80; tobacco, 7 |
| Haiti | Coffee, 62; sisal, 18 |
| Dominican Republic | Sugar and molasses, 44; cocoa, chocolate, and preparations, 21; coffee, 18 |

SOURCE: *United Nations Yearbook of International Trade Statistics*, 1958.
[a] The combined total of lead, zinc, and copper exports (ores, concentrates, and metal) accounted for 21 percent of all exports over the three-year period 1955–1957.

large holdings, most of which are owned by citizens of the country involved. Banana plantations (photo, below), found principally along the hot, moist, coastal lowlands, are in large measure under the control of the United Fruit Company, an

Large-scale commercial plantation agriculture in Central America. The photo shows a banana plantation of the United Fruit Company on the Pacific coastal plain of Guatemala. Barracks of workers front on the company-owned railroad in the center of the picture. (Foreign Agricultural Service, U. S. Department of Agriculture.)

American concern. Because careful management and precision timing are needed to market the ripening bananas (which are picked while still green), the company's own employees manage both the plantations and a fleet of specially built ships plying between Caribbean and Pacific ports and wholesale markets, chiefly in coastal cities of Anglo-America. The main plantation districts are found in the Caribbean lowlands of Honduras and the Pacific lowlands of Panama, Costa Rica, and Guatemala.

The land problem in these countries is even more serious than in Mexico. Their average acreage of cultivated land per farm worker is less than half that of their northern neighbor—and, for comparison, less than one twelfth that of the United States. Moreover, they are the masters of their own destiny to a much more limited degree than Mexico. Catering to tastes in the world market, they manage as best they can by attracting foreign capital when possible and selling such tropically grown products of farm and forest as will be purchased by peoples with standards of living higher than their own.

In every republic of Central America, the largest city is the national capital. The two largest are Guatemala City (370,000) and San Salvador (270,000), the capital of El Salvador.

### ▶ Colombia and Venezuela

The high landforms which dominate Mexico and Central America extend southward, with interruptions, through Colombia. An outlier reaches eastward in Venezuela to the offshore island of Trinidad. Population nuclei of these South American nations are distributed in the same erratic manner as are those of the northern mainland republics, with a preference for highlands and uplands very much in evidence.

In the two countries the basic geographic ingredients do not differ so much in nature as in distribution. Both have mountains, but Colombia's areas of high mountains are much the larger; both have populations that are predominantly *mestizo*, but that of Colombia is over twice as large and the ethnic divisions within the population are more pronounced; both contain a wide range of climates, but Colombia has more of the temperate or cool upland and highland types; in both countries agriculture is the leading source of employment, but a considerably larger proportion of Colombia's labor force is employed in agriculture than is the case in Venezuela. Colombia has more cultivated land, but also has a larger population, so that ratios between man and cultivated land are about the same for the two countries. Both countries have significant mineral resources, but Venezuela has most of the known reserves and output of the two outstanding minerals—petroleum and iron ore.

Of Colombia's exports, about 77 percent by value in 1958 was represented by coffee and 17 percent by petroleum. The coffee is grown principally along the mountainous middle sections of the Magdalena and Cauca river valleys. It is shipped northward by rail, truck, river, air, or a combination of these, to the Caribbean ports of Barranquilla (380,000) and Cartagena (150,000), or westward by truck to Colombia's main Pacific seaport, Buenaventura (89,000) (map, p. 552). The petroleum fields are chiefly extensions of those in Venezuela and thus are located mainly in Colombia's northeast. Most petroleum leaves the country via two small Caribbean ports to the south of Cartagena.

The majority of Colombia's people, like their counterparts in Mexico and Central America, live in the highlands. Of the country's four cities with metropolitan populations of over 350,000, three are in the *tierra templada* or the *tierra fría* of the mountains. These are Bogotá (900,000), Medellín (565,000), and Cali (385,000). Colombia has five other cities or metropolitan areas with more than 100,000 people; of these four are in the highlands (map, p. 552). Each highland city serves as a market center for an agricultural basin or series of basins. One of these cities, Medellín, is the country's leading manufacturing center. Its factories produce a variety of consumer goods, but particularly textiles.

In broad outline, Venezuela is comprised of (1) a large, sparsely populated or unoccupied hinterland of tropical savanna climate in the basin of the Orinoco River, (2) an irregularly settled east-west trending mountain cordillera, largely *tierra templada,* in the northern and northwestern parts of the country, and (3) a discontinuous coastal lowland, which centers around petroleum-rich Lake Maracaibo in the northwest and around the Orinoco River delta in the northeast.

Except for the mining of iron ore by United States corporations at Cerro Bolívar and El Pao in the Guiana Highlands—operations supplying tidewater iron and steel plants in the United States—the savanna country is essentially the domain of the livestock ranch (photo, p. 529). Ranching, however, is largely confined to the half of the country that lies north and west of the Orinoco. Areas to the south and east of the river, largely in the Guiana Highlands, are mostly unoccupied except for small numbers of primitive and little-known Indians. In contrast, the *tierra templada* of northern Venezuela contains two of the country's four cities with metropolitan populations of 100,000 or over—Caracas, the capital (1,000,000), and Barquisimeto (155,000). (The remaining cities are Maracaibo [355,-000] on the northern coastal lowland and Valencia [120,000] in the intermontane basin of the same name.) It also contains the most important farming districts. Coffee from the *tierra templada* zone is Venezuela's principal export crop. However, corn, grown in all of the country's agricultural areas, occupies a much larger total acreage than any other crop. It is primarily a subsistence crop.

Petroleum, amounting to over 14 percent of the estimated world output in 1958, constituted 91 percent of Venezuela's exports by value in that year. It is extracted in Venezuela by American and British firms, but refined, for the most part, on the islands of Aruba and Curaçao in the Netherlands Antilles or at overseas refineries. Less than one fifth is refined in Venezuela itself. Most of the country's oil is procured in the northwestern fields centering on Lake Maracaibo (photo, right), but petroleum extraction is also important in a rather large area between the Orinoco River and the northern mountains. By far the greater part of Venezuela's petroleum exports move to the United States or Europe.

A rural landscape in the Andean *tierra fría* of Colombia about 30 miles north of Bogotá. Level land is at a premium here, and fields and pastures are carried as far up the mountain slopes as possible. (Foreign Agricultural Service, U. S. Department of Agriculture.)

Petroleum is the leading Latin American mineral in value of production. The photo shows oil being extracted from beneath the shallow waters of Lake Maracaibo in western Venezuela. (Standard Oil Company, N. J.)

In recent years Venezuela has experienced a rapid development of manufacturing, as Colombia has at a somewhat slower rate. Consumer-type industries are greatly in the majority in both countries, though Venezuela has a new iron and steel plant on the Orinoco River in the port area which serves the iron mines of the Guiana Highlands. Venezuela's new industries also include an impressive cluster of chemical plants on the coastal plain about 100 miles west of Caracas.

## ▶ Mainland Units Affiliated with Overseas Nations

British Guiana, French Guiana, Surinam or Dutch Guiana, British Honduras, and the Panama Canal Zone are the mainland units of Caribbean America that are affiliated with overseas nations.[5] The two British units are colonies, though British Guiana manages its own internal affairs to a greater extent than does British Honduras. French Guiana is an overseas department of France, and Surinam is officially an integral part of the Kingdom of the Netherlands. The Panama Canal Zone, a United States government reservation, is essentially a district 10 miles wide trending in conformance with the Panama Canal. Over one half of its population of around 60,000 (including armed forces) lives in urban centers at either end of, or along, the canal. The Canal Zone enjoys substantial economic support from the United States.

The three Guiana units and British Honduras have much in common. They have been among the farthest outposts of Euro-

[5] Although the three Guianas, like the Bahama Islands and El Salvador, do not touch the Caribbean Sea proper, they lie near by, and like the latter units they may be discussed without strain in the general context of Caribbean America.

pean colonialism in Latin America. Their physical environment is chiefly that of tropical rainy, disease-ridden lowlands. On the whole they have received comparatively little attention from the European colonial powers which have controlled them. An important exception has been the development of large-scale bauxite mining in Surinam and British Guiana. In 1958 the former supplied 14 percent and the latter nearly 8 percent of the total world production of this aluminum-bearing ore. Employment opportunities are relatively few, however, as most of the work is done with machines.

Only a small fraction of the total land area of the three Guianas has been cleared for cultivation, though agriculture supports most of the people. Plantations, clustered along the coast, yield exports of cane sugar (from British Guiana) and rice (from Surinam and British Guiana). Some farming of a subsistence nature is carried on, with rice and yams as the principal crops.

French Guiana is economically the poorest of the Guianas, partly because it lacks mineral exports and partly because it has only recently been elevated from the status of a penal colony. The more docile prisoners were kept on the mainland and those more difficult to manage on Devil's Island, a few miles offshore. Most of the prisoners were from France. Many, now freed, still live in French Guiana.

In British Honduras, forest products replace those of the mine and farm as major exports. Lumber, primarily mahogany or pine, is by far the largest item on the export list. Chicle, used as a base for chewing gum, is a second forest export of some importance. Corn, grown mostly as a subsistence crop, is the main agricultural product. Foodstuffs constituted more than a fourth of all imports into British Honduras in 1958.

### ▶ The Islands

The islands of Caribbean America are an extremely varied group. A wide range of physical types and sizes is represented, racial and cultural variations are very great, and there is notable variety from island to island in political arrangements and in economic mainstays.

Cuba, the largest island, is comprised primarily of lowlands with low to moderate relief, the principal exception being a mountainous area that occupies the southern end of the island. The islands that rank next in size—Hispaniola (Haiti), Jamaica, and Puerto Rico—are very mountainous or hilly. The island of Trinidad, a detached fragment of the South American continent, has a low mountain range in the north (a continuation of the Andes) and level to hilly areas elsewhere. The small islands of Aruba, Curaçao, and Bonaire, affiliated with the Netherlands, also lie near the mainland. They have low to moderate elevations and slopes. Most of the remaining islands of Caribbean America, all comparatively small, fall into two broad physical types. (1) Low, flat, limestone islands rimmed by coral reefs include the Bahamas, northeast of Cuba (see n. 5, p. 545), and a few others. (2) Most islands in the Virgin Island, Leeward, and Windward groups, stretching along the eastern margin of the Caribbean from Puerto Rico toward Trinidad (map, p. 539), are of volcanic origin. Such islands consist of one or more volcanic cones, most of which are extinct or inactive, with limited amounts of cultivable land on lower slopes and small plains. Some cones are thousands of feet high, while others have been greatly worn down by erosive processes. Intermixed with the volcanic islands are a small number of low limestone islands. Barbados, located east of the Windward Islands, is a limestone island with moderately elevated, rolling surfaces.

All of the islands have warm temperatures throughout the year, though extremely hot weather is uncommon. The difference between the average temperatures of the warmest and coolest months ranges from about 4°F in Barbados to about 10°F in northern Cuba. Precipitation, however, varies notably from island to island, and from one section of mountainous islands to another. Windward slopes of mountains often receive very heavy precipitation, amounting in some instances to more than 200 inches annually, whereas leeward slopes and very low islands may have rainfall so scanty as to create semiarid conditions. In some areas a moisture deficiency is created or abetted by porous limestone bedrock into which precipitation rapidly disappears. The natural vegetation of the islands varies from luxuriant forests in areas of abundant moisture to a sparse, scrubby woodland in very dry areas. Most areas experience two rainy seasons and two dry seasons a year. Hurricanes, approaching from the east and then curving northward along rather well-defined tracks, are a scourge of the northern islands in the late summer and autumn.

The majority—in most islands a very large majority—of the inhabitants are Negroes or mulattoes. People of relatively unmixed European descent comprise most of the remainder, aside from a considerable Asian element (mainly Hindu or Moslem Indians) in Trinidad. The cultural heritage of the different islands varies greatly, and includes Spanish, British, French, Dutch, American, Danish, African, and (in Trinidad) Hindu and Moslem influences in practically endless combinations. Political arrangements also are diversified. Only three units—the republics of Cuba and Haiti, and the Dominican Republic—are sovereign nations; the remaining units exhibit varying degrees of dependence on overseas nations and are tied to those nations under a variety of governmental forms (Table 27). For the islands as a whole and for most individual islands, agriculture is by far the leading source of livelihood. A large share of the production is for subsistence or for sale in local markets. Corn, manioc, yams, rice, and bananas are among the prominent subsistence crops. But single-crop plantation agriculture is the economic activity for which these islands are best known, and it is still the commercial mainstay of most islands. Generally a particular island will specialize heavily in one crop—sugar cane being favored in the majority of cases, as it has been for centuries. Other commercial crops that are prominent on some islands include coffee, sea-island cotton, bananas (particularly in Jamaica), tobacco (primarily in Cuba), cacao, spices, limes and other citrus fruits, and coconuts. Though most of the value of commercial production for the islands as a whole has up to the present been accounted for by large plantations or estates worked by tenant farmers or hired laborers, some crops—such as the coffee of Haiti or the bananas of Jamaica—are produced primarily by small landowning farmers. On most islands mineral production is absent or unimportant, the most conspicuous exceptions being Jamaica (bauxite), Trinidad (petroleum), and Cuba (metals). Manufacturing has made very large gains in Puerto Rico in recent years and significant gains in Cuba, but in most of the other islands industrial progress has been slow or absent. Tourism is of growing significance in the island area as a whole, though American tourism practically ceased in Cuba following the revolution which brought the government of Fidel Castro to power in 1959. Most tourists in the islands are from the United States.

### The Island Republics

In area the island republics of Cuba, the Dominican Republic, and Haiti fall into a general class with the independent countries of Central America. Population densities, however, are generally much higher than on the mainland, except in the case of densely-populated El Salvador.

Cuba's has been essentially a sugar economy. Approximately one fifth of the world's sugar has normally been produced here each year, most of it for export. Cane sugar, mainly in raw form, accounted for slightly more than three fourths of all exports by value in 1957 and 1958, while molasses represented an additional 3 to 5 percent. The United States has been the principal market for Cuba's sugar and molasses. Production of sugar cane has been carried on primarily by tenants on small parcels of land belonging to large estates—a situation which may or may not be fundamentally altered by land redistribution under the Castro regime. Only about a tenth of Cuba's raw sugar has normally been refined within the country; the remainder has moved to refineries in seaports of other countries, primarily the United States. Foreign capital, much of it from the United States, has played a dominant role in the development of Cuba's sugar industry. Prior to the Castro revolution, more American capital had been invested in Cuba than in any other Latin American country except Venezuela and Brazil. At the time of writing (early 1961), it seemed probable that the investors would suffer heavy losses as a result of the nationalization of nearly all American-owned properties by the revolutionary government. Cuba's seizure of these properties, plus the apparent drift of the Castro government toward the Communist political and economic orbit, had roused a bitter controversy with the United States. What the ultimate effects of this would be on political and economic relationships between Cuba and its giant neighbor to the north was quite unpredictable.

Tobacco and metalliferous ores (primarily nickel and copper ores, with some manganese ore, chrome ore, and iron ore) account for most of Cuba's exports other than sugar and molasses. Mining is largely confined to two mountainous areas, one in the far south of the island and the other in the extreme northwest. Copper comes primarily from the latter area and other metals from the former. The island has experienced a considerable development of manufacturing industries in recent years. Prominent among these are industries that process food and tobacco and that manufacture cotton and rayon textiles, cement, chemical fertilizers, and automobile tires. Havana (Habana; 1,315,000) is Cuba's main industrial center, as well as its political capital, largest city, and main seaport.

Haiti and the Dominican Republic share uneasily the island of Hispaniola or Haiti. Although the diversity of natural features on this mountainous island is not inconsequential, that of culture and society is even more pronounced. Haiti is a Negro republic in which the rapidly growing population has already attained a density more than twice as high as that of any other republic in Caribbean America except El Salvador (Table 27). Its present-day agricultural economy, largely of a subsistence character, reflects little influence from the French who once controlled the country. The Dominican Republic, though containing some Negroes and a large majority with some Negro blood, is proud of its Spanish cultural heritage. Although the Dominican Republic has nearly twice the area of Haiti, its small farm-plantation economy supports a population which is somewhat smaller than that of its western neighbor.

The boundary line between these two countries is one of long-standing instability, and local border incidents have been rather frequent.

The largest cities of Hispaniola are the two national capitals, Ciudad Trujillo (295,000) in the Dominican Republic and Port-au-Prince (235,000), in Haiti.

### Islands Affiliated with Overseas Nations

The statement that Caribbean America is not the master of its own destiny is most applicable to the islands that are affiliated politically with overseas nations. In these units, severe population pressures and poverty are almost omnipresent. One unit in which conditions are better is Puerto Rico. A determined effort on the part of Puerto Ricans to raise their standard of living has brought great changes to the island during the past two decades. Hydroelectric power resources have been harnessed, a land classification program has provided a basis for sound agricultural planning, and a thriving development of manufacturing industries and tourism, financed in large measure by capital attracted from mainland United States, is under way. But in the islands generally, including many of those that belong to the new West Indies federation (see p. 523), movements for political, economic, and social improvement tend to be sluggish, and in some cases are essentially absent. Most islands continue to suffer from the traditional ills of poverty, illiteracy, disease, excessive dependence on single-crop plantation agriculture, absentee ownership of land, and, particularly on some of the smaller islands, an undesirable measure of control by plantation or estate owners over the lives of the inhabitants.

In the islands affiliated with overseas nations, the only cities with metropolitan populations of more than 100,000 are San Juan (590,000) and Ponce (140,000) in Puerto Rico; Kingston, Jamaica (346,000); and Port-of-Spain, Trinidad (240,000).

## ▶ Transportation and Urbanization in Caribbean America

Caribbean America is not noteworthy for a highly developed system of transportation facilities or for a conspicuous degree of urbanization. However, connections with the outside world are afforded by the many important shipping lanes which converge on the region, attracted in no small measure by the great interocean passageway through Panama. A modest number of large cities exist, including one, Mexico City, with a metropolitan population of nearly 4 million, and five others—Havana, Caracas, Bogotá, San Juan, and Medellín—with metropolitan populations of over 500,000.

### The Panama Canal

The Panama Canal is one of the two major man-made waterways which have caused a gross reorientation of the world's ocean shipping lanes. Like its counterpart, the Suez Canal, its economic importance lies chiefly in the intensity of ocean traffic it attracts by providing a passage through a narrow land bridge connecting two continents. In this sense, it is only about 30 percent as important as the Suez channel: in 1958 it freighted approximately 48.1 million long tons of cargo as compared with 139.3 million long tons moving through the Suez. Nevertheless, it is a major focus of shipping lanes, being particularly important in the funneling of vessels from the Far East, the west coasts of the Americas, and other Pacific Ocean ports into the Atlantic. The return volume of cargo is less than one half as large as this prevailing west-to-east flow.

Again like the Suez, the Panama Canal has military as well as economic importance. Although the military implications vary with current events, they are never absent.

At the present time there is agitation for increasing the canal's present depth of 42 feet (actually, the minimum depth is now 37 feet at low tide in the harbor of Balboa) to 60 feet—thus permitting the largest naval and merchant ships, present and prospective future, to negotiate the channel. The possibility of converting the present vulnerable lock system into a sea-level waterway is also under consideration.

Unlike the other transportation facilities of Caribbean America, the Panama Canal tends to be superimposed upon, rather than meshed into, the local economies. The traffic of most Caribbean countries would not be seriously altered if the canal were not used.

### Local Transportation

The remaining transportation facilities are, in the main, designed to serve Caribbean America. Mexico and Cuba have rather loosely woven rail networks with gauges that are generally the same as the standard gauge in the United States and Canada. A railway freight car can thus move from Canada to Mexico or (by car ferry) to Cuba.

Highway systems tend to parallel the

railways. In Honduras, Panama, Haiti, the Dominican Republic, and most small islands, highways take precedence in importance over railroads. The Inter-American Highway is gradually reaching completion, although a few segments tend to be dry weather roads only, and a few breaks still remain.

Ocean shipping and commercial aircraft are of primary importance as media of transportation within Caribbean America. Nearly every city of 100,000 or over has access to one or the other, or both.

**Urbanization**

Relatively few of Caribbean America's people live in major cities. In Venezuela, about 1 inhabitant in 5 lives in a city of 50,000 or over. In Costa Rica the ratio is 1 in 14; in El Salvador, 1 in 10; in Haiti, 1 in 20. These ratios are crude indices of comparative stages of industrial development, for factory-type industries in Caribbean America, as in many other parts of the world, tend to be heavily concentrated in the larger cities. A large majority of Caribbean America's factories and cities of 100,000 inhabitants or more (map, p. 539) are found in the four largest countries—Mexico, Colombia, Venezuela, and Cuba. Industrial production per capita is far smaller in most other political units of the region than in the four countries named, though Puerto Rico is a noteworthy exception.

## THE NATIVE INDIAN COUNTRIES OF SOUTH AMERICA

Ecuador, Peru, Bolivia, and Paraguay are the predominantly native Indian countries of South America. Each has a high proportion—at least 50 percent—of native Indians in its population. The ratio in Peru—50 percent—is the smallest; in Bolivia it is 57 percent, in Ecuador 58 percent, and in Paraguay 64 percent.[6] Except for Guatemala in Central America no other Latin American country contains a comparable proportion of native Indians.

These countries are further characterized by their very low per capita national incomes—ranging from $94 per year in Paraguay to $150 in Ecuador. They rank near the bottom of the Latin American scale in this respect.

Still another distinctive feature of these four countries is the very small contribution they make to Latin America's total exports. Peru, the most important exporting nation of the group, is responsible for slightly more than 3 percent of all Latin American exports by value.

Furthermore, the native Indian countries have an unusually high ratio of rural to urban population. Cities with metropolitan populations of 100,000 or over include only Guayaquil and Quito in Ecuador, Lima-Callao and Arequipa in Peru, La Paz and Cochabamba in Bolivia, and Asunción in Paraguay.

In each of these countries, except Paraguay, a major segment of the total population resides in mountain valleys of the Andes. In Bolivia most of the people live at high altitudes; in Ecuador and Peru the population is distributed among high, intermediate, and low elevations; and in Paraguay it is found at low elevations. Obviously the

---

[6] Donald D. Brand, "The Present Indian Populations of Latin America." In *Some Educational and Anthropological Aspects of Latin America.* Austin: University of Texas Press, 1948. P. 51. Other sources state that Paraguay's population is overwhelmingly *mestizo.* But all sources agree that the predominant racial strain in that country is Guarani Indian.

range from *tierra fría* through the *tierra templada* to the *tierra caliente* is well illustrated here.

## ▶ *Bolivia*

Of Bolivia's more than 3 million people, most are residents of the *tierra fría* zone of the Andes, which constitute the western third of the country (maps, pp. 552 and 553). It is here that the Andean system reaches its widest extent—over 400 miles, if one includes the small portion to the west in Chile. Most of this highland country in Bolivia is above the level of the *tierra templada*. It is essentially comprised of two high mountain cordilleras, separated by a high intermontane plateau. The Western Cordillera, reaching elevations of 20,000 feet above the sea, is the most inhospitable of these areas to human settlement and the most formidable barrier to traffic routes. The intermontane plateau, the Altiplano, contains Lake Poopó, a salt-water lake at an elevation of about 12,120 feet; Lake Titicaca, a fresh-water lake which Bolivia shares with its neighbor Peru at a height of about 12,500 feet; and the Desaguadero River connecting the two lakes. The Eastern Cordillera, although attaining elevations of more than 20,000 feet, is more thoroughly dissected by streams than its western counterpart. In addition, it contains some very rich vein deposits of tin and other metals. These metals were sought and to some extent exploited by the Spanish, and they still form Bolivia's principal exports.

### Settlement in the *Tierra Fría*

Most of Bolivia's people live in either the Altiplano or the Eastern Cordillera. As has been stated, the majority of these are native Indians whose ancestors, once the subjects of the Inca Empire, have inhabited these highlands for centuries. The population density seldom exceeds 25 persons per square mile except around the shores of Lake Titicaca, which is surrounded by a closely spaced fringe of native Indian settlements. Although the lake with its attendant cluster of settlements is bisected by the political boundary line between Bolivia and Peru, the local inhabitants form a unitary community and customarily pay little heed to the boundary. Where left alone, they continue to live as their ancestors have done— grazing their sheep, llamas, and burros in the grassy area of the Altiplano and on the *paramos* above, and growing their meager crops of potatoes, quínoa, and barley. Throughout the year the average monthly temperatures vary comparatively little— ranging generally between 40°F and 50°F. Rainfall varies greatly from valley to valley, with a rough average of perhaps 30 to 50 inches annually. It is a dreary life in a dreary land—a life which the native Indians ease somewhat by chewing leaves of the coca plant. This is a cultivated plant that contains the drug cocaine.

Tin is the most important product taken from Bolivian mines. In 1959 the country was responsible for slightly less than 15 percent of the total world mine production of this commodity. The leading mines are in the Eastern Cordillera and, to a lesser extent, in the Altiplano. In addition, silver, tungsten, antimony, lead, zinc, and bismuth are extracted in the same general areas—often from the same mines as the tin. Until recently the mines have been privately owned—in some measure from abroad and in some measure by Bolivian citizens. However, control over most of them has lately been assumed by the Bolivian government. The native Indians provide the principal labor force of the mines. They are more effective than lowland dwellers, who become short of breath because there is less oxygen at these heights.

### La Paz

Several urban settlements at varying altitudes are situated in valleys of streams which drain eastward through the East-

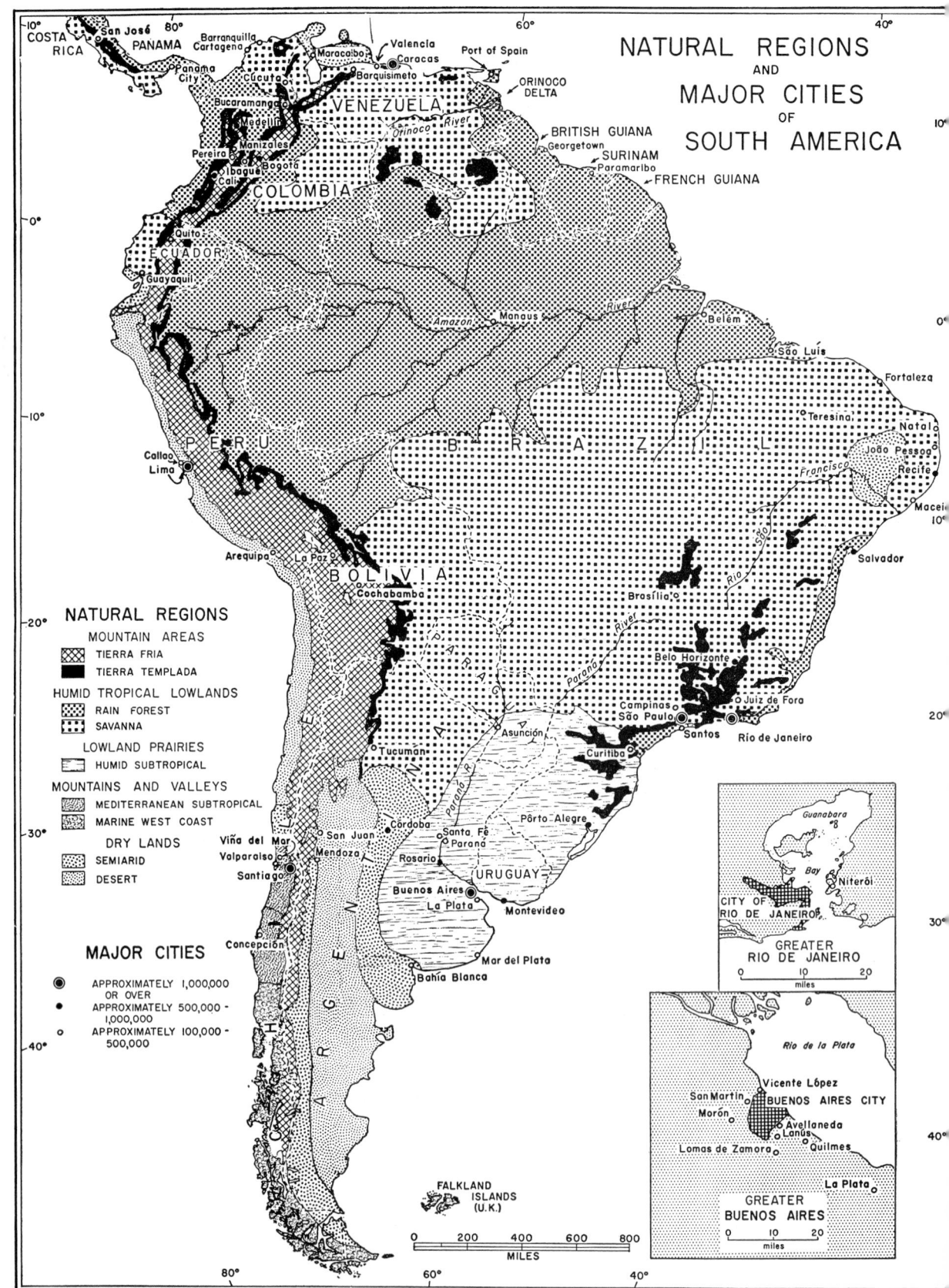

# NATURAL REGIONS
## AND
# MAJOR CITIES
## OF
# SOUTH AMERICA

## NATURAL REGIONS

### MOUNTAIN AREAS
- TIERRA FRIA
- TIERRA TEMPLADA

### HUMID TROPICAL LOWLANDS
- RAIN FOREST
- SAVANNA

### LOWLAND PRAIRIES
- HUMID SUBTROPICAL

### MOUNTAINS AND VALLEYS
- MEDITERRANEAN SUBTROPICAL
- MARINE WEST COAST

### DRY LANDS
- SEMIARID
- DESERT

## MAJOR CITIES
- APPROXIMATELY 1,000,000 OR OVER
- APPROXIMATELY 500,000 - 1,000,000
- APPROXIMATELY 100,000 - 500,000

GREATER RIO DE JANEIRO
0   10   20
miles

GREATER BUENOS AIRES
0   10   20
miles

FALKLAND ISLANDS (U.K.)

0   200   400   600   800
MILES

The city-size symbols are based on metropolitan-area estimates.

ern Cordillera. The most noteworthy of these is the city of La Paz (395,000). Lying in a gorge immediately beneath the rim of the Altiplano (photo, p. 537), this unusually placed city is the *de facto* capital of Bolivia, although Sucre (45,000), 350 miles to the southeast, has long been officially designated as the capital, and the Bolivian Supreme Court actually sits there. La Paz is a true highland capital of a highland country. In addition, it is a redistribution point for agricultural products from the lower mountain valleys to the northeast and from the Altiplano, and for necessities brought by rail from either the Atlantic or the Pacific coast. Its manufacturing industries process food and make textiles, clothing, and other items needed by Bolivians.

**Settlements of the Lower *Tierra Fría* and Upper *Tierra Templada***

At lower elevations, especially to the south and east in the *tierra templada,* are found a number of settlements where European-induced forms of agriculture prevail. The most heavily populated of these is centered around Cochabamba, a city of approximately 100,000 inhabitants. Food products from the small commercial agricultural district surrounding the city move chiefly to the mines in the highlands. In all of the four native Indian countries this district is the only sizable area within which the average population density exceeds 250 per square mile.

The eastern and northeastern wilds of Bolivia, a lowland countryside dominated by tropical savanna climate and ranging in vegetation from high forest in the north to scrub forest on the Paraguay border, is as yet very thinly inhabited.

### ▶ *Peru*

North and west of Lake Titicaca, the Altiplano comes to a rather abrupt end. The two cordilleras which have been distinct in Bolivia merge into a series of echelonlike ranges and groups of mountains. This series

continues through Peru, where the Andean system becomes narrower until, at the Ecuadorian border, it is only about 150 miles wide.

### The *Tierra Fría*

The native Indians living in the high mountain valleys of Peru follow ways of life similar to those of highland Bolivia. Indeed, the highland Indians of both countries are descended from subjects of the ancient Incas, who once controlled a considerable empire with its capital at Cuzco

(68,000). As in Bolivia, the *tierra fría* supports primarily a subsistence agricultural economy, especially to the northwest and to the southeast.

In the center of the Peruvian Andes is a rich mining district in the vicinity of Cerro de Pasco (28,000), producing copper, silver, gold, zinc, lead, and bismuth. Some commercial farming is carried on in valleys not far from the mines. The wheat, corn, and other products grown here are shipped by rail to the mines or—farther downslope —to the capital city of Lima.

### The Arid Coast

The Andes drop sharply on the west to a narrow desert coast. Water from the numerous streams draining from the mountains into the Pacific provides irrigation for approximately 40 intermittently distributed oases (photo, below). Some of these are the sites of commercial plantations specializing in cotton, others of similar plantations growing sugar cane. In still others the farm-ing is predominantly of a subsistence character. Rice grown for local consumption is an important crop in most oases. No continuous rail route parallels the coast, and each oasis has its own seaport. Quality rather than quantity is emphasized in the production of both cotton and sugar. The cotton is chiefly a long staple variety similar to that of the Nile Valley in Egypt. Peru supplies approximately 1 percent of the total annual world production of both commodities.

Lima, the capital (1,169,000), is also on the arid coastal lowland. It was built by the Spanish and with its seaport Callao became the focus of routes leading not only from nearby mines of the Andes but also from more distant points. It is today an important manufacturing and university metropolis. Its manufacturing is mainly devoted to food, apparel, and other necessities for Peruvian consumption.

A series of small petroleum fields, situated at the northern edge of this arid coast,

Irrigated agriculture and sheep-raising in an oasis on the desert coast of Peru 150 miles north of Lima. The view shows a commercial sugar-cane plantation owned and operated by an American corporation. In the foreground is the main control gate of the plantation's irrigation system. (Foreign Agricultural Service, U. S. Department of Agriculture.)

extends across the border into Ecuador.

### The Eastern *Tierra Caliente*

The eastern part of Peru lies beyond the Andes and almost wholly within the Amazon Basin. Here is a broad lowland area of rain forest and sluggish river, of untamed Indian and venturesome trader. Iquitos (54,000), at the upper limit of effective steamboat navigation on the Amazon River, is the major focus of commerce and transportation. From the city move wild animal skins, crude rubber, certain gums used in the manufacture of chewing gum, tagua nuts, and other extracted forest and animal products. Some cotton is also shipped. In turn, the city acts as a supply center for a large, sparsely settled hinterland. Its traders sell to the natives and a few immigrant settlers such items as drugs, groceries, hardware, and buttons. Iquitos is connected to Callao and Lima by regular steamer service involving a total journey of over 6000 miles down the Amazon River, through the Panama Canal, and along the Pacific coast. Air service is also available.

### ▶ *Ecuador*

Ecuador, like Peru, has a lowland strip on its Pacific side, a high-mountain central segment, and a section of the Amazon River basin. The Pacific lowlands are more hilly than their Peruvian counterparts. In climate, the coastal desert of the south gives way to tropical savanna and, in the extreme north, to tropical rain forest.

The Andes Mountains, having narrowed increasingly from central Bolivia through Peru, are generally only 100 to 150 miles wide in Ecuador. They broaden again to the north in Colombia. Their areal arrangement in Ecuador becomes once again that of two rather distinct cordilleras, separated by a structural depression—or, more strictly, by a series of mountain valleys which together constitute such a depression. Volcanic peaks, very much present in

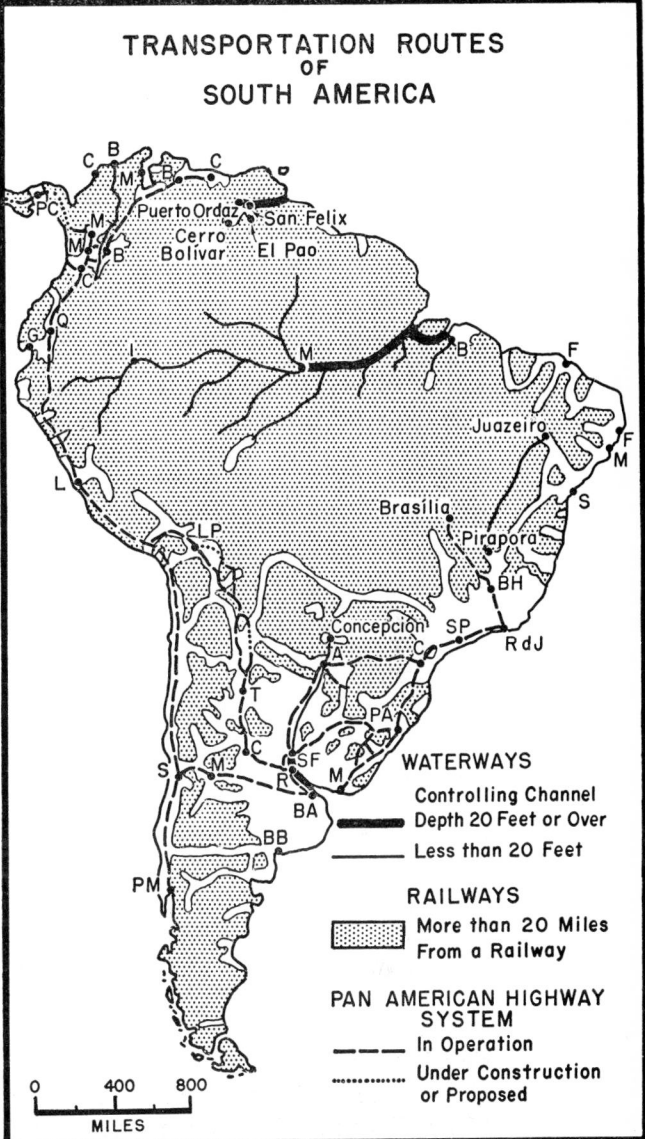

Bolivia but relatively few in Peru, reappear conspicuously in either cordillera. The highest, Mount Chimborazo in the Western Cordillera, reaches 20,577 feet. The Amazonian lowland of Ecuador to the east of the Andes is not unlike that of Peru and southeastern Colombia in general character, but it is smaller in extent.

### Settlement Pattern and Economy of the Highlands

A majority of the people in Ecuador live in the Andean *tierra fría* at elevations

higher than 7000 feet. They are clustered mainly in mountain valleys between the two cordilleras. Valleys of the far north, like their counterparts across the border in Colombia, are mainly occupied by highland Indians, as are those of the south. Quito, the capital and second largest city (elevation about 9350 feet; population 255,000), lies in a high basin in the north central part of the country. In the surrounding countryside the subsistence economy of the native Indian gives place to commercial farming dominated by *mestizos* and whites, who also form a majority of the population in Quito itself. Barley, corn, quínoa, potatoes, and livestock are grown, chiefly for sale in Quito. The manufacturing industries of the city, like those in so many isolated Latin American urban centers, concentrate on the processing of locally grown agricultural produce for local consumption. Another valley characterized by commercial forms of agriculture and a predominantly *mestizo* or white population surrounds Ecuador's third city, Cuenca (67,000), approximately 300 miles south of Quito. The country's only noteworthy railroad connects Quito and Cuenca with the important seaport of Guayaquil on the Pacific.

The highland economy of Ecuador differs sharply from that of Peru and Bolivia in the comparative unimportance of minerals. Many different minerals are present, but few in deposits sufficiently large or rich to justify the costs of mining.

**The Pacific Lowlands**

On the Pacific coast lives the other substantial portion of Ecuador's population. Here is found the port of Guayaquil (320,-000), the largest city in Ecuador. A low alluvial area inundated regularly by the Guayas River surrounds the port. Here, under a tropical savanna climate, is grown rice, primarily for domestic use but to some degree for export. Bananas, coffee, and cacao, respectively comprising 37, 28, and 22 percent of the country's exports by value

(1958), also are grown on the Guayas River lowland or its margins. Most of the land of the drier section along the western margin of the lowland is devoted to the raising of livestock, chiefly for domestic consumption.

▶ *Paraguay*

Paraguay is lowland. Only along its western margin and in a few scattered hills to the east does the elevation exceed 1000 feet. It is sparsely populated. The three fifths of the country situated to the west of the Paraguay River contains fewer than 2½ persons per square mile. Except for a corridor of settlement along the railway from the capital, Asunción (235,000), to Encarnación (13,000), the density to the east of the river does not generally exceed 26 persons per square mile. Effective Paraguay is, therefore, along the railway.

In perhaps no other country of South America has a not unfavorable physical environment been used so ineffectually as in Paraguay. Many of the soils, though not of the highest caliber, are reasonably fertile. The climate of the west, it is true, is a rather inhospitable, dry tropical savanna. To the east, however, where agricultural potentialities are much higher, are humid subtropical conditions where the annual precipitation, rather evenly distributed, ranges generally between 40 and 80 inches each year. Yet the country has lagged behind in the development of commercial forms of agriculture.

The Paraguayans themselves, like their Bolivian neighbors, ascribe much of their low economic status to an interior position. Of the 10 South American republics, only Paraguay and Bolivia are without a coastline. In 1865 Paraguay decided to remedy this situation by marching to the Atlantic Ocean. The latter proved a foolhardy undertaking resulting in war with Brazil, Argentina, and Uruguay. In five years of war a Paraguayan population numbering over 500,000 was reduced to approximately 300,-

000, of which only 22,000 were males. The country is today strongly dependent on the seaports of Argentina for contact with world markets. Approximately one third of Paraguay's exports are consigned to Argentine ports for overseas shipment.

Present-day Paraguayans live in a semi-subsistence economy. Their small farms grow corn, cassava, beans, vegetables, some fruit—including citrus fruit—and cotton. The much larger land area that is not tilled is devoted chiefly to the raising of cattle. Meat and cotton are the principal agricultural exports. These rank second and third, behind timber, among the country's total exports.

Paraguay sends two interesting forest products to the regional and, to a lesser degree, the world market. One of these is extract from the quebracho tree which thrives along the Paraná and Paraguay rivers. The extract is used in the tanning of leather. The second product is comprised of leaves from a South American holly plant.

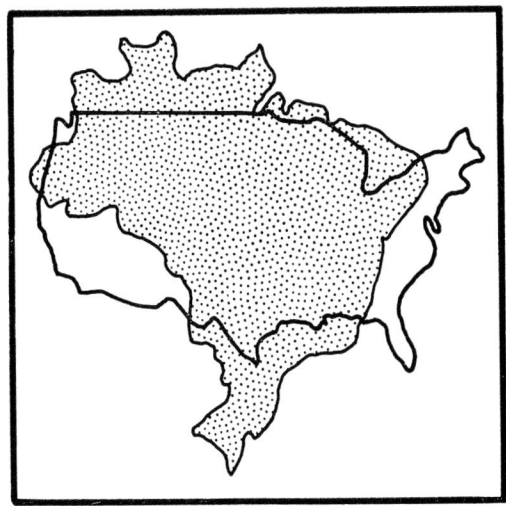

Brazil compared in area with the continental United States.

These leaves are used to make yerba maté, a form of "tea" which is an important item of diet not only in Paraguay but also in other—especially nearby—sections of South America.

# BRAZIL

Brazil, although a single nation, forms a major subdivision of Latin America comparable in extent and importance to regions containing several different countries. Both the area and the population of Brazil are impressive, especially in comparison with other Latin American nations. Its area exceeds that of continental United States (excluding Alaska) (map, above). Its population, while little more than a third as large as that of the United States, is nearly double that of Mexico, the second Latin American country in population. Brazil contains nearly a third of all the people in Latin America.

### ▶ Some Major Characteristics of Brazil

Brazil occupies a central position in Latin America. Situated on the equator, the coun-

try has extensive coastlines fringing the Atlantic Ocean in both the Northern and Southern hemispheres. Its westernmost margin is not far from the Pacific. Smaller Latin American neighbors, including all of the other South American political units except Ecuador and Chile, flank its northern, western, and southern boundaries.

Much of its large area is undulating lowland or low upland. Unlike most other nations of comparable size, it is lacking in truly high mountains. At no place does it reach the Andes. Still, it has mountains and associated rough country in the Brazilian Highlands which flank most of the southeast coast; and, to the north across the Amazon River, in a small segment of the Guiana Highlands which reach over the border from Venezuela.

It encompasses nearly the whole of the

drainage basin of the Amazon and its tributaries, one of the world's greatest river systems.

It includes the major portion of Latin America's tropical climates, vegetation, and soils. Except for the *tierra templada* of the highlands and the humid subtropical climate of the far south, Brazil is essentially a tropical nation.

It is the only Latin American nation in which Portuguese is the official language.

Its people are predominantly rural dwellers, yet it contains Rio de Janeiro and São Paulo, two of Latin America's eight metropolises that exceed one million in population. In addition, it possesses 19 metropolitan cities with populations ranging from 100,000 to 860,000.

It is a nation in which manufacturing industries and service occupations are growing rapidly in size and importance.

It contains the largest expanses of uninhabited or sparsely settled and yet potentially productive land in Latin America. According to some estimates, nearly four fifths of Brazil could be made productive and support at least a moderately dense population. At present, however, only about a fourth of the country is effectively occupied.

## ▶ Major Land Divisions

The land surface of Brazil falls generally into three major divisions: (1) the Atlantic coastal lowland strip; (2) the eastern highlands and uplands, sloping generally toward the continental interior; and (3) the lowlands of the Amazon, Paraná–Paraguay, and Uruguay rivers.

### The Atlantic Coastal Strip

Although recognizable along the northeastern shorelines of Brazil, the Atlantic coastal strip is best developed on the country's southeastern margin between the cities of Recife (860,000) and Pôrto Alegre (530,000). It is narrow, varying in width from almost nothing to about 100 miles.

From Salvador (500,000) almost to Pôrto Alegre its western side is flanked by a steep series of terraces—or, in a few places, by a single terrace—customarily referred to as "the great escarpment." The coastal strip is predominantly a lowland of uneven surface, of tropical rainy or savanna climate and associated natural vegetation (much of which has been removed by man) and of rather infertile tropical soils. This coastal lowland is the most densely populated and intensively utilized of the three major surface divisions of the country.

The trend of the great escarpment is in conformance with that of the seacoast. Attaining elevations of 2500 feet—and, in isolated mountains up to 8000 feet—above sea level, this escarpment is the "height of land" in Brazil. It tends to separate headwaters of the numerous short rivers draining to the Atlantic Ocean on the east from those of longer arteries extending to the Amazon and Paraná–Paraguay systems on the west. The single major exception is the large São Francisco River, which reaches the Atlantic Ocean between Recife and Salvador.

### The Brazilian Highlands

The great escarpment forms the eastern edge of the Brazilian Highlands, which slope gently toward the interior. The irregular terrain has a tropical savanna climate, but with much variation in total rainfall from place to place and also in types of associated vegetation. This area is sparsely populated at present, except for parts of its seaward margin. It contains much of Brazil's potentially productive land.

### The Interior Lowlands

In general the surface of the interior lowlands is uneven, although the flood plains proper are quite flat. To the north, the great Amazon system lies under tropical rainy climate, with tributary waterways extending into the adjacent tropical savanna—particularly that of the Southern Hemisphere. During the rainy summer months (December–

February) these tributaries bring floods to the main river. Such floods are large enough to destroy sedimentary islands deposited the preceding year, together with the luxuriant jungle vegetation which establishes itself annually on these islands. Meanwhile, islands are again created, upon which the jungle will grow anew. Above the high-water mark are the tall broad-leaved evergreen trees of the tropical rain forest proper.

To the south, the Paraguay, Paraná, and Uruguay rivers also flow through uneven terrain. The climate varies from tropical savanna along the middle Paraguay to humid subtropical along the middle Paraná and upper Uruguay. Settlement of the river lowlands ranges from almost empty areas of rain forest in the Amazon River basin to moderately peopled subtropical grasslands in the south.

## ► Population Distribution

Brazil is predominantly an area of sparse, unevenly distributed, rural population. The majority of the inhabitants are concentrated within two major clusters along the southeast coast. One of these lies around and between the cities of Recife and Salvador. The other extends from Rio de Janeiro (3,750,-000) and its hinterland to São Paulo (3,300,000) and its hinterland. Smaller clusters are found around the other major cities and at other, less prominent places, of which most are near the sea. In no sizable area does the population exceed 250 persons per square mile.

## ► Brazilian Agriculture

The people of Brazil look primarily to agriculture and grazing for a livelihood. These engage about two thirds of all employed workers, excluding a very large number who are domestic servants. The principal farming areas are found along, or relatively near, the southeast coast. They form a series of discontinuous districts separated by lightly occupied areas where grazing and shifting cultivation are the primary activities. There is considerable variety in the crops that are emphasized from one district to the next. The northermost important district is a cotton-growing area that extends inland from Natal (140,000). Short-staple cotton is grown here largely as an adjunct of local cattle ranching, the pressed seeds (oilcake) being in great demand for cattle feed. Farther south, sugar cane is grown in a series of coastal districts extending discontinuously to the vicinity of Salvador. The largest district is near Recife. Immediately inland from it are districts producing coffee, cotton, and agave (the plant from which sisal fiber is secured). A small area to the west of Salvador specializes in tobacco. Well to the south of Salvador, the country's main cacao district occupies an elongated strip parallel to the coast but some distance inland. Brazilian cacao accounts for 15 to 20 percent of the world's commercial output, and the country is the second largest cacao exporter (after Ghana).

The climate of the foregoing districts is tropical rain forest around Salvador and in the cacao district to the south, and tropical savanna in districts north of Salvador. Commercial production tends to be dominated by *fazendas,* which are large holdings not greatly unlike the *haciendas* discussed elsewhere. Workers on *fazendas* may be tenants or hired employees, but are usually the former. Some are permanently attached to the land (more by custom than by law), while others tend to move about. Although definitely subordinate to *fazendas* in extent and importance, farms of a subsistence or semi-subsistence nature are also present.

In the far north of this coastal strip the majority of the landowners are of relatively unmixed European descent. Around Salvador, however, Negroes and mulattoes constitute approximately two thirds of the total population and a sizable proportion of the property owners.

A coastal area of tropical rain forest climate around Rio de Janeiro grows bananas, oranges, and truck crops, while irrigated rice is grown in an elongated strip along the Paraíba River valley to the west of the city. A large share of the food produced in the immediate hinterland of Rio de Janeiro is consumed by the nearly 4 million people of that city's metropolitan area.

In the *tierra templada* and tropical savanna hinterland of São Paulo nearly one half of the world's annual coffee crop is produced. Unlike Brazil's agricultural districts discussed thus far, this area reaches far over the crest of the great eastern escarpment of the Brazilian Highlands. It is still moving outward. Each year tenant farmers are assigned virgin land to clear, upon which they grow food crops for the following two years. Subsequently, the land is planted to coffee, though food continues to be grown between the rows of immature trees. When the coffee trees begin to bear (about four to six years after they are planted), the tenants will move again to unbroken deciduous forest land. Cotton is the second most important crop of the coffee region, and the bulk of Brazil's cotton is produced here. The country is Latin America's second largest producer, after Mexico.

Coffee was by far the largest export from Brazil in 1958 (55 percent of all exports by value), as it has been for many years. Cocoa beans ranked second, with 7 percent, and cane sugar third, with 5 percent, of the country's total export value.

In contrast to areas near Rio de Janeiro and Salvador, the coffee area, most of which lies in São Paulo state, is chiefly a district of Europeans and *mestizos* (in Brazil called *mamelucos*). There are few Negroes or mixed Negroid types. The *fazendas* otherwise do not differ sharply from those farther north.

As one proceeds toward Uruguay into humid subtropical climate, he finds himself first in an area of coniferous evergreen forest—a general counterpart to the softwoods of southeastern United States. Beyond this is a discontinuous belt of semideciduous woods which quickly gives way to prairie grasses. Colonies of Slavs (mostly Poles),

Germans, Italians, and Japanese have developed in the forested areas—flourishing, after a slow start, in a diversified agricultural economy based on that of their homelands. The populations of these immigrant communities are currently increasing biologically at a rate without parallel in most of Latin America.

To the south, long-established cattle ranching dominates the rolling prairie lands. Important on the western side of all the Brazilian Highlands, this form of livelihood is perhaps the most picturesquely represented here where the Brazilian *gaucho*—in most cases, a *mameluco*—rules supreme.

## ▶ Manufacturing and Mining

In two other livelihood industries—manufacturing and mining—Brazil is increasingly significant, although neither industry is yet very active when measured in terms of labor force. Manufacturing accounts for only about 6 percent and mining less than 2 percent of all workers. However, Brazil has important potentialities for future development in both fields.

As in other Latin American countries, manufactured products are made primarily for home consumption. In addition to iron and steel made at the Volta Redonda plant (largest in Latin America) on the Paraíba River and at older, smaller mills in the Brazilian Highlands, there are important industries engaged in producing foodstuffs, cotton textiles, leather and leather products, cement, and a substantial variety of other commodities.

The city of São Paulo leads in this industrial trend, employing over one third of all the country's manufacturing labor force, and producing more than 40 percent of all manufactured goods by value. There is a secondary concentration of manufacturing in Rio de Janeiro, and a scattering of industries among the other cities of the country, especially those exceeding 100,000 in population.

Brazil lacks supplies of good coal (although some deposits of low to medium grade exist in the southeast), but has substantial reserves of water power. The country has a large number of hydroelectric generating plants, the bulk of which are concentrated in the Brazilian Highlands. Unfortunately, much of the undeveloped hydroelectric power is along the Paraná River in southeastern Brazil, and therefore well removed from the main industrial areas.

Both the foreign investor and the Brazilian government—the latter acting often with borrowed funds—have been active in developing Brazil's manufacturing industries. Most foreign capital has come from the United States and West Germany. Especially in recent years, such government agencies as the Export-Import Bank of the United States and the International Bank for Reconstruction and Development of the United Nations have made funds available to the Brazilian government for development purposes, particularly for hydroelectric power.

Some Brazilian mines antedate European settlement. Yet, except for precious metals and stones, the mineral deposits of the country have not been exploited to the same degree as many deposits in other parts of Latin America. The most important concentration of minerals lies in the Brazilian Highlands, in the general district of Belo Horizonte (450,000). This area contains one of the world's largest reserves of high-quality iron ore. Manganese is also in good supply. Other Brazilian minerals include copper, bauxite, lead, zinc, nickel, chromium, quartz crystals, and diamonds (chiefly for industrial purposes).

▶ *Transportation and Urbanization*

In a country where most of the inhabitants live on or near the seacoast and where many live within the framework of an essentially subsistence economy, inland transportation routes are less important than might otherwise be the case. Nevertheless, coffee, cotton, minerals, livestock, meat, and other commodities must get to market, and consumer goods and other necessities must be shipped back. Brazil's rather poorly developed railways assume most of the responsibility for such shipments. The networks converge upon Rio de Janeiro and São Paulo. Recently they have been forged into a single system that is financed and managed by the national government. The highway pattern conforms generally to that of the railways, but is less extensively developed. The Amazon River, and its tributaries, and the São Francisco River (the latter not navigable over the great escarpment) provide inland water transportation which varies in depth and therefore in utility with the season, for both river systems extend into the zone of seasonally rainy climate. The airplane is increasingly important as a means of quick access from the interior to the coast, where connections exist with the world's major air lanes.

Although a large proportion of Brazil's people live essentially outside of a commercial economy, there is a close coincidence between the general distribution of the country's population and that of its major cities. Brazil has 19 cities or metropolitan areas with populations of 100,000 or over. In areal distribution they form a sinuous linear pattern beginning at Manaus (169,000) in the central Amazon Basin, extending downstream to Belém (295,000), and thence southeastward along or near the coast. Each city tends to stand alone, acting as a manufacturing center and/or trade focus for a distinct hinterland.

The two metropolises of Rio de Janeiro and São Paulo, although separated by an approximate distance of only 250 miles, differ rather markedly. Rio de Janeiro was the nation's capital until April 1960, as attested by its many beautiful government buildings. The city is a major tourist center, offering easy access to both the sea and a mountain countryside. It is particularly attractive during the drier winter months. It is also a major shipping, manufacturing, and trade center. Its port, which can accommodate ships drawing as much as 40 feet of water, accounts for nearly half of the nation's total imports and ranks second only to Santos in volume of exports. Its railroads reach toward São Paulo and Santos on the southwest, past Belo Horizonte and the mining district of the Brazilian Highlands on the northwest, and toward Salvador on the northeast. Therefore, its hinterland is sizable in area and population, and it is diversified in economic activity.

São Paulo and its port, Santos (285,000), depend chiefly upon an economic base of commerce and manufacturing. Much of the commerce involves coffee, shipped through São Paulo to ocean ships at Santos. The hinterland of these cities includes not only the major Brazilian coffee district, but also some of the lumber district to the southwest and the northern portion of the livestock ranching area beyond. To the northeast, it merges with the trading area of Rio de Janeiro in the vicinity of the Volta Redonda steel mill. Through the port of Santos move nearly half of Brazil's exports by value and approximately 40 percent of its imports.

The manufacturing of São Paulo is comparatively new and growing rapidly, as, indeed, is the city itself. A major portion of the Volta Redonda iron and steel products come here for further fabrication into textile and electrical machinery, finished steel and wire, and railway rolling stock. Automobiles (final assembly only) are also produced. Textiles, including cotton, wool, rayon, jute, and silk, are important, as are chemicals, leather products, and processed foods. The factories of São Paulo produce goods principally for Brazilian consumption.

## ▶ Brazil's New Capital—Brasília

For many years, Brazilians gave consideration to the possibility of shifting their national capital to an interior location. In April 1960 this idea was consummated when Brasília, more than 500 miles inland, was officially proclaimed the capital. An entirely new, carefully planned, and spectacular creation in the midst of sparsely settled frontier country, Brasília has been constructed at enormous cost as a strictly governmental city. Construction was authorized by the Brazilian Congress in 1957, following forceful recommendations by a new president (Juscelino Kubitschek de Oliveira, inaugurated in 1956). By mid-1960 the population of Brasília was reported to be nearing the 100,000 mark. The site, enclosed within a Federal District, lies in a gently sloping part of the Brazilian Highlands on the border between the states of Minas Gerais and Goiás. The tropical savanna climate, here associated with a vegetation of savanna grasses interspersed with patches of scrubby deciduous woods, is tempered by an elevation of about 4000 feet above the sea.

Brasília symbolizes the aspiration of Brazilians to occupy the empty interior lands of their enormous country. It is hoped that the government, in its new location, will be able to give effective direction to Brazil's westward movement, and will be able to view the nation's over-all problems in a broader and more balanced perspective than was possible in the old seaboard location at Rio. It is further hoped that the shift will encourage settlement away from the coast.

## COUNTRIES OF THE SOUTHERN MIDDLE LATITUDES

Argentina, Chile, and Uruguay are the Latin American countries of the southern middle latitudes. Their populations live mainly on subtropical lowlands, although sparsely settled portions of Argentina and Chile extend poleward into cooler climates.

Agriculture is an important element in the economies of these countries, although the proportion of the labor force that is employed in agriculture is considerably lower in Argentina and Chile than in any of the other Latin American republics (Uruguay or Venezuela would rank next to the two leaders in this respect). Unlike most other Latin American units, the three countries compete in world markets with the powerful agricultural economy of the United States, as well as with the agricultural economies of Canada, Australia, South Africa, New Zealand, and other middle latitude nations. Argentina, Chile, and Uruguay lie largely outside the tropics (Uruguay entirely so), and thus in general they must grow crops and types of livestock that duplicate those of other subtropical and middle latitude areas.

With respect to total exports, Argentina ranks very high among the countries of Latin America (third, after Venezuela and Brazil), while Chile and Uruguay occupy a middle position. All three nations rank higher in value of exports per capita than in value of total exports. The exports of Argentina and Uruguay consist mainly of agricultural products (Uruguay's exports almost entirely so), while Chile's exports are comprised predominantly of minerals. Total exports of all three nations have declined, both absolutely and relatively, since the end of World War II.

The three countries are among the few units in Latin America with economies that may be classified as technically or economically advanced. Among the Latin American republics, their per capita incomes are exceeded only by that of oil-rich Venezuela.

The countries of the southern middle latitudes have a further distinctive characteristic in their ethnic composition. Over 90 percent of the aggregate population in the three countries is either European or *mestizo*. In all of Latin America only Nicaragua, Costa Rica, Colombia, Venezuela, and Mexico approach this very high ratio. In Argentina and Uruguay approximately 90 percent of the people are of European descent. Chile, with 10 percent of its population native Indian and over 65 percent *mestizo*, is more diversified ethnically. In all three countries Negroes are few.

## ▶ *Argentina*

Of the three countries, Argentina is by far the largest. But, as in the case of so many Latin American countries, effective Argentina is far smaller than total Argentina. Nearly 70 percent of the people live in the immediate hinterland of Buenos Aires (5,750,000)—an area encompassing only slightly more than one fifth of the entire nation.

### The Agriculture of the Humid Pampa

The populous core of Argentina is essentially the humid pampa, a crudely circular district bordering on the Atlantic Ocean and extending outward from Buenos Aires as far as 350 miles. It is characterized by a humid subtropical climate that merges into drier conditions on the south and west. Precipitation ranges from 20 to 40 inches annually. Toward the west and south there is a tendency for a decrease in total amount, for a summer maximum, and for a great degree of unreliability in rainfall. The most highly prized farm land is found southwest of the Paraná River between Buenos Aires and Rosario (630,000). Temperatures are moderate; monthly averages vary within a general range of 45° to 75°F. The black, waxy, and highly fertile prairie and chernozem soils have developed over a nearly flat residual accumulation of windblown and stream-deposited materials—a mantle that is, in places, over 1000 feet deep.

Labor for the *haciendas* is supplied principally by tenant workers, who—like their counterparts in Brazil (particularly in São Paulo state)—are often utilized to open up new land. Upon this virgin land the tenant plants wheat for himself (although a part of the crop may be paid as rent) and alfalfa for the *hacienda* owner. After the initial wheat crop has been harvested, the alfalfa establishes itself firmly in the field—to be used in succeeding years as pasture or feed for livestock belonging to the landowner. Meanwhile, the tenant moves to another plot of land. In areas where no new land is available, the tenant is, of course, more closely bound to one section of the estate.

Extending outward from Buenos Aires are a series of districts, each characterized by a rather distinct type of rural land use. Near the city itself is a fruit and vegetable district supplying urban residents with garden produce. To the northwest, the fertile lands between Buenos Aires and Rosario are devoted chiefly to corn, alfalfa, and livestock. Most of Argentina's corn is grown here. Although its annual harvest of the grain is small compared to that of the United States, Argentina is normally the world's second exporter of corn, though its exports are far less than those of the United States.

Farther to the north, west, and south, a combination of wheat and livestock becomes more important. These same commodities also are predominant in a coastal district somewhat removed from Buenos Aires, between La Plata (375,000) and Mar del Plata (165,000). Argentina provides nearly 30 percent of all beef and 10 percent of all wheat entering world markets.

Between Buenos Aires and Mar del Plata are a series of swamps that have not as yet been drained sufficiently to be tilled. These soggy lands are devoted principally to the grazing of sheep, beef cattle, and dairy cattle.

Livestock, wheat, alfalfa, corn, and truck garden products, are thus the principal agricultural commodities of the humid pampa. Except for the truck garden products (grown primarily for the Buenos Aires market) and the alfalfa (grown chiefly for livestock feed and pasture), these commodities are produced mainly for export. Products of lesser significance include barley and flax.

### Agriculture in the Outlying Areas

The outlying countryside of Argentina beyond the humid pampa is sparsely settled. The existing population is generally clustered into districts of agricultural specialization—districts that are superimposed upon an extensive livestock grazing economy. Thus, in the far northeast of the area between the Paraguay–Paraná and Uruguay rivers, yerba maté—the tea of Argentina and nearby lands—is grown. In the north, along the Paraguay–Paraná River, the quebracho tree is cut—as it is in Paraguay—for its tannin. Beef cattle comparable to those of the savannas of Venezuela, are also raised here. In the semiarid west and southward into even drier Patagonia, grazing is the characteristic land use, with the cattle of the west giving way to the sheep of Patagonia. Irrigated valleys support an intensive form of agriculture built around specialized crops. Tucumán (245,-000) is the center of an irrigated sugar cane district, and Mendoza (270,000) has developed a reputation for its fine vineyards. Other, lesser oases are scattered along the eastern piedmont of the Andes.

### Manufacturing and Mining

More workers are employed in manufacturing in Argentina than in any other Latin American country except Brazil. Over a million wage earners—approximately one in seven of the entire Argentine labor force —are so engaged.

Manufacturing has been stimulated not only by local investment but also by a comparatively heavy influx of foreign capital—particularly from the United States and Britain. The former has invested heavily in manufacturing industries and the latter in communication and transportation facilities. In recent years, however, the Argentine government has been nationalizing an increasing number of enterprises—especially transportation and communication facilities.

Mechanical energy is obtained largely from petroleum products. About two thirds of the country's annual consumption of petroleum is imported and one third secured from domestic sources. Argentina's petroleum fields are situated along the Patagonian seacoast and in the far northwest. A small amount of energy comes from domestic hydroelectric plants, notably those clustered near Córdoba (490,000) and Mendoza—sites appreciably removed from the concentrated market for power at Buenos Aires. Some energy is secured from thermoelectric plants burning imported coal and gas, as well as from direct use of these fuels.

The older industries of Argentina are engaged primarily in the production of foodstuffs, textiles, boots, shoes, and other "soft" consumer goods. Many of the more recently established factories produce such hard durables as cement, iron and steel, and machinery, as well as chemicals and electronic equipment. This latter group has grown much more rapidly than the former during the past decade, but neither has recorded outstanding growth. This is attributable in no small measure to chaotic economic policies of the regime of former dictator Juan Perón—policies from which the country is still seeking to recover. Most of Argentina's manufacturing is concentrated within Greater Buenos Aires, an urban agglomeration containing 8 of the country's 16 cities of 100,000 or over.

Argentina is poor in known minerals. Besides modest deposits of petroleum the country possesses some copper, lead, silver, tin, manganese, iron, and low-grade lignite. None of the deposits is of more than local importance.

**Transportation and Urbanization**

Reaching well beyond the core of settlement in the humid pampa is the most extensive railway network in all of Latin America (map, p. 555). It serves not only Argentina, but also Paraguay and much of Bolivia and ties into the railways of Chile, Brazil, and Uruguay. All major routes converge on Buenos Aires. Most of the key lines, built by the British, have been nationalized.

Highways are numerous, but poorly developed. This is due in large measure to the fact that the smooth pampa, with a surface conducive to such roads, is comprised of very fine clay and/or loess. It contains, therefore, neither a good base upon which roads can be built nor good materials for road construction. Even gravel is scarce. There are, however, a few hard-surfaced roads, including the Pan American Highway, which reaches Buenos Aires. Steamship service and air service—both excellent—are, as elsewhere in Latin America, vital to the country's economy.

Argentina is without parallel in Latin America with respect to the number and close juxtaposition of major cities. Nearly one third of the total population lives in cities of 100,000 or over. About one fourth lives in the cluster of major urban units comprising Greater Buenos Aires. It is in these and other sizable cities that most of Argentina's major industries are concentrated. Of these industries, many are either managed by, or provide employment for, Italians, Spaniards, and other recent European immigrants or descendants of comparatively recent immigrants. Although the main tide of immigration has waned, its effects are still felt in Argentina—particularly in the coastal cities.

### ▶ Chile

Across the Andes from Argentina lies Chile, which has the distinction of possessing the greatest latitudinal extent of all Latin American countries except Brazil. In width, however, it seldom exceeds 225 miles. To the north, more than one third of the country is in the exceptionally dry Atacama Desert. To the south, an even larger portion is comprised essentially of windswept, fiorded, inhospitable mountain country. In the center, primarily within an area of mediterranean climate, is effective Chile, where most of the people live. The summer deficiency and winter maximum of precipitation and the moderate temperatures resemble those previously described for the borderlands of the Mediterranean Sea. This district is bordered on the south by a habitable section of marine west coast climate, with conditions not unlike those in Portland, Oregon, or Vancouver, British Columbia.

## The System of Agriculture

The populous middle section of Chile has traditionally been a land of the *hacienda*. A small, well-educated, wealthy upper class has held most of the land, which has been worked by a large, poverty-stricken tenant population. In recent decades a rapid breakup of large properties has greatly increased the number and proportion of small landowners, though many large units continue to function.

The main agricultural products of middle Chile are wheat, livestock, vegetables, grapes, and other products characteristic of mediterranean climates. The major portion of these commodities do not reach the export market. In fact, despite its relatively small population and its agricultural economy, Chile must import considerable amounts of food.

## Importance of Mining for the Export Trade

Exports from Chile consist mainly of minerals. Of these copper is by far the most important, accounting for 55 percent of all exports by value in 1957 and 63 percent in 1958. The primary deposits are in the Atacama Desert, as are those of the second-ranking export, nitrate. Thus the major exports of the country come from one of its most sparsely populated sections. The copper ore of the Atacama, located in the Andes on the eastern edge of the desert, is poor in quality, averaging approximately 2 percent metal. Yet Chile contains over one third of the world's known reserves of this important metal. Besides the desert production centered chiefly at Chuquicamata and Potrerillos (map, p. 553), there is a third production center at El Teniente, in the Andes south and east of Santiago in middle Chile.

Nitrate currently accounts for about a tenth of Chile's exports. The Atacama Desert contains the only extensive deposit of commercially recoverable nitrate in the world. It has been exploited for over a century. But Chilean nitrate faces an uncertain future, due to competition with synthetic nitrate—competition which first made itself felt effectively soon after World War I, and was abetted by an export tax levied by the national government which amounted to nearly one third of the total sale price.

Chile is endowed with two other significant minerals. Iron ore is mined at El Tofo, in the southern portion of the Atacama. Controlled by the Bethlehem Steel Company, the ore taken from this deposit moves through the Panama Canal to Sparrows Point near Baltimore, Maryland. Ore from this district is also carried 500 miles southward to a small iron and steel plant in the Chilean city of Huachipato, a suburb of Concepción (245,000). Here it meets coal, which is Chile's fourth major mineral. This is a poor grade of coal that is mined still farther south at Lota, a coastal location on the Lebu Peninsula, 50 miles southwest of Concepción.

## Chilean Manufacturing

The manufacturing industries of Chile, less important on the basis of employment than the industries of Brazil, Argentina, Peru, Mexico, or Cuba, are currently receiving much attention. In 1939 the Chilean government established the Chilean Development Corporation for the express purpose of increasing the country's manufacturing output. The primary industries are not unlike those mentioned elsewhere, ranging from foodstuffs and tobacco through textiles, metals and metal products, chemicals, leather and rubber goods, and lesser industries. Producing chiefly for home consumption, most are centered in and to the immediate south of Santiago (1,600,000) and Valparaíso (335,000).

**Transportation and Urbanization**

With its 2600 miles of coastline and its narrow width, Chile is oriented toward the ocean. Ports along the Atacama Desert, however, are hampered by the fact that no good harbors exist in the northern third of the country. Steamers must anchor some distance offshore and accept or discharge cargo via smaller craft. Valparaíso in Middle Chile is the seaport for Santiago, the capital. Lesser ports stud the coast as far south as Puerto Montt (21,000).

A railway line trends along the central valley of the country from a point north of Iquique (40,000) to Puerto Montt. Its usefulness is somewhat limited, however, by the fact that it is narrow gauge (3.28 ft) in the northern desert, and broad gauge (5.5 ft) from Santiago southward. Thus goods shipped the length of the network by rail must be transferred from one freight train to another. From Santiago and Valparaíso a railway climbs over high Uspallata Pass in the Andes to reach the Argentine piedmont city of Mendoza. It is not a heavily traveled route. From the Atacama two small northern lines also reach into the Andes, in Bolivia.

Of the roads, the most noteworthy is the Pan-American Highway, which provides Santiago and Valparaíso with access to coastal Peru on the north and, over Uspallata Pass, to Mendoza on the east. The remaining roads tend to form a pattern not unlike that of the rail net.

Airways from Santiago lead not only to other major world cities, but also to Arica (18,000) in Chile's far north, Punta Arenas (27,000) in the far south, and points in between.

Nearly one fifth of Chile's people live in the two major cities of Santiago and Valparaíso. Most of Chile's manufacturing industries are located in or between these two cities.

In May 1960, the southern parts of Chile, including Concepción and other cities, were devastated by some of the greatest earthquakes and seismic sea waves ever recorded. Extensive alterations were made in the topography of sizable areas, large numbers of buildings were destroyed, and many small coastal settlements were swept into the sea. The Andean region, including the adjoining coast, lies in a belt of seismic activity which girdles the Pacific, and all of the countries along the Pacific margin of South America have been visited from time to time by disastrous earthquakes.

## ▶ *Uruguay*

Uruguay, like its large neighbors on either side, is primarily a rural country. It is also like Argentina and Brazil in that more of its land is pastured than is cultivated. The agricultural district is mainly a small crescent around the city of Montevideo (860,000). Here, under a humid subtropical climate that encompasses the entire country, are grown wheat, flax, barley, oats, and some truck crops. The pastoral section includes nearly all of the remainder of the country. From it comes wool amounting to nearly one half of the country's exports, but only about 4 percent of the wool exports of the world.

About one third of Uruguay's people live in the capital city of Montevideo. The rest are distributed rather uniformly throughout the city's hinterland, which essentially coincides with the nation's entire extent. A railway network focusing on Montevideo connects with the rail systems of Brazil and Argentina. Steamship services, both passenger and freight, between Montevideo and Buenos Aires add to the capital's commerce. Manufacturing in Montevideo largely involves the processing of meat and other agricultural commodities from the hinterland, the making of textiles and beverages, and the refining of imported petroleum.

# Introduction to Anglo-America

The colonizing activities of Great Britain have left a major imprint on the United States and Canada. Hence these two countries are commonly distinguished, under the term "Anglo-America," from the rest of the Americas, which have received primarily the Latin imprint of Spain and Portugal. For some purposes the large Arctic island of Greenland is conveniently included in the concept of Anglo-America. This procedure is justified by Greenland's proximity to Canada (map, p. 576) and its strategic importance to both of the Anglo-American countries, but not by the island's culture (a blend of native Eskimo and imported Danish elements) nor by its present political status as an integral part of the Danish state. The same general considerations apply to the small French island possession of St. Pierre and Miquelon, south of Newfoundland, except that the latter is French in culture and is administered as a dependency of France.

## TIES WITH BRITAIN

Effective British settlement of the present United States and of Newfoundland began in the early seventeenth century. Effective settlement of the Canadian mainland by Brit-

The massive towers of the financial district in lower Manhattan symbolize the great wealth and world-wide financial power of Anglo-America. (Standard Oil Company, N. J.)

ain commenced in the later eighteenth century, after Canada had been wrested from France in the French and Indian Wars. Continued immigration from the homeland and a high rate of natural increase in the newly colonized areas led to a rapid growth in the number of British settlers. Consequently, a basically British form of culture became firmly established and has remained dominant in Anglo-America to the present day, despite the entry of large numbers of settlers from continental Europe and smaller numbers from Africa, Latin America, the Orient, and the Middle East. These non-British elements in the Anglo-American population have now been largely (though not completely) assimilated into the general culture of the United States and of Canada.

The most obvious and probably most important evidence of the cultural tie with Britain is the dominance of the English language in Anglo-America. Other evidences of the British heritage are found in the political and legal institutions of the Anglo-American countries, as well as in a multitude of everyday customs and practices among the people. Present-day cultural and political affiliations with Great Britain are closer and more openly acknowledged in Canada than in the United States, despite the large French-Canadian element in Canada's population. Canada retains membership in the Commonwealth of Nations and gives formal allegiance to the British Crown. The basic cultural bonds between the United States and Britain, on the other hand, were weakened by a long period of political antagonism beginning in colonial times and continuing for many years after the American Revolution. Indeed, this antagonism is still evident at times among some segments of the American and British populations, although the two peoples as a whole have been drawn closer together by the great world crises and military conflicts of the twentieth century.

## ANGLO-AMERICAN WEALTH AND POWER

In the twentieth century Anglo-America has become the main center of wealth and power in the world. Consequently, this region exerts an immense influence in world affairs. The United States, although hard pressed by the competition of the Soviet Union, is still in all probability the world's most powerful nation. Canada, with a population of only 17.81 million (mid-1960 estimate) is a less powerful nation in its own right but is an exceedingly valuable ally of the United States and wields an influence disproportionately greater than might be expected of a country with such a small number of inhabitants.

The material wealth of the Anglo-American countries finds an expression in their exceptionally high standards of living. Most estimates place the United States first and Canada second among the nations of the world in this regard.

Although the success of the Anglo-American nations in achieving such high levels of wealth, power, and influence is a matter too complicated to be fully explained, it is clear that these countries possess a number of rather specific assets on which they have been able to capitalize. Some of the more important assets may be stated as follows:

1. The Anglo-American countries are large in area.

2. They possess effective internal unity.

3. They are outstandingly rich in natural resources.

4. Their combined population is impressively large (the United States alone being the fourth most populous nation of the world), yet neither country is overpopulated.

5. They possess highly mechanized economies which lead the world in over-all production per capita.

6. They occupy a strong defensive position, due to relative isolation from other major centers of population and military power.

7. Their relations with each other are friendly and cooperative.

Each of the foregoing statements will be discussed at some length in the remainder of the present chapter. These points, when elaborated, not only help to explain the success of the United States and Canada in reaching their present eminence in world affairs, but also throw much light on the general character of Anglo-America as a world region.

## LARGE AREA OF THE ANGLO-AMERICAN COUNTRIES

Possession of a large area assures a country of neither wealth nor power. But it does afford at least the possibility of finding and developing a wider variety of resources and, other things being equal, of supporting a larger population than might be expected in a small country. In the twentieth century two of the world's largest countries, the United States and the Soviet Union, have surpassed the older and smaller states of western Europe as world powers. Both the United States and the Soviet Union have resources which are much superior to those of the west European nations, but until the twentieth century neither country had yet found the means to occupy and organize its national territory effectively and thus to take adequate advantage of its resources.

That there is no direct relationship between area on the one hand and wealth and power on the other is amply attested by the comparative areas of the Anglo-American countries themselves. Canada is the larger country of the two, but is much the lesser in total wealth and political, economic, and military power. The United States, the world's wealthiest and probably most powerful nation, measures 3,615,208 square miles, while the area of Canada is 3,851,000 square miles. Canada's territorial extent is second in the world only to that of the Soviet Union and possibly China (see p. 384) while the United States ranks behind all three of these countries. Even the United States, however, has nearly twice the area of Europe outside the Soviet Union. France, the largest European country in area, is only about one seventeenth the size of the United States.

## INTERNAL UNITY OF THE UNITED STATES AND CANADA

The welding of their large national territories into effectively functioning units represents a major accomplishment by the Anglo-American countries and a major source of their wealth and power. They are not weakened by chronic political separatism in any of their parts. Their economic welfare and, indirectly, their political unity are promoted by constant and large-scale interchange of goods between sections far removed from one another.

Political separatism in the world's countries is often based on ethnic differences.

The cultural unity of Anglo-America is strikingly in contrast to the large number of different ethnic groups found in such areas as Europe and the Orient. The aboriginal population of American Indians was overwhelmed by the tide of European settlement and has now been reduced to an insignificant minority concentrated mainly in the western and northern parts of Anglo-America. The Indian population is gradually being absorbed into the main stream of American and Canadian life. Non-British immigrants have been gradually absorbed

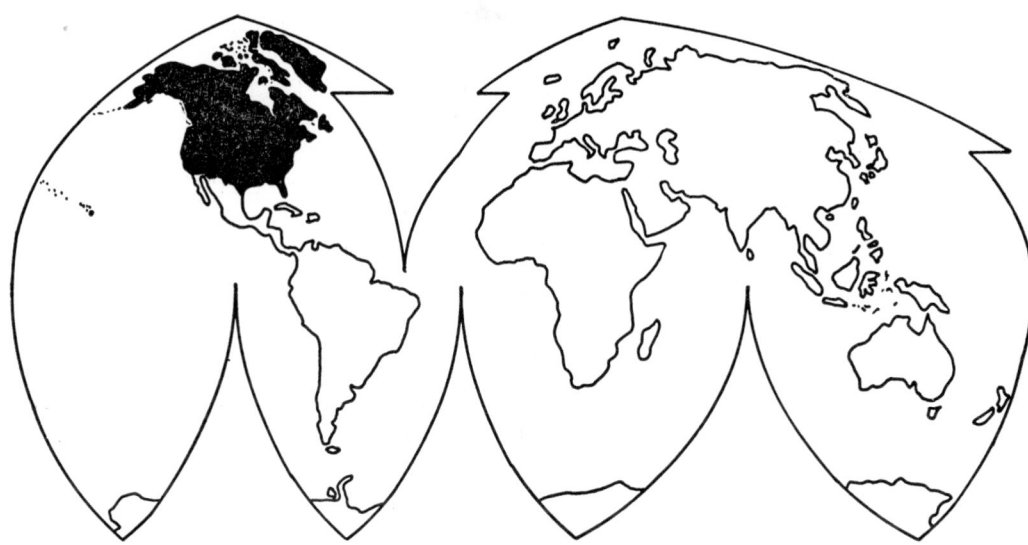

Location of Anglo-America. (Boggs Eumorphic Equal Area Projection, copyright A. J. Nystrom & Co.)

also, though not without making valuable contributions to the Anglo-American society they have entered.

Each of the Anglo-American countries has one major ethnic minority, and in each case this minority has been the focus of serious problems of national unity. About one third of Canada's people belong to the French-Canadian group, which is differentiated from the rest of the Canadian population not only by language but by religion, being overwhelmingly Roman Catholic while the rest of Canada's population is predominantly Protestant. The French-Canadians are concentrated, for the most part, in the lowlands along the St. Lawrence River in the province of Quebec (photo, right), although they have also spread to some extent into adjoining areas. The ancestors of this group, some 60,000 to 70,000 strong, were left in British hands when France was expelled from Canada in 1763. They did not join the English-speaking colonists of the Atlantic seaboard in the American Revolution and by their abstinence laid the basis for the division of Anglo-America into two separate countries. Since the eighteenth century the French-Canadians have increased rapidly in numbers and have clung tena-

ciously to their distinctive language and culture. At times major controversies have arisen between this group and other Canadians, and separatist sentiments have occasionally been voiced by the French minority. The Canadian government has achieved and preserved national unity through the recognition of French as a second official language and the provision of legal protection for French-Canadian institutions. Although not yet assimilated in a cultural sense, French Canada has been incorporated into the nation to the extent that it has provided a number of outstanding Canadian leaders, including prime ministers.

The principal minority group in the United States is the American Negroes, numbering about one tenth of the total population. Unlike the French-Canadians they do not form a coherent minority which is numerically dominant in any major political division or section of the country. Neither have the Negroes as a group been an active force toward disunity in the United States. Nevertheless, a conflict of attitudes toward Negro slavery was among the important factors which nearly split the United States into two nations in the nineteenth century, and dif-

An agricultural village in French Canada on the south shore of the St. Lawrence River about 200 miles northeast of Quebec City. The long, narrow farms extending back from the closely spaced farmsteads along the road are characteristic of this part of Canada. (Canadian National Railways.)

fering attitudes toward the Negro are still a source of friction between the South (which contains more than half of the total Negro population) and the rest of the nation.

Even without strong ethnic contrasts and antagonisms, however, regional conflicts of interest are bound to occur in countries of such large extent and varied physical and economic conditions. In this connection it is a striking and significant aspect of Anglo-America that both of its countries employ a federal structure of government. A multitude of powers and functions are assigned to the fifty states of the United States and the ten provinces of Canada, giving latitude for governmental expression of regional differences and the solution of regional problems which might otherwise work toward the disruption of national unity.

Another notable and important political characteristic of Anglo-America lies in the fact that this region represents an outstanding stronghold of democratic representative government. Governmental responsiveness to majority opinion, combined with safeguards for the minority, tends to prevent

revolutionary pressures from building up. The effectiveness of the political system is strengthened by the fortunate economic circumstances of the region, which lead most of its inhabitants to congratulate themselves on being Americans or Canadians and to feel that their institutions have provided opportunities and results beneficial to themselves.

The result is that Anglo-America has been characterized thus far by great stability of government. The American Civil War is the only large-scale, violent civil conflict that has ever occurred in either nation. In neither country has the national government ever been overthrown by force. Thus the governments of the United States and Canada have not been obliged to devote large energies merely to preserving the state's existence or its territorial integrity against internal stresses.

The governments of both countries have assiduously fostered national unity through the provision of adequate means of internal transportation. In both, the development of transportation networks has had to be ac-

ANGLO-AMERICA
INTRODUCTORY LOCATION MAP

URBAN AREAS (NATIONAL CAPITALS
UNDERLINED)

◉ OVER 1,000,000

● 500,000 - 1,000,000

○ SELECTED SMALLER URBAN UNITS

A-S-T Albany-Schenectady-Troy

0    200    400    600    800
MILES

On this map and subsequent Anglo-America maps, city-size symbols for Canadian cities are based on recent metropolitan-area estimates. Symbols for United States cities are based on 1960 census data for Standard Metropolitan Statistical Areas (see footnote, p. 594).

complished not only over long distances but primarily against the "grain" of the land, since effective transport links between east and west have been most imperative, while most of the mountains and valleys in Anglo-America have a north-south trend, thus opposing themselves as a series of obstacles to cross-country transport. Both the United States and Canada were tied together as effectively functioning units by heavily subsidized transcontinental railroads built during the latter half of the nineteenth century. These fostered national unity not only directly, through the connections they afforded between sections, but indirectly through their promotion of settlement and of general economic development. Later, automobile transportation on publicly constructed highway networks and, still later, the development of air transportation further solidified internal unity.

## THE LARGE AND DIVERSIFIED NATURAL RESOURCES OF ANGLO-AMERICA

The natural resources which the Anglo-American countries have within their boundaries are outstanding in both variety and abundance. In part, this fact is simply a reflection of the large territorial extent of each nation. Countries of such magnitude are almost bound to contain a sufficient diversity of physical conditions to produce resources that are out of the ordinary in size and utility. Nevertheless, it is probable that no area of the earth's surface of comparable extent contains so much natural wealth as Anglo-America. The abundance of resources also reflects the inventiveness and skill of the Anglo-American peoples in the exploitation of nature, in the "making" of resources. It should not be forgotten, however, that the value of Anglo-American resources is partly due to scientific and technological advances in other lands. The usefulness of coal, for example, was discovered in England long before the superior coal resources of Anglo-America were more than vaguely known.

Certain important aspects of the world position of the Anglo-American countries with regard to resources and production are summarized in Table 30.

▶ *Agricultural and Forest Resources*
Large areas of Anglo-America are suited by topography and climate for cultivation. The United States, although the fourth largest country in total area, is second only to the USSR in total area of arable land and is easily first in the world in arable land of high quality. A much smaller proportion of Canada is arable, but even in that nation the total arable acreage is still greater than that of any country other than the Soviet Union, the United States, India, or China. With only 18 million people Canada is the world's richest country in arable land per capita (almost 6 arable acres per person). The United States, despite its much larger population (179 million at the 1960 census), ranks behind only Canada, Australia, and Argentina in the amount of arable land it possesses per capita, which is over 2½ acres. In contrast, no country in Europe has even 2 acres of arable land to support each member of its population. Furthermore, the United States ranks third, after the USSR and Australia, in total area of meadow and pasture lands, while in Canada such lands, although much less extensive than in the United States, are sufficient to allow a perennially important export of meat and live cattle in addition to a high domestic consumption of livestock products.

Anglo-America is estimated to contain about 17 percent of the world's forested area. Canada and the United States rank third and fourth among the nations of the world in this regard, behind the Soviet Union and Brazil. The intensively exploited forests of the United States can no longer supply the needs of the country for wood, although American forest resources are still extremely large and varied. In fact, the United States now ranks second only to the United Kingdom as an importer of forest products, with Canada, the largest exporter of such commodities, being the main source of supply. Canadian forest resources are larger in extent than those of the United States, but are not so varied in type. For example, Canada has no forests comparable to the redwoods of California or the pine forests of southeastern United States, and is far behind the United States in both acreage and variety of deciduous hardwoods.

## ▶ *Mineral Resources*

Not only is Anglo-America rich in agricultural and forest resources, but estimates of mineral reserves give a picture of a region possessing outstanding mineral wealth, probably greater than that found in any part of the earth of comparable size.

Power resources are especially plentiful. The United States is estimated to possess about one third of the world's known coal of bituminous grade or better, ranking well ahead of any other country in total reserves. Canada, however, is relatively poor in coal, although not totally devoid of it. Various ways of defining and estimating petroleum resources lead to estimates which differ substantially, but most estimates credit the United States with more than one tenth of the world's petroleum reserves. It normally produces nearly two fifths of the world's total output of petroleum, although even this immense production is not sufficient to supply the nation's needs, and substantial imports are required. Canada is a growing producer of petroleum and has noteworthy reserves, though in neither reserves nor production is it comparable to the United States (Table 30). The United States currently produces an estimated four fifths of the world's

natural gas, and has very large reserves. Estimates of the world's total hydroelectric potential do not give Anglo-America an outstandingly high proportion. Canada and the United States are each credited with about 5 percent of the world total. But they lead the world in *developed* water power, with the United States having about one quarter and Canada about one tenth of the world total, and neither country has developed more than a small fraction of its potential as yet.

With regard to metals the general picture is also one of outstanding wealth and great variety. The United States originally had huge deposits of high-grade iron ore, but the enormous scale of exploitation by the iron and steel industry has seriously depleted these reserves and dependence on imported ore has increased considerably in recent years. However, the country still has an estimated one fifth of the world's "potential" iron ore reserves—reserves only approximately estimated as to extent, and often composed of lower grade ores than those usually mined in the past—and new methods of treating ore now give promise of making more and more of these "potential" reserves economically usable. Canada also has substantial deposits of iron ore. Canadian reserves are smaller in total quantity than those of the United States, as far as is known, but are larger per capita and are at a much earlier stage of exploitation. A selection of other important metals shows the following estimated percentages of world reserves in Anglo-America: copper, United States 19 percent, Canada 4 percent; lead, United States 17 percent, Canada 9 percent; zinc, United States 12 percent, Canada considerably less; nickel, United States little or none, but Canada well over half of the world total. Anglo-America is also outstandingly rich in a considerable number of important nonmetallic minerals other than power minerals: the list includes phosphate, potash, sulfur, industrial salt, gypsum, and asbestos. Anglo-American reserves

## TABLE 30

## ANGLO-AMERICA'S SHARE IN THE WORLD'S KNOWN WEALTH AND PRODUCTION: SELECTED ITEMS

| ITEM | APPROXIMATE PERCENT OF WORLD TOTAL[a] | | |
|---|---|---|---|
| | UNITED STATES | CANADA | ANGLO-AMERICA |
| Area | 7 | 7 | 16 |
| Population | 6 | 0.6 | 7 |
| Agricultural resources and production | | | |
| Arable land | 14 | 3 | 17 |
| Permanent meadows and pastures | 10 | 1 | 11 |
| Production of: | | | |
| Wheat | 14 | 5 | 19 |
| Corn (grain) | 52 | — | 52 |
| Soybeans | 52 | — | 52 |
| Cotton | 27 | — | 27 |
| Tobacco | 23 | 2 | 25 |
| Oranges | 30 | — | 30 |
| Milk | 17 | 2 | 19 |
| Number of: | | | |
| Cattle | 11 | 1 | 12 |
| Hogs | 13 | 1 | 14 |
| Forest resources and production | | | |
| Area of forests and woodlands | 8 | 9 | 17 |
| All wood cut | 19 | 6 | 25 |
| Sawn-wood production | 30 | 6 | 36 |
| Wood-pulp production | 40 | 19 | 59 |
| Minerals, mining, and smelting | | | |
| Estimated coal reserves, bituminous and better grades | 32 | 1 | 33 |
| Coal production, bituminous and better grades | 29 | 1 | 30 |
| Estimated petroleum reserves | 12 | 2 | 14 |
| Crude-oil production | 39 | 3 | 42 |
| Crude-oil refinery capacity | 42 | 4 | 46 |
| Natural-gas production | 84 | 2 | 86 |
| Potential iron-ore reserves | 20 | 2 | 22 |
| Iron ore mined | 27 | 6 | 33 |
| Pig iron produced | 36 | 2 | 38 |
| Steel produced | 37 | 2 | 39 |
| Bauxite reserves | 2 | — | 2 |
| Bauxite mined | 7 | — | 7 |
| Aluminum produced | 43 | 16 | 59 |
| Copper reserves (copper content) | 19 | 4 | 23 |
| Copper mined (copper content) | 27 | 9 | 36 |
| Copper smelted | 28 | 8 | 36 |
| Lead reserves (lead content) | 17 | 9 | 26 |
| Lead mined (lead content) | 12 | 7 | 19 |
| Lead smelted | 20 | 6 | 26 |
| Zinc reserves (zinc content) | 12 | I.D. | I.D. |
| Zinc mined (zinc content) | 13 | 12 | 25 |
| Zinc smelted | 28 | 8 | 36 |
| Nickel mined (nickel content) | — | 59 | 59 |
| Gold mined | 4 | 11 | 15 |
| Phosphate rock mined | 43 | — | 43 |
| Potash produced ($K_2O$ equivalent) | 25 | — | 25 |
| Sulfur produced | 74 | — | 74 |
| Asbestos mined | 2 | 48 | 50 |
| Water power | | | |
| Undeveloped water power | 5 | 5 | 10 |

TABLE 30 (Continued)

| ITEM | APPROXIMATE PERCENT OF WORLD TOTAL [a] | | |
| --- | --- | --- | --- |
| | UNITED STATES | CANADA | ANGLO-AMERICA |
| Capacity of existing hydroelectric plants | 24 | 9 | 33 |
| Manufacturing other than metals | | | |
|   Raw cotton consumed industrially | 19 | 1 | 20 |
|   Raw wool consumed industrially | 13 | 1 | 14 |
|   Sulfuric acid produced | 37 | 3 | 40 |
|   Motor-vehicle production (all units) | 51 | 2 | 53 |
|   Steel consumed industrially | 34 | 2 | 36 |

SOURCES: A considerable number of sources were used in the preparation of this table, including the *Encyclopaedia Britannica* and *Collier's Encyclopedia* books of the year, the United Nations statistical yearbooks, the FAO production yearbooks, the United Nations publications *World Iron Ore Resources and their Utilization* (1950) and *Economic Survey of Europe in 1958* (for some data on USSR production not found in other sources), the minerals yearbooks of the United States Bureau of Mines, and others. While the data are believed to convey as accurate an impression as is possible with a single set of figures, the student must be warned that they can give a false impression of stability, reliability, and detail. Actually, many of the percentages are subject in varying degree to (1) errors in estimation and compilation, (2) fluctuations over a period of time, and (3) misinterpretations due to differences in quality or ease of exploitation of particular resources from one area to another. The percentages show *volume* rather than *value* of production and reserves. In general, percentages given for production were computed on the basis of two-year or three-year averages for the period 1956–1958.

[a] The notation (—) indicates none or no appreciable amount. The notation I.D. indicates insufficient data for a reasonably accurate percentage to be stated.

and production of the latter minerals are concentrated mainly in the United States, except for asbestos, of which Canada is the world's greatest producer.

Such is the wealth of the region that it is easier to summarize the gaps in the resource structure than to describe the resources themselves. Agriculturally, the lack of any large producing area for certain tropical specialty crops is felt, necessitating the import of such commodities as coffee and tea, bananas, rubber, and tropical vegetable oils. The major mineral deficiencies are in chromite, manganese, tungsten, tin, diamonds, graphite, and high-grade bauxite. However, the industrial development of the United States has progressed to the point that large imports are normally required even of minerals with which the United States is itself well endowed and of which it is a major producer. Canada is an important source of supply for some of these imported minerals.

Such estimates as those given in the foregoing paragraphs and in Table 30 serve adequately to outline the general picture of Anglo-American advantages with respect to resources. However, these estimates should be understood as only approximations. They are subject to a certain amount of error and change and tend to underemphasize the factor of quality. The contrasts and rankings they show are the result not only of differing natural conditions, but also of differences in technical knowledge and ability, in general economic conditions, and in cultural emphases among the countries concerned. Estimates of mineral reserves, in particular, must be used with caution, since the figures cited by various authorities often differ widely, and the known quantities and distributions of minerals are constantly changing as a consequence of new ore discoveries and the development of new processes for making use of ores previously considered to be substandard.

## ANGLO-AMERICA'S FAVORABLE POSITION WITH RESPECT TO POPULATION

In 1960 the United States had a census population total of 179.3 million, while Canada had an estimated 17.8 million inhabitants at mid-year. Thus Anglo-America contained about 197 million people. Three of the world's countries—China, India, and the Soviet Union—surpass all of Anglo-America in population. Nevertheless, the United States ranks fourth among all countries, with a population total nearly as large as the combined totals of Europe's four most populous countries—West Germany, the United Kingdom, Italy, and France. Most of Anglo-America's people live in the southeastern quarter of the region, from the St. Lawrence Lowlands and Great Lakes south, and this part of Anglo-America is one of the world's four extensive areas of dense population, along with the continent of Europe (including European Russia), China, and the Indian subcontinent.

From the beginning of settlement Anglo-America has been a region of rapidly growing population, and this growth continues at the present time. By 1800, approximately two centuries after the first settlements were firmly established at Jamestown and at Quebec, there were over 5 million people in the United States and several hundred thousand more in Canada. Population growth since that time is summarized in Table 31. Continuing rapid growth is evident in an increase of about 28 million in the United States between the 1950 and 1960 censuses.

The population of this region has been increasing at a rate more rapid than that of the world as a whole. Between 1900 and 1950 the increase in world population is estimated at around 50 percent, while that in Anglo-America was over 100 percent.

Thus one element in the mounting world importance and power of Anglo-America, and particularly of the United States, has been its possession of an increasing share of the world's population. The older world powers of western Europe, especially, have been surpassed. In 1870, at the time of the Franco-Prussian War, the United States had almost exactly the same population as each of the two belligerents, Germany and France, but in 1960 it had over 1½ times as many people as France and the two Germanies combined.

However, the Anglo-American share of the world's population is still not an excessively large one. The United States and Canada have together about 7 percent of the estimated world total. This compares with their possession of about 14 percent of the world's land area. The average population density of the two countries considered as a whole is only 26 per square mile, as compared with about 50 per square mile for the world as a whole. However, the figure for average density obscures the contrast between the United States, with 50 persons per square mile, and Canada, with only 5 per square mile. The very low figure for Canada is due to its tremendous expanse of sparsely settled northern lands, the effectively occupied part of the country in the south being much more densely populated, although far smaller in areal extent.

It is evident that judged by the world as a whole even the United States is far from

## TABLE 31

### POPULATION GROWTH IN THE UNITED STATES AND CANADA, 1850–1960

| YEAR | U. S. POPULATION (MILLIONS) | CANADIAN POPULATION (MILLIONS) | TOTAL (MILLIONS) | TOTAL INCREMENT | |
|---|---|---|---|---|---|
| | | | | MILLIONS | PERCENT |
| 1850 | 23.3 | 2.4 | 25.7 | | |
| 1900 [a] | 76.1 | 5.4 | 81.5 | 55.8 | 217 |
| 1950 [a] | 151.1 | 14.0 | 165.1 | 83.6 | 103 |
| 1960 | 179.3 | 17.8 [b] | 197.1 | 32.0 | 19 |

[a] Actual dates for Canada are 1901 and 1951. The decennial census is taken one year later in Canada than in the United States. The table shows census data except for Canada's population in 1960.
[b] Official mid-year estimate.

overpopulated, considering its exceptional resources and enormous production, and Canada, if anything, is underpopulated. Thus the Anglo-American countries have a combined population sufficiently large to exploit the resources of the region effectively but not so large as to press heavily on those resources and thus prevent surplus production to supply military strength when the latter is needed.

## MECHANIZED AND PRODUCTIVE ECONOMIES OF THE ANGLO-AMERICAN COUNTRIES

On the whole, economic production per person involved is higher in Anglo-America than in any other part of the world. This regional characteristic is reflected in, and to some extent can be measured by, the high per capita incomes of the United States and Canada. It is attested by the results of comparative studies of industries in the United States and in overseas countries, as well as by the efforts of other nations to learn American production methods. High production per worker is a basic factor leading not only to a high income level and high standard of living in Anglo-America, but also to military power, since it means that there is a large surplus of productive capacity available beyond that needed to supply the necessities of the people. This surplus capacity can be used to produce military equipment when the need arises.

Anglo-American production methods are not easy to imitate in the rest of the world because they are so closely related to other outstanding characteristics of the region and to its distinctive historical development. The use of machines and mechanical energy on a scale greater than anywhere else in the world is basic to Anglo-American productivity. But this superior mechanization has been achieved in a region which has had an abundance of resources and a shortage of labor throughout most of its history; which has possessed resources sufficiently large and rich both to attract foreign capital and, through large-scale and often wasteful exploitation, to make possible large domestic accumulations of capital; and which has been superlatively endowed with the necessary fuels to drive machinery. Furthermore, it has been achieved in a region where a free and fluid society has encouraged full development of the abilities of the people; where free and untrammeled economic progress has generally been encouraged, fostered, and subsidized by government; where the energies of the people have not had to be too much diverted into war; and where large segments of the population have subscribed with an almost religious fervor to the ideals of hard work and economic success since early times. Finally, in the United States, a large and unified internal market has allowed great economic organizations to specialize in the mechanized mass production of a few articles, thus lowering the unit costs of production. The foregoing combination of circumstances has been essentially unmatched in any other part of the world, much of which seeks mechanization under comparatively severe handicaps.

## DEFENSIVE ADVANTAGES OF RELATIVE ISOLATION

Anglo-America is essentially a huge island, bordered on the east by the Atlantic Ocean, on the north by the Arctic Ocean and on the west by the Pacific. The only land connection with another world region is along the boundary between the United States and Mexico, which mostly runs through sparsely populated territory and is far removed from the core area of either country. No good land route yet connects the United States and Canada with South America, and most of Anglo-America's contacts with Latin America, as well as with other world regions, are made by sea and air.

The closest land approaches of Anglo-America to Eurasia are at the northeastern and northwestern corners of the region. A series of islands bridges the North Atlantic between Canada and Europe, and includes Greenland, Iceland, the Faeroes, the Shetlands, and Svalbard. Only the Bering Strait separates Asia from Alaska. The first historic contact between Europe and North America, that of the Vikings from the ninth to the eleventh centuries, was made via the island stepping stones of the North Atlantic. Contacts with Asia occurred earlier, since the North American Indians are thought to have entered the continent in prehistoric times from Asia via the Bering Strait area. In the eighteenth century Russian fur traders entered Alaska, which only passed from Russian to American control by purchase in 1867.

But harsh climatic conditions in the latitudes of these land approaches have prevented them from serving as major avenues of movement between Anglo-America and Eurasia during historic times. The North Atlantic approach is dangerous to navigate and leads, on the American side, only to the wasteland of tundra and coniferous forest which occupies northern Canada. Bering Strait is backed on both sides by similar stretches of wasteland. Between the two approaches Eurasia and North America are separated by the ice-jammed Arctic Ocean, again backed by tundra and taiga on both sides.

Consequently, the main connections between the two great land masses of the Northern Hemisphere have lain across the oceans farther south, although the routes generally followed do swing north to approximate great circle courses. From the Atlantic seaboard ports of Anglo-America

south of the taiga the sea distance to Britain is about 3000 miles (only about 2000 between the outer extremities of Newfoundland and Ireland), and from Puget Sound to Japan is about 4000. If the Pacific is crossed via Hawaii to Japan, the distance becomes well over 5000 miles. These have been the real distances separating the states of Anglo-America from the world's other centers of political and military power—distances not over long for peaceful commerce but constituting a major obstacle to military operations. Such distances (added to inherent strength) have so reduced the danger of a successful military attack on Anglo-America that the region was able in the past to proceed with its domestic development while paying relatively little attention to considerations of defense and the entanglements of world politics.

However, three new factors have arisen in relatively recent times to lessen the value of Anglo-America's protected position and to make the psychological attitude of isolationism which it engendered a dangerous one. In the first place, the destruction of the the balance of power in Eurasia has raised the possibility that while no individual Eurasian power could successfully overcome Anglo-America, a Eurasia united wholly or in large part under one dominion might well aspire to do so. A united Eurasia would change the position of Anglo-America from that of an isolated region protected by distance to that of an area semisurrounded by its possible antagonist. Secondly, the development of air power, including guided missiles, has seriously compromised the protective function of the oceans and the northern wastes. Finally, the development of nuclear armaments has raised the possibility of devastating or even decisive effect by attack from the air.

The relatively isolated position of Anglo-America has allowed the region to develop in relative peace and security, and remains a valuable asset and source of strength, since it is still harder to attack effectively over long than over short distances. But the protective value of this position has declined sharply in recent years, and the people of the region can no longer afford to harbor such feelings of isolation, immunity, and security as have been habitual in the past.

## COOPERATIVE RELATIONS OF THE ANGLO-AMERICAN STATES

For many years after the American Revolution the political division of Anglo-America between the independent United States to the south and a group of British colonial possessions to the north was accompanied by serious friction between the peoples and governments on either side of the boundary. A heritage of antagonism was present due to the failure of the northern colonies to join in the Revolution, their use as British bases during that war, the large element of their population which was composed of Tory stock driven from American homes during the Revolution, and uncertainty and rivalry as to ultimate control of the central and western reaches of the continent.

The War of 1812 was largely an American effort to conquer Canada. Even after the failure of this effort a series of border disputes occurred, and American ambitions to possess this remaining British territory in North America were openly expressed; suggestions and threats of annexation were made in official quarters throughout the nineteenth and into the twentieth century.

In fact, Canada as a unified nation is in good part a result of American pressure. After the American Civil War the military power of the United States took on a threatening aspect in Canadian and British eyes. Suggestions were made in some American quarters that Canadian territory would be a just recompense to the United States for British hostility toward the Union during the war. The British North America Act, passed by the British Parliament in 1867, brought an independent Canada into existence. Britain sought, and as the event has proved, successfully, to establish in Canada an independent nation capable of achieving transcontinental unity, of maintaining its independence and integrity, and of relieving Britain of some of the burden of defense in North America.

Hostility between the United States and its northern neighbor did not immediately cease with the establishment of an independent and unified Canada; in fact, a certain amount of friction is evident from time to time even today. Nevertheless, relations between the two Anglo-American nations have improved gradually to the point where these countries are often cited as an outstanding example of international amity and cooperation, and the frontier between them has ceased to be a source of mutual insecurity and weakness. This frontier, stretching completely unfortified across a continent, has become more a symbol of friendship than of enmity.

The bases of Canadian-American friendship are cultural similarities, the material wealth of both nations, and the mutual need for and advantages of cooperation. Despite certain vexatious tariff restrictions, a very large volume of trade moves across the frontier and strengthens both countries economically and militarily. Each country is the other's principal foreign market and source of supply, although Canada is much more dependent on the United States in this regard than is the United States on Canada. In 1958, for example, Canada supplied 21 percent of all United States imports by value and took 19 percent of all United States exports; while the United States supplied 69 percent of Canada's imports and took 59 percent of its exports. In addition, the United States supplies large quantities of capital which have been an important factor in the rapid economic development of Canada during recent decades. Major items moving from the United States to Canada include automobiles and parts, and other machinery; steel; chemicals; and coal. Those moving from Canada to the United States include paper, pulp, and lumber; nonferrous ores and metals, including ferro-alloys; and iron ore.

In defense arrangements the two nations work together so closely as to form almost a single unit. Important aspects of their relationship include (1) a structure of joint command, (2) cooperative military ma-neuvers in far northern areas, (3) cooperative installations to warn against air attack, and (4) cooperation in the production and supply of military equipment. These arrangements mean essentially that Canada is protected by its more powerful neighbor, which would certainly regard any attack on Canada as an attack on itself. But at the same time, of course, Canada's resources and strategic assets greatly strengthen that neighbor. Meanwhile, as an independent nation Canada continues to guard its sovereignty and cultural identity and to maintain its ties with the United Kingdom and the other states of the Commonwealth of Nations.

# Anglo-American Regions

Among the most notable characteristics of Anglo-America as a world region are a certain broad uniformity of culture and a simplicity of political organization which contrast sharply with the cultural and political complexity of such areas as Europe or the Orient. Nevertheless, even Anglo-America is sufficiently different from place to place that a multiplicity of cultural and political regions and subregions can be distinguished. The regional complexity becomes much greater when physical and economic factors are considered. Since a regional treatment of some type seems essential in presenting the geography of such a vast and varied segment of the earth's surface, the problem arises as to what scheme, or schemes, of regional division should be chosen.

One possible solution to this problem is provided by certain grand divisions which are commonly recognized by scholars in various fields and the public generally: in the United States the Northeast (including its distinctive subrealm of New England), the South, the Middle West, and the West; in Canada the Maritime Provinces, Newfoundland, Quebec, Ontario, the Prairie Provinces, British Columbia, and the vast,

A landscape along the southern margin of the Dairy Belt section of the Interior Plains. This view was taken in southeastern Minnesota near the Wisconsin border. The tilled field in the foreground bordered by pasture contains, in order from bottom of photo, contour strips of hay, wheat (in shocks), and corn. The silo beside the large barn at the right indicates a dairy operation. (United States Information Service, Department of State.)

586

years it has accounted for a larger share of Texas' cotton production than either of the Coastal Plain districts.

*Effects of Cotton Growing on the Regional Life of the South.* More than any other economic activity, cotton production has given distinctive regional qualities to Southern life. The large Negro population of the South, in many ways the most important element differentiating this section culturally and politically from the rest of the nation, is descended from African slaves who became mainly concentrated on cotton plantations in the period between the invention of the cotton gin (1793) and the close of the Civil War. Today the heaviest densities of rural Negro population are commonly found in present or former areas of concentrated cotton production. The prevalence of cotton culture has had a primary bearing on the relatively low income levels and standards of living, the long-retarded development of other forms of economic activity, and the general economic difficulties which have been outstanding characteristics of the South, at least up to recent years. The attraction of cotton as a cash crop, its adaptability to systems of farm tenancy, especially sharecropping, and its heavy demand for hand labor, coupled with the poverty-stricken condition of the post-Civil War South and

This mechanical cotton picker in operation near the eastern edge of the Mississippi Lowland between Memphis and Vicksburg symbolizes the high degree of mechanization which characterizes the agriculture of the United States as a whole. It also symbolizes one aspect of the agricultural revolution that is overtaking large sections of the Cotton Belt. (Standard Oil Company, N. J.)

the lack of alternative sources of employment, created a situation which allowed a relatively small class of large landowners, cotton ginners and dealers, storekeepers, fertilizer merchants, and bankers to accumulate profits and even become wealthy, while at the same time the much larger group of actual cultivators, unable to acquire sufficient capital to improve their situation, were living fairly close to the margin of subsistence. Continuous cropping in cotton wore out the soil, and dependence on overseas markets resulted in increasing difficulties under the stress of a growing foreign competition. The depths of distress in the cotton South were reached in the Great Depression of the early 1930s, when the price of cotton sank to unprecedented lows and large numbers of cultivators and their families were forced to seek government relief in order to live. In the twentieth century, particularly since 1930, cotton culture in the South has experienced a drastic decline in the face of these mounting difficulties and under the stimulus of a concentrated attack on Southern problems. Great acreages have been removed from cotton cultivation, and communities which were formerly dependent on cotton have groped, with varying degrees of success, toward new types of agriculture and other means of support. Now the mechanical cotton picker is rapidly being adopted (photo, p. 601) and is releasing labor from cotton in a Southern economy that was long nearly static but today is characterized by vigorous growth and change.

### Citrus Fruit

Most of the output of citrus fruit in the United States is concentrated in a few localities on the Gulf–Atlantic Coastal Plain. The danger of frost in areas farther north restricts citrus growing on the plain to the extreme southern sections of the zone of humid subtropical climate. There is some production scattered along most of the Gulf Coast, but the southernmost areas, Florida and the lower Rio Grande Valley, contain the major producing districts. Florida, in which fruit growing is the most important type of agriculture, normally accounts for about two thirds of the total United States output of citrus. Most of the Florida production comes from a belt in the center of the peninsula east of Tampa Bay (map, p. 598). This part of Florida has many lakes and low hills which give a certain amount of added protection against frost damage. Citrus production is the principal element in the irrigated agriculture of the lower Rio Grande Valley. It is supplemented by truck farming, as in Florida, and by cotton. The only other major area of citrus growing in Anglo-America is found in southern California, principally south of Los Angeles.

### Sugar

No part of the continental United States is sufficiently tropical for really efficient production of cane sugar. However, two districts specializing in this product have developed behind tariff protection. The larger and more important of the two is the so-called "Sugar Bowl" in the southern Mississippi Delta of Louisiana; the other is near Lake Okeechobee in Florida (map, p. 598). Their combined production amounts to only a small percentage of American sugar consumption, considerably less than the percentage supplied by the beet-sugar industry, which is localized in other parts of the country. Most of the sugar used in continental United States is cane sugar from tropical sources, principally Cuba, Puerto Rico, the Philippines, and Hawaii.

### Rice

The United States supplies its own needs for rice and even exports a certain amount to the Orient. Rice consumption per capita in the United States is relatively small, and American rice is produced with extreme efficiency by machine methods. About half of the American crop comes from the prairies along the coasts of Louisiana and Texas and another fourth from the Arkansas and Mississippi portions of the Mississippi Lowland (map, p. 598). The remainder comes almost entirely from California. The total American production is quite small when measured on a world scale, but rice growing is an important phase of the economy in the areas where production is centered.

### Other Crops

In addition to the major specialties of Coastal Plain agriculture described above, many other crops are grown, sometimes as basic specialties in small areas, sometimes in combination (often in rotation) with the major crops. The most widespread and important of these secondary crops is corn. Among the others are soybeans, some wheat, sorghums toward the drier west, tree crops such as pecans and tung, and a variety of grasses and legumes grown as hay, forage, and soil-building crops.

### The Growing Importance of Livestock

A growing emphasis is being placed on livestock, principally beef cattle, in many parts of the Coastal Plain, and the amount and proportion of land devoted to feed crops and pasture has definitely increased in recent years. Ranching districts are found in south central Florida and along the Texas and Louisiana coasts. The Black Belt of Alabama and Mississippi has redeveloped from a cotton-growing to a livestock-farming area, and cattle are being emphasized along with soybeans in a movement toward greater diversification of the Mississippi Lowland cotton district.

## ▶ Forestry, Tourism, and Fishing

Three other important economic activities are widely scattered over the Coastal Plain or along its shores. These are the forest industries, the tourist and resort indus-

try, and commercial fishing. Most of the original natural forest of the Coastal Plain has been cut, but very large areas are in second growth timber of varying size and quality. One of the great natural assets of the southern Coastal Plain, as well as of other areas in the South, is the rapid growth of trees in the subtropical climate. The forests of southeastern United States furnish approximately one third of the country's total production of lumber and over half of its wood pulp. At least half of the South's lumber and pulp production comes from the Coastal Plain. Southern pine is the outstanding Southern source both of lumber and of pulpwood, and in addition supplies more than half of the world output of naval stores. But the production of hardwoods from river bottom lands is also important. Memphis, Tennessee, on the Mississippi, is the country's chief commercial center for hardwood lumber. Thus over wide areas wood industries vie with agriculture as the principal basis of economic life. Only in the areas of natural prairie and in the sections north of Virginia, where trees grow more slowly, are forest industries absent or unimportant on the Coastal Plain.

Resort establishments and fishing villages dot the shore from Cape Cod to Texas. Miami (935,000), St. Petersburg (with Tampa 772,000), Orlando (318,000), and West Palm Beach (228,000), all in Florida, are highly developed resort centers and are the largest cities of the United States in which the resort function plays so great a role. Atlantic City, New Jersey (161,000), is the most important resort city on the Atlantic coast outside of Florida. Many of the larger cities along the coast besides those named count the resort business as an important element in their economies, while many smaller settlements are primarily dependent on it. Commercial fishing is sometimes carried on in the same communities as the resort trade, sometimes in separate villages and towns. Nearly half of the commercial fish catch of the United States by value is ordinarily landed along this coast. Major areas of concentration are found in Chesapeake Bay and off the Texas coast, where oysters and shrimp, respectively, are the main specialties.

## ▶ Mineral Resources

Most of the Coastal Plain is poor in mineral resources. A conspicuous exception is phosphate. Several parts of the plain have phosphate deposits, but three quarters of the American production by volume, and about a third of the total world production, comes from a narrow belt inland and north from Tampa in western Florida. Much of the production is marketed in the South, which uses more chemical fertilizer per acre than most regions of Anglo-America. A small area in central Arkansas near the Interior Highlands produces almost all the bauxite mined in the United States. This production, however, represents only a small percentage of the total American consumption of bauxite ore, most of which must be imported.

### Superior Resources and Industrial Development of the Texas-Louisiana Coast

The most valuable mineral resources of the Coastal Plain are found in Texas and Louisiana. Areas of the Coastal Plain in these states, and to a lesser extent in Mississippi and Arkansas, produce an important share of the total American output of petroleum and natural gas. Major oil fields are widely scattered along the immediate coast and also inland in eastern Texas and western Louisiana. Increasing amounts of oil are being produced offshore from beneath shallow waters overlying the continental shelf. Texas, which has many fields outside the Coastal Plain, accounted for about 40 percent of the total United States petroleum production by volume and Louisiana for another 13 percent during the late 1950s. The Coastal Plain contribution to American oil production can hardly be stated as less than 35 to 40 percent, which is well over a tenth of the petroleum production of the world. To their wealth in oil, coastal Louisiana and Texas add large deposits of sulfur and salt. Around two thirds of the total world production of natural sulfur comes from this area.

The abundant resources of oil and natural gas, which are important chemical raw materials as well as fuels, plus sulfur, salt, inland timber, agricultural wealth, and access to ocean and coastwise water transportation go far toward explaining the rapid development of industry along this coast in recent years. During this period most of the Coastal Plain has experienced industrial development on a much smaller scale, and it has been confined primarily to the processing of local agricultural products or timber. The major industries that have developed in coastal Texas and southern Louisiana include oil refining, chemical and synthetic rubber production, aluminum manufacture from imported bauxite, and the smelting of other imported ores such as zinc and tin. However, a scattering of other types of factories exist, including even a small iron and steel plant at Houston.

## ▶ Urban Development

That the Coastal Plain is not, on the whole, an outstanding industrial area is reflected in the size and functions of its major cities. Twelve of its twenty most populous metropolitan areas (excluding Fall Line cities—see p. 606) are seaports, the main ones being Houston, New Orleans, and the cluster of cities around Hampton Roads, especially Norfolk. Houston (1,243,000), the largest city on the Coastal Plain, is the main commercial and supply center for the Gulf Coast oil fields. New Orleans (868,000), the "natural" port for the Mississippi Valley, long ago lost most of the trade of the Middle West to east-coast ports, but it is still the fifth-ranking port in the United States in tonnage of foreign trade (after New York,

factures are electrical equipment and clothing. The next largest city along the valley route is Utica–Rome (331,000) at the western end of the Mohawk Valley. The principal manufactures here include machinery, brassware, and textiles.

The circular mass of the Adirondack Mountains is geologically an upraised outlier of the Canadian Shield. The hard-rock formations which tie it to the main body of the Shield emerge in the St. Lawrence River as the picturesque "Thousand Islands" and are responsible for the rapids which blocked navigation on the St. Lawrence above Montreal until they were bypassed by small canals in the nineteenth century. Very recently the possibilities for navigation of the St. Lawrence have been greatly enlarged by construction of the St. Lawrence Seaway, which permits good-sized oceangoing vessels to enter the Great Lakes. The highest peak of the Adirondacks exceeds 5000 feet in elevation. These mountains form an island of rugged, forested land and sparse population surrounded on all sides by more populous lowlands. The Adirondacks are important as a recreational area, however, and there is some production of pulp and paper around their margins, as well as a small production of iron ore.

## ▶ Physical Subdivisions of the Central and Southern Appalachians

South of the Hudson–Mohawk line the Appalachians fall into three major subdivisions. From east to west these are the Blue Ridge, the Ridge and Valley Section, and the Appalachian Plateau (maps, pp. 609, 598, and 613). Each of the three trends northeast-southwest, and they roughly parallel each other.

The *Blue Ridge,* long and narrow, can be traced from near the mouth of the Hudson to Alabama. Often it rises abruptly from the Piedmont to the east, and throughout much of its length it is but a single ridge. It has been given various local names.

In some places, especially in the north, the Blue Ridge is discontinuous, and lowland gaps provide important east-west routes for transportation. One of these gaps to the east of Harrisburg, Pennsylvania, is utilized by the main line of the Pennsylvania Railroad and by the Pennsylvania Turnpike, both connecting Philadelphia and the eastern seaboard with the Interior Plains via Pittsburgh, Pennsylvania. The Blue Ridge widens into several ranges and becomes higher and more continuous toward the south. Although the northern sections of the Blue Ridge often fail to reach 1000 feet in elevation, the section in western North Carolina known as the Great Smoky Mountains has a number of peaks over 6000 feet. Mount Mitchell in the Great Smokies, at 6684 feet, is the highest peak in the entire Appalachian system and in eastern United States.

West of the Blue Ridge, the *Ridge and Valley Section* of the Appalachians extends from southern New York to Alabama. Long, narrow, roughly parallel ridges trend generally north and south and are surrounded and separated by narrow valleys. The ridges are often 3000 to 4000 feet high, the valley floors 1000 to 2000 feet lower. On the east, immediately adjacent to the Blue Ridge, a valley somewhat wider than the rest extends almost continuously throughout the length of the Ridge and Valley Section. It is known in general as the Great Appalachian Valley, although it has many local names such as Shenandoah Valley in Virginia and Lehigh Valley in northeastern Pennsylvania. The Great Valley is a historic north-south passageway, and its productive limestone soils have provided the basis for an agricultural development superior to that of most parts of the Appalachians.

The *Appalachian Plateau* lies west of the Ridge and Valley Section. It covers most of southern New York State and extends southward into Alabama, narrowing toward the south. Although geologically a plateau (more precisely a series of plateaus), it is so deeply and thoroughly dissected in most places that it is actually an area of tangled hills and low mountains separated by narrow, twisting stream valleys. Most summit elevations are between 2000 and 3500 feet above sea level. The northern part is often called the Allegheny Plateau and the southern part the Cumberland Plateau. Notable escarpments, the Allegheny Front in the north and the Cumberland Front in the south, mark the eastern edge of the plateau area, while the frayed western edge merges into the Interior Plains.

### ► The Northern Appalachian Plateau (Allegheny Plateau)

The Northern Appalachian Plateau occupies parts of the states of New York, Ohio, Pennsylvania, West Virginia, Maryland, Virginia, and Kentucky. It has important forest and water power resources and some oil and natural gas. But its greatest importance lies in the fact that it contains what is probably the world's best coal field (map, right), considering the quantity and quality of coal available and the extraordinary ease of working it. Among the states sharing the Northern Appalachian Plateau, only New York has no noteworthy coal resources or production. About two thirds of the United States output of bituminous coal, or some 15 percent of the world's total production, comes from the Northern Appalachian Plateau. The West Virginia, Pennsylvania, and Kentucky portions of the plateau, ranking in that order, produce about 60 percent of the United States output, and the Ohio portion another 5 percent.

This enormous power resource drives industry and heats homes on the Atlantic Coast and in the Middle West, and it makes the Northern Appalachian Plateau itself one of the leading areas of heavy industry in the world. Pittsburgh, Pennsylvania (2,405,-000), strategically located where the navigable Allegheny and Monongahela rivers, flowing from the coal fields, unite to form the navigable Ohio River leading to the Midwest and South, is the area's outstanding steel-producing and urban center. Long the greatest center of primary iron and steel production in the world, the Pittsburgh metropolitan area has now been slightly surpassed by the Chicago area and possibly by Germany's Ruhr. But the plants strung along the river valleys that radiate from the city still represent about 16 percent of all United States steel capacity, or at least 5 percent of world capacity. The Northern Appalachian Plateau includes one other iron and steel center of major importance. This is Youngstown, Ohio (509,000 with nearby Warren), located in a valley which leads from Lake Erie to Pittsburgh. Smaller centers include the Steubenville, Ohio–Weirton, West Virginia area (168,000), the Huntington, West Virginia–Ashland, Kentucky area (255,000), the Canton, Ohio, area (340,000), and the Johnstown, Pennsylvania, area (281,000). In the aggregate, the steel industry of the Northern Appalachian Plateau represents about one third of all United States steel capacity. The iron and steel plants of the area draw their ore mainly from the Superior Upland, and probably could not have reached their present great development without the fortunate interposition of the Great Lakes to allow cheap transportation of ore most of the way to their various locations in or near the Appalachian coal fields.

Other important industries in the Northern Appalachian Plateau manufacture secondary metal products, rubber, chemicals, glass, and clay products. Akron, Ohio (514,-000), the original center of the rubber industry, is still the leading center of rubber manufacturing, with nearly a fifth of the national output by value. A district extending along the valley of the Kanawha River in the vicinity of Charleston, West Virginia (253,-000), and westward to Huntington specializes in chemicals, glass, and synthetic fabrics. Wheeling, West Virginia (190,000), another Ohio River city, carries on secondary processing of steel and manufactures clay products and glass. The only sizable in-

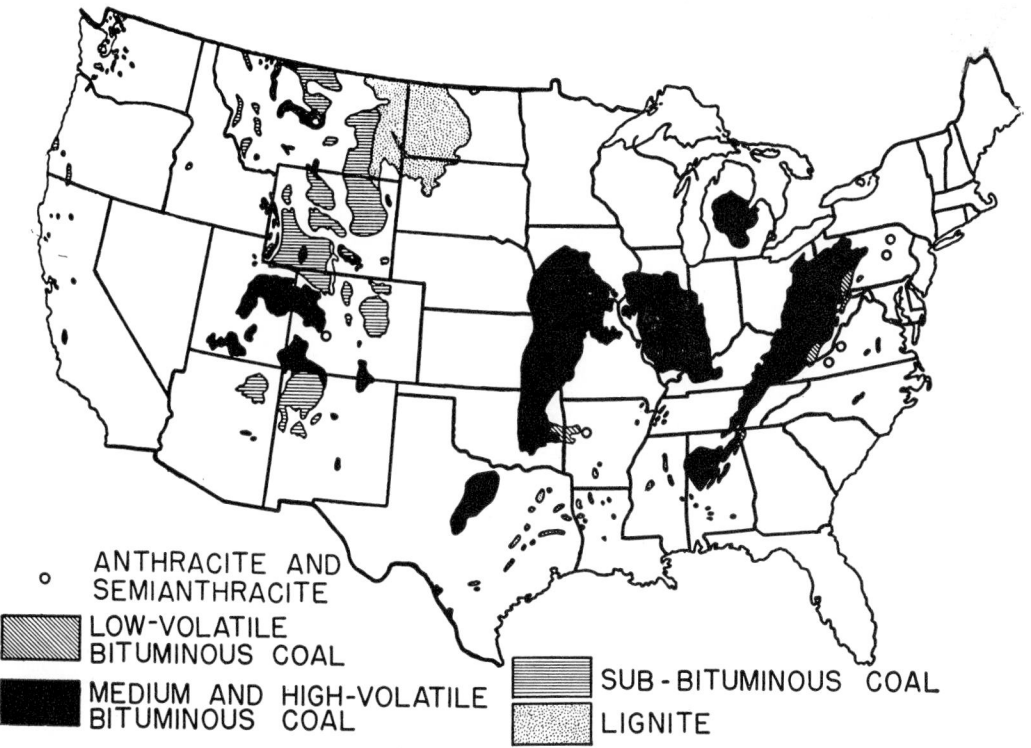

ANTHRACITE AND
SEMIANTHRACITE

LOW-VOLATILE
BITUMINOUS COAL

MEDIUM AND HIGH-VOLATILE
BITUMINOUS COAL

SUB-BITUMINOUS COAL

LIGNITE

Coal fields of the United States. (After a map by W. S. and E. S. Woytinsky in *World Population and Production: Trends and Outlook,* New York: Twentieth Century Fund, 1953.)

dustrial center of the Northern Appalachian Plateau that is clearly outside of the coal-producing area is Binghamton, New York (213,000), which is atypical in its kind of industry as well as in location, being primarily a shoe-manufacturing center.

Agriculture is overshadowed by industry and mining in the Northern Appalachian Plateau, although much of the land is in farms and there is a fair-sized farm population scattered along many of the valleys. Level land for crops is scarce, and farming is for the most part not a very rewarding or productive enterprise. West Virginia is fairly typical. Here much farming is done on a part-time basis, and a sizable part of the state's farm products are used at home. Livestock are the principal source of cash income to farmers. In the northern part of the region, especially in New York, the topography is somewhat more subdued and adequate mar-

kets are more easily reached so that a considerable dairy industry has developed. As a state New York is second only to Wisconsin in dairy products, and its Appalachian Plateau section makes a considerable contribution to the state's total dairy production. The Finger Lakes district at the northern edge of the Plateau is a well-developed fruit- and truck-farming area.

▶ *The Appalachian Ridges and
Valleys of Pennsylvania*

A small district in the Ridge and Valley Section of northeastern Pennsylvania produces almost the entire United States output of anthracite coal. Two main cities, Wilkes-Barre–Hazelton (347,000) and Scranton (235,000) have developed on the anthracite field. Their principal business is mining, and with the twentieth-century decline in the demand for anthracite they have become two of the major problem cities of the United States, suffering chronic unemployment and a considerable decrease in population. Some apparel and textile firms have come in to take advantage of the surplus labor supply created by the decline of the anthracite industry.

The early development of the anthracite fields, plus small local deposits of iron ore, led to the rise of a sizable iron and steel industry in eastern Pennsylvania which far antedates the recent construction of tidewater plants in the Philadelphia area. Three urban areas in the Ridge and Valley Section of the state are still important steel producers: Allentown–Bethlehem–Easton (492,-000), Harrisburg (345,000), and a much smaller producer, Reading (275,000). These cities are all located in the Great Valley on rivers whose valleys provide superior passageways into the rugged country to the west and through the Blue Ridge to the east. Their steel industries have now remained relatively static for some time, and textile and clothing industries have developed which at present tend to overshadow steel. The Allentown–Bethlehem–Easton area has also had an extraordinary development of the cement industry. This industry has been favored by its access to coal, the limestone of the Great Valley, and the very large and easily reached markets near by. The area is the foremost center of the cement industry in the United States and probably in the world.

The valleys of this section of eastern Pennsylvania are almost completely occupied by farms, primarily dairy farms, though livestock and subsistence farms are found in valleys more remote from markets.

### ▶ The Southern Appalachians

Most parts of the Appalachians south of the Potomac River and Northern Appalachian Plateau are still in the process of emerging from relative isolation and a poor agricultural economy. With the exception of the Great Valley, agriculture is largely on a subsistence basis, although commercial livestock production is increasing. The Great Valley has long been a superior agricultural section. It is now devoted principally to livestock and dairy farming or to general commercial farming. The Shenandoah Valley section is in addition one of the principal apple-producing areas of the United States. Alabama sections of the Appalachians are far enough south to have a considerable cotton production.

There is some coal production in Virginia, Tennessee, and Alabama, but the major stimulus to increased industrialization in recent decades has been water power, produced largely by the Tennessee Valley Authority (TVA) as a major aspect of its program to control the Tennessee River and its tributaries and to develop the resources of the Tennessee River Basin.[6] The main industrial growth has been in the fields of chemicals, aluminum, rayon and other textiles, and atomic energy. Only four cities in the Southern Appalachians reach 150,000 in metropolitan population. Birmingham, Alabama (635,000), at the extreme southern end of the Appalachians, is by far the largest and is a special case. Here large deposits of coal and iron ore in close proximity present one of the world's most favorable natural situations for the development of an iron and steel industry, and the city is the main center of that industry in the southern part of the United States. The remaining cities include Knoxville (368,000 with adjacent Oak Ridge), the main commercial center of the Tennessee portion of the Great Valley and an important center of federal government activity connected with the Tennessee Valley Authority and the production of atomic energy; Chattanooga, Tennessee (283,000), located

---

[6] Although a series of great dams and associated hydroelectric stations along the Tennessee and various tributaries are the best-known aspect of TVA, the demand for current has far outstripped the existing hydroelectric capacity, and TVA has now moved heavily into the production of electricity at coal-powered thermal stations.

where the Tennessee River cuts a natural passageway through the southern end of the Appalachian Plateau; and Roanoke, Virginia (159,000), a rail center and industrial city located at a gap through the Blue Ridge opposite the port of Norfolk.

## THE INTERIOR HIGHLANDS

The Interior Highlands, often called the Ozark or Ozark-Ouachita Highlands, occupy most of southern Missouri, the northwestern half of Arkansas, and adjoining parts of eastern Oklahoma (maps. pp. 588, 598, and 609). They constitute an island of hill country and low mountains in the midst of a sea of plains: the Interior Plains on the north and west and the Coastal Plain on the east (Mississippi Lowland) and south. The Interior Highlands are divided into two major segments by the east-west valley of the Arkansas River. The northern segment consists of the Boston Mountains, overlooking the Arkansas Valley, plus the more extensive Ozark Plateau of northern Arkansas, southern Missouri, and northeastern Oklahoma. South of the Arkansas Valley are the Ouachita Mountains, constituting the other principal segment of the Highlands.

The Interior Highlands display a great deal of internal variety in form and relief. North of the Arkansas Valley most of the area consists of dissected plateau surfaces bearing a certain physical resemblance to the Appalachian Plateau. However, the plateau section of the Interior Highlands is lower in elevation and relief and lacks the coal deposits of the Appalachian area. The Ouachita Mountains consist of roughly parallel ridges and valleys resembling the Ridge and Valley Section of the Appalachians, except that in the Ouachitas the trend of the topography is east and west. The peak elevations in the Interior Highlands lie generally between 1000 and 2000 feet. No crest in the entire area reaches 3000 feet, although the highest summits of the Ouachitas approach that elevation. There are notable differences in local relief within the Highlands. A number of fairly level upland surfaces occur, but other areas are quite rugged. Most areas fall between these topographic extremes.

Farming and lumbering are the economic mainstays in most parts of this landform division. Much of the agriculture is of a subsistence character. On the better lands, especially where adequate transportation is available, an important commercial livestock industry has developed, emphasizing dairying in some areas and the raising of beef cattle in others. Commercial poultry farming on a sizable scale is a relatively recent development in some districts. Cotton is the major crop of the Arkansas River Valley.

The Interior Highlands were originally in forest, and most parts are still forested (map, p. 596), generally with a rather poor grade of second growth timber. Deciduous hardwoods predominate north of the Arkansas Valley and coniferous softwoods in the Ouachita Mountains.

Many deposits of minerals exist in the Interior Highlands, but most deposits are not of sufficient value to justify exploitation at present. Two areas, however, are important producers of metals. In the northeastern part of the Highlands, about 60 miles south of St. Louis, a small district supplies over a third of the annual United States production of lead. It is the leading lead-mining district in the country. In northeastern Oklahoma and adjoining parts of Kansas and Missouri is the Tri-State mining district, for many years the leading area of zinc production in the United States and still important, although declining as a mining area. A number of other mineral resources are exploited on a small scale in various parts of the Highlands.

Manufacturing is poorly developed, aside

from sawmilling. A scattering of factories exist in a few towns and small cities. Springfield, Missouri (126,000), located in a well-developed dairy-farming area, is the largest city of the Highlands and the most important focus of highways and rail lines.

Recent years have witnessed a marked expansion in the tourist and resort industry. A considerable number of private resort developments cater to populations of the surrounding lowlands. In addition, state and federal government agencies have been active in the development of public recreational facilities. The impoundment of lakes behind federally built dams has been an important factor in increased tourist trade, and the electricity created in generating stations at these dams appears to offer a basis for increased industrial development in the Highlands.

## THE INTERIOR PLAINS

The interior of Anglo-America, between the Rocky Mountains on the west and the Appalachian Highlands and Canadian Shield on the east, is essentially composed of a vast expanse of plains (map, right). These plains lie mostly within the drainage basins of four important rivers: the Mississippi, the Mackenzie, the Saskatchewan, and the St. Lawrence. Most parts of the Interior Plains are many hundreds of miles from the sea; their location, in other words, is essentially continental rather than maritime. However, the Interior Plains reach the sea in the northwest and northeast of Anglo-America, respectively, along two narrow corridors —the Mackenzie River Lowlands and the St. Lawrence Lowlands. In the south the Interior Plains extend into Mexico, merge with the Gulf–Atlantic Coastal Plain, or abut against the Interior Highlands and Appalachian Highlands. The western edge of the plains can be traced through the Northwest Territories, British Columbia, Alberta, Montana, Wyoming, Colorado, New Mexico, and Texas; their northeastern edge through the Northwest Territories, Alberta, Saskatchewan, Manitoba, Minnesota, Wisconsin, Michigan, Ontario, and Quebec; and their southeastern edge through Quebec, New York, Ohio, Kentucky, Tennessee, Alabama, Missouri, Oklahoma, and Texas. Besides parts of the states, provinces, and territories already mentioned, the Interior Plains include the whole of seven states: the Dako-

tas, Nebraska, Kansas, Iowa, Illinois, and Indiana. Approximately the western third of the Interior Plains, from Mexico north to the southern part of Saskatchewan and Alberta, is known as the Great Plains.

### ▶ Physiography, Climate, Vegetation, and Soils

The Interior Plains are seldom flat, although considerable areas are very nearly so. Most of the land is gently rolling, but some areas are hilly and occasional areas rather rugged. Most parts of the Interior Plains north of the Ohio and Missouri rivers were covered with a mantle of glacial debris during the Great Ice Age and the topography was somewhat smoothed thereby. Thus the more hilly sections tend to be outside the area of glaciation, although some unglaciated portions are also fairly level. The principal unglaciated hilly areas are in the southeast from southern Indiana across Kentucky into Tennessee, and in an "island" of unglaciated terrain in southwestern Wisconsin. Other areas of hilly terrain exist (1) in eroded strips along major stream courses, (2) in areas of terminal moraine deposition, (3) along cuesta escarpments separating different plain levels, (4) in fantastically eroded badlands of the western sections such as the famous ones in western South Dakota, and (5) in small, isolated mountain areas near the western border, of which the Black Hills of South

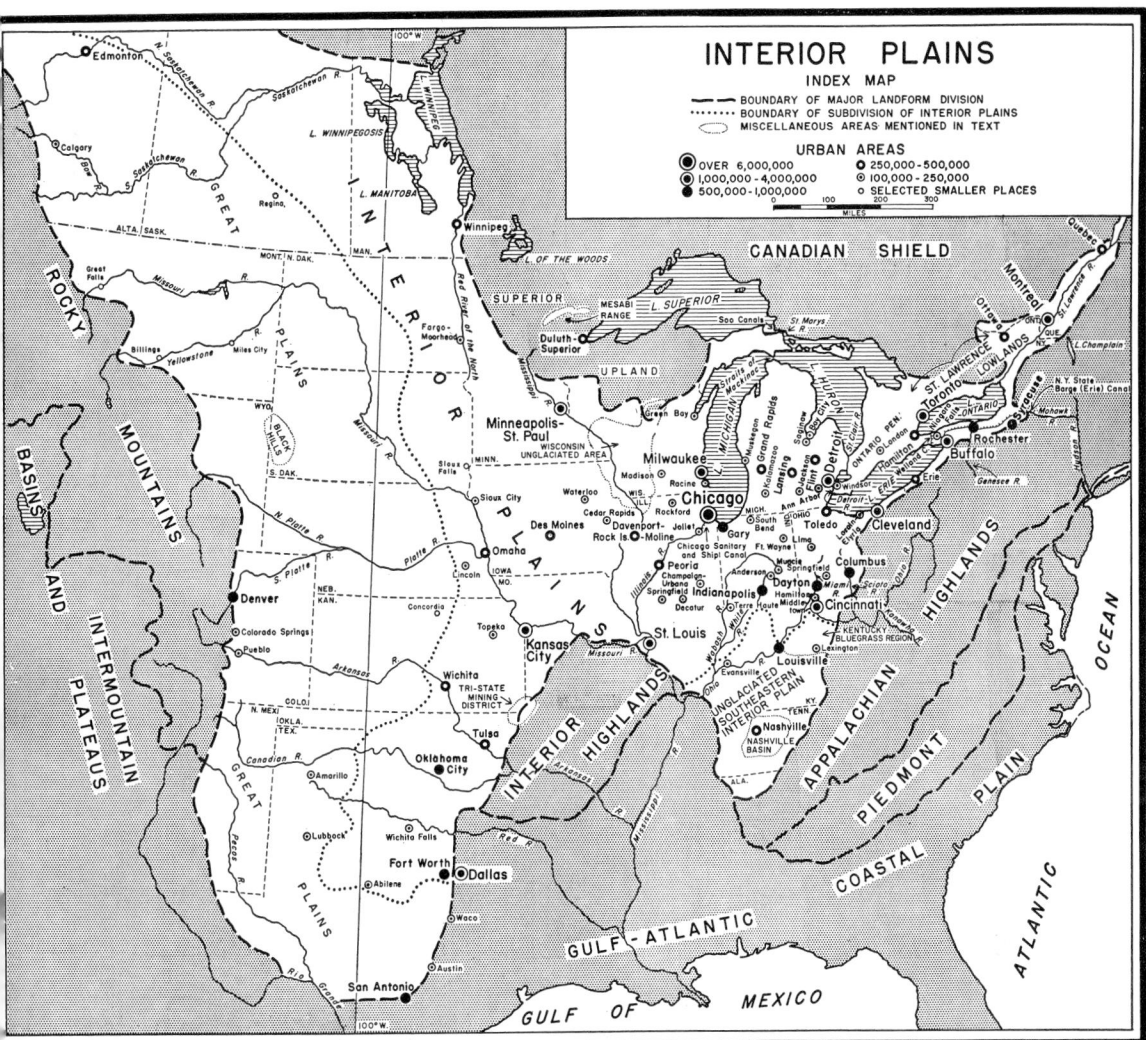

Dakota are the most notable example. These various exceptions, however, do not essentially damage but only refine the over-all concept of a huge plains area with enormous expanses of land level enough for cultivation.

An interior area of this size extending from the margins of the low latitudes to the margins of the high latitudes naturally has a great range of climatic conditions, natural vegetation, and soils. The Mackenzie Delta is in the tundra zone, and the subarctic climatic zone with its coniferous forest reaches

southward into central Alberta, Saskatchewan, and Manitoba. Southern Alberta and Saskatchewan and areas west of approximately the 100th meridian in the Great Plains section of the United States are semiarid and have a short grass, or steppe, vegetation. South of the general latitude of the Ohio River and east of the belt of steppe, considerable sections of the Interior Plains fall within the zone of humid subtropical climate. But the most important and productive agricultural areas of this landform division lie within the humid continental climatic zones: humid continental with short summers in a belt from Alberta to the Atlantic which includes southern Canada and large sections of the northern tier of states in the United States, and humid continental with long summers in a belt reaching from Nebraska and Kansas to the Appalachians. Large areas within the humid continental zones were originally in forest, with deciduous hardwoods predominating in most places, but with a belt of mixed hardwoods and conifers in the north. However, tall grass, or prairie, vegetation occupied a roughly triangular area with its apex in Illinois and widening westward toward the steppe. The deep, black soils originally developed under a vegetation of tall grass are outstandingly fertile and some soils developed under the deciduous forest are above average in natural fertility, though not equal to the grassland soils. Such soils, combined with adequate rainfall and wide expanses of land sufficiently level for cultivation, have provided a natural setting for the development of one of the world's most important and impressive agricultural areas. All things considered, the Interior Plains represent the agricultural heartland of Anglo-America.

## ▶ Agricultural Regions

Relatively smooth topography, good soils, and the existence of a number of major climatic regions, each occupying a broad area, has permitted the development of several large and rather distinct agricultural regions. These display considerable internal uniformity rather than the intricate and broken pattern of agriculture characteristic of many of Anglo-America's landform regions. The major agricultural regions of the Interior Plains, as considered herein, include (1) the Corn Belt, (2) the Dairy Belt, (3) the Spring and Winter Wheat Belts, (4) the Unglaciated Southeastern Interior Plain, (5) the Texas–Oklahoma Red Prairies, and (6) the Great Plains Region of Ranching and Irrigated Agriculture.

## The Corn Belt

The famous Corn Belt of the United States lies wholly within the Interior Plains (map, p. 597). It extends from western Ohio to eastern South Dakota, Nebraska, and Kansas, and includes most of Indiana and Illinois, northern and most of western Missouri, practically all of Iowa, southwestern Minnesota, and small areas in southern Michigan, southwestern Wisconsin, southeastern North Dakota, and northwestern Kentucky. It lies essentially within the humid continental long-summer climatic zone of the Interior Plains, and except for its Indiana and Ohio sections is generally within the region of prairie or chernozem soils. Physically its limits are set (1) on the east by the more rugged land and poorer soils of the Appalachian Plateau, (2) on the south by the eroded northern margin of the Ohio River Valley and by the Ozarks, (3) on the west by semiaridity (approximately the line of 20 inches average annual rainfall), and (4) on the north by summers too short and cool to insure a mature corn crop.

The Corn Belt system of agriculture emphasizes the production of hogs and cattle for cash sale. The principal feedstuff is corn, which has a high feed value and grows exceedingly well in this region of fertile soil, long hot summers, and ample moisture. Most of the livestock are bred within the area, but many Western range cattle are brought into the Corn Belt for fattening before their final trip to the slaughterhouses. Oats, winter wheat, hay, pasture grasses and legumes, and soybeans are grown in a variety of rotations with corn. These latter crops contribute to livestock production, or they may, if the market favors it, be marketed as cash crops, especially the wheat and soybeans. In addition, corn is often marketed as a cash crop if the market is more favorable than for livestock. This practice is the usual one in some parts of the Corn Belt that are especially near major markets, as in large sections of Illinois where cash grain farming of corn has largely replaced livestock production.

Iowa and Illinois may be considered the heart of the Corn Belt. In total farm production, by value, Iowa ranks second among the states and Illinois fourth. Together these states account for about 12 to 14 percent of the country's total agricultural production by value. They produce about a third of the nation's corn and hogs, and the Corn Belt as a whole accounts for well over half of the national output of these items. Although quite important within the Corn Belt, especially toward the west, the beef cattle industry of the United States is not so highly centered in the area as is the production of corn and hogs. Nevertheless, Iowa ranks second only to the much larger state of Texas in the production of beef cattle.

### The Dairy Belt

Dairy farming is the principal form of agriculture in those portions of the Interior Plains that lie in Wisconsin and adjacent parts of Minnesota, in most Michigan and New York sections of the Plains, in Illinois and Indiana sections near Chicago (map, p. 597), and in sizable parts of the Ontario and Quebec sections. Outside the Interior Plains, dairy production is also important, though generally less intensive, in adjoining sections of the Appalachians and the southern margins of the Canadian Shield. Thus dairy farming is particularly an enterprise of the humid continental short-summer climatic zone in Anglo-America. The southern limit of the Dairy Belt within the Interior Plains is set primarily by warmer summers that allow production of mature corn; its northern boundary, lying generally outside the Plains, is essentially the northern climatic limit of agriculture itself; and its western limit is set by semiaridity and distance from adequate markets.

The principal items of sale from the dairy farms of this agricultural region are fluid milk, where city markets are sufficiently near, or butter and cheese in sections more distant from large cities. However, calves, nonproductive milk cows, hogs, poultry, and cash crops are also marketed. The feed for these animals is supplied mainly by crops of hay, oats, and silage corn, by permanent and rotation pastures, and by creamery wastes and surplus milk. Approximately one quarter of all United States dairy products by value originate in the Interior Plains sections of the Dairy Belt, Wisconsin alone accounting for about 12 or 13 percent. The Interior Plains of eastern Canada—comprised of lowlands along the St. Lawrence River in Quebec and the Ontario Peninsula, between the edge of the Shield and the Great Lakes, in Ontario—are Canada's most productive agricultural area. Much of this area may be classed as part of the Dairy Belt. But in the Ontario Peninsula, the southernmost section of Canada, feed grain and livestock production somewhat like that of the Corn Belt overshadows dairying. In addition, small and scattered specialty areas producing such items as fruits and vegetables, tobacco, potatoes, and sugar beets are relatively prominent in these Canadian dairy and livestock regions. Such specialty areas are also found in the United States portions of the Dairy Belt, though their relative importance is less than in the Canadian portions. The main ones are fruit and truck districts that are located close to the shores of the Great Lakes and benefit from the moderating climatic influence of the lakes.

### The Spring and Winter Wheat Belts

Most of Anglo-America's large production of wheat originates in two zones of specialized wheat growing within the Interior Plains (map, p. 597). One of these zones grows spring wheat, the other winter wheat. The Spring Wheat Belt occupies the western edge of Minnesota, nearly all of North Dakota, part of northeastern South Dakota, much of northern Montana, and most of the plains area of the Canadian Prairie Provinces of Manitoba, Saskatchewan, and Alberta. It thus occupies the drier margins of the humid continental short-summer climatic zone and the wetter margins of the steppe. In general its limits are set by an increasingly short growing season on the north, sufficient moisture for more intensive forms of agriculture on the east, summers too warm for spring wheat on the south, and increasing aridity on the west. The Winter Wheat Belt centers in central and western Kansas and extends into adjoining parts of Nebraska, Colorado, and Oklahoma and into the Texas Panhandle and small sections of eastern New Mexico and southeastern Wyoming. It occupies principally the drier margins of the humid continental long-summer climatic zone and the wetter margins of the steppe. In general its limits are set by winters too cold for winter wheat on the north, adequate moisture for more intensive forms of agriculture on the east, and insufficient moisture for wheat on the west and south. The actual limits of wheat growing undergo marked changes from one period of years to another due to severe climatic and market fluctuations.

Large-scale, highly mechanized commercial wheat production completely dominates the agriculture of these areas. The extensive use of machinery and the scale of operations tend to offset the disadvantage of crop yields that are generally low despite the excellent grassland soils. There is relatively little diversification, although small acreages are devoted to hay, oats, barley, rye, flax, and corn in the Spring Wheat Belt and to corn, sorghums, and hay in the Winter Wheat Belt. Fallow land, stubble, and some of these secondary crops provide forage for cattle, which represent a supplementary source of income and a means of avoiding disaster in case the wheat crop fails.

Statistics vary considerably from year to year, but in general the Winter Wheat Belt supplies close to 40 percent of the United States wheat crop, with Kansas (the leading wheat state) accounting for almost a fifth of the national output. The Spring Wheat Belt supplies approximately a quarter of the American crop, with North Dakota (the second ranking wheat state) accounting for not quite half of this. Practically all of the Canadian wheat crop is grown in the Spring Wheat Belt.

Commercial wheat farming in the Spring and Winter Wheat Belts is a risky and uncertain type of enterprise. These areas are climatically marginal, and relatively slight deviations from normal conditions can result in disastrous crop failures. The heavy dependence on one-crop farming makes it difficult for farmers to weather a year, often a series of years, of wheat failure. Most of the Canadian crop and a considerable share of the American are destined for export markets, in which the demand for Anglo-American wheat fluctuates considerably. The result of these factors is a great variation in farm incomes from year to year, often leading to the adoption of radical political programs by state and provincial governments in the wheat belts. North Dakota and the three Prairie Provinces of Canada are particularly known for such programs.

### The Unglaciated Southeastern Interior Plain

The Unglaciated Southeastern Interior Plain lies south of the Corn Belt. Its northern edge is found in dissected lands near the Ohio River in southern Indiana, and Illinois, and it extends southward to include sizable areas in Kentucky and Tennessee between the Appalachians and the Mississippi River embayment of the Gulf–Atlantic Coastal Plain, plus a small part of northern Alabama (map, p. 623). The topography of this southeastern section of the Interior Plains has not been smoothed by glaciation, and it is essentially a hilly area. The climate is mostly humid subtropical, albeit a cool phase of this climatic type.

The Unglaciated Southeastern Interior Plain is distinguished from other large agricultural regions of the Interior Plains by the fact that no well-established, highly developed, and specialized system of farming has evolved in the area as a whole. For the most part the type of agriculture resembles that of the Corn Belt, combining corn, winter wheat, and livestock production. But as the land is poorer than that of the Corn Belt, so is the agriculture poorer and less productive in almost every way. In addition, tobacco and, toward the Coastal Plain, a little cotton often enter the farming picture. Included within the general region, however, are two small but outstanding agricultural districts, both developed in basinlike areas where soils of more than average fertility have been derived from underlying limestone formations. These are the Bluegrass Region of north central Kentucky, specializing in tobacco production and also famous as the home of fine horses, and the Nashville Basin of central Tennessee, an area of livestock farming resembling that of the Corn Belt to the north.

### The Texas–Oklahoma Red Prairies

South of the Winter Wheat Belt in Texas and Oklahoma a major area of intensive cotton cultivation has developed on reddish prairie soils (map, p. 598). Cotton can be grown without irrigation here, and extensive mechanization helps to compensate for low average yields. However, in recent years a considerable amount of irrigated cotton acreage has been developed. Until the comparatively recent development of large-scale cotton culture, this was principally a ranching district. Today some areas exhibit a mixture of cotton cultivation, ranching, and some wheat and sorghum production. However, cotton is the dominant agricultural interest for the region as a whole.

### The Great Plains Region of Ranching and Irrigated Agriculture

A north-south belt of country which is too dry for wheat except in abnormally wet years extends along the western edge of the Interior Plains from Alberta and Saskatchewan to the Mexican border. This area of steppe climate in the western portion of the Great Plains is culturally and economically a zone of transition between the farming country of the humid and subhumid East and the range livestock country of the West. Sheep and cattle ranches occupy most of the land, although goat ranching is important in the extreme south. The population is generally sparse, but islands of greater density are found in scattered irrigated areas. The largest of these are in Colorado, especially along the South Platte River. The agricultural mainstays of the Great Plains irrigated areas are hay, grown as supplemental feed for range animals, and sugar beets, which supply both a cash crop and fodder for livestock.

### ▶ Urban and Industrial Development

The Interior Plains are not only the leading agricultural area of Anglo-America, but contain many of the largest cities and much of the manufacturing industry of this world region. Most of the urban and industrial development is found in the eastern half of the Plains. Of 52 metropolitan areas in the Interior Plains numbering 150,000 inhabitants or more, 39 lie either on the Mississippi or east of it. Sixteen of the 20 metropolitan areas numbering 500,000 or more are on the Mississippi or east of it, as are all but one of the 11 that number more than a million inhabitants.

Most of the major cities in the eastern part of the Interior Plains lie within the American Manufacturing Belt, a zone of concentrated industrial activity extending eastward from the Mississippi River to the northeastern Atlantic seaboard. The western limit of the belt lies in the vicinity of a line connecting St. Louis and Milwaukee; the northern limit along or near the line Milwaukee–Toronto–Montreal–Portland, Maine; and the southern limit along the general line St. Louis–Cincinnati–Charleston, West Virginia–Baltimore. The American Manufacturing Belt thus includes large portions of the American Middle West and

Northeast, as well as several districts in southeastern Canada. It represents one of the two largest concentrations of relatively continuous industrial development in the world, the other being the great manufacturing region of western Europe. In terms of major landform divisions, the American Manufacturing Belt lies partly in the Appalachian Highlands, partly in the northern Piedmont and adjacent Coastal Plain, and partly in the Interior Plains.

In general, the individual cities of the Interior Plains have been favored in their development by one or more of the following factors: (1) access to the agricultural wealth of the plains; (2) access to coal, iron, and steel; (3) advantageous location with respect to transportation. Most of these cities began as commercial centers serving an agricultural hinterland. Many of them had particular advantages with respect to water transportation, which was of exceptional importance during the time they were first developing. Later the coming of railroads provided a further stimulus to growth, although many cities have continued to be important centers of water transportation as well as railroad centers. The manufacturing industries which have been developed in these cities of the Interior Plains fall under two main categories: (1) industries engaged in processing the agricultural products of the plains and (2) industries manufacturing machinery, vehicles, and other secondary metal products from iron and steel produced in or near the Interior Plains. Position between the Appalachian coal fields and the iron-ore resources of the Canadian Shield and its extension in the Superior Upland, with the Great Lakes–St. Lawrence waterway providing cheap and efficient water transportation for both iron ore and coal, gives the manufacturing centers of the eastern Interior Plains a superior access to the basic raw materials needed by the iron and steel industry.

For purposes of description and analysis, the major cities and industries of the Interior Plains may be conveniently divided into the following four groups according to location: (1) cities and industries of the Ontario and Quebec lowlands, (2) United States cities and industries on or near the Great Lakes, (3) cities and industries of the southeastern section of the Interior Plains, and (4) cities and industries of the Interior Plains west of the Great Lakes.

### Cities and Industries of the Ontario and Quebec Lowlands

The core region of Canada is found in a group of lowlands bordering the Great Lakes or the St. Lawrence River from the vicinity of Detroit to Quebec City. The entire lowland area is often termed loosely the "St. Lawrence Lowlands," although the Ontario Peninsula between Lakes Huron, Erie, and Ontario is frequently recognized as a separate section (maps, pp. 613 and 623). Well over half of Canada's manufacturing is carried on in the Ontario and Quebec lowlands, and most of the large Canadian cities are found here. The industries of this Canadian section of the Interior Plains are very diversified, although generally smaller in scale than those found in the United States sections. The major manufactures include textiles, clothing, pulp and paper, shoes, rubber; flour, meat, and other food products, iron and steel, automobiles, machinery, and electrical equipment. Among the factors that have favorably influenced the development of these industries are (1) the availability of water power and minerals from the Canadian Shield, (2) the availability of coal from the Northern Appalachian Plateau, (3) access to good transportation facilities, especially water transportation, (4) the agricultural wealth of the surrounding lowlands, and (5) markets provided by the relatively large population of these lowlands.

Most of the main cities in the Ontario and Quebec lowlands are located either on the Great Lakes or on the St. Lawrence River. The St. Lawrence is navigable for large ships

An air view of Montreal, Canada's largest seaport. Note the prominent grain elevators in the middle foreground. The St. Lawrence River appears at the upper right. (Photographic Services, Quebec.)

as far as Montreal, although it is blocked by ice for a considerable period in winter. Beyond Montreal, canals bypassing rapids on the river gave small ships access to Lake Ontario before completion of the St. Lawrence Seaway in 1959. The new Seaway allows relatively large oceangoing ships to enter the Great Lakes. The obstacle of Niagara Falls, between Lakes Ontario and Erie, is circumvented on the Canadian side by the Welland Ship Canal.

The largest of Canada's cities, aggregating almost a tenth of the country's population in its metropolitan area, is Montreal (1,621,000). It lies at the convergence of several major passageways: the St. Lawrence River and Valley leading to the Atlantic and the Great Lakes; the Champlain Lowland leading south toward New York City; and the Ottawa River Valley along which Canada's transcontinental railroads find a natural passage west and north into the Shield. Montreal is Canada's chief seaport and its largest manufacturing center. Its industries are highly diversified, with the manufacture of textiles and clothing the most important. Quebec (310,000), on the St. Lawrence below Montreal, was the original center of French settlement and administration in Canada, chosen because of its fortress position at the head of the estuary where the river became narrow enough to be controlled by the cannon of the time. Its advantages for commerce, however, have proved far inferior to those of Montreal, though it, too, is an active ocean port.

Montreal's great rival among Canadian cities is Toronto (1,429,000), which has the finest natural harbor on Lake Ontario. Toronto has become the financial center of

Canada and the commercial center of Ontario, as well as Canada's second city in population and manufacturing. Together Montreal and Toronto account for about a third of the total value of Canada's manufactures. Toronto's manufacturing industries, like those of Montreal, are highly diversified.

Other Ontario cities include Ottawa (335,000), Canada's capital, which is located on the Ottawa River in the section where the river forms the boundary between the country's two largest provinces; Hamilton (325,000), a Lake Ontario port which is one of Canada's principal centers of iron and steel manufacture; Windsor (184,000), located opposite Detroit and thus favorably situated for its role as Canada's main center of automobile production; and London (191,000), an inland commercial and industrial center in one of the most productive agricultural areas of lowland Ontario. In addition to the cities mentioned, a great deal of manufacturing is carried on in smaller industrial centers of the Ontario and Quebec lowlands.

### United States Cities and Industries On or Near the Great Lakes

Some of the largest cities in the United States, including the largest ones in the Interior Plains, are found along or near the southern shore of the Great Lakes. Their locations generally reflect past or present advantages deriving from such factors as natural harbors on the lakes, portages between rivers, river valley passageways leading from the lakes to the interior, or other factors relating to water transportation.

Ready access to coal and steel has been an advantage of the greatest importance to the manufacturing industries of the lake cities. Most of the coal comes from the Appalachian Plateau, as does much of the steel. However, a number of the lake ports are themselves major steel producers. The leading ones in this respect are Chicago (where the industry is largely centered in the Indiana suburbs, especially Gary), Detroit, Cleveland, and Buffalo. The production in these four cities and their suburbs alone, not including smaller installations in other lake ports, represents about a third of the United States total. The Chicago metropolitan area is the country's—and probably the world's—greatest center of steel production, with about 18 percent of all United States steel-manufacturing capacity. The steel mills of the lake ports draw most of their ore from the Superior Upland via the lakes and their coal mainly from the Appalachians, but Chicago benefits also from relative proximity to the Eastern Interior coal field of central and southern Illinois and adjoining parts of Indiana and Kentucky. This field produces about 17 percent of the United States output of bituminous coal. Much of the coal can be used for coking when mixed with higher-grade Appalachian coal. Most of the lake cities are highly industrialized, and the group as a whole is of great importance in the iron and steel, machinery, vehicle, and other metal industries. In addition, two cities in the group, Chicago and Buffalo, are major world centers of food processing, and another city, Rochester, is the world's greatest center of the photographic equipment industry.

Chicago's metropolitan area (6,794,000 including Gary and other Indiana satellites and suburbs) is the second largest in the United States and in Anglo-America. Chicago is by far the largest city of the Interior Plains. It has developed on a harbor formed by the mouth of the Chicago River at the southern end of Lake Michigan. Here the Great Lakes make their farthest penetration into the agricultural heartland of the United States. An old portage, first canalized a century ago, connects Lake Michigan drainage and Mississippi drainage in the vicinity of the city. Today a modern commercial waterway, following the old canal route, connects Chicago with the Mississippi and the Gulf of Mexico via the Illinois River. The city has become the world's greatest railway center, a result partly of the diversion of east-west tracks around the southern end of Lake Michigan, but more largely due to Chicago's original importance as a lake port. The relation of Chicago to the agriculture of the Corn Belt and the wheat belts is seen in its function as a major grain market, in its important meat-packing industry and in its unquestioned world leadership in the manufacture of agricultural machinery. However, most of the city's industries are engaged in producing a diverse array of metal products, including many different types of machinery.

Milwaukee (1,194,000), north of Chicago, is the second most important Lake Michigan port and industrial center. It has a better natural harbor than Chicago, but in other respects its location is less advantageous. Nevertheless it is a major industrial center, known for its large production of heavy machinery, beer (probably the result of its large population of German origin), automobile bodies, and a miscellany of other goods.

The second largest city of the Interior Plains, and second largest on the Great Lakes, is Detroit (3,762,000, excluding the Canadian suburb of Windsor). Its position on the Detroit River linking Lakes Huron and Erie has long made it a city of considerable importance. However, its meteoric rise in the twentieth century into the top group of American population and industrial centers has been connected mainly with the equally meteoric rise of the American automobile industry. Despite some decentralization of the industry in recent years, Detroit still has no significant rival as a center of automobile manufacturing. Probably no city in the world of comparable size is so dependent on a single industry. Smaller cities around Detroit are also dominated by auto-making—either complete cars or components. The group includes Flint (374,000), Lansing (299,000), and Saginaw (191,000) in Michigan; Toledo (457,000) in Ohio; and South Bend (239,000) in Indiana, as

well as many smaller places. Only two of the larger cities between Lake Michigan and the western end of Lake Erie are not dominated by the auto industry. These are Grand Rapids, Michigan (363,000) and Fort Wayne, Indiana (232,000). Grand Rapids, located at a waterfall in an area originally in mixed forest, has become famous as a center of furniture manufacture, although that industry is now overshadowed by the manufacture of a variety of secondary metal products. Fort Wayne stands at a portage on a water route once affording an important connection between Lake Erie and the Ohio River. It, too, is mainly a producer of secondary metal wares. Even in these cities the motor vehicle industry is of some importance, as it is in most of the main manufacturing centers of the Great Lakes group outside the major areas of automobile production.

Two other major Great Lakes ports of the United States are Cleveland, Ohio (1,797,000), and Buffalo, New York (1,307,000). Between them lies the much smaller port city of Erie (251,000), the only Pennsylvania port on the lakes. Cleveland has a good harbor and lies in the path of rail lines skirting the Appalachian Plateau along the level coastal plain of Lake Erie, and others following relatively easy valley routes into the interior of the Plateau. The city is important in both the steel and automobile industries, and is noteworthy for the production of machinery and assorted metal wares. Several ports along the Ohio shore of Lake Erie handle large tonnages of iron ore (inbound) or coal (outbound). Cleveland and the small cities of Conneaut and Ashtabula (map, p. 613) are the main ore ports, while Toledo is by far the leading coal port. Buffalo is pre-eminently the port where transportation along the Hudson-Mohawk Valley and the Lake Ontario Plain intersects that of the Great Lakes. Until the building of the Welland Canal it was the head of navigation on the upper Great Lakes, and it was the western terminus of the Erie Canal. Buffalo has important steel and automobile industries, and is the world's greatest center of flour milling. Hydro-electricity from Niagara Falls has provided a basis for a considerable development of electrochemical and electrometallurgical manufacturing. East of Buffalo, along the Erie Canal route, are two other important industrial centers, each connected by canal with a small port on Lake Ontario. Rochester (586,000) grew originally where the lowland route passed a waterfall on the Genessee River. It was primarily a flour-milling center in the early days, but it has now become the world's leading center for the production of photographic equipment. Its other manufactures are dominantly of a type requiring highly skilled labor. Syracuse (564,000) is located where the lowland route along the Mohawk Valley widens into the Lake Ontario Plain. Large salt deposits in the vicinity of the city fostered an early growth of chemical manufacturing, but the chemical industry is now greatly outweighed in importance by a variety of secondary metal products.

### Cities and Industries of the Southeastern Section of the Interior Plains

During the early days of settlement in the Middle West, people and goods moved westward along three great routes issuing from the Appalachians into the Interior Plains. One of these routes was the Great Lakes, one was the Ohio River, and the other was the first land highway in the Middle West, the National Road, which pursued its westward course between the other two. Important cities are now found at intervals along each of these routes. Those along the Great Lakes have already been described. The principal Ohio River cities are Cincinnati, Ohio (1,072,000), located on the great northern bend of the river where tributaries enter from both sides; Louisville, Kentucky (725,000), located at a stretch of falls and rapids which long interrupted traffic until by-passed by a canal; and Evansville, Indiana (199,000), located not far from the mouth

of the Ohio's major north bank tributary, the Wabash, which once carried a considerable amount of commerce. The main cities along the old National Road are Columbus, Ohio (687,000), located where the road issued from the Appalachian Plateau and intersected the Scioto River leading toward the Ohio; Dayton, Ohio (695,000), where the road intersected the Miami River leading southward to the Ohio at Cincinnati; and Indianapolis, Indiana (698,000), located at the intersection of the road with an Ohio tributary thought, erroneously, to be navigable at the time the city was founded. Despite the error with regard to the availability of water transport, Indianapolis became the capital of Indiana, for which its central location favored it, and also became a major rail center. The only large city in the southeastern part of the Interior Plains that is not on either of these old transport routes is Nashville, Tennessee (400,000) which lies considerably farther south and is the commercial center of the fertile Nashville Basin, besides being the state capital and a minor center of chemical production.

With the exception of Nashville, each of the cities described in the preceding paragraph has an industrial structure dominated by the manufacture of machinery and other secondary metal products. In addition, some of them have secondary specialties such as beer and soap in Cincinnati, whiskey and tobacco products in Louisville, and drugs and meat products in Indianapolis. Cincinnati is the greatest single center of the machine tool industry in the United States, Columbus is noted for its mining machinery, and Dayton for light manufactures, such as calculators, cash registers, and various automobile components, which require a high degree of skill to make.

### Cities and Industries West of the Great Lakes

In the Interior Plains west of the Great Lakes cities are more widely scattered and smaller than farther east, and, in general, this becomes increasingly so the farther

A roundup of range cattle in the Montana Rockies south of Butte. This semiarid landscape in the upper valley of the Ruby River is characteristic in many ways of vast areas of range land in the Rocky Mountains and Intermountain West. Note the small trees lining the water course in the foreground. (Charles W. Herbert from *Western Ways*.)

United States, north of Yellowstone Park, does the linear outline break down. Here the mountains rise in jumbled masses.

Easy passes through the Rockies are almost nonexistent, and the system has been a major barrier to transportation. Seven east-west trunk railroads cross the mountains: the Canadian National, Canadian Pacific, Great Northern, Northern Pacific, Milwaukee, Union Pacific, and Denver and Rio Grande Western (map, p. 637). The easiest route, followed by the Union Pacific, lies through southern Wyoming, where the Wyoming Basin almost breaks the mountain system in two, and thence through low passes in the Wasatch Range to the Great Salt Lake district. Elsewhere, three routes in Canada, three through Montana, and one through Colorado cross the Rockies via passes varying from 3700 to 10,000 feet.

## ▶ *The Important Mining Industry*

Mining is the most important economic activity of the Rocky Mountains from the standpoint of value of production. Scattered mining towns from New Mexico to British Columbia produce a variety of minerals, often from complex ores yielding several end products. The major minerals in terms of value are molybdenum, copper, silver, lead, zinc, and, in the Wyoming Basin, oil, uranium, and coal. But many others are produced. Among the many small and scattered mining communities, a few are of outstanding importance. They include Butte, Montana, where the famous copper mines also yield silver, lead, and zinc; Coeur d'Alene, Idaho, producing gold, silver, lead, and zinc; Kimberley, British Columbia, which mines most of Canada's lead

Major physiographic features of western United States and southwestern Canada. (The base map is a portion of A. K. Lobeck's Physiographic Diagram of the United States, copyright, The Geographical Press, a division of C. S. Hammond & Company, Maplewood, N. J.)

and much of its zinc; and Climax, Colorado, the site of the world's largest molybdenum mine. Some of the ores are refined and smelted in or near the mining districts. Anaconda, Montana, near Butte, and Trail, British Columbia, are among the world's greatest centers of nonferrous metallurgy. Many "ghost towns" in the Rockies tell of mineral deposits once important but now exhausted. Awaiting future exploitation, however, are widespread deposits of coal, now mined on a large scale only in the Wyoming Basin, and large reserves of phosphate and oil shale in the central and northern U. S. Rockies and adjoining parts of the Intermountain Basins and Plateaus.

## ▶ Other Economic Activities

Ranchers graze sheep and cattle in many parts of the Rockies (photo, p. 635), and many valleys contain small agricultural communities. Agriculture is generally dependent on irrigation, however, and is limited by short growing seasons. Fodder crops are grown to supplement natural forage for grazing animals; and specialties such as tree fruits, potatoes, and vegetables have developed in some areas. The Rockies are forested, largely with varieties of pine, fir, and other coniferous softwoods, up to the tree line, and a certain amount of lumbering is found in various sections. However, large-scale lumbering has developed only in northern Idaho and adjoining areas. A very important and growing activity is the tourist and resort trade. Most of the land in the Rockies, in both the United States and Canada, is owned by the respective national governments. The latter exert control over the exploitation of mineral, timber, and water resources within their properties in the interests of conservation and sustained economic development of their countries. They have contributed to the growth of tourism by setting aside areas containing spectacular scenery or other natural or historical attractions as national parks or monuments. Tourist facilities have been developed in many of these recreational areas. In addition, a large number of privately owned resorts are found in the Rockies. They are often in close proximity to areas that have been developed as public recreational facilities.

On the whole, the economy of the Rocky Mountains is handicapped by the relative isolation of much of the area. This isolation is partly a consequence of remoteness from important centers of population, and is partly due to the difficulty of constructing adequate transportation lines in such rugged terrain. The mountain area as a whole is sparsely populated, and urban development is very limited. The largest city, Butte,

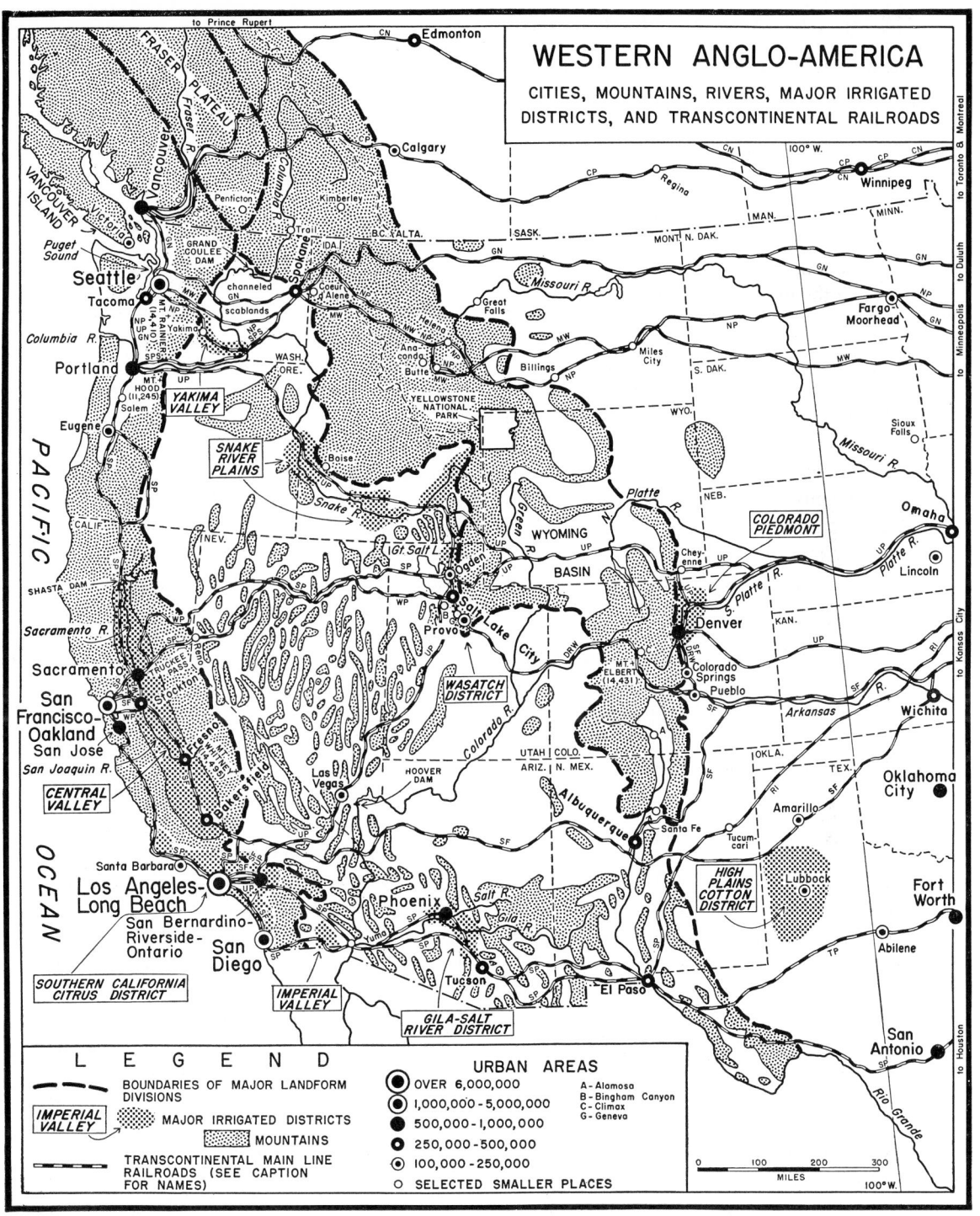

# WESTERN ANGLO-AMERICA
## CITIES, MOUNTAINS, RIVERS, MAJOR IRRIGATED DISTRICTS, AND TRANSCONTINENTAL RAILROADS

### LEGEND

— — — BOUNDARIES OF MAJOR LANDFORM DIVISIONS

IMPERIAL VALLEY · · · MAJOR IRRIGATED DISTRICTS

MOUNTAINS

TRANSCONTINENTAL MAIN LINE RAILROADS (SEE CAPTION FOR NAMES)

#### URBAN AREAS

- OVER 6,000,000
- 1,000,000 - 5,000,000
- 500,000 - 1,000,000
- 250,000 - 500,000
- 100,000 - 250,000
- SELECTED SMALLER PLACES

A - Alamosa
B - Bingham Canyon
C - Climax
G - Geneva

0   100   200   300
MILES

Key to railroads: CN, Canadian National; CP, Canadian Pacific; DRW, Denver and Rio Grande Western; GN, Great Northern; MW, Milwaukee; NP, Northern Pacific; RI, Rock Island; SF, Santa Fe; SP, Southern Pacific; SPS, Spokane, Portland and Seattle; TP, Texas and Pacific; UP, Union Pacific; WP, Western Pacific.

has a population of only 28,000 in the city proper. The commercial capitals of the various sections of the Rockies generally lie just outside the mountains, in such cities as Denver, Colorado (929,000), Salt Lake City, Utah (383,000), Spokane, Washington (278,000), and Calgary, Alberta (240,000).

# THE INTERMOUNTAIN BASINS AND PLATEAUS

The Rocky Mountain System and the mountains near the western shore of Anglo-America are separated from each other, from Alaska to Mexico, by the Intermountain Basins and Plateaus (map, p. 588). This landform division occupies an immense part of western Anglo-America. In general, while lower than the bordering mountains, the Intermountain Basins and Plateaus lie at comparatively high elevations above the sea. Few sections lie below 3000 feet, and very few below 2000. There is a great deal of variety in elevations, landforms, and local relief from place to place. Most of the land is composed of plateau surfaces in various stages of dissection so that rolling uplands and rugged hilly and mountainous sections are included, in addition to the large areas which are comparatively level or actually flat. Over much of the area the river valleys are deeply incised, forming spectacular canyons and gorges. The most famous of these, the Grand Canyon of the Colorado River, is an enormous gash cut in the surface of the Colorado Plateau in northern Arizona. In many places isolated mountain ranges project far above the general surface level.

Climatically, the Intermountain Basins and Plateaus are distinguished by low rainfall due to the position of this landform division between two shielding mountain systems. Most of the Intermountain area has a semiarid (steppe) climate, although there are a number of sizable desert areas. The heaviest precipitation occurs on the higher surfaces. In the more northerly sections the effects of low precipitation are offset to some degree by the lessened evaporation attendant on lower temperatures. Temperature conditions range from sub-

arctic in Alaska and northern Canada to subtropical along the Mexican border. Locally, there are great temperature as well as rainfall contrasts resulting from differences in elevation.

## ▶ *Major Subdivisions*

The Intermountain area may be divided into a number of major subsections, as follows (maps, pp. 636, 637, and 640): (1) the Basin and Range Country, (2) the Colorado Plateau, (3) the Columbia-Snake Plateau, (4) the Fraser-Nechako-Stikine Plateaus, and (5) the Yukon River Basin.

The *Basin and Range Country* extends from southern Oregon and southern Idaho to the Mexican border. It includes parts of Oregon, Idaho, California, Utah, Arizona, New Mexico, and Texas, as well as practically the entire state of Nevada. The section lying between the Wasatch Mountains of Utah and the Sierra Nevada of California is often referred to as the Great Basin, although the latter includes many smaller basins. The basins of the Basin and Range Country, many of which have no external drainage, are often separated from each other by blocklike mountain ridges rising high above the general level. Semiarid climatic conditions of northern sections and most eastern sections produce such vegetation forms as short grass, bunch grass, and sagebrush. In the southwestern part, true desert with extremely sparse vegetation prevails over a wide area in California, Nevada, and Arizona, and extends eastward into southern New Mexico and southwestern Texas.

The *Colorado Plateau* occupies parts of Colorado, Utah, Arizona, and New Mexico.

Rolling uplands lie at varying levels, often separated by steep escarpments. Mountain areas rise above the general surface in various places. Rivers, principally the Colorado and its tributaries, flow in deep canyons. The latter have been a great hindrance to transportation and have kept many sections extremely isolated. The climate is generally semiarid, although some higher sections have sufficient precipitation to produce a forest growth.

The *Columbia-Snake Plateau* is found in eastern Oregon and Washington and southern and western Idaho. It is characterized by extensive areas of level land, the result of massive lava flows in the past which buried the previous topography. The soils formed from these volcanic materials are exceptionally fertile. Isolated mountains occur, and the streams often flow in canyons. The Columbia River, the master stream of the area, has cut many alternative channels in the past, which now form rugged "scablands" in parts of Washington. The Columbia's giant tributary, the Snake, flows along the border between Oregon and Idaho in a canyon rivaling the Grand Canyon of the Colorado. The climate is semiarid.

The *Fraser-Nechako-Stikine Plateaus* of British Columbia form a considerably more narrow and constricted section of the Intermountain region than their counterparts in the United States. The Fraser Plateau in the south is a deeply dissected and rugged area, but in the north the Intermountain section of British Columbia presents large areas of rolling upland, interrupted by several mountain ranges. The semiaridity of the area is moderated by lower temperatures toward the north, where the grasslands and parklike forests of the south trend into the subarctic or taiga forest.

The *Yukon River Basin,* which occupies most of Canada's Yukon Territory and the greater part of Alaska (map, p. 640), has a varied topography of rolling uplands, hill country, low mountains, intrenched streams, and comparatively small areas of flat alluvial plains. As the elevations decline toward the sea in the Alaska section of the Basin, marshy areas become more prominent. The extreme subarctic climate of the Yukon Basin sets it apart from other areas in the Intermountain Basins and Plateaus. Cold rather than aridity is the dominant climatic factor, and the subarctic taiga forest is the prevailing vegetation type.

### ▶ *Population, Economy, and Urban Development*

Population is very sparse in the Intermountain Basins and Plateaus, being almost nonexistent over wide stretches, especially in the north. The major economic activities are grazing, irrigated agriculture, and mining. Most of the land as far north as the subarctic area of British Columbia is grazed, but the pasturage is generally poor. Ranches must perforce be large, and the ranching population, in consequence, is small and scattered. Here and there definite clusters of population are associated with irrigated areas or, to a lesser extent, with mining districts. Among the many scattered irrigated districts or oases, the following are outstanding in size and importance (map, p. 637): (1) the Imperial Valley of California, watered by the lower Colorado River, (2) the Gila–Salt River district around Phoenix, Arizona, (3) the Wasatch district in Utah at the western foot of the Wasatch Range, (4) the Snake River Plains in Idaho, and (5) a series of irrigated valleys along the eastern slopes of the Cascade Mountains in Washington and Oregon, the most important of which is the Yakima Valley with its massive production of apples, pears, peaches, and other fruits. There is much variety in types of production from one irrigated district to another. Different oases specialize in one or a combination of such crops as alfalfa, cotton, citrus fruits, early vegetables, sugar beets, potatoes, and apples.

Mining activity characterizes almost the whole extent of the Intermountain area in

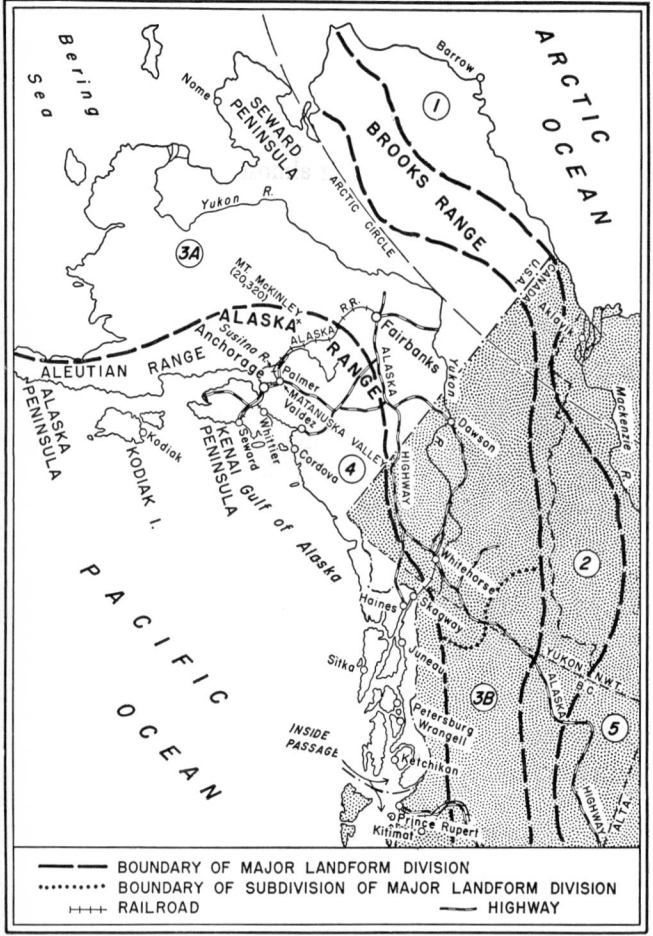

Alaska and northwestern Canada. Canadian areas are stippled. Some minor highways are not shown. Key to circled numbers: 1, Arctic Coastal Plains; 2, Rocky Mountains; 3A, Yukon River Basin; 3B, Fraser-Nechako-Stikine Plateaus; 4, Pacific Mountains and Valleys; 5, Interior Plains.

Production of oil and uranium in the Colorado Plateau sections of Utah, Colorado, and New Mexico has developed rapidly in recent years and is breaking down some of the isolation that has characterized large parts of the Plateau. In addition to copper, oil, and uranium, Utah mines both coal and iron ore and has, south of Salt Lake City at Geneva, the only iron and steel plant in the Intermountain region. In the Yukon Basin section of the Intermountain area, gold mining is a mainstay of the economy.

Nonirrigated cropping is important in only one district, the Columbia Plateau, which is able to produce large quantities of wheat thanks to soils that are exceptionally fertile and water retentive. The tourist and resort industry is also limited mainly to one section—the southern deserts. Visitors are attracted to the latter for reasons of health as well as recreation. The intrenched rivers of the Intermountain area, flowing from adjacent mountain regions, produce a tremendous hydroelectric potential, much of which has been developed. The Columbia River and its tributaries have a greater hydroelectric potential than any other river system in Anglo-America. The largest and most famous power installations in the Intermountain area are Grand Coulee Dam on the Columbia River and Hoover Dam (formerly Boulder Dam) on the Colorado. Power from these dams is largely transmitted to points outside of the Intermountain Basins and Plateaus and has given rise to relatively little manufacturing within the area itself.

The general sparsity of population is indicated by the comparatively small size of the major metropolitan areas. These are few in number and are scattered over a huge area. They include two state capitals, Phoenix, Arizona (664,000), and Salt Lake City, Utah (383,000), each identified with a major irrigated district; El Paso, Texas (314,000 excluding suburbs in Mexico), an important rail center and international border crossing on the Rio Grande River;

greater or less degree, being least important in the Columbia–Snake Plateau and the plateaus of British Columbia. The leading mineral products by value for the area as a whole are copper, oil, and uranium, though a great variety of others are extracted. Arizona mines about half and Utah about a fifth of the United States output of copper. The main producing centers include mines in southeastern Arizona and a great open-pit operation at Bingham Canyon, Utah.

Albuquerque, New Mexico (262,000), also on the Rio Grande, and Tucson, Arizona (266,000), each an educational, health resort, and rail center; and Spokane, Washington (278,000), a major rail junction (map, p. 637) and commercial center serving the Columbia Plateau wheat belt.

In British Columbia the largest Intermountain town, Penticton, has only about 12,000 people; in Yukon Territory the largest settlement, Whitehorse, has 3000; while in the Alaskan section of the Yukon Basin Fairbanks, with 13,000 people, easily surpasses any other settlement.

## THE PACIFIC MOUNTAINS AND VALLEYS

The Pacific shore of Anglo-America is bordered by a series of mountain ranges extending from Mexico to the Aleutian Islands. In the United States several large lowlands are included within this mountainous region.

▶ *Physical Description of the Major Subdivisions*

For purposes of introductory physical description, the Pacific Mountains and Valleys may be conveniently discussed in terms of the following major subdivisions (maps, pp. 636, 637, and 640): (1) the Coast Ranges of California, Oregon, and Washington, (2) the Sierra Nevada, (3) the Central Valley of California, (4) the Klam-

ath Mountains, (5) the Cascade Mountains, (6) the Willamette–Puget Sound Lowland, (7) the Coastal Ranges of British Columbia and southeastern Alaska, and (8) the Alaska Range and other mountains of southern Alaska north of the southeastern "Panhandle."

The coasts of California, Oregon, and Washington are fronted by the *Coast Ranges*. The section in northwestern Washington known as the Olympic Mountains has peaks reaching approximately 8000 feet and in the south some sections east of Los Angeles exceed 10,000 feet. However, the peak elevations more commonly lie at 3000 to 5000 feet in California and at only 1000

A field of potatoes in the Yukon River Basin near Fairbanks, Alaska. Potatoes are one of the few crops that can be grown successfully in the subarctic climate zone. Vast areas of the Alaskan and Canadian subarctic are covered by a straggling growth of small trees, mainly conifers, such as cover the low uplands in the background. (United States Information Service, Department of State.)

to 3000 feet farther north. Along most of the western coast of the United States there is no coastal plain, or almost none, and even the lower parts of the Coast Ranges are often quite rugged. However, a few valleys are available for agriculture, especially in California; and from Los Angeles to the Mexican border the ranges lie a few miles inland and a lower, hilly district containing much of California's population fronts the sea.

The *Sierra Nevada* forms the inland edge of the Pacific Mountains and Valleys in central California, merging with the Coast Ranges north of Los Angeles and with the Klamath and Cascade ranges in northern California. The Sierra Nevada is an immense upraised, tilted, broken, and eroded block presenting a long and comparatively gentle slope to the west and a precipitous face eastward toward the Basin and Range Country. It is very high and rugged, and constitutes a major barrier both climatically and with regard to transportation. Mount Whitney (14,495 feet) in the southern Sierra Nevada is the highest peak in the continental United States.

The *Central Valley,* a level-floored alluvial trough some 500 miles long by 50 miles wide, occupies the center of California between the Coast Ranges and the Sierra Nevada. It is completely surrounded by mountains except where San Francisco Bay breaks the continuity of the Coast Ranges and brings the Central Valley into contact with the Pacific.

The *Klamath Mountains* form a link between the Coast Ranges and the Sierra Nevada and Cascade ranges, and separate the northern end of the Central Valley of California from the southern end of the Willamette Valley of Oregon. The Klamath Mountains are physiographically a dissected plateau. The valleys are deeply incised, giving an extremely rugged aspect to the terrain. Summit levels are frequently at 6000 to 7000 feet or higher.

The *Cascade Mountains* extend north-ward from the Sierra Nevada and the Klamath Mountains across Oregon and Washington and into British Columbia. Much of the area of the Cascades lies between 5000 and 9000 feet in elevation, and the mountains are surmounted by a series of volcanic cones reaching much higher elevations. Mt. Rainier (14,410 feet) and Mount Hood (11,245 feet) are probably the most famous of these. The Cascades are broken into two sections at the Oregon-Washington boundary by a spectacular gorge through which the Columbia River flows westward toward the Pacific.

The *Willamette–Puget Sound Lowland* lies between the Coast Ranges and the Cascades. Its Oregon section, from the Klamath Mountains in the south to the lower Columbia River in the north, is the valley of the Willamette River, while the northern section is commonly known as the Puget Sound Lowland. This latter section extends all the way across western Washington and north into British Columbia to include a small area along the lower course of the Fraser River.

In British Columbia and the southeastern "Panhandle" of Alaska a northward extension of the Cascades lies along the coast and is known as the *Coastal Ranges.* These Ranges are generally higher and more rugged than the Coast Ranges in the United States. Many peaks reach 9000 or 10,000 feet. The mountains rise abruptly from the sea and are penetrated by fjords, resembling in this respect the coasts of Norway and southern Chile. West of the Coastal Ranges a valley analogous in position to the Central Valley of California and the Willamette–Puget Sound Lowland has subsided below sea level and now forms the famous "Inside Passage" to Alaska. The mountains in British Columbia and southeastern Alaska which correspond in position to the Coast Ranges of the United States are partly submerged, and form a string of rugged islands along the outer edge of the Inside Passage.

Most of southern Alaska is mountainous.

Just north of the Panhandle, spectacular glaciers descend the mountains to the sea. The highest mountains, however, are found farther to the north and west in the *Alaska Range,* where Mount McKinley reaches 20,320 feet, the highest elevation in Anglo-America. In a more subdued form the mountains continue from the Alaska Range into the Alaska Peninsula and the Aleutian Islands. A fair-sized area of lower land is found south of the Alaska Range in the Susitna River Valley and along the western side of the Kenai Peninsula.

### ▶ Distribution of Population

From southern California to southern British Columbia the Pacific Mountains and Valleys contain a rather large population, especially considering that most of the included land is mountainous. This Pacific littoral forms an island of relatively dense population separated from the populous eastern areas of Anglo-America by the thinly peopled Intermountain, Rocky Mountain, and Great Plains regions. At least 19 million people live in the parts of the Pacific Mountains and Valleys that lie within continental United States, as compared with a total of less than 7 million in all the interior states eastward to the western boundaries of the Dakotas, Nebraska, Kansas, and Texas. California is by far the largest center of population in the western third of Anglo-America. With 15,717,000 people (1960 census), it ranks second in population among the states. In Canada around three quarters of the 1,600,000 people of British Columbia live in small lowland areas along or near the lower Fraser River and on the southern part of Vancouver Island. North of this southwestern corner of British Columbia there is little population in the Pacific Mountains and Valleys, but even so, the population is larger than in the adjacent regions of the interior. Two thirds or more of Alaska's 226,000 people (1960 census) live along or near the Pacific Coast, the most concentrated area of settlement being in the Anchorage (city proper, 44,000) district.

### ▶ The Highly Developed Agriculture of California

The marked concentration of people along the Pacific littoral is partly due to the agricultural advantages of this area as compared with interior sections of the Anglo-American West. These advantages are much more pronounced in California than in any other section of the Pacific Mountains and Valleys. The lowlands of California are areas of mediterranean or dry-summer subtropical climate, except for especially sheltered spots in the southern part of the Central Valley, which grade into steppe and desert. The winter rains and mild winter temperatures permit nonirrigated grain farming to be carried on in the winter and spring, and there is enough moisture to provide fairly good pasturage for grazing. During the dry summers, nearby mountain pastures often provide valuable supplementary grazing for livestock. But the importance of California as an agricultural state derives mainly from the most extensive development of irrigation in the United States. This development has been made possible by the close proximity of high mountain ranges (especially the Sierra Nevada but also parts of the Coast Ranges) which receive very heavy precipitation. Rain and snow falling in these mountains provide large amounts of water for irrigating the lowlands of the Central Valley and southern California.

The principal products of California agriculture are a great variety of fruits. Citrus fruits, grown mainly in southern California, are the best known, and the state ordinarily accounts for over a quarter of the country's citrus production. However, California is also the leading producer of many other fruits, including apricots, dates, figs, olives, peaches, pears, plums, and, of greatest value, grapes. It is also the leading state in vegetable production, usually accounting for

Mediterranean agriculture in southern California. The irrigated orange grove in this view lies at the foot of rugged mountains in the Coast Ranges east of Los Angeles. In the vicinity of Los Angeles is found one of the three greatest citrus districts of the United States. (Los Angeles Chamber of Commerce.)

between a quarter and a third of the country's total output by value. The Imperial Valley, located in the Intermountain area of southeastern California and supplied with water by an irrigation canal from the Colorado River, plays an important part in the irrigated vegetable production of the state, along with the Pacific sections. The southern part of the Central Valley, known as the San Joaquin Valley, produces over a tenth of the American cotton crop, and the northern part (Sacramento Valley) about a quarter of the country's rice crop. In addition, large dairy, livestock, and poultry industries have developed in some sections, stimulated by the state's rapid growth in urban population. Grazing, dry farming, and irrigation farm-

ing combine to give California a remarkable diversity in agriculture and a production great enough to make it the leading state in total value of farm products.

### ▶ Agriculture in the Area of Marine West Coast Climate

North of California the lowlands of the Pacific area have a marine west coast climate characterized by mild, wet conditions similar to those of the corresponding climatic region in northwestern Europe. In the Willamette–Puget Sound Lowland, agricultural development has emphasized principally dairy farming and the production of tree and bush fruits, with some truck gardening. But agriculture has been handicapped, especially in the Puget Sound Lowland, by the difficulty and expense of clearing the land of immense stumps in cutover forest areas, and by soils which are often poorly drained and heavily leached. Nor does this section have a climate permitting it to produce specialties of the type which have allowed California to largely overcome its problem of great distance from major consuming centers in eastern United States. Consequently, agricultural development here is on a considerably smaller scale than in California, and there is much farming on a part-time subsistence basis. North of the Fraser lowlands and Vancouver Island, there is very little land sufficiently level for agriculture, and the largest agricultural area, found in lowlands north of Anchorage (Matanuska Valley), contains only a few hundred farms.

▶ *Nonagricultural Resources*

The principal nonagricultural resources of the Pacific Mountains and Valleys are water power, oil, timber, and fish. Hydroelectricity is a major source of power for both domestic and industrial uses, and helps to overcome the region's shortage of coal. Electricity is supplied by many installations within the Pacific area, of which Bonneville Dam in the Columbia gorge and Shasta Dam on the Sacramento River in northern California are probably the outstanding examples. In addition, large amounts of power are transmitted from installations in the Intermountain Basins and Plateaus such as Hoover Dam and Grand Coulee Dam. The location of a large part of the United States aluminum industry in Washington and Oregon is closely related to the superior water power resources of these states. Now this industry is extending northward along the coast of British Columbia where the Kitimat installation will be possibly the world's largest when fully completed.

Oil is another major source of power along the Pacific Coast, but its production is confined to California. Southern Califor-

nia and the southern end of the Central Valley supply about 13 percent of the national total, and California ranks third, after Texas and Louisiana, as an oil-producing state. Los Angeles and San Francisco and their environs are major centers of oil refining.

The softwood forests which occupy the mountainous portions of the Pacific Coast region from the Sierra Nevada and San Francisco Bay northward are the most valuable in Anglo-America from the standpoint of size of trees and total reserves of saw timber. These large trees can be cut into long, high-quality boards, and represent the greatest reserve of saw timber in the United States. The famous Douglas fir of Oregon and Washington is the outstanding species, although the immense redwoods of northern California and various other species are important. Oregon, Washington, and California, in that order, are the first-, second-, and third-ranking American states in sawmilling, accounting together for 44 percent of the total United States production of sawn lumber, while British Columbia ranks first among Canadian provinces in this phase of the forest industries. Pulp and paper milling is relatively less important here than in most other forested areas in Anglo-America, but the Pacific area does produce more than 15 percent of all United States wood pulp. In fact, Washington is the leading American state in pulp and paper milling. In Alaska the forests are, on the whole, less impressive; nevertheless, they offer a major resource which has been very little exploited as yet. The first Alaskan pulp mills recently began operations in the Panhandle section.

The fishing industry is important along the Pacific Coast from San Diego to the Aleutian Islands. In terms of value of catch, California is the leading fishing state with over a tenth of the United States total. Tuna and sardines are the principal species landed by the California fishing fleet. The other Pacific Coast states, led by Alaska, land an additional 15 percent of the total

United States catch. British Columbia also has important fisheries, being in fact the leading Canadian province in total value of fishery production. Salmon, halibut, and herring are the major species landed by the Pacific fisheries north of California. The fishing industry is relatively more important as a phase of the total economy in northern British Columbia and Alaska than in areas farther south. Little other economic development has occurred in these more northerly sections, and fishing affords the principal support for most of the small and scattered coastal communities. The Anchorage area, dependent largely on United States military installations, is an exception to this generalization.

Finally, the scenery of the Pacific area and the climate of southern California must be considered as major resources since they afford the principal basis for a large and growing tourist trade.

### ▶ Urban and Industrial Development

The Pacific border from Vancouver southward includes an impressive number of large cities. In general, the importance of commerce seems somewhat greater than that of manufacturing in these cities, although a rapid development of industry has occurred in recent years. The six largest cities are all seaports. Their locations reflect advantages deriving from natural harbors or passes through the mountains to the east, or both. The largest city on the Pacific Coast, Los Angeles (6,743,000 with Long Beach and many other suburbs and satellites), is located in the northern and wider part of the coastal lowland of southern California. San Francisco (2,783,000 with Oakland; the San Jose metropolitan area immediately to the south has 642,000) has developed on one of the world's best natural harbors. It lies west of the center of the Central Valley nearly opposite the important Truckee Pass over the high Sierra Nevada. San Diego (1,033,000) as also developed on an excellent natural harbor and has be-

come the main Pacific Coast naval base of the United States, although its development as a commercial port has been handicapped by inferior connections to the interior. Seattle, Washington (1,107,000), lies on a natural harbor on Puget Sound west of passes through the Cascades. Portland, Oregon (822,000), is located on the lower Columbia River at the head of the Willamette Valley. Improvement of the lower Columbia's channel has made it an ocean port, and the Columbia gorge through the Cascades gives it access to the interior. Vancouver, British Columbia (684,000), has an excellent natural harbor near the mouth of the Fraser River. The Fraser Valley affords a passageway through the mountains to the east. Among Canadian ports Vancouver ranks second only to Montreal, drawing traffic not only from its immediate hinterland but to some extent from the Prairie Provinces also.

The Pacific Coast region has a number of other metropolitan areas that deserve mention. Most of these are inland in southern California and the Central Valley. In southern California the San Bernardino–Riverside–Ontario area (810,000) is an important commercial, industrial, and transportation center immediately to the east of Los Angeles. It has developed in the midst of passes through the Coast Ranges that channel major rail lines from the east (the Santa Fe, Southern Pacific, and Union Pacific) into Los Angeles (map, p. 637). In the Central Valley, Bakersfield (292,000) is the commercial center of the oil-producing southern end of the valley, while Fresno (366,000) is the commercial center of the section of the valley that lies within the drainage basin of the San Joaquin River, and Stockton (250,000) is a seaport on the San Joaquin near its junction with the Sacramento River. The largest city of the Central Valley, Sacramento (503,000), is the state capital and the commercial center of the central and northern sections of the valley. North of California the largest cities of the

Pacific Coast region besides Seattle, Portland, and Vancouver are Tacoma, Washington (322,000), an industrial city on Puget Sound that is especially important in the sawmilling industry, and Victoria (142,-000), the capital of British Columbia, on Vancouver Island.

Three types of manufacturing dominate the industries of the Pacific region: aircraft (including missile and rocket) production, sawmilling, and canning and other industries that process the region's surpluses of agricultural products and fish. Los Angeles, with possibly a third of the American aircraft industry, is the greatest center of aircraft production in the United States and probably in the world. Aircraft production also dominates the industrial structure of

San Diego and is important in Seattle. Sawmilling is most important in Oregon, Washington, and British Columbia, though it is also present on a considerable scale in northern California. Food processing is important in most large sections of the Pacific Coast region and is the leading industry of many towns and cities. It is especially well developed in California. Other industries worthy of note include oil refining and automobile assembly in the Los Angeles and San Francisco areas, the movie and apparel industries in Los Angeles, the aluminum industry of Washington, British Columbia, and Oregon; and iron and steel production carried on between San Bernardino and Ontario, California, by the only large steel plant of the Pacific region.

## THE ARCTIC COASTAL PLAINS

Fairly extensive coastal plains fronting on Arctic waters are found in two distinct sections of Anglo-America, one north of the Brooks Range (map, p. 640) and the other along the southern shores of Hudson Bay (map, p. 592). The Alaskan coastal plain is an area of tundra, while that along Hudson Bay is largely subarctic in climate and forested, though grading into tundra in

some sections. These areas are extremely thinly populated and play almost no part in the economic life of Anglo-America, although there are a few fur-trading posts in the Hudson Bay section. Subsistence hunting and fishing are the principal means of support of the Eskimo population of the Alaska section.

## GREENLAND

Greenland is the world's largest island, with an area of approximately 840,000 square miles. While not culturally or politically a part of Anglo-America, it may be regarded as a marginal part of the latter region from the standpoint of proximity and strategic geography. Roughly 85 percent of the surface is covered by an icecap and most of the island's 28,000 permanent inhabitants live in rugged strips of tundra along the southwestern and southeastern coasts. These people are primarily Eskimo but with a strong admixture of Scandinavian blood.

Fishing (carried on both commercially and on a subsistence basis), hunting, trapping, and sheep herding are their chief means of livelihood. The population includes about 2000 Danes, mainly traders and government officials. The island is known to have considerable mineral wealth, but little of this has yet been exploited except for cryolite, a material useful in the glass, chemical, and aluminum industries. Greenland has practically a world monopoly of natural cryolite.

Politically, Greenland is an integral part

of Denmark. The latter, a member of the North Atlantic Treaty Organization, has granted permission for the establishment of several NATO air bases along the Green-land coast. The United States has played a leading role in the development of these bases. The largest is located at Thule on the far northwestern coast.

# HAWAII

Hawaii, admitted to the American Union as the fiftieth state in 1959, has been mentioned briefly in Chapter 20 on the Pacific Islands. A volcanic, mountainous tropical area populated originally by Polynesians, the new state is comprised of eight main islands (inset map, p. 430), one of which is uninhabited. The islands lie in the path of trade winds which bring heavy rainfall to windward slopes throughout the year. Leeward and low-lying areas, however, may receive as little as 10 to 20 inches of rainfall annually.

The Hawaiian Islands lie just south of the Tropic of Cancer and slightly more than 2000 miles from California. The island of Hawaii is by far the largest of the group and contains the only active volcanic craters. The state's population, however, is heavily concentrated in the island of Oahu, where the capital and only large city, Honolulu (500,000), is located. The total area of the state, 6423 square miles, is greater than the combined areas of Connecticut and Rhode Island, and its population of 633,000 (1960 census) ranks it 44th among the states. Caucasian and Japanese elements comprise the principal groups in the popula-tion, but are augmented by much smaller groups of native Hawaiian, Filipino, Chinese, Korean, Puerto Rican, or Samoan ancestry. Much racial and ethnic mixing has taken place. Most of the population is thoroughly Americanized.

Hawaii's economy leans heavily on commercial agriculture, defense, and tourism. The main agricultural products and exports—cane sugar and pineapples—are grown on large estates owned and administered by Caucasian family and corporate interests but actually worked by non-Caucasian labor. Both products are marketed primarily in mainland United States, though some exports go to foreign countries. Most sugar cane is grown in irrigated fields, while pineapples are largely an unirrigated crop. Military installations, including the famous naval base at Pearl Harbor, are a vital source of income for the state, as is the rapidly expanding tourist industry. Urban development, tourism, and business administration are overwhelmingly concentrated in Honolulu, and most of the main defense installations, including the Pearl Harbor base, are near the city.

# Index

*All page references to maps are in italics following general entry for topic.*

Aachen: *119;* coal field of, 121, 147

Abadan: 312, 315, *279, 313, 323*

Abidjan: 491, 492, *466, 467*

Abqaiq oil field: 316, *313*

Accra: 496, *466, 467;* climatic data for, 469

Ackerman, Edward A.: 408

Adana: 321, *294, 323*

Addis Ababa: 327, 328, *279, 281, 323, 466, 467;* climatic data for, 283

Adelaide: 449, *430, 443, 447;* climatic data for, 445

Aden (city): 319, *279, 323*

Aden (colony and protectorate): 319, *279;* area and population of, 276

Adirondack Mountains: 590, 617, *609, 613*

Adriatic Sea: 192, 198, 208, 209, *40, 181, 202*

Aegean Sea: 25, 187, *40, 181*

Afghanistan: 319, 324–326, *279, 324;* agriculture of, 326; area and population of, 276; Helmand Valley irrigation and power project of, 325; historical background of, 324–325; karakul lambskins, exports of, 325; Moslem clerical influence in, 326; population of, 325; and the Pushtunistan issue, 326; regional areas of, 325; relations of, with Great Britain, 324, 326, with Pakistan, 325, 326, with the U. S., 325, with USSR, 324, 325

Africa: 8, 455–511, *5, 12, 13, 35, 39, 87, 95, 459, 466* (index map), *467, 502;* agriculture of, 476–478; animal life in, 472; area and population of, 458, data for political units of, 460–462; Belgian colonial empire in, 137, *see also* Congo, Republic of the; climate of and vegetation of, 468–470, data for climatic stations, 469; colonial powers and policies of, 482–483; Commonwealth states and British dependencies in, 493–500; cultural divisions

of, 458; disease in, 471–472; elevations of, 464–465, *467;* European colonial possessions, emancipation of, 34, 457–458, 481–482, *35, see also specific areas;* European settlers in, 482; French Community in, 94–96, 489–493, *95,* area and population of, 460; German colonial empire in, 116, 117; grasslands of, 480; Great Rift Valley of, 465, *467;* historical background of, 459–463; hydroelectric development and potential of, 465–468; Italian colonial empire in, 188, 307, 327–328; lakes of, 465; Latin America, compared with, 526–536; livestock in, 479; minerals of, 457, *467,* production of, 310–311, 472–475; modernization of, 458; mountains of, 465; natural environment of, 464–475; partitioning of, by European nations, 463; pastoralism in, 478–480; peoples of, and their economy, 475–480; population density of, key areas, 458; ports of, studies concerning, 484*fn;* Portuguese possessions in, 188, 483–485; recent problems and changes in, 463; rivers of, 459, 465–466; slave-trading in, 459–460; soils of, 470–471; Spanish possessions in, 188, 485; topography of, 464–465; transportation in, 465, 484*fn, 467;* water resources and problems of, 470; world interest in, 457–458; *see also specific regions and countries*

Africa, British: *see* British Africa

Africa, British East: *see* British East Africa

Africa, Belgian: *see* Belgium; Congo, Republic of the (former Belgian Congo); Ruanda-Urundi

Africa, French: *see* French Community

Africa, northwest: *see* Maghrib, the, *and individual countries*

Africa, Portuguese: *see* Angola;

Mozambique; Portuguese Africa

Africa, South: *see* South Africa

Africa, South West: *see* South West Africa

Africa, Spanish: *see* Africa, Spanish possessions in

Africans: in South Africa, 501, European legal restrictions on, 501

Afrikaans language: 510, 511

agriculture: in Africa, 476–478; in Anglo-America, 577–578, 579; characteristic of underdeveloped areas, 18; culture system of, 380–381; early development of, 18; and economy of area, 18; in Europe, 52–53, *54, 55;* in Latin America, 532–533; importance of Middle East to, 277–278; intensive subsistence, 340–341; in the Orient, 340–342; in the Pacific Islands, 434–439; shifting cultivation, 370, 477; in USSR, 226–229; world cultivated land area, 13; *see also specific regions and countries*

Agricultural Triangle: *see* Slavic Coreland

agricultural villages: as feature of geography, 21–22

Ahmadi: 318

Ahmedabad: 346, 358, 359, *347;* housing conditions in, 351

Ainoids: 429

Ainu: 407

Akmolinsk: *232;* climatic data for, 242

Akron: 618, *613, 623*

Alamosa: *637;* climatic data for, 591

Alaska: *576, 640;* Arctic coast of, 647; Brooks Range in, 634; compared with Northern Europe, 163; fisheries of, 645, 646; forest resources and pulp mills of, 645; Inside Passage to, 642, *640;* Matanuska Valley of, 645; military installations in, 646; Panhandle of, 643, 645, *640;* Peninsula, 643, *640;* population distribution in, 643;

Bengal: 349, 353, *347;* and jute industry, 358
Benghazi: 307, *279, 309*
Benguela Current: 509, *502*
Benguela Railway: 484, *467*
Ben Nevis: 62
Berbers: 288, 308
Berezniki: 258, *232, 255*
Bergen: 170, *164;* climatic data for, 46
Bering Strait: 583, *640*
Berkshire Hills: 614, *613*
Berlin: 118, 123, 127, 129, 131, 132, *27, 41, 91, 119, 122;* Airlift (1948–1949), 129; climatic data for, 46, 120; photo of, 115
Bern: 153, *27, 91, 150*
berseem (clover): 302*fn*
Bessarabia: 203, 204, 235, *202*
Bessemer converter: 70
Bethlehem (Pa.): 620, *613*
Betic Mountains: 186, *181*
Bhakra Dam: 360, *347*
Bhutan: 343, *344, 347, 388;* area and population of, 343
Bihar: *347*
Bihor Mountains: 215, *202*
Bikini (Marshall Is.): 428, *430*
Bilbao: 190, *91, 181*
Billiton: 374, 381, *368*
Bingham Canyon: 640, *637*
Binghamton: 618, *613*
Birmingham (Ala.): 620, *576, 596*
Birmingham (Eng.): 71, 76, *61, 66, 78, 81, 91*
Bismarck Archipelago: 411, 428, *430–431*
Black Belt: 600, 603, *596*
black-earth belt (USSR): 241, *252;* agriculture of, 261–262, 266
Black Forest: 99, 100, 120, 207, *91, 97, 119*
Black Hills: 622, *636*
Black Sea: 25, 51, 208, 234, 238, 243, *40, 202, 232*
Black Waxy Prairie: 600, 605, *596*
Bloemfontein: 511, *502*
Bluegrass Region: 627, *596, 609, 623*
Blue Nile River: 306, *279, 301, 323*
Blue Ridge: 617, *596, 609, 613*
Boer colonists: 510–511
Boer War (Anglo-Boer War): 511
Bogotá: 543, 549, *518, 539, 552*
Bohemia: 156, 207, 210, 211, 212, 214, 216, 218, *202; see also* Czechoslovakia
Bohemian Basin: 207; industrial development of, 216, 218; *see also* Bohemia
Bohemian Forest: 120, 207, *91, 119, 202*
Bohemian Hills: 149, *151*
Boliva: 519, 530, 550, 551–553, *518, 552, 553, 555;* area and population of, 521; Eastern

Cordillera of, 551; mineral resources of, 531, 532, 533, 551; settlements of, 551–553; subsistence agriculture of, 551; tin mines of, 551; Western Cordillera of, 551
Bologna: 188, 192, *91, 181*
Bombay (city): 346, 358, 359, *347;* climatic data for, 337; housing conditions in, 351
Bombay (state): *347*
Bomi Hills iron-mining district: 498, *467*
Bonaire: 546, *539*
Bonin Islands: 410, *410, 430*
Bonn: 123, *27, 91, 119*
Bonneville Dam: 645, *637*
Bordeaux: 111, *91, 97*
Borneo (Indo.): 366, 374, 380, 381, *368*
Borneo, British: *see* British Borneo
Borneo, North: 367, *368*
Bosporus: *see* Turkish Straits
Boston: 615, *613*
Boston Mountains: 621, *596, 609*
Bougainville (Solomon Is.): 428, 434, *430–431*
Bougie: 311, *309*
Boulder Dam: *see* Hoover Dam
Boulogne: 107, *91, 97*
Bourke: *443;* climatic data for, 445
Bowman, Isaiah: 117
Bradford (Eng.): 73, *66*
Brahman caste: 363
Brahmaputra River: 390, *345, 347, 388*
Braila: 208, *202*
Brand, Donald D.: 550
Brandenburg Gate: photo of, 115
Brasília: 562, *518, 552*
Bratislava: 207, *202*
Bratsk: 270, *255*
Brazil: 517, 519, 523, 524, 530, 535, 557–562, *518, 552, 553, 555;* agriculture of, 559–560; area and population of, 521; capital of, 562; coffee crop of, 560; foreign investments in, 561; "the great escarpment" of, 558; immigrant communities of, 560; land divisions of, 558–559; landholdings in, 559; manufacturing and mining of, 560–561; mineral resources of, 530–531, 560–561; population distribution in, 559, 561–562; transportation in, 561–562, *555;* urbanization of, 561–562
Brazilian Highlands: 557, *553*
Brazzaville: 492, *466, 467*
Bremen: 123, 129, 130, *91, 119;* climatic data for, 120
Bremerhaven: 129, *119*
Brenner Pass: *150*
Breslau: *see* Wroclaw
Brest: 107, *91, 97*
Breton language: 29
Bridgeport (Conn.): 615, *613*

Bridgetown: 539, climatic data for, 531
Brighton-Worthing: 76, *66*
Brisbane: 449, *430, 443, 447;* climatic data for, 445
Bristol (Eng.): 70, *61, 66, 79, 91*
British Africa: component units as of 1955, 493, as of 1960, *466;* recent political changes in, 493–494; *see also individual units and areas*
British Borneo: 367, *368;* area and population of, 369
British Cameroons: 493, 495, *466, 467;* area and population of, 461
British East Africa: 484*fn,* 497–499, *466, 467*
British Guiana: 533, 546, *518, 539, 552;* area and population of, 520
British Honduras: 545–546, *518, 539;* area and population of, 520
British Isles: *see* Great Britain; Ireland
British North America Act: 584
British Petroleum Company: 312–313, 319
British Somaliland: 327; *see also* Somali Republic
British Virgin Islands: 523*fn,* 538, *539*
British West Africa: transportation in, 484*fn*
Brittany: 29, 100, 106, 107, *40, 97*
Brno: 213, *202*
Brockton: 615, *613*
Broken Hill: 451, *443*
Bronx: 615, *613*
Brooklyn: 615, *613*
Brooks Range: 634, *640*
Broome: 442, *443*
Brown, W. Norman: 345–350, 351–352, 363
Bruges: *135;* photo of, 144
Brunei: 367, *368*
Brunhes, Jean: 13
Brunswick: 123, *91, 119*
Brussels: 102, 138, 139, *27, 91, 135;* climatic data for, 46
Bucharest: 213, *27, 202*
Budapest: 207, 213, *27, 202;* climatic data for, 209
Buddhism: in China, 386; in India, 362; Lamaist branch of, in Tibet, 389–390; in the Orient, 339; in Southeast Asia, 375, 376, 377, 378
Buenaventura: 543, *552*
Buenos Aires: 535, 563, 564, 565, *518, 552*
Buffalo: 616, 631, *613, 623*
Bukhara: 265, *232*
Bulawayo: 465, 500, *466, 467*
Bulgaria: 28, 55, 200–201, *27, 36, 202* (index map); agriculture in, 210, 211, 212; area and population of, 201; boundary problems of, 203–204; climate

of, 210; cities of, 213; industry in, 214; language and religion of, 31, 205–206; political history of, 203–204; topography of, 207, 208; uranium in, 216; *see also* Europe, East Central
Bullard, Sir Reader: 300
Bureya Basin coal field, 271, *254*
Bureya River: 271, *233*
Burgan oil field: 317–318, *313*
Burgenland: 149, *151*
Burgundian Gate: *see* Belfort Gap
Burgundy: *97*
Burma: 366–367, 375–376, *334, 368, 376;* area and population of, 369; commercial rice in, 373, 376; minerals of, 374; *see also* Southeast Asia
bush fallowing: 477
Bushmen: 476; photo, 475
Bush Veld: 503, *502*
Butte: 635, *637*
Byzantine Empire: Constantinople as capital of, 187, 322; relation to Kievan Russia, 249

Cabinda: 485, *466*
Cadiz: 199, *181*
Cairo: 281, 288, 292, 303, *279, 281, 294, 301, 323, 466, 467;* climatic data for, 283
Calais: *91, 97*
Calcutta: 346, 358, 359, *334, 347;* climatic data for, 337
Calder Hall: 69, *66*
Calgary: 634, 638, *592, 623, 637;* climatic data for, 591
Cali: 543, *539, 552*
Callao: 550, 555, *518, 552*
Cambodia: 366–367, 373, 377–378, *35, 334, 368, 376*
Camden (N. J.): 607, *613*
Cameroun Mountain: 496, *467*
Cameroun, Republic of (former French Cameroons): 94–96, 489–492, *466, 467;* area and population of, 462
Campania: 185, 187, 194, *181*
Campine: 146, *135;* coal field of, 147, *92*
Canada: 571–595, 608–611, 617, 622–630, 634–647, *576, 588, 592, 613, 623, 637, 640;* climate of, *see* Anglo-America; comparison with Europe and the Mediterranean Sea, *41,* with Australia, 444–446, with USSR, 271; landform divisions of, *see specific division;* member of Commonwealth of Nations, 85; natural resources in, percentage of world, 579–580, *see also* United States and Canada; population, growth of, 581; subarctic region, photo of, 14; trade turnover of, *39; see also* Anglo-America; United States and Canada; *specific landform divisions*

Canadian National Railways and Canadian Pacific Railway, 635, *592, 637*
Canadian Shield: 590–595, 617, *588, 592, 609, 613;* agriculture in, 595; forest industry of, 592–593; hydroelectricity in, 593; mining industry of, 593–594, 628; tourism in, 593; urban development in, 594–595
Canary Islands: 188, 460, 485, *466*
Cantabrian Mountains: 186, 190, *181*
Canterbury Plains: 453, *453*
Canton (China): 387, 394, *388;* climatic data for, 337
Canton Delta: 393, 394, *335, 388*
Canton Is.: 432, *431*
Cape Chelyuskin: 234, *233, 234*
Cape Cod: 599, *609, 613*
Cape Colony (So. Africa): 510
Cape Comorin: 350, *347*
Cape Dezhnev (East Cape): 231, *233*
Cape of Good Hope Province: 507–509, *502;* agriculture of, 507–509, photo of, 508; inland districts of, 508–509; "Coloured" of, 507
Cape Town: 501, 507, 510, 511, *466, 467, 502;* climatic data for, 469, 506
Cape Verde Islands: 485; area and population of, 460
Cape York: *443;* climatic data for, 445
Cape York Peninsula: 451, *443*
Caracas: 530, 535, 544, 549, *518, 539, 552;* climatic data for, 531
Carcassonne Gap: 98, 111, *97*
Cardamon Hills: 350, *347*
Cardiff: 69, 71, *66, 91*
Caroline Islands: 411, 428, *410, 430*
Carpathian Mountains: 206–208, 215, 235, *202, 245*
Caribbean America: 537–550, *539;* area and population of, 520–521; Central American Republics of, 542–543; Colombia and Venezuela, 543–545; diversity of units, 538; exports of republics of, 542; islands of, 546–549; island dependencies in, 548–549; island republics of, 547–548; mainland dependencies in, 545–546; Mexico, 538–542; transportation in, 549–550; urbanization of, 550
Cartagena: 543, *539, 552*
Casablanca: 308, *279, 309, 466, 467;* climatic data for, 469
Cascade Mountains: 639, 642, 646, *636, 637*
Caspian Sea: 25, 243, 260, 262, 263, 314, *232, 255, 279, 323*
Catalan language: 30, 193
Catalonia: 193, *181*
Cauca River: 543, *518*

Caucasus Mountains: 25, 262–264, *245, 252*
Caucasus Region: 237, 242, 244, 262–264, *252*
Cawnpore: *see* Kanpur
Cayman Islands: 523*fn, 539*
Celebes: 366, 381, *368*
Celtic languages: 29
Central African Republic (former Ubangi-Shari): 490, *466, 467;* area and population of, 460
Central American republics: 542–543, *518, 539;* area and population of, 520; exports of, 542
Central Industrial Region: *see* Moscow Region
Central Tanganyika Railway: 489, 499, *467*
Central Treaty Organization: 315
Central Valley: 641–646, *636, 637*
Cerro Bolívar: 544, *555*
Cerro de Pasco: 554, *553*
Ceuta: 277*fn, 309*
Ceylon: 366–367, 374–375, *368;* area and population of, 369; paddy fields of, 341; tea exports of, 372
Chad, Republic of: 490, 491, *466, 467;* area and population of, 461
Champagne: 105, *97*
Champlain Lowland: 612, 616, 629, *609, 613*
Changchun: 396, *388*
Channel, English: 65, *40, 66;* English cities on, 76, 77
Channel Islands: 59, *40*
Chao Praya River (Menam Chao Praya) and Delta: 373, 376, *335, 368, 376*
Charleroi: 139, *91, 135*
Charleston (S. C.): 605, *596*
Charleston (W. Va.): 618, *596, 613*
Charlotte (N. C.): 607, *596*
Chattanooga: 620–621, *596*
Chelyabinsk: 258, 259, *232, 255*
Chemnitz: *see* Karl-Marx-Stadt
Chenab River: 349, 363, *347*
Chengtu: 404, *388;* climatic data for, 333
Chengtu plain: 393, *388*
Cherbourg: 109, *91, 97*
Cheremkhovo: 271, *233, 254, 255*
Cherepovets: 270, *232, 255*
chernozems: definition and distribution of, 241
Cherrapunji: 350, *347*
Chesapeake Bay: 596, 607, *596, 613;* commercial fish catch of, 604
chestnut soils (USSR): 241, 266
Chiang Kai-shek: 387
Chiatura: 257, 263, *232, 254, 255*
Chicago: 630–631, *613, 623*
Chicago River: 630

This Book Belongs To Loretta E. Perry

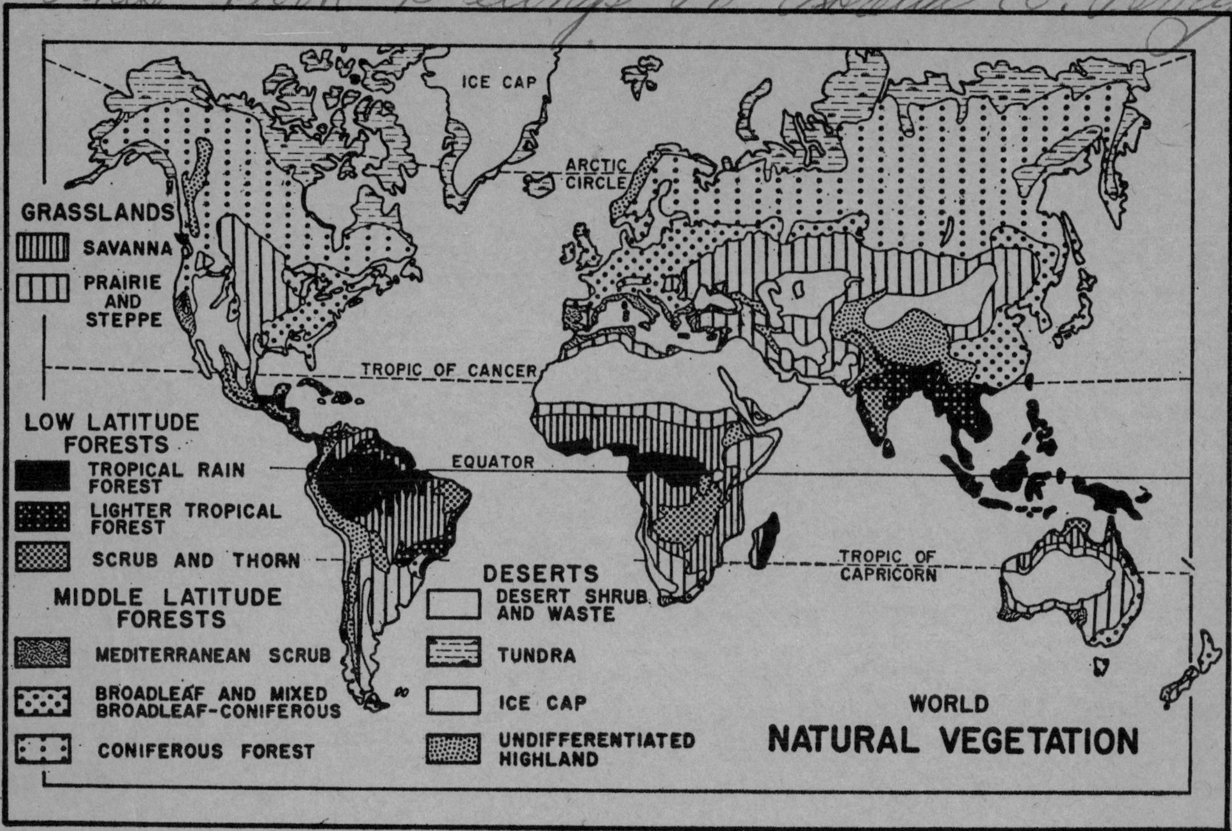

## WORLD NATURAL VEGETATION

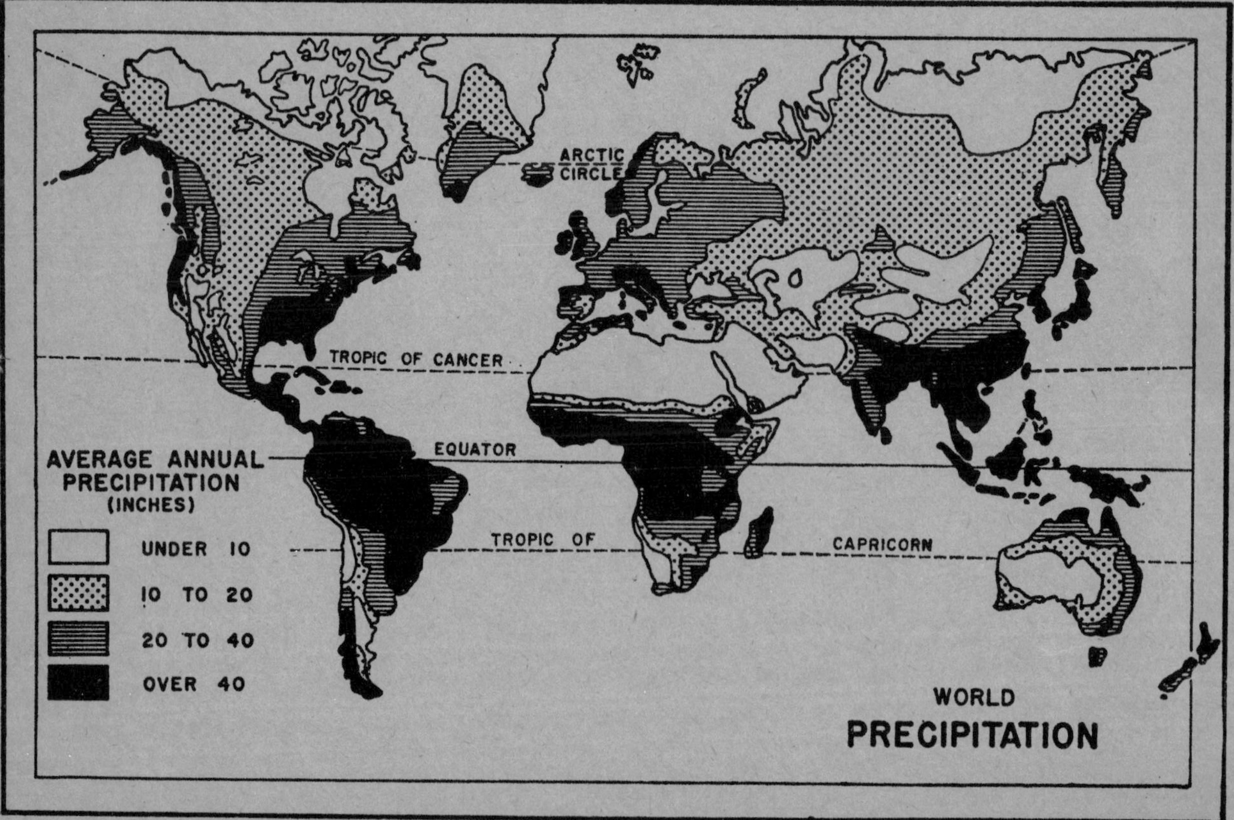

**GRASSLANDS**
- SAVANNA
- PRAIRIE AND STEPPE

**LOW LATITUDE FORESTS**
- TROPICAL RAIN FOREST
- LIGHTER TROPICAL FOREST
- SCRUB AND THORN

**MIDDLE LATITUDE FORESTS**
- MEDITERRANEAN SCRUB
- BROADLEAF AND MIXED BROADLEAF-CONIFEROUS
- CONIFEROUS FOREST

**DESERTS**
- DESERT SHRUB AND WASTE
- TUNDRA
- ICE CAP
- UNDIFFERENTIATED HIGHLAND

ICE CAP
ARCTIC CIRCLE
TROPIC OF CANCER
EQUATOR
TROPIC OF CAPRICORN

## WORLD PRECIPITATION

**AVERAGE ANNUAL PRECIPITATION (INCHES)**
- UNDER 10
- 10 TO 20
- 20 TO 40
- OVER 40

ARCTIC CIRCLE
TROPIC OF CANCER
EQUATOR
TROPIC OF CAPRICORN